THE ANALYSIS OF
MANAGEMENT DECISIONS

The Irwin Series in Management

Consulting Editor John F. Mee *Indiana University*

THE ANALYSIS OF MANAGEMENT DECISIONS

William T. Morris

PROFESSOR OF INDUSTRIAL ENGINEERING
THE OHIO STATE UNIVERSITY

REVISED EDITION

RICHARD D. IRWIN, INC.
HOMEWOOD, ILLINOIS   •   1964

Revised Edition
First Printing, May, 1964
Second Printing, December, 1965
Third Printing, September, 1966
Fourth Printing, June, 1967

Library of Congress Catalogue Card No. 64-17249

PRINTED IN THE UNITED STATES OF AMERICA

PREFACE

THIS BOOK attempts to use the decision process as a conceptual structure for organizing a variety of examples of scientific staff assistance to management decision makers. It is not for those who are interested in mathematical analysis alone, but for those who wish to apply it to real decision problems experienced by real managers.

Several cautions may assist the reader. An elementary background in economics, accounting, and probability theory is presumed. While sections on these topics appear at appropriate points throughout the book, the discussions are for review and reorganization of ideas only. They should not be used as introductions. The book covers a number of examples of analysis and thus no single technique in detail. Only the basic ideas in such areas as inventory theory, waiting line theory, or game theory could be presented. Suggestions for further reading hint at the extensive literature which the interested reader might pursue. No specific attention is devoted to machine computation, although it will be obvious that many of the examples, such as those of Chapter 9, provide good opportunities for instructional use of computers. Finally the reader is warned that many of the problems require a creative extension of the ideas in the text, not simply the search for the right formula into which to substitute some numbers. As in reality, there may be no "right" answer, but one learns by considering the variety of different answers which together help illuminate a problem.

I have learned much from the students, teachers, and managers who have commented on the earlier version of this book. Many of them devoted time and patience to the task of educating me, for which I am most thankful. The shortcomings which remain are mine, not theirs.

WILLIAM T. MORRIS

To M. L. M.

TABLE OF CONTENTS

Chapter 1

STAFF ASSISTANCE
FOR MANAGEMENT DECISIONS

A POINT OF VIEW

ONE NEEDS SOME sort of organizing concept to make sense out of the complex world of management and the fascinating possibilities for using science to assist managers. This book uses management decision making as such an organizing concept. It attempts to examine the processes by which business decisions are made, looking for the contributions of the scientifically trained analyst and the contributions of the experienced manager. The notion of a decision is thus a sort of model or logical structure which is used to bring some conceptual order out of the endless variety of observations that one might make about management, about science, and about the uses of science in the assistance of managers. Perhaps the best way to begin is with a simple example.

A TYPICAL DECISION PROBLEM

The management of a manufacturing firm is undertaking the production of a new product which it hopes to sell both commercially and to the military services. Much effort has gone into the study of the market for this product, its design, its production, and the possibilities for profit. At a rather advanced stage in this effort, the management of the firm must make a decision as to what type of lathes should be purchased to carry out one stage in the production of the product. A staff analyst is asked to study this problem and make a recommendation to management. He undertakes a study of the lathes which are available from various machine tool manufacturers, getting as much data as possible on the prices, operating costs, performance characteristics, maintenance costs, service lives, and salvage values of the various machines. His objective is to find

1

the type of machine which will perform the anticipated operations on the product with the required precision and so forth, and will do this as economically as possible. As he accumulates and studies the information, it becomes clear that the machines fall into two general groups. There are special-purpose lathes which can do a limited variety of production operations, but do them very economically at a high rate of output. There are also general-purpose lathes which can do a greater variety of operations, but for any given set of operations their output rate is lower than that of the special-purpose machines. On the basis of various considerations such as price, precision, and reliability, he is able to select what seems to be the best of the special-purpose machines and the best of the general-purpose machines. Let us refer to these as machine A and machine B, respectively.

In studying the relative desirability of machines A and B, the staff analyst decides to compute the unit production cost for each type. Using the data he has obtained, he comes up with the following result. If the product is to be produced at an annual rate of 20,000 units or more, machines of type A will have the lower unit production cost. If less than 20,000 units per year are produced, machines of type B would be cheaper on a unit cost basis. He reports this conclusion to the head of his staff group who adds the following idea. If for some reason the firm eventually ceases to make the product, machines of type B would be more useful for making other products than would those of type A. The two analysts then present their findings to a meeting of the firm's management. At this meeting many other factors are discussed, such as the availability of capital, the reputations of the machine tool manufacturers, the possibilities of getting a substantial military contract for the product, plans for other new products in the future, and so on. The orderly thought processes of the analyst may even become a little confused at the variety and vagueness of the considerations discussed. Finally a show of hands is called for, and the majority of the managers are seen to favor type B machines. A small but vehement minority argues on in favor of type A. Time passes, perhaps tempers are lost, but eventually those in the minority reluctantly agree to type B machines. At this point the president of the firm directs the treasurer to make the necessary funds available and the purchasing agent to begin negotiations to buy the equipment. This little drama represents an instance of the kind of situation examined in this book.

Decision making is such a prominent management activity that it is seldom considered analytically by those who do it regularly. Indeed, managers are seldom capable of explaining their own decision process. As one prominent manager stated it, "You don't know how you do it; you just do it." One may begin to understand the process, however, by turning an analytical eye to the little episode described above. The events might be organized as follows:

1. *Explicit Recognition of a Decision Problem.* As plans and preparations for the new product advanced, the decision about lathes required management attention. Fortunately there was time to study the decision before they were forced into action.

2. *Seeking Staff Assistance.* Somehow management decided that this decision was one for which the assistance of the staff could usefully be sought.

3. *Search for Alternatives.* The analyst searched for various courses of action which management might choose. His task was to predict the consequences of various acts. He could not go on searching indefinitely but had sooner or later to stop and get on with the problem.

4. *Prediction.* The analyst attempted to predict what would happen if various alternatives were adopted. This was difficult because of such uncertainties as future sales rates, military contracts, and product life.

5. *Evaluation.* The analyst tried to calculate the value or worth of the action in the light of various future events. He did this in terms of production cost but recognized that this might not capture such considerations as reliability, flexibility, availability of capital, and so forth.

6. *Production of an Explicit Model.* The result of the analyst's effort was the production of an explicit model or conceptualization of the decision problem.

7. *Application of Managerial Judgment.* Management recognized that the analyst's efforts were a considerable help but not an exhaustive statement of the problem. They added factors which were not included in the model, weighing them and combining in an implicit judgmental process.

8. *The Management Decision Process.* The final conclusion was reached by pooling the judgments of the management committee, ostensibly by a vote. When the vote failed to be unanimous, efforts were made to reach a consensus. A great deal of bargaining and persuasion may have been involved here, which are often quite difficult to understand. These last two steps seem to have brought

considerable confusion to the analyst's orderly rendering of the decision.

APPROACHES TO DECISION MAKING

One interesting way to study history is to view it in terms of the variety of approaches to the problem of making decisions which it reveals. It would be impossible to review these approaches, but one calls to mind such interesting extremes as the royal astrologers and the Prussian general staff, democracy and dictatorship, the government economist and the existentialist philosopher. Our approach to decisions is the result of a long effort on the part of many engineers, scientists, and managers to remove decisions, at least to some extent, from the realm of pure guesses, intuition, or judgment, and into the area of logical analysis and careful empirical observations. This is the attempt to make decisions by the methods of science. In this connection there is a good deal of discussion as to whether many decisions can ever be made on a completely scientific basis and whether we can really have "scientific management." The best answer to this seems to be that it is the wrong question to ask. It is more sensible to inquire, "How far can we go in using the methods of science to assist the responsible decision makers in industry and the government?" Recent years have brought developments in the use of scientific approaches to decision making which encourage one to think that we can go further than we had imagined years ago. This is the result of the advent of high-speed computers and of intensive research efforts directed toward scientific approaches to important decisions.

The approach in this book rests upon the following premise. It is true at the present stage of scientific advance that almost all interesting decisions encountered by the analyst and the manager are to some extent beyond purely scientific study. Indeed, for many of these decisions little if anything can be done scientifically. Nevertheless, the way to better decision making lies through the use of the scientific approach as far as possible, to supplement the judgments which must finally be made. If we want to characterize the extremes in approaches to decision making, we might call one extreme analytical and the other judgmental. Our premise might then be refined into the following statement: "In making decisions it is best to go as far as is technically or economically feasible with analysis, then appeal to judgment and experience." This is the whole theme of this book.

Clearly it is hard to draw a firm distinction between analysis and judgment, but we have in mind the everyday meanings of the terms. The exact meaning will emerge as the presentation progresses. The words "it is best" in the foregoing statement will seem acceptable enough to some, but others will call upon us to prove that what is suggested is really best. In some simple decisions it is easy to show how one decision maker employing analysis might do better than another using judgment alone, but in most situations no such demonstration can even be imagined. One need only recall the stories of a few major corporation executives or stock market millionaires who were not troubled in the slightest by any need or desire to approach their decisions analytically. Nevertheless, the mounting success of analytical approaches to decisions in the fields of industrial engineering and operations research make it possible to view our premise as something more than simply an article of faith. There is sufficient evidence of actual improvement in decision making through analysis to have considerable confidence in its possibilities. Almost every decision eventually, however, involves judgment to some extent.

GETTING STARTED

The analyst sets out to produce an explicit model or conceptualization of the decision process. Explicitness simply means that the process of making a decision is consciously carried through and that all the elements and steps in the process can be spelled out. Explicitness means that we can state exactly what alternatives were considered in a decision, exactly how the results of choosing the various alternatives were predicted, exactly how these results were evaluated, and so on. To the extent explicitness is achieved, decisions can be checked and reviewed by others, ways of improving bad decisions may be sought, and decision making may be talked about and taught. If a decision is not made explicit it cannot be checked, improved, or yield principles which can be taught. Actually, of course, the analyst never really makes all the aspects of a decision explicit. It is a goal which he aims at but never quite reaches. His study of a decision may begin with a model of the situation which is vague, incomplete, doubtful, and confused. As he works, he studies the deductive consequences of his model and seeks empirical verification of them through experimental or historical data. He can never go as far as he would wish in the development of the model. The complexities of the real management situation are too great; there are things he cannot measure; and the pressures of cost and time limit the achievement of full explicitness. Yet the first vague model evolves through deduction and observation into something which may be of considerable assistance to management.

We begin with an example of a decision which will illustrate the elements of the basic decision model that will be used throughout the book.

A MODEL OF A DECISION

Consider the decision problem encountered by the roulette player who wishes to place a $1.00 bet on either red, black, or zero and double zero. The rules of the game are simple. If the wheel is spun and the ball stops at a position which corresponds to his wager, he wins. Otherwise he loses. For winning bets of $1.00 the house pays as follows:

Red..........................$ 2.00
Black........................ 2.00
0 and 00..................... 18.00

In approaching this decision the player observes that there are 38 possible positions on the wheel, 18 of which are red, 18 of which are black, and the remaining two are labelled 0 and 00. Although no wheel is absolutely perfect, the imperfections are usually so slight as to become evident only after extremely long periods of study. Thus, the usual assumption made by the player is that the ball is equally likely to stop at any position on the wheel. Using this assumption, the probabilities or relative frequencies of the various outcomes are estimated as follows:

Red..........................$^{18}/_{38}$
Black........................$^{18}/_{38}$
0 and 00.....................$^{2}/_{38}$

It is helpful to summarize all this information about the decision in a matrix. The rows of the matrix correspond to the alternative bets among which the player must choose. The columns correspond to the various results of a spin of the wheel, with the probabilities noted for each possible result. The cells of the matrix then indicate whether the player wins or loses and the corresponding net money return.

The net return in each case is obtained by subtracting the dollar wagered from the amount which the house pays. Thus, if the player chooses red and the ball stops at red, the house pays $2.00, but he wagered $1.00, so his net return is $2 - 1 = 1$. Having displayed a good deal of information about the decision in this matrix form, perhaps the player is ready to actually make his choice. How should he place his bet? As we shall see later on, a number of arguments could be advanced to answer this question. At present we will consider only one such argument, which suggests that the player should choose so as to maximize his long-run average or expected return. Thus we might compute the average or expected return for each possible choice, and select the one for which this quantity is the largest.

		The Ball Stops at:		
		Red Prob. = 18/38	Black Prob. = 18/38	0 and 00 Prob. = 2/38
The player chooses	Red................	WIN $1	LOSE −$1	LOSE −$1
	Black................	LOSE −$1	WIN $1	LOSE −$1
	0 and 00............	LOSE −$1	LOSE −$1	WIN $17

The expected return for a bet of $1.00 on red is

$$(18/38)(\$1) + (18/38)(-\$1) + (2/38)(-\$1) = -\$.053$$

This means that if we bet on red a large number of times, the net return each time tends toward an average loss of 5.3 cents. The prospect of such a loss is not attractive, but if the expected returns for bets on black, and 0 and 00 are computed, they turn out to be precisely the same. The decision maker may then draw several conclusions:

1. Using expected return as an index, it makes no difference how he places his best.
2. No matter how he bets, this sort of gambling will not be profitable in the long run.
3. There is no way of improving his analysis of the decision unless he can study the wheel for a very long time to check the probabilities more carefully.

A similar study of other commercial gambling games would show that all have negative expected returns, since otherwise gambling houses would soon go out of business. Our point is not to dwell on the folly of gambling but to suggest that the elements of this decision are typical of many decisions and that a model can be set forth making these elements explicit.

In any decision of interest, there are two or more alternative courses of action among which the decision maker must choose. (In the foregoing example, bets on red, black, or 0 and 00.) We will use the symbol a_i to represent the ith alternative course of action. The result of deciding upon a course of action depends on other events which are beyond the control of the decision maker. (Where the ball stops.) We shall call these other events "possible future states of the world" or simply "possible futures." In many decisions it turns out that the possible futures may be described very simply. (We can summarize the very complicated series of events which take place when the wheel is spun and describe the relevant possible futures as "the ball stops on a red position," etc.) The symbol S_j will stand for the jth possible future. The result of selecting a particular course of action and having a particular possible future happen is an event which we will refer to simply as an outcome. (Win or lose.) The outcome of choosing alternative a_i and having possible future S_j happen, is the event θ_{ij}. In studying the outcomes, the decision maker will wish to evaluate them or measure their worth in terms of his objectives and value system. Often the value of an outcome may be expressed in terms of dollars of profit or loss which it may represent, but sometimes intangible considerations will enter. (How can we evaluate the pleasure the player obtains from playing roulette and winning?) If we can evaluate an outcome, we write $V(\theta_{ij})$ for the value of θ_{ij}. (Net dollar returns to the player.) We may now present our matrix representation of the elements of a decision in symbolic terms.

	S_1	S_2	S_3		S_j		S_m
a_1	$V(\theta_{11})$	$V(\theta_{12})$	$V(\theta_{13})$	$\cdots$	$V(\theta_{1j})$	$\cdots$	$V(\theta_{1m})$
a_2	$V(\theta_{21})$	$V(\theta_{22})$					
a_3							
$\cdot$	$\cdot$	$\cdot$					
$\cdot$	$\cdot$	$\cdot$					
$\cdot$	$\cdot$	$\cdot$					
a_i				$\cdots$	$V(\theta_{ij})$	$\cdots$	$V(\theta_{im})$
$\cdot$	$\cdot$	$\cdot$					
$\cdot$	$\cdot$	$\cdot$					
$\cdot$	$\cdot$	$\cdot$					
a_n				$\cdots$			$V(\theta_{nm})$

If the probabilities of the possible futures are known, the symbol p_j may be used to stand for the probability of S_j. In terms of these symbols, the expected return from a_i may be written:

$$E(a_i) = \sum_j V(\theta_{ij}) p_j$$

This then is the kind of a model which will be used to represent the elements of a decision.

TWO BASIC CONCEPTS

Two fundamental ideas kept in mind may help considerably as one sets out to study decision making.

By a decision we mean a conceptualization of a choice situation, whether in the form of a mental image or an explicit model.

Each of us perceives a choice situation differently and thus has different concepts, models, or images of it. Although the scientifically trained analyst attempts to express his conceptualization as an explicit model, what goes into this model is necessarily a function of his experience, the selective character of his perception, and his judgments as to what should or should not be included.

All decision making involves the simplification of reality.
Because of the limited capacity of the human mind (and of the computer) all conceptualizations of choice situations are produced by abstracting from the rich complexity of reality. This is true for both the experienced manager and the analyst, although they may simplify to very different degrees and in very different ways. When we examine models of decision situations, it is well to keep in mind that they are necessarily simplifications and that the way in which the situation has been simplified is a product of the analyst's perception and judgment. The key to understanding any decision process is to understand the way in which it reduces the unmanageable complexity of the management situation.

THE BASIC TYPES OF DECISIONS

There are many useful ways of classifying decisions, but the most appropriate for analytical purposes depends upon the amount of information we are able to obtain. Many important management decisions are notable for the difficulties involved in obtaining the information which the decision maker would ideally like to have. For example, the decision to manufacture a new product may be based upon careful design and processing studies, detailed cost and profit analyses, market research studies, and even pilot runs and test sales. Even with all this, a vast amount of uncertainty is associated with the decision. We cannot know the future, and even the most sophisticated prediction techniques are sometimes wrong. Often too, the decision to manufacture a new product must, under the pressures of business necessity, be made without the benefit of some or all of these kinds of information. Almost every significant business or personal decision involves this troublesome shortage of information.

Much of our analytical effort will be devoted to the attempt to make good decisions in the face of something less than complete information.

DECISIONS UNDER ASSUMED CERTAINTY

For some decisions it is convenient and practical to assume that we have complete information and that there is no uncertainty connected with the analysis of the decision. Such a case will be called a decision under assumed certainty. For example, the decision to purchase a United States Government Bond is one in which it is reasonable to assume complete information about the future. For practical decision-making purposes, most people will agree that there is no doubt that the federal government will in fact pay the interest as it falls due and the principal at maturity. Thus, in predicting the outcome of such an action, certainty is a reasonable assumption. One should never lose sight of the fact, however, that such a model is a result of one's decision to simplify by suppressing uncertainties about the future. Its "reasonableness" is a matter of judgment at first and what sort of results it leads to ultimately. It does not mean that the future is certain, only that one studies the decision *as if* the future were certain.

In terms of our decision model, assumed certainty means that only one possible future has probability 1 and that the outcome for each alternative can be stated definitely. In matrix form a decision under assumed certainty would appear as follows:

$$S$$

a_1	$V(\theta_1)$
a_2	$V(\theta_2)$
a_3	$V(\theta_3)$
.	.
.	.
.	.
a_i	$V(\theta_i)$
.	.
.	.
.	.
a_n	$V(\theta_n)$

DECISIONS UNDER RISK

A decision problem in which the analyst elects to consider several possible futures, the probabilities of which can, in his view, be stated, is called a decision under risk. The roulette player's decision noted earlier is a typical example of a decision under risk. Less information is available than in a decision under certainty, since it is not definitely known what the outcome will be. However, it is possible to estimate the probabilities of the various possible futures, in the view of the analyst.

DECISIONS UNDER UNCERTAINTY

A decision for which the analyst elects to consider several possible futures, the probabilities of which *cannot*, in his judgment, be stated is called a decision under uncertainty. In matrix form a decision under uncertainty looks much like a decision under risk, except that the probabilities of the various possible futures are missing. Thus, decisions under uncertainty contain even less information than decisions under risk, and both contain less information than decisions under certainty. As an example, consider the construction firm which wishes to decide whether or not to submit a proposal for a certain government contract. The cost of preparing the proposal is taken to be $10,000 which will be lost if the firm is not awarded the contract. If the contract is won, the firm expects a profit of $100,000 to result. The decision might be expressed in the form

	Win	Lose
Propose	$100,000	−$10,000
Do Not Propose	0	0

The analyst, not knowing which other firms would be proposing, the nature of their proposals, or the details of how the government would evaluate proposals, may well make the judgment that he has little grounds on which to base any statements of the probabilities of the possible futures. Thus the model, at this point, might be one of a decision under uncertainty. Of course, the analyst might try to obtain data or opinions on which to base statements about the probabilities, thus transforming the decision into one under risk. As the model now stands, reflecting his judgment that he cannot state the probabilities, it would, however, be an example of uncertainty.

We have chosen these particular meanings for the terms risk and uncertainty, but the literature is by no means unanimous in this regard. These meanings were suggested by Professor Knight of the University of Chicago many years ago (78)* and have been used by some but not all recent writers (84).

OTHER CLASSIFICATIONS OF DECISIONS

While the relative completeness of information which characterizes a decision may be the most important way of classifying it, at least at the outset, it is helpful and suggestive to examine some other ways of classifying decisions. Several such classifications are suggested in the succeeding paragraphs.

1. *Investment and Operating Decisions.* Investment decisions involve funds which will be recovered over an extended future period, usually spent for plant and equipment. Operating decisions involve expenditures which will be recovered in the near future and are concerned with alternative methods for utilizing existing facilities.

2. *Organizational Level.* It is often helpful to classify decisions according to the level in the organization at which responsibility for them is lodged. Thus we speak of top-management decisions, middle-management decisions, and so on.

3. *Degree of Pressure.* Most decisions in actual situations are made under various degrees of time pressure. There is almost always some sort of a limit on the time which can be devoted to making the choice. The differences between emergency and crisis decisions, on the one hand, and those which can be approached in a more deliberate fashion, on the other, are well known.

4. *One Time and Repetitive Decisions.* Some decisions will be made repeatedly in the life of an organization. With these, skill and experience can lead to the development of policy, which is simply the premeditation of decision. Other decisions will be unique in the history of the organization, and policy will not arise. This distinction also is important in the way certain decisions are made, as will be seen in Chapter 11.

5. *Magnitude of Possible Results.* One of the more obvious ways to classify decisions is with respect to the magnitude of the results which might be expected. Thus, the corporation finds itself confronted by some decisions which involve millions of dollars and the very existence of the organization. Other decisions will involve small and even insignificant results.

---

* Numbers in parentheses refer to the bibliography at the end of the book.

6. *Feasibility and Optimization Decisions.* Often the analyst who is connected with some technological development program finds that in the early stages of the program the decisions have mainly to do with feasibility or "how to do it." As the technology matures he more often encounters optimization decisions which relate to the question of "how to do it best." For example, early lunar expeditions will involve decisions largely aimed at getting the job done somehow. Later expeditions will involve decisions as to the most economical or the safest way of doing the job.

7. *Possible Anticipation.* Decision situations differ widely with respect to our ability to anticipate them. Sometimes a decision can be foreseen and extensive preparation made for it. At other times we will be suddenly confronted with the necessity for making a decision which we could not foresee.

8. *Analytical Possibilities.* As the science of decision making develops, some types of decisions emerge for which analysis is important and makes considerable contribution. Inventory decisions form one such class. Other decisions will remain largely beyond analytical efforts, in the domain of judgment.

These and other classifications which might be suggested serve to emphasize some of the characteristics of decisions which make them difficult subjects for analysis. Many of these factors can be dealt with in one way or another as we shall see. Before making a frontal attack on the problem of decision making, something of the background against which many decisions appear will be suggested.

PROBLEMS

1–1. From your own experience select a personal decision or a management decision which you would take to be an example of each of the following types:

　a) A decision under assumed certainty.

　b) A decision under risk.

　c) A decision under uncertainty.

For each example identify the elements of the decision, including the alternatives, possible futures, outcomes, and so on.

1–2. A series of holes must be drilled in a casting which forms the housing for a motor. The holes may be located and drilled without the aid of a jig by a skilled machinist whose wage rate is $2.50 per hour. His production time will be 1.5 minutes per plate. A jig could be built at a cost of $150 permitting the holes to be drilled by a machinist at a lower skill level. In this case the wage rate would be $2.20 and the production rate would be two housings per minute. Which alternative would you suggest if *a*) 2,000 housings are to be made.

b) 4,000 housings are to be made.

c) 3,300 housings are to be made.

1–3. Suggest examples of decisions to illustrate the eight classifications given in the chapter. What other classifications appear interesting?

1–4. If you had $1,000 to invest in common stocks, to what extent could you rationalize the choice of which issues to buy?

1–5. A firm is considering the possibility of installing on its punch presses safety devices which are designed to protect the operators from injuring their hands. What data would you want to rationalize this decision? Show explicitly how you would use the data if they were available. What data would you expect to actually be able to obtain in a typical firm?

1–6. Two different types of bituminous concrete plants are available to a contractor. On the basis of the following data which choice would you suggest?

	Plant A	Plant B
Income (per year)	$100,000	$100,000
Expense (per year)	50,000	70,000
Investment	200,000	400,000
Useful life	10 years	10 years
Salvage value	0	200,000

1–7. A Christmas tree retailer has one opportunity to buy his stock for the season. If he buys too many trees he suffers a loss on those which he cannot sell. If he buys too few trees he does not get the profit on some sales which he might have made. Make his decision problem explicit.

1–8. Rank the following jobs according to the degree to which the decisions they involve may be made explicit:

Personnel manager	Design engineer
Sales manager	Director of research
Purchasing agent	Department foreman

1–9. Make the following decisions explicit using the model developed in this chapter:

a) To flip or not to flip with a man who owes you $100 for double or nothing.

b) To solve a problem by hand computation or by computer.

c) Which of two job offers to accept.

d) The amount of extra inventory a steel user should maintain in anticipation of a steel strike.

1–10. What explanation could be offered for the fact that many people who face the choice of whether or not to gamble, say at roulette, decide in favor of gambling? Could your explanation be stated in the terms used in this chapter to describe a decision?

1–11. In what important ways is the decision as to which horse to bet on in a race different from the roulette decision described in this chapter?

1–12. Consider the decision as to the size of cable to be used for an electrical transmission line. Assuming we are not restricted to a finite number of standard cable sizes, the line might be designed with an infinity of possible cross-sectional areas. Suppose in this decision the relevant costs include the investment in the cable (on an annual basis) and the annual cost of energy loss. If the current in the line is known, then the energy loss might be assumed to be inversely proportional to the cross-section area of the cable. Let us also assume that the investment in the line is directly proportional to the cross-sectional area. If we let A stand for this area, then the total cost for any particular decision with respect to A is given by

Total Cost = Investment Cost + Cost of Energy Loss

or symbolically

$$TC(A) = C_1 K_1 A + \frac{C_2 K_2}{A}$$

where C_1 is the unit investment cost, C_2 is the unit cost of energy, and K_1 and K_2 are constants of proportionality.

a) How is this problem related to the basic decision model in the chapter?

b) What cable area would you recommend to a manager in such a situation?

1–13. From your own experience suggest the relationships you might expect to find between

a) The amount of time available to make a decision and the amount of analysis which is likely to be done on it.

b) The amount of analysis done on decisions and the level of management at which they are made.

c) The amount of analysis done on decisions and the dollar value of the largest outcome.

1–14. Consider a construction firm which has a chance to buy some street paving equipment at an advantageous price. Suppose the firm's engineers, in studying the decision to purchase or not to purchase the equipment, discover that all street paving contracts are awarded by the municipality in which the firm operates and that a municipal election is in the offing. Further investigation reveals that Party A is committed to an extensive street repair program, but Party B has made no such commitment and is expected to balance the municipal budget by keeping street repairs to a minimum. The firm's engineers make estimates of the profit to the firm over some future period, including and excluding street paving operations, and under both kinds of street repair programs. Suppose the values in the matrix represent profit in thousands of dollars.

	Party A Wins Election	Party B Wins Election
Paving Equipment Purchased	42	26
Paving Equipment Not Purchased	31	31

a) What action would you recommend to management if you were unable to obtain any further information? Why?

b) What information would you suggest the engineers try to obtain? What would they do with it? How would it be reflected in a modified model of the decision problem?

c) What would you predict an experienced manager would do when faced with the above model of the decision?

Chapter 2

SOME BASIC
MANAGERIAL ECONOMICS

ECONOMICS OF THE FIRM

To SET THE STAGE for the analysis of management decisions, one must examine the firm or organization within which these decisions arise. Although most of what follows applies equally well to governmental, retail, wholesale, or service organizations, we will assume an industrial enterprise. In order to be definite we will also assume that the primary objective of the management of such an enterprise is profit, although this assumption must be severely questioned later. We will study some mathematical models of these enterprises which, while too simple to capture the full flavor of reality, are sufficient to suggest some of the major policy decisions which confront the management of such an enterprise. The analysis which will be set forth may be recognized as managerial economics, the analysis of the firm under conditions of imperfect competition, or as the formulation of some major policy decisions under assumed certainty. Our purposes then are to provide an introductory description of the firm within which management decisions take place, to introduce some basic considerations and criteria which will enter directly into the analysis of decisions, to give an overview of some of the major policy decisions which managements face, and, quite incidentally, to begin the development of some fluency in the use of mathematical models.

In this chapter we will use systems of equations and inequations to represent decisions under assumed certainty. The reader should identify for himself the alternatives open to management and the values of the outcomes which would correspond to the matrix representation of the previous chapter.

THE FIRM AND ITS MARKET

Imagine an industrial enterprise which competes with several others in an industry. The firm produces a single product, has some control over the price which it will charge, and is primarily devoted to making a profit. Imagine further that the major characteristics of the market, the competitors, and the firm's own internal technology are well known to management and essentially static in time. Under these conditions we will explore some of the major economic decisions which might be made. Our plan will be to start with the evironment in which the firm exists and work our way inward, reaching eventually the level of decisions at which the analyst often works.

In studying the firm's environment, one might wish to study in detail the firm's customers, competitors, suppliers, and the legal, political, social, and geographic factors which bear upon its operations. To avoid some of the chaos which this might involve, we will assume that all these things can be expressed by the demand curve of the enterprise. The demand curve expresses a part of the firm's relationship with its market by simply giving the amount of product which can be sold as a function of the price charged for it. In this simple model price is taken to be the major determining factor in the amount the firm can sell, and such obvious other factors as quality, advertising, sales effort, reputation, and service are left out of the picture. Thus we suppose that management knows that the relationship between the price of their product and the amount they can sell is given by some function such as

$$P = a - bD \qquad \text{for } 0 \leq D \leq a/b$$
$$= 0 \qquad \text{otherwise}$$

·Here P is the unit price in dollars, D is the amount of product sold, and a and b are positive constants. We assume that the amount of product, D, is a continuous variable. This causes no trouble if the product is gasoline and is measured in gallons, but if the product is automobiles some uneasiness may result. Actually, however, the rate at which automobiles are sold may be a continuous variable, or, if necessary, the analysis may be reformulated in terms of discrete variables with no difficulty. The straight-line example we have given might have been a curve, but the point is that one usually expects large volume to be associated with low price and small volume to be associated with high price (Figure 2–1).

The manager who knows his firm's demand curve may then

decide what price he will charge and the curve will tell him how much he can sell, or he may decide what volume to produce and the curve will indicate the highest price at which he will be able to dispose of his production. Ultimately he will wish to make this choice

FIGURE 2–1

A Demand Curve

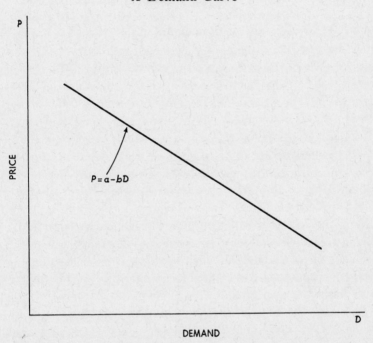

so as to maximize profit, and profit may be defined simply as the difference between total revenue or gross sales (TR) and total cost (TC).

$$\text{Profit} = TR - TC$$

The total revenue resulting from any price-volume choice may be computed directly from the demand curve.

THE TOTAL REVENUE FUNCTION

Total revenue to the firm is simply the amount of product sold multiplied by the unit price charged.

$$TR = (\text{unit price})(\text{volume}) = PD$$

Using the demand function, total revenue can be expressed in terms of D alone.

$$TR = (a - bD)D = aD - bD^2 \qquad \text{for } 0 \leq D \leq a/b$$
$$= 0 \qquad\qquad\qquad\qquad \text{otherwise}$$

Now if we are dealing with a peculiar firm which has no costs at all, or has only costs which are independent of the volume of production, then maximizing profit would be achieved by maximizing total revenue. The volume which will maximize total revenue can be found by the usual methods of the calculus (Figure 2–2).

FIGURE 2–2

A Total Revenue Function

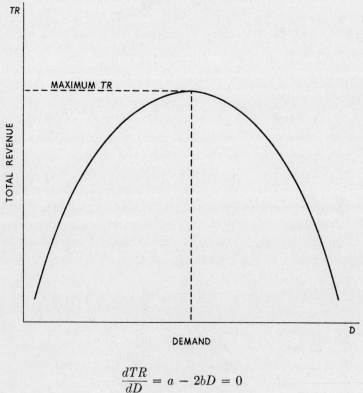

$$\frac{dTR}{dD} = a - 2bD = 0$$

$$D = \frac{a}{2b}$$

We are assured of a maximum by noting that

$$\frac{d^2 TR}{dD^2} = -2b$$

is negative since b is a positive constant. It may be noted also that the derivative of total revenue with respect to volume is given the name "marginal revenue." It expresses the rate at which revenue increases with increases in the volume of sales.

Most firms, however, would not find that maximum total revenue resulted in maximum profit, thus we must investigate the problem of total cost of production in order to compute profit in the more usual way.

THE TOTAL COST FUNCTION

Imagine now that the manager is able to examine the productive operations of his firm, and from his accountants and engineers learn a good deal about the costs of production. At this point he may be especially interested in how total cost changes as the volume of production changes. In estimating total cost it is helpful to divide the components of this sum into two classes called fixed costs and variable costs.

Fixed costs include all costs which are independent of the volume of production. These are the costs which must be met whatever the level of production, such as real estate taxes and interest on debts.

Variable costs include all costs which vary more or less directly with the volume of production. These costs include such things as direct labor costs and raw materials costs which tend to rise as the number of units produced goes up. Now it usually happens in actuality that it is hard to classify costs as being absolutely fixed or absolutely variable. It may be difficult to discover just exactly how variable costs do vary with the level of production. Further, costs which are fixed in the short run may not be fixed in the long run. For example, if production is stopped, the firm may meet its fixed expenses for a short period in anticipation of renewed activity; however, this cannot go on for long without resulting in liquidation or some other drastic modification of the cost structure. In spite of these difficulties, these cost classifications are sufficiently suggestive to give some important insights. To clarify these ideas, let

$$TC(D) = \text{total cost at a production level of } D \text{ units}$$
$$FC = \text{fixed costs, independent of } D$$
$$VC(D) = \text{variable costs at a production level of } D$$
$$TC(D) = FC + VC(D)$$

This is the general form of the firm's total cost function.

Consider first a simple case in which the variable cost function turns out to be a simple linear function of the volume of production.

$$VC(D) = vD$$

The rate of change of the variable costs with the volume of production is called the "marginal cost" or sometimes the "incremental cost." In this case we have simply

$$\text{Marginal cost} = \frac{dVC(D)}{dD} = v$$

This implies that marginal costs are constant and that the cost of producing a small additional amount is always the same. If D is taken to be a discrete variable then the marginal cost is simply the

FIGURE 2–3

A Total Cost Function

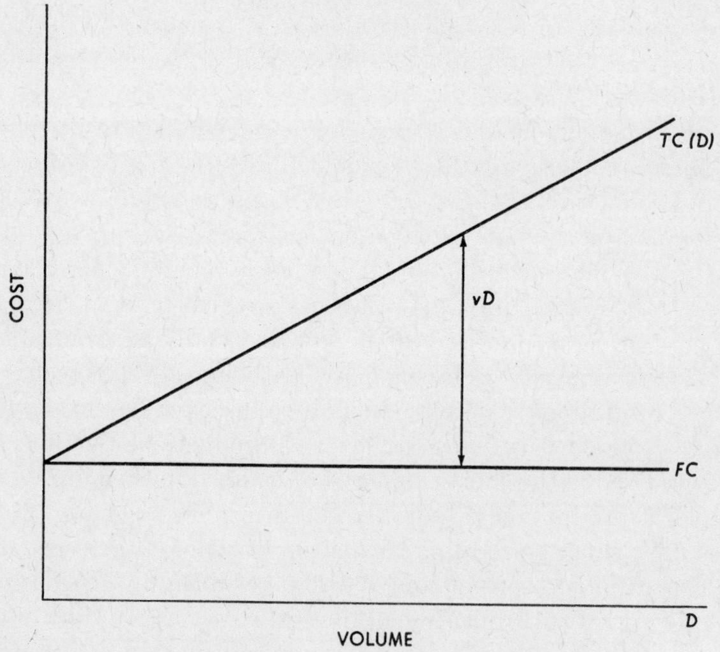

cost of producing one additional unit of product when the production is at some given level.

$$VC(D + 1) - VC(D) = \text{marginal cost}$$

Using the simple linear variable cost function (Figure 2–3), the total cost function becomes

$$TC(D) = FC + vD$$

and profit is given by

$$
\begin{aligned}
\text{Profit} = TR(D) - TC(D) &= (aD - bD^2) - (FC + vD) \\
&= -FC + (a - v)D - bD^2 \qquad \text{for } 0 \le D \le a/b \\
&= 0 \qquad\qquad\qquad\qquad\quad \text{otherwise}
\end{aligned}
$$

The manager who wishes to maximize profit under these conditions will then be interested in the value of D which maximizes this function. Thus if

$$a - v > 0$$

$$\frac{d(\text{profit})}{dD} = a - v - 2bD = 0$$

$$D = \frac{a - v}{2b}$$

FIGURE 2–4

A Profit and Loss Function

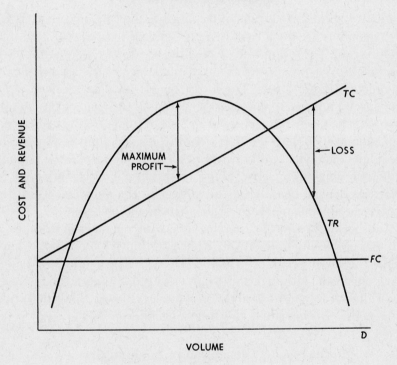

If

$$a - v \leq 0$$

the profit will be maximized for

$$D = 0$$

The reader should satisfy himself that this does in fact yield a maximum. The situation which confronts the manager is shown graphically in Figure 2–4, in which we assume

$$a - v > 0$$

An important principle emerges here if one observes that at this level of production, marginal cost is equal to marginal revenue. For

$$D = \frac{a - v}{2b}, \quad \frac{dTR(D)}{dD} = a - 2bD = v \qquad (a - v > 0)$$

Thus one might formulate a decision rule which says, "To maximize profit, increase production as long as marginal revenue is greater than marginal cost, but stop when the two are equal." Alternatively, "To maximize profit, increase production until the revenue from the last unit of product is just equal to the cost of producing it."

BREAK-EVEN AND SHUTDOWN POINTS

From Figure 2–4 certain other insights may be obtained. There are two points at which total revenue is equal to total cost, and thus profit is zero. These points are called the break-even points. Between the break-even points the firm will make a profit, but outside of them it will suffer a loss. The lower, or left-hand break-even point is of special interest to managers since this is the level of production that must be reached to get the firm "out of the red." Thus one hears hotel managers remarking that their break-even point is 80 per cent occupancy, and steel mill operators speaking of a break-even point at 67 per cent of capacity. Many of the firm's decisions about its activities depend heavily on the answer to the question, "Will the venture be able to operate at or above its break-even point?"

Another decision which may confront the manager is whether or not to cease production entirely when conditions force volume down below the lower break-even point. This decision might be studied using our model although this is not essential. Suppose the manager finds himself forced to produce at some level lower than his break-even point. He has then the following alternatives:

$$a_1 = \text{stop production}$$
$$a_2 = \text{continue production at some level}$$
$$D_1 \text{ below the break-even point}$$

Assuming that no uncertainty or risk is involved in the analysis of this decision, we could compute the profit associated with each alternative:

	Profit
a_1	$-FC$
a_2	$TR(D_1) - TC(D_1)$

The profit for a_2 may be computed as follows:

$$TR(D_1) - TC(D_1) = TR(D)_1 - (FC + vD_1)$$

Alternative a_2 will be preferred if

$$TR(D_1) - (FC + vD_1) > -FC$$
$$TR(D_1) > vD_1$$

Thus we have the decision rule, "As long as total revenue exceeds variable costs, do not stop production." This rule must obviously apply in the short run, since generally the firm cannot go on sustaining a loss for very long. It is the kind of rule which would be sensible if the manager felt that better prospects lay in the future. Otherwise the best choice would be to liquidate the firm completely. The point at which total revenue is equal to the variable cost of production is called the shutdown point.

In our example the manager would not wish to shut down until production actually was forced down to nothing. This of course is not true in general, and one often finds firms willing to do business under conditions where total revenue is less than total cost in order to cut their losses. The losses are clearly those that would be sustained if production were stopped entirely.

PRODUCTION

The problems and decisions discussed so far are largely the concern of top management, since they are in the realm of major company policy. The analyst, at least early in his career, is more likely to be associated with decisions which are specifically related to the methods of production and operation employed by the firm. Thus he may be concerned with alternative production processes, alternative designs for the product, alternative operating procedures, and so on.

Ideally, of course, all the decisions should be studied from the over-all viewpoint of the firm, with the aim perhaps of maximizing total profit as was shown previously. For obvious practical reasons, not every decision can be approached immediately from this "global" viewpoint, and thus one uses other, more immediate criteria. Typically, much effort is devoted to reducing costs through the improvement of the product, the process, or the operating procedures. While it may sometimes be true that if costs are reduced by a dollar, profit will increase by a dollar, things are usually not this simple. Suppose, for example, that the analyst can show that by refusing to disrupt production in order to push through "rush" orders, costs can be reduced. Clearly, profits may not be increased by an equal amount, since the customers may no longer be satisfied with the increased delivery time on rush orders and may take their business elsewhere. In practice, however, many decisions are approached from the viewpoint of minimizing costs, since it may be difficult to measure profit directly, and good judgment indicates that higher profits are likely to result.

ECONOMIES OF MASS PRODUCTION

Suppose that management is confronted with the following decision. If the production process and equipment are kept substantially the same, what volume of production will minimize the average unit cost of production? This is the question of the economic operating level for a plant. If we assume that the plant's costs under these conditions are given by a linear total cost function as in Figure 2–3 then the average unit cost is simply given by

$$AC(D) = \frac{TC(D)}{D} = \frac{FC + vD}{D} = \frac{FC}{D} + v$$

In this situation, the more we produce, the lower the average unit cost. This phenomenon is so important that it is given the name "economies of mass production," and forms the entire basis for much of our industrial development. The simple linear cost function leads to the conclusion that production may be increased indefinitely, always with the result of lowering average unit cost. Recalling that the plant and production process are being held substantially constant, this conclusion does not appear realistic. As we try to obtain more and more production from the plant, the facilities are strained to their limit, expensive overtime operation is necessary, scrap may increase, maintenance may be neglected, and average cost may go up (Figure 2–5). We would have noted this if we had assumed a somewhat more realistic total cost function such as

$$TC(D) = FC + v_1D + v_2D^2$$

In this case average cost is given by

$$AC(D) = \frac{FC}{D} + v_1 + v_2D$$

and will be minimized when

$$\frac{dAC(D)}{dD} = -\frac{FC}{D^2} + v_2 = 0$$

This yields

$$D = \sqrt{\frac{FC}{v_2}}$$

The phenomenon of rising average cost which sets in when production goes above this level suggests that we might formulate the general hypothesis: *As we try to get more and more production out of a given plant and process, the unit cost will eventually go up.*

FIGURE 2–5

An Average Cost Function

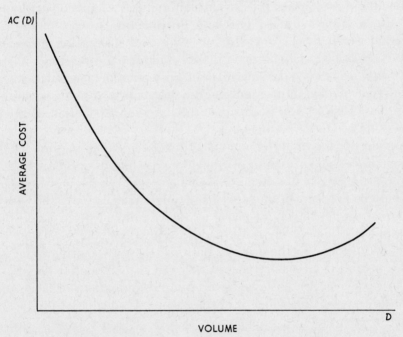

Thus we have to compromise between the conflicting effects of economies of mass production and the eventual upturning of the average cost function. The best compromise in the sense of minimizing cost is given by the result obtained above.

At this point another helpful decision rule may be obtained. At the point where average cost is minimum it is easy to show that

$$AC(D) = \text{marginal cost at } D = v_1 + 2\sqrt{FCv_2}$$

Thus we could say: *Average cost will come down as long as marginal cost is below it. But when marginal cost exceeds average cost, it*

*will rise. To minimize average cost, find the level of production where
it is equal to marginal cost.* A little thought will confirm the common sense of this rule.

Instead of seeking the best production volume for a given plant
facility, let us turn the problem around to a form in which it rather
commonly is encountered by analysts. Suppose management has
already decided upon a level of production, and the analyst is given
the task of finding the plant, production process, and operating
methods which will minimize the cost of this volume of production.
Now this is an extremely complicated problem which is beyond the
grasp of a single person in most cases. However, an analyst often has
the task of evaluating at least some alternative production processes
and operating methods. This task is really the subject of the remainder of this book, but again we will study a simple overview of
the problem which helps to set the stage for detailed analysis.

Suppose it were possible to summarize all our knowledge about
different production technologies for the plant by a single equation.
Suppose further that in this case the different production methods
and operating procedures may be simply characterized by the
amount of labor and the amount of machinery they require. Thus,
to produce a given amount, one might have a highly automated plant
consisting largely of automatic machinery and relatively little labor
would be needed. On the other hand, one might use only the barest
necessities in the way of machines, leave most of the work to the
employees themselves, and thus have a relatively large amount of
labor consumed in the process. Between these two extremes lie all
the possible degrees of mechanization and automation for the plant.
The manager then has a wide variety of combinations of labor and
machinery, each of which, we will assume, is capable of producing
the desired amount. Suppose we were to measure labor in man-
hours and machinery usage in terms of machine-hours. Our summarizing function would then be of the form

$$D = f(L, M)$$

where L stands for labor in man-hours, and M for machine usage in
machine-hours.

This function says that any pair of values for L and M which
satisfy the relation will yield D units of output, or L man-hours, and
M machine-hours will yield D units of output according to the
function. Thus it may be thought of as summarizing all the efficient
techological possibilities for production by relating input to output.

Such a relation is usually called a "production function" (Figure 2–6). Now the manager who sets out to minimize the cost of a given level of production must know his production function, although in actuality he may know only a small part of it, and he must also know the costs of the various inputs which are represented by the function. Let us assume a linear cost structure for the inputs.

FIGURE 2–6

A Production Function

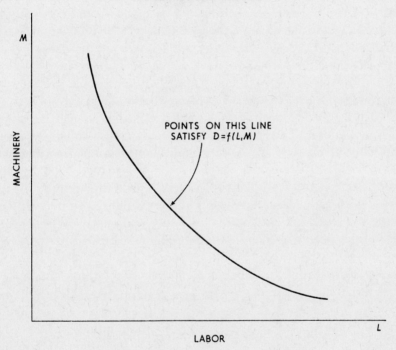

POINTS ON THIS LINE
SATISFY $D = f(L, M)$

M

MACHINERY

LABOR

L

C_1 = cost of a man-hour of labor
C_2 = cost of a machine-hour of usage

Total outlay is then given by

$$TO = C_1 L + C_2 M$$

where the values of L and M must be chosen to satisfy the production function for an output of D units. To illustrate this decision, let us assume a production function such as

$$D = aL + bM - cM^2$$

If we solve the production function for L, and then substitute in the total outlay function, we obtain

$$TO(M) = C_1 \left\{ \frac{D - bM + cM^2}{a} \right\} + C_2 M$$

We wish to minimize $TO(M)$ subject to the constraints that neither the number of man-hours, L, nor the number of machine-hours, M, take on negative values. Since

$$L = \frac{D - bM + cM^2}{a}$$

L will be nonnegative if

$$M \leq \frac{b - \sqrt{b^2 - 4cD}}{2c} = M_0$$

We will consider only the case in which

$$b^2 - 4cD \geq 0$$

The problem is thus to find the value of M in the interval

$$0 \leq M \leq M_0$$

which minimizes $TO(M)$. The value of M which satisfies the equation

$$\frac{dTO(M)}{dM} = 0$$

is

$$M^* = \frac{C_1 b - C_2 a}{2C_1 c}$$

If $0 \leq M^* \leq M_0$, then M^* is the solution. If $M^* < 0$, then the solution is to take $M = 0$, and if $M^* > M_0$, then the solution will be to take $M = M_0$. This amount of machine-hours and the corresponding amount of man-hours obtained from the production function yields the technology which minimizes the cost of producing D units. Another useful decision rule may be drawn from this analysis by stating the conditions for minimum total cost slightly differently.

$$\frac{dTO(M)}{dM} = \frac{dC_1 L}{dM} + \frac{dC_2 M}{dM} = 0$$

Here we understand that L is a function of M. It follows that

$$\frac{dC_1 L}{dM} = - \frac{dC_2 M}{dM}$$

This may be interpreted as follows: *Go on substituting machinery for labor until the rate at which costs are being reduced by declining labor requirements just equals the rate at which costs are being in-creased through the addition of machinery.* In another form: *Con-tinue to mechanize until the marginal cost of the last machinery added is just balanced by the marginal savings from the last labor replaced.* This gives the manager a key to the amount of automation which will be economic.

This point of view is somewhat oversimplified in relation to the detail and complexity of the actual decision-making tasks. How-ever, it does suggest the importance of an economic balance among the inputs to the production activity.

A PRODUCTION MANAGEMENT DECISION

The work of the analyst is partly that of transforming manage-ment problems into mathematical problems. If he can discover or create a mathematical structure which reasonably reflects the man-agement decision, then he is in a position to use the mathematical structure or model to predict the results of various managerial choices. One way, and perhaps the only way, to become acquainted with the art of model building is to study some examples. Let us take a somewhat more detailed look at production by means of an especially useful model which may be used to capture some of the complexity of production management decisions. Instead of consid-ering a plant in terms of a production function, we now look more closely at what is inside the plant.

Suppose we have a food-processing plant, and our business con-sists of buying vegetables from farmers, preparing them, and pack-ing them in cans of our own manufacture. The plant consists of three departments: the can department which produces the containers, the preparation department which cleans and cooks the vege-tables, and the packing department which fills and labels the cans. At the moment, farmers are offering both peas and tomatoes, either of which could be processed in our plant. Our whole cost and revenue structure is so simple that we can say each can of peas yields us 2 cents profit and each can of tomatoes yields 3 cents profit. These profits are the same no matter what level of production for either vegetable we decide upon. If we are planning for the coming week, then our profit for the week will be (in cents)

$$\text{Profit} = 2P + 3T$$

where P is the number of cans of peas we turn out and T is the number of cans of tomatoes. At this point it may appear that, since

tomatoes are more profitable, we should forsake peas entirely and
turn out all the tomatoes possible. However, things are not usually
that simple. First of all, we discover that the farmers in the area will
have available no more than the equivalent of 20,000 cans of tomatoes and no more than the equivalent of 25,000 cans of peas. Thus
our choices of P and T are limited by the availability of vegetables.
It must be that

$$P \leq 25,000 \qquad T \leq 20,000$$

Next, we note that the capacity of our departments is limited also.
Suppose both vegetables are packed in the same type of can, and
that the can department has a capacity of 30,000 cans per week.
This puts another restriction on our production program.

$$P + T \leq 30,000$$

The preparation department, which operates 40 hours per week, requires .001 hours to process enough peas to fill a can and .002 hours
to process a can of tomatoes. We have then a processing department restriction which says

$$.001P + .002T \leq 40$$

or

$$P + 2T \leq 40,000$$

The packing department has a capacity of 50,000 cans of either type
for the week, giving

$$P + T \leq 50,000$$

One might go on adding restrictions and conditions to make the
problem more and more realistic, but the decision about a production program is sufficiently complicated at this point to suggest the
difficulties that might be encountered. The problem is still simple
enough so that its solution may be illustrated graphically. Any
decision as to a production program can be represented by a point
on Figure 2–7, that is, a particular pair of values for P and T. By
plotting the inequations which express the restrictions we can see
exactly how our choice is limited. Because of the limited production
by farmers our choice of P must lie on or below the horizontal line
$P = 25,000$. Similarly, our choice of T must lie to the left of a vertical line $T = 20,000$. The other two restrictions are similarly plotted,
with the result that our decision is limited in fact to P and T combinations lying in or on the edge of the shaded area in Figure 2–7.

The capacity of the canning department does not need to be considered in this particular decision, since the other restrictions prevent any possibility of reaching this capacity. At the moment we have more capacity than necessary in this department.

Now let us plot, on this same diagram, lines of equal profit. That

FIGURE 2–7

Possible Production Programs and Restrictions

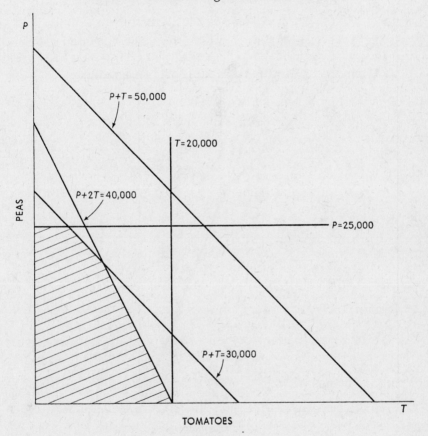

is, let us plot combinations of P and T which will yield a given amount of profit. For example the lines

$$.02P + .03T = \$150$$
$$.02P + .03T = \$300$$

and so on for profits of $450, $600, and $700 have been plotted on Figure 2–8. The manager's problem is then to pick the production program, or combination of P and T, which lies in or on the boundaries of the polygon of programs which satisfy the restrictions, and yet maximizes profit. Examination of the diagram will show that the equal profit lines are parallel, and that as we move in a northeasterly direction from the origin, profit increases. The line for profit equal to $700 is thus the maximum profit line which still passes through a

FIGURE 2–8

Lines of Equal Profit

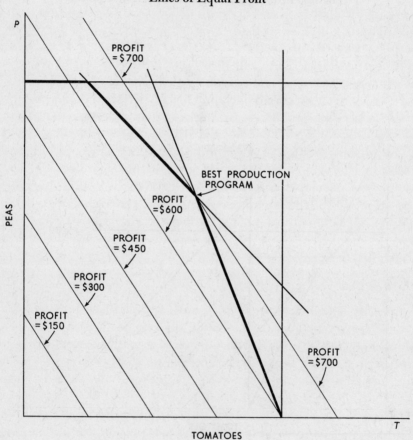

possible production program. This best production program lies on the vertex of the polygon where

$$P = 20,000 \text{ cans}$$
$$T = 10,000 \text{ cans}$$

This problem is one of a well-developed class of linear programming problems. It emphasizes the viewpoint that the manager's decisions about production often involve the choice of alternative programs for the employment of available facilities, and that these decisions must always be made within the limitations of a wide variety of restrictions.

THE PROJECT

Having suggested this overview of the firm and some of the larger decisions involved in its design and operation, we can move somewhat closer to the realm of "everyday" decision problems encountered by the analyst. These decision problems are many and varied, but they may involve such things as the choice between machines, between methods of operation, between designs for a product, or between materials. The analyst also encounters decision problems involving organization and administration, personnel policy, inventory policy, maintenance policy, purchasing policy, and so on. These kinds of decision problems, which are encountered repeatedly and form the day-to-day activity of the analyst, are sometimes referred to as "projects." Often it is useful to organize this work in terms of such projects, where each project involves a particular decision. The methods of undertaking these decision-making projects will occupy our attention for the remainder of the book. Before moving ahead, however, it is important to suggest some of the ways in which the firm determines the considerations relevant to decisions at the project level.

CRITERIA

Clearly, decisions made at any level within the firm should be made in such a manner as to advance the firm as a whole toward its objectives. Now this little truism is harmless enough until one tries to take it seriously in an actual decision problem. Let us pass over the fact that in many firms the objectives are not made explicit by anyone, and it may be very difficult to find out exactly what they are. Let us pass over the fact that the firm may have a number of objectives, and that some of these may be in conflict with one another. Let us also pass over the fact that the objectives may change from time to time, that different people may have widely differing ideas as to objectives, and that most people in the firm are making decisions on the basis of some mixture of their personal objectives, those of their work unit or department, and those of the firm itself. Let us simply assume the firm is interested in making a profit. This is a very ordinary assumption, but it certainly does not solve the problem. Somehow we must decide whether this means immediate profit, or long-run profit, or some continuing rate of profit over time. We must decide just how profit is to be computed for the firm, since this may depend heavily on which accounting conventions are used and just how the firm's operations are viewed. We must decide how to consider decisions which involve "gambles" or risks. For example, how are we to choose between a small but certain profit and a large but highly uncertain profit?

Supposing that we could make our way through this maze of problems, we would then have a measure of profit which could be used as a criterion for making decisions. In selecting a machine we would try to select the one which results in the most profit to the company in the sense in which we have decided to define profit. (We are still overlooking the problem of whether the firm wishes to maximize profit, make a "fair" rate of profit, or what.) If we have decided that what we are after is to maximize the profit on the firm's profit and loss statement at the end of the year, then presumably the ultimate criterion in every decision is: "Which alternative will make the profit figure for the firm as large as possible?" This type of thinking has been called the "systems approach." It simply means that in every decision we consider the impact of the alternatives on the firm or system as a whole. From a strictly practical point of view, two difficulties with this criterion still remain. First, it would mean that we would have to trace the consequences of every decision throughout the entire firm. Now a certain amount of this kind of investigation is vital. There is little use in making a decision in one department which will generate difficulties in other departments, resulting ultimately in a loss rather than a profit to the firm. However, in much day-to-day decision making it is neither possible nor economically feasible to study all the ramifications of a decision through the entire company. Every analyst knows that he should do this as a good "systems" man, but he knows also that very often he is forced to make decisions from a somewhat more provincial point of view. The classic example is that of the firm in which financial management, production management, and sales management find their perceived goals in conflict. The sales department demands large inventories of a wide variety of products in order to satisfy their customers. Production wants to make long runs of a few products and to avoid special orders and rush orders. This, coupled with ample in-process inventories, makes for easy production scheduling, high machine utilization, and low unit cost of production. Those concerned with finance aim for low inventories turning over rapidly and thus a modest drain on the firm's working capital.

The second difficulty is that, for many decisions, it is simply impossible to predict the profit which will result from the various alternatives. Thus, if we are deciding which of two materials to use in the manufacture of a product, it is often far easier to discover which will have the lesser cost than it is to find out how much profit will be attributable to the use of the materials and whether this profit will differ among them.

The net result of all this is, in practice, that every decision really should be made from the point of view of its effects on the over-all objectives of the firm, but many decisions must utilize some proximate criteria instead. It then becomes the fondest hope of the decision maker that the proximate criterion is highly correlated with the ultimate criterion. Thus, when we select the least-cost material, we do so in the hope that this will result in increased profits. We will have more to say about the criterion problem as we progress.

Three other economic considerations are often brought to bear upon decision problems at the project level and are largely determined by the firm in which the decisions arise—taxes, interest, and depreciation. Taxes will be discussed in Chapter 8; however, it is convenient to introduce the other two considerations immediately.

INTEREST

Calculations involving interest have become a traditional part of the analysis of investment decision problems. The particular interest rate used and the way in which it is used derive directly from considerations of the firm within which the decision is made. There are a variety of situations which lead to the use of interest in the analysis of these problems.

The Cost of Borrowed Funds. Interest considerations first found their way into the analysis of management actions in the days of active railroad construction. Much of the railroads' money came from bonds, and thus it was natural in comparing alternative projects to include the cost of the money that would have to be invested in them. Many firms continue to obtain some part of their funds by means of bonds or loans, as opposed to equity capital. Thus, if one is considering the purchase of a plant which is to be financed by a mortgage, interest charges on the loan will be relevant in comparing the cost of alternative plants. Typically, such a mortgage contract might specify that the lender makes a loan of, say, $100,000 to be secured by the plant itself. This is to be paid back in 20 equal annual payments, with interest on the unpaid balance at 5 per cent compounded annually. This means that each year the firm must pay $8,024, some of which reduces the amount of the loan and the remainder of which pays the interest on the amount owed during the year. The method of making such computations is presented in Appendix A.

The Opportunity Cost of Investments Foregone. Suppose the firm always has available certain investment opportunities. It may, for example, be able to invest funds in its own operations for improvement or expansion, and perhaps money thus invested earns a return of 10 per cent. Alternatively, the firm may be able to invest in stocks or bonds, loans to its customers, and so forth. Such a possibility is often called a "standard investment opportunity." The firm may then wish to establish the following kind of policy: "Since we can always obtain a return of X per cent from our standard investment opportunity, we will not put money in any project unless it will earn at least X per cent." Thus, in computing the cost of various alternatives, the analyst may simply add on X per cent of the amount invested. Such a cost may be thought of as the opportunity cost of not investing the funds in the standard investment opportunity.

This leads also to the interesting idea of the "time value of money." Since receipts and disbursements resulting from a particular project may occur at various points in time, the question arises, "Is an income of one dollar today equivalent to an income of one dollar at the end of a year from today?" Clearly, if the firm receives a dollar today, it will immediately invest the dollar in the standard investment opportunity, or some other project yielding the same or greater return. Thus, at the end of the year the firm will have the equivalent of one dollar plus X per cent of one dollar. Thus a "present dollar" is worth more than a "future dollar," and the relationship between the two depends on the interest rate. If the firm uses an interest rate of 5 per cent compounded annually, then a dollar today is "equivalent" in the time value sense to

> $1.05 at the end of 1 year
> $1.103 at the end of 2 years
> $1.158 at the end of 3 years
> $1.629 at the end of 10 years
> $2.653 at the end of 20 years
> and so on

This means that the cost of a project will depend not only on the incomes and outlays involved, but also on the times at which these occur and the interest rate used by the firm.

Satisfactory Return. Another situation closely related to the standard investment opportunity arises when the firm simply establishes a policy that any project which it undertakes must yield at least a certain rate of return. This rate of return it takes to be a satisfactory return or a "minimum attractive return." The only reason for distinguishing this situation is that such a policy may be used even if the standard investment opportunity is not in fact available. Thus the firm may decide that, for the purpose of examining alternative courses of action, it will simply rule out all alternatives which do not result in at least the satisfactory rate of return. Here again, the analyst looking for the least-cost alternative may simply add on a return at the satisfactory rate to the costs of each alternative before choosing.

Deferred Consumption and Risk. Another notion leading to the use of interest suggests that when the firm earns a dollar it might pay that dollar to the owners who would presumably use it for their own pleasure or consumption. If the firm instead invests the dollar in a project, the owners will have to defer their consumption of the fruits of that dollar until a later time. To compensate the owners for this deferment of consumption, an interest charge must be made. Still another view suggests that many of the projects which are undertaken involve a certain risk of loss. The interest rate serves in part to compensate the firm for running this risk. The rate is theoretically set so that the interest earned by those projects which succeed will pay for the losses suffered due to the projects which fail. Since we will try to approach the problem of risk more directly later on, this view will not be stressed.

Thus, for one or more of these reasons interest computations often become a part of the analysis of decision problems.

DEPRECIATION

It is of course the hope of the firm that in undertaking any project it will eventually recover the amount invested in the project, as well as earn an additional profit or return. A major problem in the analysis of alternatives is thus to discover those which will in fact fulfill this hope.

One of the accountant's duties is to report the past performance of the firm in terms of profits and losses. In computing profits he "charges off" each year a part of the investment in an asset against the income for the year. This charge is called a depreciation charge and the rules for deciding how much to charge each year are called a depreciation policy. Several considerations may be brought to bear by the firm in setting up a depreciation policy. Usually every attempt will be made to report accurately the profits of the firm. Thus, careful estimates must be made of the useful life of the asset to the firm and of how it declines in effectiveness, productivity, and value to the firm over this useful life. Depreciation charges will then be set to reflect this decline as closely as possible. However, since this decline in value to the firm is generally very difficult to estimate, management often relies on one of several standard methods of depreciation, such as those to be discussed in the following paragraphs. A major consideration for the firm is that of income taxes which are, of course, based upon profits. Management may adopt a particular depreciation policy largely for the purposes of gaining certain income tax advantages, and may be perfectly within the law in so doing. The usual depreciation policies are as follows:

Straight-Line Depreciation. A fixed amount is charged each year for depreciation. This amount is determined by the following relation:

$$\text{Annual depreciation charge} = \frac{I - S}{n}$$

where I is the initial investment or first cost of the asset, n its estimated useful life to the firm in years, and S is its estimated salvage value at the end of n years of service.

Fixed Percentage of a Declining Balance. Each year a fixed percentage of the undepreciated value (book value) of the asset is charged off for depreciation. If $p(100)$ is the fixed percentage used, then the undepreciated balance at the end of year $j - 1$ will be

$$I(1 - p)^{j-1}$$

and the amount of depreciation for year j will be

$$d(j) = pI(1 - p)^{j-1}$$

To depreciate an asset requiring an initial investment I and having a salvage value $S \neq 0$ over a service life of n years, the percentage is given by

$$p = 1 - \sqrt[n]{S/I} \qquad (S \neq 0)$$

If the asset has no salvage value it cannot be fully depreciated by this method alone.

Sum of the Years' Digits Method. Depreciation for the year j in the life of an asset having a service life of n years given by

$$d(j) = \frac{n - j + 1}{\sum_{j=1}^{n} j} \ (I - S) = \frac{2(n - j + 1)}{n(n + 1)} \ (I - S)$$

Thus, for an asset with a $10,000 investment and no salvage value **after** a service life of five years, this method would yield

Year	Depreciation		
1	$10,000(5/15)	=	$3,333
2	10,000(4/15)	=	2,667
3	10,000(3/15)	=	2,000
4	10,000(2/15)	=	1,333
5	10,000(1/15)	=	667

Sinking Fund Depreciation. A real or imaginary sinking fund is established and a fixed deposit is made in the fund at the end of each year in the life of the asset. The deposit is so computed that the amount put into the fund plus the interest earned on it will just equal the amount by which the asset is to be depreciated. The actual depreciation charge is equal to the sum of the sinking fund deposit plus the interest on the amount in the fund during the year.

There are other methods of depreciation but these will suffice to illustrate their general nature. As has been pointed out, these methods are used to record the history of the company in terms of profits and losses.

The analyst approaching decisions about the acquisition or disposal of assets may utilize a slightly different point of view. His problem is first to predict the life of the asset in the service of the firm, which he may do using both economic and technological considerations. Next he must predict whether or not the asset will produce earnings sufficient to recover the investment required to obtain it. The analyst may later restudy the decision as to the service life of the machine, and continually reopen the question of when it should be replaced. When this decision is studied, it is not the depreciated value on the accountant's book which is useful, but the actual salvage value or market value of the asset at the time replacement is contemplated. This point is more clearly established in the next section.

IRRELEVANCE OF PAST OUTLAYS

From the viewpoint of the firm, most decisions which arise concern the future and the selection of future courses of action. This means that in many respects what has happened as the result of past decisions is irrelevant, except as it affects the outcome of present and future decisions. One cannot rewrite history, and one must "let bygones be bygones." The important questions are: "Where does the firm stand at present?" and "Where does it go from here?" Consider the retailer who desires to maintain a constant inventory of one of his commodities during a period of rising prices. Let us suppose that he has purchased in the past a quantity of this commodity at a unit price of $6.00. Applying his usual markup, he now sells these at $9.00 each. When he goes to replenish his stock he discovers that the price has gone up to $10.00. He thus finds himself in the unhappy position of having sold goods at $9.00 which he can only replace at a cost of $10.00. Now in this case it is clear that the fact that he originally paid $6.00 is irrelevant in fixing the selling price at present. He would have been wiser to overlook this entirely and to reason that since it will cost him $10.00 per unit to replace the goods, he should sell them for, say, $15.00.

The notion of "letting bygones be bygones" is also important in the following decision problem. The firm bought a machine two years ago for $5,000, and since that time has recovered $1,000 of its investment. The unrecovered balance is thus $4,000. The used machine can be sold, however, for only $2,000. A salesman offers the firm a more modern and efficient machine for $6,000, which will perform the same functions. The old machine costs $1,000 per year to operate, but the new machine will cost only $500 per year to operate. Assuming a useful life of ten years for both machines, no salvage value for either machine at that time, and neglecting interest considerations, should the firm buy the new machine? The answer is yes. From the decision maker's point of view the old machine could be sold for $2,000 today; thus, if it is not sold, he is in fact paying this amount to keep it. The fact that it originally cost $5,000 and that the books presently show an unrecovered balance of $4,000 do not enter into the analysis of the decision. The difference between the unrecovered balance and what the machine would presently bring if sold is called a "sunk cost" or a "bygone." Thus, if the present machine is kept, the cost of ten years' service will be (interest is neglected)

Investment	$ 2,000
Operating cost	10,000
(10 years at $1,000)	
Total	$12,000

For the new machine we have:

Investment................$ 6,000
Operating cost................ 5,000
(10 years at $500)
Total................$11,000

There is a tendency among some decision makers to require the new machine to pay also for the sunk cost loss of $2,000 which will be suffered if the old machine is sold. If this amount is added on to the cost of the new machine, the old one will be retained. In order to establish clearly that this latter approach is wrong, and to forestall other mistaken approaches to the problem, consider the following simple demonstration.

Consider a time scale on which T_0 represents the present.

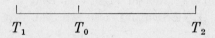

$$T_1 \qquad T_0 \qquad\qquad T_2$$

Assume

1. At time T_1 a machine called A is purchased with an investment of amount I_A.
2. From T_1 until T_0 machine A is operated at a total operating cost of C_A' and earns a gross revenue of R_A.
3. The salvage or resale value of A is S_{A0} at T_0, and S_{A2} at T_2.
4. At T_0 a new machine called B becomes available at a cost of I_B, which will have a salvage value of S_{B2} at T_2.
5. From T_0 to T_2 either machine may be used to earn a gross return of R. The operating cost during this period will be C_A if A is used, and C_B if B is used.

Now suppose the firm overlooks the irrelevance of past outlays, and asks the question, "Which machine should we choose at T_0, so as to maximize profit over the entire period T_1 to T_2?" To answer this, let

$$a_1 = \text{buy machine } B \text{ at } T_0$$
$$a_2 = \text{keep machine } A \text{ until } T_2$$

The total profit over the entire period is

Profit for $a_1 = R_A - C_A' - I_A + S_{A0} + R - C_B - I_B + S_{B2}$
Profit for $a_2 = R_A - C_A' - I_A + R - C_A + S_{A2}$

Now compute the difference between these two profits:

Profit for a_1 − profit from $a_2 = \{S_{A0} + C_A - S_{A2}\} - \{I_B + C_B - S_{B2}\}$

Since we have assumed that the gross revenues are equal in both cases, the difference in profits is simply the difference in costs. The costs which are relevant for a_1 include neither the original investment in machine A nor the amount of this investment recovered (or unrecovered) up to T_0. The costs in each case are exactly those used in the foregoing analysis, that is, investment at T_0 plus future operating cost less future salvage value (if any). Clearly the proper investment for machine A at T_0 is its salvage value at that time.

This leads us to a general rule about bygones or sunk costs: "In making decisions about the future of an asset, the present investment in this asset is what could be obtained for it if disposed of at the present time."

SUGGESTIONS FOR FURTHER STUDY

GRANT, EUGENE L. and IRESON, W. GRANT. *Principles of Engineering Economy.* New York: Ronald Press Co., 1960.

SAMUELSON, PAUL A. *Economics.* 5th Ed. New York: McGraw-Hill Book Co., 1961.

PROBLEMS

2–1. Assume that total revenue and total cost for a firm are given by the following functions:

$$TR(D) = PD \qquad TC(D) = FC + vD \qquad (D \geq 0)$$

Find the break-even point. How can the firm maximize profit, assuming P is constant? What essential features are missing from this model?

2–2. A firm estimates that its total cost and total revenue functions are

$$TC(D) = FC + vD \qquad \begin{aligned} TR(D) &= aD - bD^2 \quad &&\text{for } 0 \leq D \leq a/b \\ &= 0 \quad &&\text{otherwise} \end{aligned}$$

where

$$FC = \$500.00 \qquad v = \$2.00 \qquad a = \$4.00 \qquad b = .001$$

Find

a) Production volume which maximizes profit.

b) Maximum profit.

c) Marginal cost and the marginal revenue for the volume computed in part a.

d) Break-even points.

2–3. An electronics firm decides to convert one of its plants to the manufacture of color television sets. A study of the market suggests that the gross income (in dollars ÷ 10,000) might be

$$\begin{aligned} \text{Gross income} &= 50X - .3X^2 \quad &&\text{for } 0 \leq X \leq 166 \\ &= 0 \quad &&\text{otherwise} \end{aligned}$$

where X is the number of sets produced each year (in thousands). A study of the production process suggests that the total cost of production (in dollars $\div$ 10,000) will be

$$\text{Total cost} = 100 + 50X - 3X^2 + .1X^3$$

Find

  a) Break-even points.
  b) Maximum profit point.
  c) Range of X in which economies of mass production are found.
  d) Range of X in which average cost increases.
  e) Point at which the plant should be shut down.

2–4. A machine is purchased for $10,000 and, being a highly specialized machine, has essentially no salvage value. The operation and maintenance costs for successive years of use are estimated as follows:

Year	Cost
1	$2,000
2	3,000
3	3,500
4	3,500
5	4,000
6	5,000
7	6,500
8	7,500
9	9,000

Show that the following principle is true: "To minimize the average annual cost of service from the machine, it should be replaced at the end of the year for which the average annual cost to date is exceeded by the marginal cost of obtaining one more year of service."

2–5. An electronic computer is purchased for $100,000 and is expected to be obsolete in ten years. At that time it will have a resale value of $10,000. Compute depreciation for each year using the straight-line method, a fixed percentage of a declining balance, and the sinking fund method with interest at 6 per cent. Which method gives the best protection against early obsolescence? What would be the advantage of leasing the computer, rather than purchasing it?

2–6. A firm has spent $500,000 on research to develop product A. It is estimated that A will yield an annual profit of $200,000 for five years. Before A is put into production, the firm is offered the patent rights on product B at a cost of $100,000. The firm may produce either product, but not both. Which would you recommend, if B is expected to yield a profit of $230,000 each year for five years?

2–7. Under what conditions will a firm find that maximizing total revenue is equivalent to maximizing profit?

2–8. As a car owner, what costs would you take to be fixed (independent of mileage driven) and what costs would you consider variable? How would you compute the marginal cost of a summer vacation trip?

2–9. For a typical manufacturing firm, give examples of
  a) Fixed costs.

   b) Variable costs.

   c) Costs which are fixed in the short run but variable in the long run.

2–10. Assume that profit for a firm is given by the function

$$\text{Profit} = aD - bD^2 - FC - vD \qquad \text{for } 0 \le D \le a/b$$
$$= 0 \qquad\qquad\qquad\qquad \text{otherwise}$$

Show that maximum profit occurs when

$$D = \frac{a - v}{2b} \qquad \text{if } a > v$$

Why is the optimum production volume independent of *FC?*

2–11. What reasonable argument can be advanced to convince one that marginal cost and marginal revenue will be equal at the point of maximum profit?

2–12. A construction firm has leased some equipment for a project which is finished ahead of schedule. The equipment lease still has 30 days to run and cannot be canceled. Under the lease a rent of $300 per day is paid for the equipment. Daily operating costs for the equipment are $75 for wages and $15 for fuel and supplies. If the contractor can find some small jobs to keep the equipment busy, what would be his minimum bid per day?

2–13. Give examples of how economies of mass production are achieved in

   a) An automobile assembly plant.

   b) A retail grocery business.

   c) Medical care clinics.

   d) Educational institutions.

2–14. How might the eventual upturn of the average cost function arise in the situations suggested in problem 2–13?

2–15. A firm has spent $300,000 for a plant site and the foundations for the building. If the project were sold in its current condition it would bring about $50,000. What conditions would have to be met by a second site to make it reasonable for the firm to give up its present site in favor of a second one?

2–16. A firm's total cost function is

$$TC(D) = FC + v_1 D + v_2 D^2$$

Show that average cost decreases as long as marginal cost is below it, and increases only when marginal cost rises above it.

2–17. A plant can make either product *A* or product *B* or some mix of the two. The profit from *A* is $1.50 per unit, and from *B*, $2.00 per unit. The firm has a contract to supply the government with 100,000 units of *A* each month. Its marketing group estimates that at most 200,000 *A*'s and 150,000 *B*'s could be sold each month. There is a bottleneck step in the production process which limits the output rate of the plant. This step, which operates 220 hours per month at most, requires .001 hours to process one unit of A and .002 hours to process one unit of B. Find the production program which will maximize profit.

2–18. The following statements describe the basic economic features of a manufacturing firm:

a) As production volume increases, total production cost first increases at a decreasing rate, and then increases at an increasing rate.

b) As sales volume increases, total revenue increases at a decreasing rate.

Translate these statements into a mathematical model and then use the model to find the economic production volume for the firm.

2–19. A gas station sells gasoline for 25 cents per gallon. The total cost for a day's operation is given by

$$TC(X) = (.00001)X^2 + .15X + 25$$

where X is the number of gallons sold in a day. What sales volume will be most profitable for the station?

2–20. A firm has two plants, A and B, which produce the same product. The production cost for x units at plant A is

$$TC_A(x) = a_0 + a_1x + a_2x^2 \qquad a_0,a_1,a_2 > 0$$

The production cost for y units at plant B is

$$TC_B(y) = b_0 + b_1y + b_2y^2 \qquad b_0,b_1,b_2 > 0$$

The total revenue for the firm is given by

$$TR(x + y) = c_0(x + y) - c_1(x + y)^2 \qquad c_0,c_1 > 0 \qquad 0 \le x + y \le = \frac{c_0}{c_1}$$

Find the production quantities for each of the plants, x and y, which will maximize profit for the firm.

2–21. Set up a mathematical model which would be an example of the situation described by the following statements. A firm must store a given amount of inventory, and it has two warehouses available. The cost of storing goods in warehouse 1 increases at an increasing rate as the quantity stored increases. Costs at warehouse 2 are similar in their behavior but of different magnitudes.

Use the model to show how one would determine the amount of the inventory to be allocated to each warehouse so as to minimize the total storage cost for the firm.

2–22. A firm with a fixed advertising budget sells in both the industrial and consumer markets. The return from advertising expenditures directed at the industrial market increases at a decreasing rate. Similar (but not identical) behavior is exhibited by the returns from advertising expenditures directed at the consumer market. How should the firm go about deciding what portion of its advertising budget to expend for each type of advertising?

2-23. Surveys of business investment policies indicate that some firms employ the following practice. If the book value of an old machine is greater than its salvage value, the difference is considered a part of the cost of replacing it with a new machine. What sort of argument would you present to a management which does this?

Chapter 3

DECISIONS UNDER ASSUMED CERTAINTY

SIMPLIFYING REALITY

THE KEY TO understanding any decision-making process is to discover the ways in which the decision maker simplifies the complex fabric of the environment into workable conceptions of his decision problems. The human mind has limited information-handling capacities; thus both analysts and managers deal with decisions in terms of conceptual simplifications or models of reality. Perhaps the most obvious of these simplifications is that of suppressing one's necessary ignorance of the future and considering a decision *as if* only one possible future could occur. This is not to pretend that one *knows* the future with certainty but is simply an act of conceptual simplification. It allows one to answer the question, "If this particular set of circumstances were to occur, what would be the reasonable course of action for management?" If a manager undertakes the course of action which results, one may think of him as *acting as if* the set of circumstances in question were sure to occur.

Likewise, when an analyst suppresses risk and uncertainty in making a management decision explicit, it does not imply that he claims knowledge of the future. It is one of the many ways in which science may simplify the real world in order to study it. None of us can know the future, but it is often very useful to ask questions about how we would act if we did.

In the previous chapter a number of managerial decisions were discussed as though the manager had virtually complete information about exactly what would happen if he chose any given course of action. No manager knows this much about his major policy decisions. Assuming certainty in such a discussion simplifies the decisions and clarifies the considerations involved but does not result in

49

a particularly realistic description of the actual situation. On the other hand, consider a decision as to which of two arbor presses to purchase. If, after reasonable investigation, we conclude that the two machines are equal in terms of output, operating costs, service life, and salvage value, then perhaps the only remaining consideration is price. In such a decision the prices are quoted firmly and there is little risk or uncertainty involved. The assumption that we have complete information and can consider the decision as being made under conditions of certainty is a reasonable and acceptable one. Just what level of information completeness to achieve or assume in a decision is a matter largely of judgment, although later the problem will be discussed in terms of some guiding principles.

It is traditional to study the great majority of managerial decisions as decisions under assumed certainty. Thus, in the selection of equipment, the selection of materials and designs, the choice of operating methods and policies, and so on, the assumption of certainty is widely used. The underlying reasons for its use may be

1. The amount of risk involved in the decision may appear to be so small that the analyst feels safe in neglecting it.

2. Risk may be importantly involved, but the difficulty or expense of including it in the analysis of the decision may suggest that it had better be left to the managerial judgment which will be applied after the analysis has been completed.

3. The decision may be such that, even if the risk were explicitly included, the choice would depend only on average values of the outcomes. For example, in estimating the cost of using a particular machine, its salvage value at some future time may be important. While the salvage value may not be exactly known, the analysis can be carried out by using the average salvage value for such machines.

Clearly, all of these reasons include the judgment or common sense of the analyst to a great extent.

PRINCIPLES OF CHOICE

In a decision under assumed certainty, the analysis leads to a statement of exactly what the outcome will be for each alternative course of action. The matrix model for such a decision has as many rows as there are alternatives, but only one column representing the certain future. By a principle of choice, we simply mean a rule which can be applied to such a matrix and will lead to the selection of a particular course of action. In decisions under certainty the ordinary principles of choice are very simple. One such principle says: *Assuming the alternatives are equal in all other respects, select that one which maximizes profit.* Another suggests: *Assuming the alternatives are equal in all other respects, select the one which minimizes cost.* Where it is not possible to make the conditioning assumption, where objectives are involved other than cost or profit, or where it is impossible to evaluate outcomes in cost or profit terms, these principles must be modified or discarded. They are so common, however, that we will begin with a number of decision problems in which they may be applied.

A PLANT DESIGN DECISION

Consider the problem of laying out a manufacturing plant in which four machines are to be located on the production floor, one at each of four possible locations. The problem is to decide which machine to place at each location. If we assume that the analyst operates in an orderly manner, he might begin by trying to specify the alternative courses of action which are open to him in this decision. This is very easy in this case, for he must choose between all the possible ways of placing four machines at four locations. The total number of alternatives is four factorial, or 24, and they may be listed by assigning the symbols A, B, C, and D to the machines and numbering the locations 1, 2, 3, and 4.

		Location		
	1	2	3	4
	A	B	C	D
Machine	A	B	D	C
Arrangement	A	C	B	D
	A	C	D	B
	etc.			

His next task is to predict the outcomes associated with each alternative arrangement. Let us suppose that the only important result of changing the location of two machines is perhaps to change the distance between them, and thus the distance over which the material that flows between them will have to be moved. The distances between locations can be measured and are given (in feet) in the table below:

	1	2	3	4
1		90	120	270
2			140	290
3				150
4				

The production program for these machines is fairly definite, and it will be assumed that the number of moves per week between machines can be predicted with certainty. Number of moves per week:

		From			
		A	B	C	D
	A		26	4	57
To	B	38		47	23
	C	211	0		2
	D	51	110	5	

Thus, the outcome of selecting a particular arrangement will be a particular flow of traffic in the plant which could be predicted from these two tables. The next step in the decision process is to evaluate the outcomes. After some thought the analyst concludes that the revenue of the firm is independent of which arrangement is chosen, and thus changes in profit resulting from this decision will arise through changes in cost. Knowing from experience that cost figures of the sort needed here are hard to come by, and also that cost is closely related to the product of the number of moves times the distance involved, he decides to locate the machines so as to minimise the latter. He may then evaluate each alternative in terms of the number of move-feet per week it will generate, and select the minimizing arrangement. This may be done by actually evaluating each of the 24 arrangements, or by some more systematic and economical method. (2) The reader may verify that the best arrangement is

Location	1	2	3	4
Machine	D	B	A	C

and that this results in 81,660 move-feet.

In making this decision explicit, we have established the following correspondence with our basic decision model:

The Model	The Decision
Alternatives.................	Possible machine arrangements.
Possible futures..............	Only one considered. Described in terms of a predicted volume of traffic flow.
Outcomes....................	The amount of travel resulting from a particular machine arrangement.
Values of the outcomes........	Expressed in move-feet.

Several points should be noted.

1. It was very easy to discover all the possible alternatives.
2. The outcomes were quite simple to predict and it seemed reasonable to assume certainty.
3. In evaluating the outcomes, a criterion was substituted for cost, which was easier to compute than cost might have been.
4. The principle of choice used was: "Since the alternatives are equal

in all other respects, select the arrangement which minimizes the number of move-feet."

Most decisions cannot be analyzed by a process of such simplicity, but this example provides a clear illustration of a typical set of steps in the analysis method. The method may be summarized in terms of the following steps:

1. Determine the alternative courses of action.
2. Predict the outcomes.
3. Evaluate the outcomes.
4. Apply an appropriate principle of choice to determine the decision.

A final step should be added to make the method general.

5. Check the recommended decision by subjecting it to managerial judgment.

In the remainder of this chapter this method will be applied to a number of decision problems which are typically treated as decisions under certainty.

MACHINE SELECTION

An interesting and extensively studied decision problem is that of the choice among machines or other major investments. Typically, the alternatives are assets which will render equal service to the firm. The revenue of the firm is taken to be independent of the choice, and thus the principle of choice is: *Since the assets are assumed to be equal in all other respects, select that one which minimizes cost.* In principle this is a very simple type of decision, and most of the difficulties encountered are in deciding what costs are to be included and how they are to be predicted.

Consider the specific example of the choice between two machines, *A* and *B*, which are expected to render equal service in a specific application. The relevant outcomes which must be predicted usually include direct and indirect labor, materials, power, fuel, lubricants, replacement parts, maintenance effort, and so forth that will be required to operate each machine. The service life of each and its condition at the end of its service life must also be predicted. In evaluating the outcomes, one uses the initial cost quoted by the seller, the operating expenses which must be estimated, and the salvage value at the end of the service life, which must also be estimated. With this information in hand the analysis simply requires an adding up of the costs and the selection of the minimum cost asset. For example:

	Machine A	Machine B
Initial cost	$20,000	$30,000
Annual operating cost	$ 4,000	$ 3,500
Service life	10 years	10 years
Salvage value	$ 2,000	$ 4,000

The total cost for ten years' service may easily be computed.

Machine A	$58,000
Machine B	$61,000

The recommendation might then be in favor of machine A, and the analysis would be submitted to management review to ascertain if important considerations should be added.

INTEREST

If interest is to be included in the analysis for one or more of the reasons discussed in Chapter 2, the problem requires some additional calculations. The differing initial investments in the two machines in the previous example, and the differing patterns of expense and income over time will be reflected in the interest costs associated with each. To show this, consider a decision in which there are three alternative machines, all of which would render equal service in the application anticipated.

The following cost data are given:

	Machine A	Machine B	Machine C
Initial cost	$28,000	$32,000	$35,000
Service life	Five years for all machines		
Operating costs			
Year 1	$ 2,500	$ 2,200	$ 2,000
Year 2	2,500	2,200	2,000
Year 3	2,600	2,200	2,000
Year 4	2,800	2,300	2,000
Year 5	3,000	2,400	2,000
Salvage value	$ 3,000	$ 3,500	$ 4,100

Interest is taken to be 5 per cent.

To simplify the analysis, it is usually assumed that the operating costs are to be considered as lump sum expenses occurring at the end of the year in question. Two principles of choice for such a decision will be suggested, although there are a variety of principles available.

1. *Assuming the alternatives are equal in all other respects, select the one which minimizes the present worth of the costs incurred.*

2. *Assuming that the alternatives are equal in all other respects, select the one which minimizes the equivalent annual cost.*

As we will show, either of these principles may be used if the assets being compared have equal service lives. If assets having differing service lives are compared, the equivalent annual cost principle is to be used.

INVESTMENT RECOVERY AND INTEREST

In applying either of these principles the analyst must first predict the pattern of costs in time over the life of each asset. Once this has been done, the costs may be converted into an equivalent present worth or an equivalent annual cost. When dealing with productive assets it is common to view the investment as giving rise to two kinds of costs. The first of these is the cost of recovering the investment itself. Once an asset has been purchased, a depreciation policy is established which in effect determines what portion of the investment is to be "charged off" against current revenue at various points during the life. This choice of depreciation policy is equivalent to establishing a pattern of costs for investment recovery over time. As we have seen in Chapter 2, there are several depreciation policies in common use. The second cost which arises out of the investment is the cost of interest on the unrecovered portion of the investment. We shall refer to these two costs as investment recovery and interest costs.

From the analyst's viewpoint, it can be shown that it makes no difference what pattern of investment recovery costs over time he predicts as long as his prediction of service life is correct. More specifically, using either of the two principles of choice mentioned previously, the results of all predicted patterns of investment recovery cost will be the same. To show this, suppose we wish to consider an asset in which the initial investment is I, and interest costs are to be taken at $i(100)$ per cent. Let

x_k = the amount of investment recovery cost at
the end of year k $(k = 1, 2, \ldots, n)$

$$\sum_{k=1}^{n} x_k = I$$

$i\sum_{j=k}^{n} x_j$ = interest cost for unrecovered portion of the
investment during year k

The present worth of the interest costs plus the investment recovery costs over the life, n, of the asset can be computed as follows:

$$\sum_{k=1}^{n}\left\{x_k + i\sum_{j=k}^{n}x_j\right\}\frac{1}{(1+i)^k}$$

This can be expanded and rewritten as:

$$\frac{1+i}{1+i}x_1 + \frac{i}{1+i}x_2 + \frac{1+i}{(1+i)^2}x_2 + \frac{i}{1+i}x_3 + \frac{i}{(1+i)^2}x_3 + \frac{i}{(1+i)^3}x_3$$

$$+ \frac{i}{1+i}x_4 + \cdots\cdots\cdots\cdots + \frac{i}{(1+i)^n}x_n$$

This series then reduces to

$$x_1 + x_2 + \cdots + x_n = \sum_{k=1}^{n}x_n = I$$

Thus we have the result that the present worth of the investment recovery costs plus the interest costs for any pattern over time is simply equal to the initial investment itself. Since the equivalent annual cost of investment recovery plus interest could be computed directly from the present worth just obtained, the result holds also for the second principle of choice. To use this result, the analyst must be willing to assume that the asset will actually serve out its useful life, and will not be retired or replaced prior to this time.

If salvage values are to be taken into consideration, then the foregoing analysis may be modified as follows. Let

$$S_n = \text{salvage value of the asset at the end of } n \text{ years of service}$$

$$\sum_{k=1}^{n}x_k + S_n = I$$

The present worth of interest costs plus investment recovery costs now becomes

$$\sum_{k=1}^{n}\left\{x_k + i\left(S_n + \sum_{j=k}^{n}x_j\right)\right\}\frac{1}{(1+i)^k}$$

which reduces to

$$\sum_{k=1}^{n}x_k + \left(1 - \frac{1}{(1+i)^n}\right)S_n = I - \frac{1}{(1+i)^n}S_n$$

If salvage values are included, the present worth of the sum of investment recovery plus interest costs, for any pattern over time, turns out to be the original investment less the present worth of the salvage value.

THE PRESENT WORTH PRINCIPLE

Applying the foregoing result to the example yields the following analysis:

Present Worth of	Machine A	Machine B	Machine C
Investment recovery and interest cost	$25,649.50	$29,257.75	$31,787.65
Operating costs			
Year 1	2,381.00	2,095.28	1,904.80
Year 2	2,267.50	1,995.40	1,814.00
Year 3	2,245.88	1,900.36	1,727.60
Year 4	2,303.56	1,892.21	1,645.40
Year 5	2,350.50	1,880.40	1,567.00
Total present worth	$37,197.94	$39,021.40	$40,446.45

The present worth of investment recovery and interest costs is found by subtracting the present worth of the salvage value from the original investment. In the case of machine A for example:

$$\$28,000 - \left\{\frac{1}{(1.05)^5}\right\} \$3,000 = \$25,649.50$$

This analysis would thus lead to the selection of machine A. This selection is conditioned by the assumptions that the machines are equal in all other respects, that interest is to be taken at 5 per cent, and that any of the alternatives would serve out its predicted useful life.

THE EQUIVALENT ANNUAL COST PRINCIPLE

Perhaps the most widely used of the foregoing principles is the second, which suggests the use of equivalent annual cost as a criterion. It has already been shown that the present worth of investment recovery plus interest costs is simply the original investment minus the present worth of the salvage value. The equivalent annual cost of investment recovery plus interest can be easily found by converting this present worth to an equivalent series of equal end-of-period payments.

$$\text{Equivalent annual cost of investment recovery and interest} = \left\{I - \frac{1}{(1+i)^n} S_n\right\} \frac{i(1+i)^n}{(1+i)^n - 1}$$

$$= (I - S_n) \frac{i(1+i)^n}{(1+i)^n - 1} + \left\{S_n - \frac{S_n}{(1+i)^n}\right\} \frac{i(1+i)^n}{(1+i)^n - 1}$$

$$= (I - S_n) \frac{i(1+i)^n}{(1+i)^n - 1} + iS_n$$

This final expression is the one most often used to calculate the equivalent annual cost of investment recovery and interest. This computation applied to machine A in the example yields:

$$\$25{,}000.00\ (.23097) + (.05)\ \$3{,}000.00 = \$5{,}924.25$$

The operating costs for each machine may be first converted to a present worth, and then to an equivalent annual cost. The comparison of the three machines then looks as follows:

	Machine A	Machine B	Machine C
Equivalent annual cost of investment recovery and interest	$5,924.25	$6,757.64	$7,341.97
Equivalent annual cost of operation	2,667.36	2,255.13	2,000.00
Total equivalent annual cost	8,591.61	9,012.77	9,341.97

Again the choice would be machine A. It should be clear also that these two principles of choice are equivalent. They are related by the expression

$$P\frac{i(1+i)^n}{(1+i)^n - 1} = R$$

where P is the present worth and R is the equivalent annual cost. In the case of machine A, for example

$$P = \$37{,}197.94$$
$$R = \$8{,}591.61$$
$$\frac{i(1+i)^n}{(1+i)^n - 1} = .23097$$

The following equality indicates the equivalence:

$$(\$37{,}197.94)(.23097) = \$8{,}591.60$$

(Rounding in the interest tables introduces some inconsequential discrepancies.) Thus we may conclude that when we are choosing among machines having equal service lives, the equivalent annual costs will differ from the present worths only by multiplication by a constant. Thus any recommendation based upon the present worth principle will be supported as well by the equivalent annual cost principle. We may then formulate the general rule: *When choosing among assets having equal service lives either the present worth principle or the equivalent annual cost principle may be used.* Note that if the service lives of the assets in a decision are different, then the two principles are not equivalent in general. We consider this situation next.

THE MAJOR ASSUMPTION

Each of the two principles of choice suggested for decisions involving assets contained the assumption that the alternatives were equal in all respects except cost. If this assumption does not hold, then an attempt must be made to express other differences in terms of costs. If this attempt fails, then these other differences must be brought into the decision by some judgmental process. The latter situation is investigated in Chapter 7. Some typical differences which can be more or less successfully reduced to cost terms will be discussed here.

It is often the case in comparing productive assets that one will have a greater output capacity than another. If the firm can utilize only a fixed level of capacity which is within the capabilities of all the alternatives, then this excess capacity is of no value and can be overlooked. If, however, the firm can utilize the excess capacity, then it must be evaluated and made a part of the analysis. This usually requires the use of a profit maximization principle of choice rather than cost minimization principles.

It often happens also that assets being compared have different potential service lives. There are at least two ways of handling such a difference:

1. If the company requires the service of the asset selected for some given length of time only, then service lives beyond this are of no consequence, except as they reflect upon salvage values. Sometimes the analyst may be uncertain as to the exact length of time the services of the selected asset will be required, and he will define a length of time called a "planning period." The length of the planning period is essentially arbitrary but might well represent the best available estimate of the duration of the project. Having assumed a planning period, the analyst neglects service lives beyond it.

2. If the services of the selected asset are assumed to be required indefinitely, then the analyst may assume that in comparing alternatives he is really comparing indefinite sequences of identical assets. That is, each machine will be replaced with an identical successor at the end of its service life, and this process will go on indefinitely (or to a point where all alternatives are replaced at the same time). When this assumption is made, the annual cost principle of choice is especially applicable.

Suppose, for example, we face a decision between two assets described below:

	Machine A	Machine B
Investment	$10,000	$20,000
Service life	5 years	10 years

Assume that neither machine has a salvage value nor involves any operating costs. Clearly it makes little sense to compute the present worths since these are $10,000 and $20,000 for A and B respectively, whatever the rate of interest. These numbers fail to reflect that we are considering five years of service in one case and ten years in the other. We might, however, compare two machines of type A in sequence, with one machine of type B. Thus we would be considering ten years of service in both cases. If the interest rate is 10% then we obtain

Present worth of two A's $= 10,000 + (10,000)(.6209) = \$16,209$
Present worth of one B = $\qquad\qquad\qquad\qquad$ $\$20,000$

Thus A appears to be the preferred type. Since ten years are involved in each case, we can convert these present worths to equivalent annual costs by multiplying by the appropriate constant:

Equivalent annual cost of two A's $= (16,209)(.16275) = \$2,638$
Equivalent annual cost of one B $= (20,000)(.16275) = \$3,255$

What would have happened if we had simply computed the equivalent annual cost for one A and compared it with the equivalent annual cost for one B?

Equivalent annual cost for one A $= (10,000)(.26380) = \$2,638$
Equivalent annual cost for one B $= (20,000)(.16275) = \$3,255$

The results are as before. We may thus conclude that the equivalent annual cost for two identical machines in sequence is equal to that for one such machine. In using the equivalent annual cost principle in this case, we get results which are the same as those arising from a comparison of ten years of service from two A's with ten years of service from one B.

This result may be generalized to any number of identical machines in sequence. As before, consider a type of machine which requires an investment I, has service life n, but involves neither salvage value nor operating costs. The present worth of k such machines in sequence may be written

$$I\left\{1 + \frac{1}{(1+i)^n} + \frac{1}{(1+i)^{2n}} + \cdots + \frac{1}{(1+i)^{(k-1)n}}\right\}$$

This is the sum of the first k terms of a geometric series which may be expressed as

$$I\frac{1 - \dfrac{1}{(1+i)^{kn}}}{1 - \dfrac{1}{(1+i)^n}} = I\frac{\{1 - (1+i)^{kn}\}\{1+i\}^n}{\{1 - (1+i)^n\}\{1+i\}^{kn}}$$

To convert this present worth to an equivalent annual cost, multiply by the factor

$$\frac{i(1 + i)^{kn}}{(1 + i)^{kn} - 1}$$

The result is

$$I\frac{i(1 + i)^n}{(1 + i)^n - 1}$$

which is simply the equivalent annual cost of one machine. The reader may wish to verify that a similar result holds for an infinite sequence of identical machines. This leads us to a second general rule: *In decisions involving assets of different service lives, the equivalent annual cost principle should be used.*

When machines differ with respect to reliability it is sometimes possible to evaluate these differences in terms of maintenance costs, costs of stocking spare parts, and costs of production lost while maintenance was performed. If machines differ with respect to the quality of output, again it may be possible to evaluate scrap and inspection costs and thus measure the differences. Differences in such attributes as safety for the operator begin to be very difficult to evaluate in terms of costs, and must be considered in other ways.

LEASING

Many major pieces of equipment, such as automatic data processing systems, may be either leased or purchased on an installment buying plan. Either of these methods may have the important result of conserving the supply of capital which the firm has available. Naturally, one would expect to pay something for this advantage. In spite of the fact that leasing may be more costly than buying, firms in industries such as petroleum refining, aircraft, chemicals, drugs, and retail food merchandising are currently engaged in leasing their equipment. Industrial property may be sold and then leased back again. Transportation equipment including trucks, automobiles, and railroad cars may be rented.

The basic idea is to avoid tying up capital in equipment if it can be used more profitably in other ways. Instead of laying out the capital when the asset is acquired, the firm makes its payments as the asset is used. This, however, may be expensive. As an example, consider a piece of equipment which could be purchased for $100,-000. To rent this equipment the payments required might be something like those suggested in the three contracts in the following table.

Year	Contract 1	Contract 2	Contract 3
1	$38,000	$32,000	$26,000
2	24,000	25,000	24,000
3	13,000	18,000	24,000
4	10,000	10,000	11,000
5	10,000	10,000	10,000
6	10,000	10,000	10,000
7	10,000	10,000	10,000

These contracts differ also in the time at which the firm might be permitted to terminate the contract. Contract 1 might permit termination after one year, contract 2, after two years, and contract 3, at any time after three years. Clearly, in the decision to enter into such a contract, the firm must be interested not only in the reduction in capital requirements but also in the cost of renting the equipment, which depends crucially on how long the equipment will be required. In the following table the present worths of the rental payments are compared for various service lives.

Life	Contract 1	Contract 2	Contract 3
1	$ 38,000	...	...
2	60,430	$ 55,365	...
3	71,784	71,086	$69,392
4	79,947	79,249	78,371
5	87,576	86,878	86,000
6	94,706	94,008	93,130
7	101,369	100,671	99,793

We have assumed an interest rate of 7 per cent and payment of rentals at the beginning of each year. Whether or not rental turns out to be less costly than outright purchase depends on the pattern of salvage values and on the anticipated life over which the equipment will be used.

OPERATING DECISIONS

Many other management decisions are typically treated as decisions under certainty—for example, choices involving materials, tooling, processes, production methods, and so on. Since in many of these decisions no substantial investment is involved, interest may be neglected. For example, in choosing between alternative materials for a product, the firm's money usually is invested in the product itself for such a short time that interest may be entirely neglected. Many of these decisions involve no more complicated principle than cost minimization. The chief difficulties in making them are the technological problem of predicting what the outcome will be for each alternative and the measurement problem of evaluating the outcomes in terms of costs. The first of these lies within the usual realm of the analyst's professional activity, while the second will be examined in future chapters.

Among the most interesting decisions often treated as decisions under certainty are a group of operating policy problems, one of which is the famous economic lot size problem. This problem has many versions and degrees of complication, but its essence is this: There is a production process with an output rate considerably in excess of the rate at which its product is required for use. Thus, instead of running the production process continuously, it is used intermittently for the product in question. At other times it may be used for the production of different products. The basic question of operating policy is how often to make a run of the product and how much to produce each time a run is made. Stated another way, "What is the best size and frequency of lots?" In attacking this problem as a decision under certainty, it is usually assumed that a planning period of length T is used, and that the amount of product required at a uniform rate over this period is known to be D units. If the lot size is given by L, then

$$\frac{D}{L} = \text{number of lots required during } T$$

$$\frac{TL}{D} = \text{time between lots}$$

We will assume for simplicity that the demand is expected to continue at a uniform rate D/T for the indefinite future, thus we need not require the number of lots D/L to be an integer. We will also assume that the material is moved into storage in lots. Thus, each time a run is completed, the amount of material in inventory increases by L units. The inventory level then declines at a uniform rate for a period of time TL/D. As the level reaches zero (or some buffer stock level) another lot of size L arrives. The inventory fluctuations are shown in Figure 3–1. The costs which depend on the choice of L are taken to be of two kinds: those which depend on the lot size (variable costs) and those which are independent of the lot size (fixed costs). Setup costs are usually assumed to be independent of the lot size, and are defined to include all costs of getting the production of a lot under way and terminating it when completed. Storage costs are considered to vary with the size of the lot,

FIGURE 3–1

Inventory Fluctuations Resulting from Production in Lots

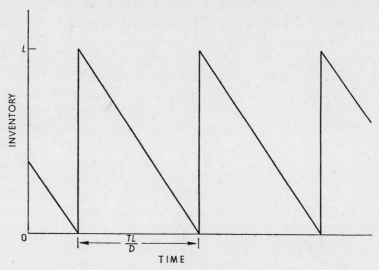

since they are often computed on the basis of the maximum or average amount of product in storage.

Assume the following costs are given:

C_1 = setup cost per lot
C_2 = storage cost per piece per unit time, based on average number of units in storage
$C(L)$ = setup cost and storage cost for a planning period T, using a lot size of L

The cost $C(L)$ may be computed as follows:

$C_1 \dfrac{D}{L}$ = total setup cost

$\dfrac{L}{2}$ = average number of units in storage

$\dfrac{LT}{2}$ = total piece-periods of storage

$\dfrac{C_2 LT}{2}$ = total storage cost

$$C(L) = C_1 \frac{D}{L} + C_2 \frac{LT}{2}$$

It is easily verified that if one takes the first derivative of $C(L)$ with respect to L, sets it equal to zero, and solves for L, the result is

$$L = \sqrt{\frac{2C_1 D}{C_2 T}}$$

This is the lot size which minimizes the sum of setup costs and storage costs. Having determined *L,* the time between lots is also determined since *D* and *T* are assumed to be known.

In terms of our basic decision model we have:

The Model	*The Decision*
Alternatives.................	Lot sizes.
Possible futures...............	Only one considered. Demand predicted at a uniform rate.
Outcomes...................	Described in terms of number of setups and inventory position over time.
Values of the outcomes........	Total cost of setups and storage.

FIGURE 3–2

The Economic Lot Size Decision

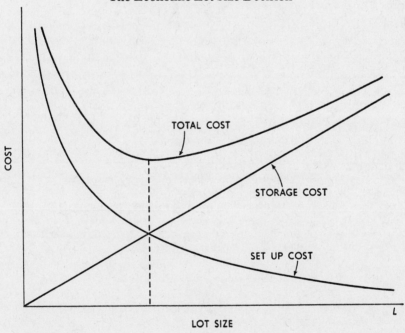

The decision is illustrated in Figure 3–2. This same analysis can be interpreted in terms of economic purchasing quantities and provides some insight into a wide class of operating decisions which involve matching an input to an output where the input rate is higher than that of the output. Figure 3–2 also provides an almost classic form for many decision problems. As the choice is moved from one extreme to another along the range of alternatives, there are some costs which increase and some costs which decrease. The best policy is not to select an extreme alternative, but a moderate one which brings about a compromise between the increasing and the decreasing costs. Moderation is thus the key to decisions of this sort.

It should also be noted that at the point where $C(L)$ is minimum the marginal storage cost is just equal to the negative of the marginal setup cost. Thus, in effect, we have an instance of the decision rule discussed in connection with the firm's production function in Chapter 2.

SELECTING A PRODUCTION METHOD

The problem of choosing among alternative methods of production is a common one which is often treated as a decision under certainty. Suppose the firm is interested in producing a small turned part which could be made on an ordinary engine lathe, on a turret lathe, or on an automatic screw machine. In examining these three alternatives let us assume that capacity could be made available on machines of any of these three types, and the decision is to be based simply on the principle of minimizing costs. Suppose further that the only costs which vary as a result of the choice of machine type are setup costs and direct labor costs. If one is willing to assume that these costs are definitely known, then the following analysis might be used:

$$C_{11} = \text{setup cost for engine lathes}$$
$$C_{12} = \text{setup cost for turret lathes}$$
$$C_{13} = \text{setup cost for automatic screw machines}$$
$$C_{21} = \text{direct labor cost per unit for engine lathes}$$
$$C_{22} = \text{direct labor cost per unit for turret lathes}$$
$$C_{23} = \text{direct labor cost per unit for automatic}$$
$$\qquad \text{screw machines}$$
$$D \ = \text{number of units to be produced}$$

If the choice is whether to use one engine lathe, one turret lathe, or one automatic screw machine, then the total cost of production in each case is given by a linear function.

$$C_{11} + C_{21}D \ \text{(engine lathe)}$$
$$C_{12} + C_{22}D \ \text{(turret lathe)}$$
$$C_{13} + C_{23}D \ \text{(automatic screw machine)}$$

When these functions are plotted, as in Figure 3–3, the cost-minimizing alternative may be selected for any level of production, D. If it is necessary to choose between a given number of machines of each type, or between mixtures of the various types, then the decision may become slightly more complicated.

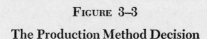

FIGURE 3–3

The Production Method Decision

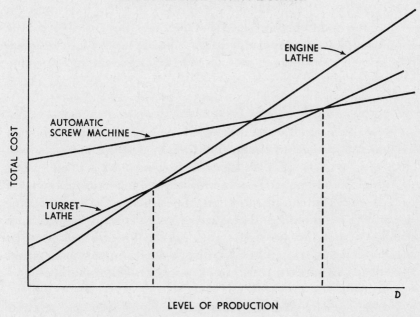

CAPITAL BUDGETING

In the previous discussion we have avoided the troublesome question of where the money is to come from to finance the projects chosen. The question is often formulated somewhat more precisely. "In the face of a scarcity of funds, which of the projects open to the firm should be chosen for investment?" The analyst who deals largely at the project level may not initially be invited to concern himself with this problem of capital budgeting or the allocation of funds, since it involves a number of difficulties which are in the province of top management. However, the basic issues may be easily outlined.

Ideally, the firm should have long-range plans for its development in a continual process of formulation and reformulation. Included in these plans would be predictions of the flow of cash into the firm and the firm's cash position at various future times. The plans would also include, as far as possible, estimates of the cash requirements and profitability of projects which might be undertaken in the future. The formulation of these long-range plans then includes the problem of allocating available cash to the candidate projects so as to best achieve the firm's objectives.

In actuality this ideal of long-range plans for the firm's realization and allocation of funds can seldom be achieved with any conviction. Perhaps a more common formulation of the problem is to view it in terms of the funds available to the firm in the present year or the coming year and the allocation of these funds to the projects which are current opportunities for the firm. Although we will discuss capital budgeting in this way, it is well to remember that the whole process requires considerable advanced planning.

Many projects require a considerable gestation period between the conception and the realization of the project. The firm may also find it necessary to obtain funds from outside sources in order to finance the project, which may itself consume considerable time.

In actuality, decisions as to how to ration funds among the various projects under consideration may be influenced to an important degree by persuasion. People and departments within the firm may actively compete for the funds, each hoping to secure support for some "pet project" or program which will enlarge a particular phase of the firm's operations. It is certain, too, that the provision and allocation of funds are heavily influenced by such factors as the preference of management for a strong cash position, the outlook for business, and the securities markets. We do not suggest that these factors are not relevant, but simply that the decision process is one of the most complex and dynamic which we have so far discussed. Actual business practice in this respect is reviewed in Chapter 24. Here we will outline some of the thinking which has been directed toward the development of a reasonable scheme for capital budgeting.

SOURCES OF FUNDS

After the initial capitalization of the firm, when it becomes a going business, there is often a strong preference for the financing of investment projects out of funds which become available from internal sources. The usual internal sources of funds for the firm are depreciation and retained earnings. Customarily the firm "charges off" depreciation of its productive assets against its current earnings. This results in a flow of cash into the firm, which may then be reinvested in other projects. It is often a policy to "plow back" or retain some of the current earnings, rather than paying all of this money to the stockholders in the form of dividends. A wide variety of policies exist with respect to the portion of current earnings which should be retained for reinvestment. As is shown in Chapter 24, recent business policy suggests a strong reliance on these sources of funds, rather than funds obtained from sources outside the firm.

The common sources of cash outside of the firm include common stock, preferred stock, bonds, leases, conditional sales, and bank loans. Each of these sources has its own technicalities which we need not examine here.

CAPITAL RATIONING

We will sketch two formulations of the problem of allocating scarce funds to candidate projects. The first of these, which stems directly from classical economic theory, involves the use of interest rates interpreted as the cost of capital to the firm. The problem is formulated in terms of the supply and demand of capital from the point of view of the firm. The firm is seen as having opportunities to obtain various amounts of capital from various sources, at prices reflected by interest rates. It is assumed that these interest rates are known, although it may be no simple matter to establish the proper cost of capital obtained from say, retained earnings. In any case the sources of funds are listed in order of increasing interest rates or cost of capital, and this list is called the "capital supply schedule" for the firm.

The demand for capital is represented by the projects which are candidates for investment. The problem is greatly simplified if one can assume that the projects are independent. The word "independent" is used here to suggest the condition that the profitability of project A does not depend on whether or not project B is undertaken. In reality, one seldom confronts a group of projects which are strictly independent, and in some cases the dependence is absolute, as in the situation where the undertaking of project A renders project B impossible. This latter condition of dependence, or mutual exclusion, has been discussed in the previous analysis.

The rate of return for a project is defined as that interest rate at which the present worth of the receipts and disbursements is equal to zero. Suppose, for example, the firm invests \$11,000 in a project which will have a life of ten years. The average annual profit from the project is \$1,360 and the equipment will have a salvage value of \$1,800 at the end of the ten-year life. Trial and error will show that if this stream of receipts and disbursements is discounted at 6 per cent, their present worth becomes zero. Thus

$$(\$1,360)(7.360) - \$11,000 + (\$1,800)(.5584) = 0$$

The project is then said to yield a rate of return of 6 per cent. Trial and error in conjunction with the interest tables is the common method of determining rates of return. Certain difficulties associated with the rate of return concept are illustrated in problems 3–8 and 3–9.

After the rates of return for all the candidate projects have been determined, the demand schedule for capital may be constructed. This is done simply by listing the candidate projects in order of decreasing rate of return. The solution of the capital budgeting problem is then simple. The two schedules are compared, and one starts at the top of the supply schedule allocating funds to the projects at the top of the demand schedule. This process continues down the two schedules until the point is reached where the rate of return from the next project is less than the cost of capital that would be used to finance it. At this point the process stops, for there is little advantage in undertaking projects which do not earn a return at least equal to the cost of the cheapest funds available to finance them. The firm will, however, wish to undertake all projects that promise a rate of return greater than the cost of their capital, since the excess represents the firm's profit. In economic theory of this sort, no firm passes up an opportunity for profit. The solution to the capital budgeting problem is then to allocate the inexpensive funds from the top of the supply schedule to the projects promising high return at the top of the demand schedule, and to continue this process as long as any possibility for profit remains.

This process, while logically satisfactory, does not agree in many respects with the realities of the capital budgeting process. Among the difficulties involved are

1. As always, one must make predictions of income and expense over the life of the project.
2. The cost of capital must be determined for each source of funds.
3. One must assume that the firm does in fact use the cost of capital as a part of its capital budgeting policy and that it has no particular aversion, say, to obtaining outside funds.

The first of these objections, being universal in character, will be examined in Chapter 6. The second forces us to face the problem of just what interest rate to use. The cost of funds obtained through debt contracts such as bonds, notes, or equipment trust certificates is usually explicitly stated and offers no great difficulty.

The proper cost to be associated with funds from other sources is, however, a matter of some question and considerable disagreement. We will suggest one possible view. (13, 123)

Common Stock. The firm may undertake to market a new issue of common stock in order to finance its major projects or expansion programs. If we neglect, for simplicity, the marketing costs, the firm might well take the cost of funds obtained in this way to be the ratio of estimated annual earnings per share outstanding (without the project) to present market value per share. This ratio is in fact the rate of return which the present stockholders are currently enjoying on their money. From their point of view it is clear that any project which produces a lower rate of return will operate to their disadvantage. Thus, this ratio should be used as the cost of funds obtained from common stock issue, and no project should be undertaken with a lower rate of return.

To illustrate, suppose that a firm presently has 10,000 common shares outstanding, with a market value of $100 per share, and with estimated future earnings (without further expansion) of $12 per share annually. Suppose the firm were to issue an additional 1,000 shares, thus obtaining $100,000 of new equity capital. Suppose further that this new capital were used to finance a project which produced an annual return of $10,000. The firm now has 11,000 shares outstanding with total annual earnings of $130,000. Under these conditions the earnings per share are about $11.82, resulting in a deterioration of the position of the original owners.

Retained Earnings. If a project is to be financed out of earnings retained by the firm, it may plausibly be argued that the same ratio might be used as the cost of capital. That is:

$$\frac{\text{ESTIMATED EARNINGS PER SHARE WITHOUT PROJECT}}{\text{PRESENT MARKET VALUE PER SHARE}}$$

Again from the stockholders' point of view, it is argued that no funds should be invested in projects promising returns of less than this amount since a better alternative is always open to them. They could always take the funds in dividends and reinvest at the aforementioned rate.

Depreciation Allowance. Funds obtained by the firm through depreciation of its assets may also be treated in this same way. From the owners' point of view, these funds are not essentially different from retained earnings, at least as far as their use is concerned.

In actual practice the firm may, as we have previously suggested, find it impossible to make these estimates, and simply establish a more or less arbitrary rate of return to be used for capital budgeting purposes. This may be called the minimum attractive return, the cutoff rate, or the acceptable rate of return. No projects promising less than this rate are supported by the firm.

Another principle may be used in this formulation of the capital budgeting problem, involving a present worth calculation instead of the rate of return calculation: *Accept all projects which have a positive present worth when discounted at the firm's cost of capital.* This principle may be somewhat easier to use and gives results identical with those based upon the rate of return criterion. (Unless the solution to the rate of return problem is not unique.)

ALLOCATING A FIXED SUM

The second formulation of the capital budgeting problem which will be explored involves the allocation of a fixed sum of money among the candidate projects. Often a firm decides to restrict its capital investment to some limited amount, rather than to continue to invest until all profitable opportunities are funded, as was suggested previously. It may be that the firm cannot in fact obtain outside funds at any reasonable cost, or, for a variety of other reasons, the decision may be made to limit investment to those funds which are available internally. The amount of internally available funds depends directly on earnings and dividend policy.

We then consider the problem of allocating a fixed amount of money among a list of possible projects. This problem may be complicated if outlays are to be made in more than one year or accounting period. We will continue to focus our attention only on the present year. Also, difficulties will arise because of discontinuity. That is, there is no assurance that the sum of the investments in any group of projects will exactly equal the fixed amount available. This is likely to be most troublesome when a small number of projects constitute a large portion of the capital budget.

One possibility is to compute the equivalent annual profit for each proposed project using the firm's cost of capital, and then form the ratio of this equivalent annual profit to the total investment required. The projects are then ranked in order of decreasing equivalent annual profit to outlay ratio. Budgeting is accomplished by investing in those projects selected by moving down the list until the fixed sum is exhausted.

A second principle suggests that the rate of return for each project be computed and the projects ranked in order of decreasing rate of return. One then moves down the list, selecting projects until the fixed sum is exhausted. While there are cases in which these two principles do in fact give different results, it is perhaps true that the differences are not, in practice, of great importance.

AN EXAMPLE

Suppose the firm is considering five candidate projects and has established the relevant cost of capital to be 6 per cent. Project A is estimated to yield an equivalent annual income of \$2,590 for a ten-year period. To obtain this, investment of \$20,000 is required with no salvage values involved. The rate of return is that interest rate for which the project will have a present worth of zero. Trial and error will show that for 5 per cent interest this will be true.

$$\text{Present worth} = (\$2,590) \frac{(1 + i)^n - 1}{i(1 + i)^n} - \$20,000 = 0$$

For $i = 5$ per cent this becomes

$$\$2,590(7.722) - \$20,000 = 0$$

Similar results for the other projects are shown below.

Project	Equivalent Annual Income	Investment	Life (Years)	Rate of Return	Present Worth at 6%
A	\$ 2,590	\$20,000	10	5%	\$ −938
B	10,816	50,000	6	8	3,182
C	15,000	80,000	8	10	13,150
D	1,100	10,000	15	7	663
E	3,255	20,000	10	10	3,957

Using the firms cost of capital to distinguish between acceptable and not acceptable projects, clearly all projects except A should be supported. This decision is the same whether the rate of return principle or the present worth principle is used.

If we now suppose that the firm has a fixed sum available, we may rank the proposals either according to rate of return or according to the ratio of equivalent annual profit at 6 per cent to outlay.

Rank	Project	Rate of Return	Ratio of Present Worth at 6% to Outlay	Ratio of Equivalent Annual Profit at 6% to Outlay
1	E	10%	.198	.027
2	C	10	.165	.027
3	B	8	.064	.013
4	D	7	.066	.007
5	A	5	...	...

Presumably in no case would project A be undertaken. This example also illustrates the problem of discontinuities. Suppose a fixed sum of $80,000 was available. Clearly it would not be sensible to invest in project E and then stop. Rather one might consider the alternatives of C alone or the combination of B, D, and E. It would then be obvious that C alone would be preferred. In small problems such discontinuites may be handled usually by inspection, while in larger problems they do not arise in such a marked fashion.

SUGGESTIONS FOR FURTHER STUDY

BERNHARD, RICHARD H. "Discount Methods for Expenditure Evaluation—A Clarification of Their Assumptions," *Journal of Industrial Engineering*, Vol. 13, No. 1. January–February, 1962.

BIERMAN, H., and SMIDT, S. *The Capital Budgeting Decision*. New York: The Macmillan Co., 1960.

SOLOMON, E. (ed.). *The Management of Corporate Capital*. Glencoe, Ill.: The Free Press, 1959.

PROBLEMS

3–1.   Three machine centers are to be located in a new plant. There are four available areas, each of which could be occupied by any one of these machine centers. The average distances between the areas are given in the distance table below.

	A	B	C	D
A	—	120	180	70
B		—	150	120
C			—	50
D				—

Material is moved between these machine centers by fork lift trucks. The predicted number of loads per week to be moved is given below.

		From		
		1	*2*	*3*
	1	—	100	200
To	*2*	50	—	150
	3	250	100	—

What arrangements of machine centers would you suggest?

3–2.   In planning future construction, a turnpike authority estimates the total cost of a four-lane toll highway to be $850,000 per mile. It plans to finance construction through the sale of 4 per cent bonds which will mature in 20 years. The authority may, however, retire bonds at its own discretion. The average toll is about four cents per mile. Highway maintenance costs about $25,000 per mile per year. How many vehicles per year must use the highway if it is to break even?

3–3.   A firm is considering diesel-powered vehicles as possible replacements for its conventional gasoline trucks. The cost of a diesel truck is $7,000, and it is expected to have a three-year service life with a resale value of $2,000. The trucks now being used cost $9,000 and are sold for $3,000 after a four-year service life. Operating costs are $.14 per mile for conventional trucks and $.12 per mile for diesels. If equipment is financed through a 5 per cent loan, at what annual mileage will the two types be equivalent?

3–4. A firm offers to lease air-conditioning equipment at a price which it claims is "comparable to bank financing." For equipment which has a five-year service life and no salvage value, what annual rental payment will be equivalent to a 6 per cent bank loan repaid in five equal annual payments?

3–5. A firm is considering buying its office furniture with $20,000 of its own working capital on which it ordinarily earns a 10 per cent return. It is offered an opportunity to lease the equipment for a ten-year period at an annual cost of $3,200. If the equipment will have a service life of ten years with no salvage value, which method of financing would be preferred? (Assume end-of-year lease payments.)

3–6. A firm is offered three different plans for leasing automatic data-processing equipment. The table below shows the annual rent payments as a percentage of the purchase price.

| | | Plan | |
Year	A	B	C
1.	.35	30	25
2.	.25	25	25
3.	.15	20	25
4.	.10	10	10
5.	.10	10	10
6.	.10	10	10
7.	.10	10	10

If the interest rate is greater than zero, which plan would be preferred?

3–7. Consider the following decisions:

Decision A: Machine A and Machine B each cost $9,000 and have service lives of seven years. Use of Machine A will result in a savings of $3,000 per year for the first three years but no savings thereafter. Use of Machine B will result in a savings of $3,000 in each of the seven years. Depreciation of the machines has not been included in computing the savings. Which machine is preferable?

Decision B: Machine X and Machine Y each cost $9,000 and will have service lives of four years. Use of these machines will produce savings shown below:

	Savings in			
	Year 1	Year 2	Year 3	Year 4
Machine X	0	$3,000	$6,000	$3,000
Machine Y	$6,000	3,000	0	3,000

Comment on the choices made in these two decisions by the following decision rules:

a) "We will invest in any machine which will pay for itself in three years."

b) "We compute the total savings over the life of the machine, divide this by the cost, and choose the machine which maximizes the result."

3–8. Consider some two-period "investment" projects which involve cash flows for the firm at the present time, at the end of period 1, and at the end of period 2. Let these amounts be represented by the symbols R_0, R_1, and R_2 respectively.

	Cash Flow		
	R_0	R_1	R_2
Project A	$1000	−$2000	$1500
Project B	−1000	2100	−1100
Project C	− 720	1700	−1000
Project D	720	− 1700	1000

The conventional definition of the rate of return on a project is that interest rate at which the present worth of the project is zero. This can be found in this case by letting

$$x = \frac{1}{1 + i}$$

and solving the equation

$$R_0 + R_1 x + R_2 x^2 = 0$$

To illustrate some of the difficulties involved in the rate of return as a criterion for selecting investments, find the rate (or rates) of return for each of the above projects. Sketch a graph of present worth as a function of interest rate for each of these projects.

3–9. An investment opportunity involves the following cash flows: an income of $1,000 at the present time, an outlay of $3,000 one year hence, and an income of $2,500 two years hence.

a) Show that the opportunity has a positive present worth for all interest rates greater than or equal to zero.

b) Show that there exists no real number greater than or equal to zero which when used as an interest rate makes the present worth zero. Thus there exists no rate of return in the usual sense. (Hint: see problem 3–8.)

3–10. Consider two investment opportunities, each of which requires an initial investment of $10,000. Opportunity A will return $800 at the end of the first year and $10,800 at the end of the second year. Opportunity B will return $10,000 at the end of the first year and $1,100 at the end of the second year.

a) Which opportunity will be preferred by a man who chooses so as to maximize the rate of return?

b) Which opportunity will be preferred by a man who chooses so as to maximize the present worth using an interest rate of 5 per cent?

c) What would be your own choice if you had money available which you could invest at 5 per cent?

3–11. A milling machine requires an initial investment of $10,000 and will have a salvage value of $1,000 at the end of its service life of

5 years. It is being considered for purchase by a company which requires 6 per cent return on its equipment investments.

Find

a) The present worth for one such machine.

b) The equivalent annual cost for one such machine.

c) The present worth of two such machines, one replacing the other after five years.

d) The equivalent annual cost for part (c).

3–12. Consider an infinite sequence of identical machines, each requiring an investment I, but having no other costs nor any salvage value. Each machine is replaced after n years with an identical replacement. Find the present worth and the equivalent annual cost for this infinite sequence.

3–13. Machine A requires an investment of $10,000, and its use will save a manufacturer $12,000 at the end of the first year but no further savings over the remaining three years of its service life. Machine B also requires an investment of $10,000 but will produce no savings until the fourth and last year of its service life. At that time it will yield a savings of $17,490. Depreciation has not been included in the computation of savings. A firm has $10,000 available which it can invest in other ways for a return of 10 per cent.

a) Which machine has the greater present worth?

b) What machine promises the greatest rate of return?

c) Which would you recommend to the management of the firm? Why?

3–14. A machine is purchased for $20,000 and is expected to have a useful life of five years. At the end of this period it will have a salvage value of $2,000. Show that the costs of investment recovery plus interest have the same present worth whether depreciation is straight line, fixed percentage of a declining balance, or sinking fund (with interest at 10 per cent).

3–15. A company is studying two machines, either of which is suitable for the application it has in mind. The following data have been obtained.

	Detroit Model 303	Giant Special
Price (delivered)	$65,000	$36,000
Installation cost	1,800	2,100
Annual operating cost	7,000	11,000
Annual maintenance cost	750	500

a) If both machines will have a service life of ten years and no salvage value at the end of that time, which machine would be preferred? The firm requires 10 per cent on its investment.

b) Which would be preferred at interest rates of 5 and 0 per cent?

c) Repeat question (a) if the firm requires 5 per cent interest and the Detroit Model 303 has a service life of eight years with no salvage value. Do the same for a service life of 12 years with no salvage value.

d) Which machine would be preferred if the Detroit Model 303 has a salvage value of $4,000 after ten years of service and the Giant Special has a salvage value of $2,000 after ten years of service? Interest is charged at 5 per cent.

3–16. A company, now in the process of building a new plant, predicts that in six years the plant will require a major addition. It is estimated that if the addition is built at the present time (during the original construction) it will cost $100,000. If, however, it is built in six years, it will cost $140,000. Construction is to be financed out of the firm's retained earnings which it generally invests at a return of at least 6 per cent. Should the firm build the addition now or wait six years?

3–17. Which of the following plans for paying for a new piece of equipment would be preferred by a company which earns 5 per cent on its capital? By one which earns 8 per cent?

a) Pay $10,000 cash now.

b) Pay $2,500 cash down now and $1,000 per year for ten years.

3–18. A firm purchased a high-precision jig-boring machine one year ago at a cost of $100,000. It was expected to last ten years and have no salvage value at the end of that time. The machine is operated by highly skilled machinists at an annual labor cost of $15,000. The firm now discovers that it can subcontract the work done on the jig-boring equipment to a reputable specialty shop at a cost of $13,000 per year. At this point it is discovered that there is little demand for used jig-boring equipment of this type and its present resale value is only $1,000. If kept, the equipment would last ten more years and have no salvage value at that time. If the firm requires a return of 10 per cent on their investments, what is the best choice at this point?

3–19. A man has $100,000 to invest. The bank holds a $20,000 mortgage on his home which carries 4 per cent interest payable annually. The principal may be repaid partially or fully at any time but must be liquidated at the end of 20 years. He may deposit money in a savings account at 3 per cent at any time. Which of the following alternatives would be most profitable?

a) Invest $90,000 in a uranium mine which has no salvage value but yields a profit of $9,700 a year for 20 years.

b) Buy a partnership in a shoe business which allows no withdrawals but which can be liquidated for an estimated $285,757 in 20 years. The partnership will cost $80,000.

c) Wait ten years to buy some special bonds which yield 20 per cent and mature in ten years. Only $50,000 worth of such bonds are sold to any one person.

3–20. A company will not make any investments on which it earns less than 8 per cent return. An improvement is suggested for one type of production machine which it uses. If the improvement will cost $1,000 per machine, how much must be saved in order that the firm will be willing to make the investment? The machines have remaining service lives of five years.

If the predicted savings are as shown below, is the investment a good one?

Year	1	2	3	4	5
Savings	$400	$300	$250	$200	$150

3–21. A railroad can earn a revenue of $1,000 by moving a flatcar carrying two loaded highway trailers piggyback between Chicago and Los Angeles. Hauling and maintenance costs for such a run amount to $200 per flatcar. Each flatcar requires an investment of $35,000, which is financed by an equipment loan at 5 per cent interest. How many one-way trips must be made by the flatcar each year in order to pay for itself in five years?

3–22. A manufacturer is exploring three new methods of metal forming for short production runs in a job shop operation. The following data have been collected for these methods:

	Method A	Method B	Method C
Initial investment	$50,000	$53,000	$59,000
Service life		10 years for each	
Salvage value	5,000	5,100	5,300

The best projection of future production plans which can be made suggests that the direct labor costs will be $15,000 per year for method A, $12,000 per year for method B, and $10,000 per year for method C.

a) If the manufacturer requires 8 per cent on his investments, which method would be preferred?

b) Which method would be preferred if the service lives were 10, 12, and 14 years for methods A, B, and C respectively.

c) Repeat part (*a*) for interest rates of 0 and 5 per cent.

3–23. A firm faces a choice among the three machines described below:

	Machine A	Machine B	Machine C
Initial cost	$40,000	$42,000	$49,000
Service life		8 years for all machines	
Annual operating costs	12,000	10,500	9,000
Salvage value	4,000	4,000	5,000

a) If the firm requires a return of 10 per cent of its investments, which machine would be preferred?

b) Which machine would be preferred if the service lives were 8 years for machine A, 10 years for machine B, and 12 years for machine C?

c) Repeat part (*a*) for interest rates of 0, 5, and 15 per cent.

3–24. Four different proposals have been made for obtaining heat-treating services in a manufacturing plant. Three of them, A, B, and C, involve buying equipment and setting up a heat-treating department. The fourth, D, involves subcontracting all the work.

	A	B	C	D
Investment	$10,000	$25,000	$ 6,000	0
Annual operating costs	17,000	13,000	17,000	$20,000
Salvage value	2,000	5,000	1,000	
Service life (years)	8	5	2	

Which method would you recommend if the firm must earn 10 per cent on its investments?

3-25. A company is offered a $200,000 plant construction loan by a community which is seeking new industry. Three repayment plans are available:

a) Pay back $400,000 at the end of 20 years.

b) Pay back $180,000 at the end of 10 years and $180,000 at the end of 20 years.

c) Pay $16,000 per year for 20 years.

What would be the rate of interest in each case?

3-26. A real estate investor is offered a tract of suburban land. He is considering buying the land, leaving it idle for ten years, and then selling it. He estimates that the land will double in value during that time. Taxes are expected to be about 2 per cent of the purchase price annually. If he can borrow the entire amount to buy the land at 4 per cent interest, should he accept the offer?

3-27. A new machine is purchased for $7,000 which has a predicted service life of 12 years. Certain modifications are proposed for the machine which would increase its service life to 15 years and reduce the annual operating costs by $300. What additional investment would be justified for these improvements, assuming no salvage value in any case? The firm requires 6 per cent return on its investments.

3-28. A certain process can be improved in either or both of two ways:

a) Product quality can be increased sufficiently to justify an increased selling price which will increase annual income by $10,000. To obtain the quality improvement, an addition to annual operating costs of $6,000 is needed as well as an additional investment in equipment of $10,000. This equipment will have a service life of 4 years and a salvage value of $2,000.

b) By using a computer to control production the firm can reduce its average investment in inventories by $50,000. The computer time required will cost about $3,500 per year.

If the firm requires 10 per cent return on its investments, what would you recommend?

3-29. What must be the prospective annual saving in maintenance cost over a five-year period in order to justify spending $5,000 for a machine overhaul? Assume the company requires at least 4 per cent return on its investments.

3-30. A factory has a power plant which originally cost $50,000 fifteen years ago. Its estimated life was 30 years; depreciation has been written off on the books on a straight-line basis so that the book value of the plant is now $25,000. The present annual outlay for running the power plant (including labor, fuel, taxes, insurance, and all other actual disbursements) is $19,000. It is estimated that a new Diesel plant would reduce these annual expenditures to $10,000. The Diesel plant would cost $60,000. Its life is conservatively estimated at 15 years. The present power plant has an estimated salvage value of $1,000. If interest is 8 per cent, is it economical to make the replacement?

3–31. Which of the following types of machines would you recommend?

	Type A	Type B
Investment	$10,000	$15,000
Salvage value	$8,000 - 500(n - 1)$	$12,000 - 500(n - 1)$
Annual operating cost	$1,000j$	$800 + 1,000(j - 1)$

Assume

        a) $n = 2$ for both types
        b) interest at 5%
        c) $j =$ age of machine

3–32. Which of the two machines described below would you recommend?

	Machine A	Machine B
Investment	$10,000	$15,000
Salvage value	1,000	1,000
Annual operating costs	$3,000 + .25x$	$2,000 + .20x$
Capacity	50,000 units per year	70,000 units per year
Service life	5 years	8 years

$x =$ number of units produced in a year

The firm can sell all of its production up to 60,000 units per year at a price of $.40 per unit. No other sales are possible. Interest is at 5 per cent.

3–33. A firm asks for your suggestion as to which of the two machines described below it should buy. Revenue, quality, reliability, and so on are considered about equal for the two.

	Machine A	Machine B
Investment	$100,000	$120,000
Annual operating cost	20,000	17,569
Salvage value	10,000	12,000
Service life	10 years	10 years

Which machine would you suggest if
    a) Interest is taken to be 3 per cent?
    b) Interest is taken to be 5 per cent?
    c) Interest is taken to be 8 per cent?

3–34. Two paving materials are being considered for a new turnpike. Material X will cost $120,000 per mile and have a service life of k years. Material Y will cost $95,000 per mile and last 20 years. If interest is taken to be 5 per cent, for what value of k will the two materials be equivalent economically?

3–35. Facing the new product committee of a diversified manufacturing firm are three new product proposals. Product A would require an investment of $182,000 in development, manufacturing, and marketing effort to bring it on the market. It is expected that product A would produce a net income (before depreciation charges) of $15,700 per year over the next 30 years. Products B and C would require investments of $200,-

000 and $220,000 respectively. Corresponding net income estimates are $15,800 for *B* and $17,600 for *C*. Both of these would also have a market life of 30 years. In no case would there be any recovery from salvage. If the firm requires at least 7 per cent return on its investments, which of these products should be considered?

3–36. A company is exploring the possibilities for automating part of its production process. The equipment which will be required may be purchased for $100,000 or leased at an annual rate of $12,000. The purchased equipment is expected to have a salvage value of $40,000 at the end of a ten-year service life. Maintenance costs are included in the rental for leased equipment, but are estimated to be $1,000 annually if the equipment is purchased. Labor and operating costs will be cut from a present $30,000 to $20,000 with the new equipment. If the firm requires a 10 per cent return on its investment, which alternative would you suggest?

3–37. A firm is considering the installation of automatic data processing equipment to handle some of its accounting, payroll, and billing operations. Machines suitable for the firm's requirements may be purchased for $80,000 or leased at an annual rental of $12,000. The purchased equipment is expected to have a salvage value of $30,000 at the end of a ten year service life. Maintenance costs are included in the rental of the leased equipment, but are estimated to run $800 annually if the equipment is purchased. Labor and operating costs for these functions will be cut from the present $60,000 per year to $20,000 with the new equipment. If the firm requires a return of 8 per cent on investments, what would you suggest?

3–38. A company is engaged in selecting a type of machine to be used in its new plant. Two types under active consideration are known as Model 774 and Model 400. The following data summarize the generally agreed upon facts about the two:

	Model 774	*Model 400*
Price	$50,000	$40,000
Installation cost	1,500	2,000
Annual operating cost	6,000	10,000
Annual maintenance cost	800	500

There is considerable uncertainty and discussion about service lives, salvage values, and interest rates appropriate for the situation.

a) If both machines have service lives of 8 years and no salvage values at the end of that time, which would be preferred? Take interest at 8 per cent.

b) Which would be preferred if interest is 5 per cent? If interest is neglected?

c) Repeat question (*a*) if the firm requires 5 per cent interest and the Model 774 has a service life of 5 years with no salvage value. Do the same if it has a service life of 14 years with no salvage value.

d) Which would be preferred if Model 774 has a salvage value of $5,000 after 10 years of service and Model 400 has a salvage value of $3,000 after ten years? Use an interest rate of 6 per cent.

e) Suppose Model 400 has a production capacity greater than Model 774 and that this extra capacity is worth $5,000 per year to the company. Using an interest rate of 6 per cent, equal service lives of 8 years, and no salvage values, which machine would be preferred?

3–39. In choosing between two machines for a particular production operation some difficulty is encountered by a firm which cannot make good predictions of its future production volumes. Find the annual production volume at which the two machines described below will be equivalent.

	Machine A	Machine B
Price	$10,000.00	$8,500.00
Salvage value	4,000.00	$3,000.00
Direct labor cost per unit	.18	.14
Service life	5 years	4 years

Assume an interest rate of 6 per cent.

3–40. Two types of paving material are being considered for a new parking lot. Type *A* will cost $10.00 per square yard. Since it is a new material, only guesses are available as to its service life. Type *B* will cost $8.00 per square yard. Previous experience with this material indicates its service life will be about 15 years. Interest is at 6 per cent and no salvage values are involved. Find the service life for Type *A* material at which the two will be economically equivalent.

3–41. A manufacturer decides to make one of his products intermittently in lots. His sales department predicts that the demand for this product will continue to be 1,000 units per month for the next several years. The cost of setting up the line to run a lot is $1,000. The cost of storing the completed product is one cent per piece per month, based on the average amount stored. What lot size would you suggest?

3–42. A particular part is required at a uniform rate of 500 units per day. The part can be produced on a multiple-purpose machine at a rate of 1,000 units per day. Units produced are moved into storage immediately. Storage costs are $.10 per unit per day, based on the average amount stored. Setup costs are $100 per run. Find the economic lot size.

3–43. A firm anticipates a continuing uniform requirement for an item at the rate of 10,000 units per month. The cost of ordering a lot is $50 regardless of the size of the lot. Storage costs are 1 cent per piece per month based upon average inventory. Interest, insurance, and taxes may be neglected. The supplier quotes a price of 13 cents per unit in lots up to 20,000, and 10 cents per unit in lots of 20,000 or more. Find the economic purchase quantity.

3–44. An ice-cream plant buys bulk milk which it consumes at a uniform rate of 1,000 gallons per week. Storage costs for the milk are $.01 per gallon per week based on the *maximum* amount stored. Each time a purchase is made there are fixed costs of $100. Milk may be stored no longer than two weeks. What frequency of purchasing would you suggest to management?

3–45. A foundry consumes scrap iron at the uniform rate of 100 tons per month. Each time scrap is purchased there are fixed costs of procurement amounting to some $200. When the scrap is delivered the unloading costs are estimated to be $1.00 per ton. The cost of storing the iron is fixed by the accounting department at $.50 per ton per month based on the *maximum* inventory. The price of scrap is $25 per ton.

a) In what quantity should scrap be purchased?

b) How many times per month should it be purchased?

3–46. Derive an economic lot size formula based upon the following considerations:

a) There is a fixed cost of ordering which is independent of the lot size.

b) Interest, insurance, and taxes are computed as percentage of the average investment in inventory.

c) Other storage charges are proportional to the maximum inventory.

3–47. A certain chemical is consumed by a process at a uniform rate. The total annual consumption is 20,000 gallons. Equipment for the production of this chemical can be brought into operation at a cost of $4,000 per run. The chemical can be stored at a cost of 5 cents a gallon per month, based on the average quantity stored. Find the economic production quantity and the number of times per year the chemical should be produced.

3–48. Solve problem 3–47 if

a) Storage costs are .4 cent per gallon per month, based on the maximum amount stored.

b) The chemical is carried in inventory at a value of $1.20 per gallon and an interest charge is incurred based upon the average investment in inventory. The interest rate is 5 per cent.

c) Storage charges (based on average inventory) are 10 cents per gallon per month up to 10,000 gallons and 15 cents per gallon per month above this level.

3–49. Develop an economic lot size model in which shortages are allowed. Assume a cost C_3 dollars per unit per period for shortages, based on the average amount short.

3–50. A firm purchases steel used in the production of its product. The costs associated with making a procurement (soliciting bids, awarding the contract, etc.) are $250 each time a purchase is made. It uses steel at a uniform rate of 500 tons per month. Storage costs are $25 per ton per month based upon the average inventory. Find the economic purchase quantity.

3–51. A machine is to be used for the production of two products exclusively. Find the optimum lot size for each product (L_1 and L_2) if the following data is given:

	Product 1	Product 2
Annual demand	D_1	D_2
Set up cost per run	C_{11}	C_{12}
Annual storage cost per unit (based on maximum inventory)	C_{21}	C_{22}

Assume that a schedule is desired under which the products alternate on the machine, a run of Product 1 being followed by a run of Product 2, and so on. The number of runs of each product per year will be equal on the average.

3–52. A firm has three sources from which it may obtain funds. It can borrow up to $100,000 from a bank at an interest rate of 10 per cent, up to $50,000 from a commercial lender at 12 per cent, and up to $20,000 from a private investor at 15 per cent. No other sources of funds are open to the firm. It has available three investment opportunities. It may invest any amount up to $50,000 in opportunity *A* with a return of 18 per cent, any amount up to $60,000 in opportunity *B* at 16 per cent return, and any amount up to $60,000 in opportunity *C* with a return of 12 per cent. What program of borrowing and investing would you recommend?

3–53. A firm has developed the following list of projects as current possibilities for investment. All projects are expected to serve for ten years.

Project	Estimated Annual Profit (before Depreciation)	Investment
A	$1,630	$10,000
B	1,952	12,000
C	1,196	6,000
D	1,416	8,000
E	1,947	11,000
F	4,200	15,000
G	2,147	9,000
H	1,490	10,000

a) Assuming that firm uses a rate of return of 12 per cent as its "cost of capital," draw up a capital budget.

b) Draw up a capital budget in which available funds amount to $30,000. Do the same for funds totaling $40,000, $50,000, and $70,000

Chapter 4

DECISION-PROCESS DYNAMICS

INTRODUCTION

IN EXAMINING DECISIONS up to this point we have been chiefly concerned with a model of the elements of a decision and the application of principles of choice. This part of the subject is often called the logic of decisions. In the next few chapters discussion will center around some of the tasks which the analyst encounters in the attempt to bring a decision problem up to the point where the elements are defined and quantified. These tasks include obtaining the alternative courses of action, predicting the outcomes, and finally evaluating the outcomes so that some principle of choice may be applied. Clearly the analyst's skill in doing these things is a result of his entire professional training and experience. However, it is important to point out some general considerations which may help him relate his professional skills more directly to the decision process.

In what follows, there will be occasion to remark on some of the things which appear to happen in actual decision-making practice. For example, it will be pointed out that the search for alternative courses of action may be impeded by a certain resistance to change on the part of the firm. The reader should be cautioned to interpret such statements as hypotheses rather than as general laws. A statement such as this is confirmed in everyone's experience to be sometimes, but not always, true. Statements of this sort included in the following discussion are more than just a rough expression of someone's experience. In most cases there is serious scientific investigation to support them, but of course no very general confirmation. These statements can best be used as clues which tend to sensitize the analyst to the environment in which he studies decision problems.

A DYNAMIC MODEL OF THE DECISION PROCESS

It cannot be emphasized too strongly that there is much more to the process of decision making than confronting a model of the decision with a principle of choice and producing a recommendation for action. In the ongoing context of management affairs, this may indeed be a very limited aspect of the decision process in terms of the time, expense, and difficulty it involves. We hypothesize that the problem of how managers make decisions or how they "ought" to make decisions is primarily an empirical problem. Most of the effort consists of developing the conception or model of the decision through the processes of searching for the alternatives, predicting the outcomes, and evaluating them in terms of the decision-maker's objectives. Once all this is done, one may turn to the question of applying a principle of choice to obtain a preferred course of action.

To understand something of the dynamics of this process, we will raise some hypotheses in the form of a simple model of decision making. We will suppose that the process begins with some events which stimulate or trigger decision-making activities. A machine breaks down, leading management to raise the question of whether it should be repaired or replaced. A competitor proudly announces the installation of a large computer, leading to an inquiry from management as to whether the staff would recommend similar action. A critical shortage in the inventory of a particular product brings about a review of the inventory policies throughout the firm. These are but a few examples of the endless variety of such events which appear to trigger decision-making activity. The manager may, of course, respond to the stimulus events in his own way, without the assistance of the analyst. If, however, he seeks help in the form of staff analysis, we may think of the staff as forming an initial model or conception of the decision situation. This initial model may be incomplete, confused, filled with doubts and uncertainties, and felt by the analyst to be totally inadequate as a basis for recommending action. Alternatively, the stimulus events may suggest a decision problem with which the analyst has had considerable experience, leading to an immediate suggestion of a preferred choice. The major question which we confront in considering the dynamics of the decision process is the question of what response or pattern of responses will be elicited by the initial conception and by its subsequent modifications. A possible view of these responses is suggested in Figure 4–1. They include

Figure 4–1

The Dynamics of the Decision Process

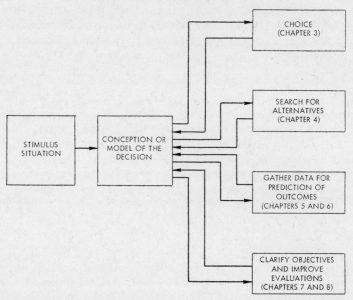

1. *Immediate Choice.* The initial model or some later modification of it will be judged by the analyst to be an adequate basis for choice. He will apply a principle to produce a recommendation. We have examined some elementary forms of this response in Chapter 3. The interesting and difficult question is that of how much effort must be devoted to developing the decision model or conception before he is willing, or is forced by the pressure of affairs, to make a recommendation.

2. *Search for Alternatives.* Instead of immediate choice the analyst may respond by deciding to search for some alternative courses of action beyond those currently being considered. The result of this search may be to modify the decision model; thus the feedback arrow in Figure 4–1. In the present chapter we will consider some elementary hypotheses about when search will be undertaken, how it will be carried out, and when it will terminate in favor of some other response.

3. *Data Gathering for Prediction.* The analyst may find his doubts and uncertainty as to the possible futures and outcomes so great that he is unwilling to suggest a choice. He sets out on a program of data collection and analysis, leading to predictions which in turn modify the decision model. Here we are considering the whole range of empirical scientific procedures involved in experimental design, statistical analysis, and the development of prediction techniques. While we assume that the

reader has been introduced to these ideas elsewhere, we will review them briefly in Chapters 5 and 6. Again, the basic question is how much data gathering will be done, or should be done, before turning to another response.

4. *Evaluation of the Outcomes.* Finally, we hypothesize that the analyst may find his image of the decision problem unsatisfactory because of doubts and uncertainties about the objectives which management seeks and the values of the outcomes in the light of these objectives. Here we try for realism by looking beyond our simple profit maximizing hypothesis. This is perhaps the most important, and at the same time, the most difficult problem in the analysis of management decisions. We have chosen to approach it in four stages, permitting the reader to move somewhat gradually out toward the research frontier. In Chapter 7 we attempt to recognize and structure the problem of multiple, conflicting management objectives. In Chapter 8 it is suggested that profit after taxes is often a closer approximation to management objectives than is profit before taxes. In Chapter 11 we examine the special problems of evaluation which come with the explicit recognition of risk in the analysis of a decision. As before, a basic question for the analyst is how much effort to devote to attempts at explicit evaluations of outcomes before turning to another response.

This simple model of choice-process dynamics raises many questions which cannot be answered at present. It is intended, however, to suggest that there is much more to the analysis of management decisions than formal exercises with principles of choice and to suggest a way of organizing the ideas which follow. We turn now to a discussion of the search for alternative courses of action.

SEARCH

Sometimes alternative courses of action are given, sometimes they are forced upon us, and sometimes they must be developed or discovered. In a decision as to the level of an inventory, the alternatives are quite obviously given. The inventory level may be fixed at any quantity from zero on up. If a machine breaks down, the alternatives are forced upon us. We must decide to repair it or to buy a replacement. If we must decide upon a material to be used in the manufacture of a rocket engine component for example, extensive research and development may be necessary to obtain the alternatives. In those decisions in which the alternatives are taken as given or are clearly obvious, then the analyst may proceed immediately with the next steps in the decision process. Before going on to the process of developing and discovering alternatives, it is important to suggest some of the conditions which lead to the assumption that the alternatives are given. Several hypotheses about these conditions are advanced in the following paragraphs.

1. If it is believed that no alternatives exist beyond those already under consideration, it is natural to assume that the alternatives are to be taken as given. If it is believed that there are no better alternatives than those under consideration, or if the cost of discovering better alternatives is believed to be excessive, then the same assumption will be made. Slogans such as "There's always a better way" caution one not to make this assumption too soon. On the other hand, nothing stimulates the search for further alternatives like the knowledge that better ones do exist. If, for example, the firm learns that a competitor has a better product or process, then aggressive efforts are launched to discover this new alternative.

2. The assumption that alternatives are given is used differently at different levels and positions in the organization. The analyst may find himself in a staff position where it is not his function to discover alternatives, but to study those suggested by others. Alternatively, in other types of staff positions his principal activity may be the discovery of alternatives, as in research and development, for example. As one moves up the ladder of line responsibility, often the opportunity and necessity to obtain new alternatives increases. Again, as the type of supervision and leadership changes, the assumption that the alternatives are given is used with more or less frequency. In authoritarian organizations, close and strict supervision often goes hand in hand with the tendency of the supervisor to specify the alternatives and thus create the structure within which the analyst works. Under more permissive or laissez-faire supervisory philosophies, freedom is created for the discovery of new alternatives, and a premium is often placed upon this activity.

3. Many of the conditions which lead to the assumption that the courses of action are given can be captured with the term "institutional rigidity." This term suggests those features of the firm which lead it to reject the search for new alternatives. Often there is an individual and collective resistance to change on the part of the decision makers in the firm. Tradition and ego involvement may play an important part in restricting the range of alternatives which are considered. Perhaps most important is the influence of past decisions on the alternatives considered. Having once been committed to a course of action, whether it be the purchase of a major asset or the adoption of an operating policy, the firm is under heavy pressure to persist in the execution of its commitment rather than look for new

alternatives. This problem has been touched on in our discussion of sunk costs in Chapter 2.

4. It is probably true that the stronger the pressures of time and routine activity upon the decision maker, the less likely is it that new alternatives will be sought. Finding new alternatives takes time, energy, and money, which may simply not be available.

5. If the conditions leading up to a decision problem have been met repeatedly in the past, then a policy may emerge which will specify the alternatives to be considered. Thus the firm may frequently encounter the problem of what to do when it falls behind some desired production schedule. Eventually a policy may be established which suggests that when production lags there are two alternatives—to work overtime or not to work overtime. When such a policy becomes formal and accepted, no thought is given to other alternatives. The possibilities of subcontracting some of the work, or revising the production schedule, or of increasing the work force are no longer considered. In such situations, the advent of a new decision maker, who may not be familiar with the policy, may lead to a dramatic reintroduction of the neglected alternatives.

ACCEPTABILITY AND SEARCH

Finally we come to a basic hypothesis which suggests a number of insights into the question of accepting the given alternatives or searching for new ones. This hypothesis, advanced by March and Simon (91) says: *Most human decision making, whether organizational or individual, is concerned with the discovery and selection of satisfactory alternatives; only in exceptional cases is it concerned with the discovery and selection of optimal alternatives.* An optimal alternative is one which is demonstrably the best of all possible alternatives. To discover an optimal alternative it is necessary to first search out all of the possible alternatives and then apply a principle of choice which will lead to a preferred course of action. A satisfactory alternative is one which simply meets some minimum standards of acceptability. To find an acceptable alternative it is not generally necessary to search out all possible alternatives. The validity of this hypothesis can be roughly checked by immediate reference to experience. Many jobs are filled, not by literally searching out the very best man, but by finding one who has the qualifications necessary to do the job. Many investments are made, not by searching out the opportunity which will literally yield the greatest return, but by taking advantage of opportunities which will yield 10 per cent return and rejecting opportunities which yield less than

this rate. Production processes are selected, not by an endless search
for the ultimate, but by selecting a process which has certain acceptable attributes of volume, quality, cost, and so on.

This hypothesis, applied to the problem of searching or not
searching for additional alternatives, suggests that, if among the alternatives presently under consideration there are one or more
satisfactory alternatives, then no search will be made. If the alternatives under consideration are not satisfactory, then a search
may be pursued until a satisfactory alternative is discovered. A clear
example of this is the whole principle of management by exception.
This principle implies that there are standards for the activities
and choices of the firm. These include a wide variety—cost standards, production standards, quality standards, and so on. Management by exception simply suggests that as long as alternatives are
available which will meet the standards, the manager need not concern himself with the search for new alternatives. This principle is
clearly useful and even necessary, because the time and energy of
the decision maker are often insufficient for the demands placed
upon him. Rarely do decision makers have time and resources to
seek out optimal alternatives, to say nothing of the knowledge and
information required to do so. This hypothesis is an important clue
to understanding the decision to search or not to search for new
alternatives.

If one decides that additional alternatives will be or must be
searched out, then it is interesting to think about how this search
should be performed and when it should be stopped. The manner in
which the search is to be carried out is itself a decision which can
be studied. Several tentative principles of search will be suggested
which may be useful as rough guides for carrying on the search
process. Although these principles will be offered in relation to the
search for alternative courses of action, it will be clear immediately
that they have application to the process of searching for any kind
of information.

THE PATTERN OF SEARCH

By the pattern of search we simply mean the principle used to
answer the question "Where do we search next for alternatives?" A
firm seeking a new plant site may divide the country up into districts, number the districts, and then search through them in numerical order for alternative plant sites. This would be an example
of a systematic search pattern. Alternatively, the firm may simply

remain alert for information on potential plant sites and investigate
the sites as they are brought to its attention. This latter process
would be an example of a more or less random search pattern. There
are some obvious reasons why systematic patterns may be preferred
if they are possible. A systematic pattern may be designed so as to
minimize the chances of missing alternatives, and it may be designed
to increase the efficiency of the search process itself. Efficiency might
be increased by reducing the costs of search and the time consumed.
The difficulty with a systematic search pattern is that it requires
some advance knowledge of the nature of the alternatives not yet
discovered and where or how they are likely to be found.

Consider as an example the problem of selecting a skin material
for a space vehicle which must re-enter the atmosphere. If one looks
for alternative skin materials by simply covering the vehicle with
whatever heat resistant materials one stumbles over and then
testing the result, the process of search is nearly random. If on the
other hand one appeals to basic theory in physics, chemistry, metal-
lurgy, and ceramic engineering, then perhaps a systematic search
process will be forthcoming. Such a systematic process would probably be more economical and more likely to produce satisfactory alternatives. The only difficulty is that some theory must be available
upon which a systematic process can be based.

To take a much more obvious example, suppose one wishes to purchase a machine to perform a certain function. Clearly, it would not
be necessary to call names in the telephone book randomly, nor even
to call machine tool manufacturers and dealers at random. The
very simplest system would be to call machine tool suppliers in al-
phabetical order. If knowledge of the relative price, quality, and variety reputations of the various suppliers were available, one might
design a simple systematic process which was based upon an ordering of their suppliers with respect to the anticipated desirability of
their products.

This leads to a very simple principle. *The more advance information one has about potential alternative courses of action, the greater
the possibility that a systematic search pattern may be designed
which will increase the efficiency of the search process.*

THE EXTENT OF SEARCH

The next decision with respect to the search process is, "How
many alternatives should be obtained before the search is stopped
and the decision made?" Two different principles may be suggested

as rough guides to the extent of search. First, it should be noted that
the Simon-March hypothesis suggests that in most cases the search
will not be exhaustive. We will not keep on searching for alternatives until we are sure we have obtained all that are possible. One
way to answer the question of when to stop is to decide in advance
how many alternatives are going to be obtained before the decision
is made. It is hard to provide a rationale for such a plan, although
it may simply be a way of limiting the amount of search activity
which is carried on. A more sensible process would be a sequential
one. This would mean that, after each alternative is obtained, its
outcomes are evaluated and the decision is then made to stop or to
continue the search process. This decision might be based upon one
of two principles.

1. *Continue search until the marginal cost of discovering an additional alternative is greater than the marginal gain to be derived
from it.* This principle is a direct application of the marginal cost–
marginal revenue ideas from Chapter 2. It is an eminently sensible
principle except that we can almost never tell in advance what the
marginal cost of discovering one additional alternative will be. Nor
do we have any way of discovering what the marginal gain from one
additional alternative will be. When a firm establishes a research
department, it may become evident in a very gross sense that the
expenditure for research is not greater than the benefits derived
from it, but just when it begins to look as if marginal costs and marginal revenue are getting close together, a brilliant discovery is
produced with great profit possibilities. The work leading to such a
discovery may itself have a very small marginal cost. All this is
difficult to predict in advance.

It may be instructive, however, to consider a highly simplified application of this marginal principle in a case where the cost of
searching for an additional alternative is assumed to be known in
the form of a probability distribution. Similarly, the alternatives
yet to be discovered are taken to be described by a probability distribution, and we consider the search decision as one under conditions of risk. Suppose a firm is searching for investment opportunities, only one of which it will undertake. The present worth of the
best opportunity so far discovered is P_0. The question is raised as to
whether they should invest in this opportunity or whether they
should search for one more before deciding to invest. We must
choose between these two alternatives in the face of two possible

futures; the next opportunity discovered will have present worth greater than P_0, or it will have present worth less than P_0.
Let

$$P_1 = \text{present worth of the next opportunity discovered}$$
$$f(P_1) = \text{probability distribution of } P_1$$
$$c = \text{cost of discovering one more opportunity}$$
$$g(c) = \text{probability distribution of } c$$

The matrix for the decision appears below.

	$P_1 > P_0$	$P_1 \leq P_0$
Search for one more opportunity	$P_1 - c$	$P_0 - c$
Invest in best available opportunity	P_0	P_0

If we are interested in the alternative which maximizes the expected value of the present worth then we might compute the following quantities. If $P_1 > P_0$ then we will invest in the newly discovered opportunity with P_1 as its present worth; otherwise we will invest so as to obtain P_0. The expected present worth if we search for one more opportunity is thus

$$\int_{P_0}^{\infty} P_1 f(P_1) dP_1 + \int_{-\infty}^{P_0} P_0 f(P_1) dP_1 - \int_0^{\infty} c g(c) dc$$

The expected present worth if we invest in the best available opportunity is simply P_0. Comparing this with the above quantity would suggest whether or not to search further. Without insisting that these functions could easily be quantified in a specific situation, this model may help to clarify the search problem. It suggests that the smaller P_0, the greater the advantage of searching for one more opportunity. It raises questions about the relevance of historical data on the costs and results of search for predicting the characteristics of future search. Can a pattern of search be discovered which will "improve" the probability distribution $f(P_1)$? Is the result of a search effort, P_1, independent of its cost, c? In what ways can the cost, c, be controlled?

2. A much more useful principle stems directly from the Simon-March hypothesis. It suggests that search be continued only until an alternative is discovered which is acceptable. This simply re-

quires a determination of the characteristic of an acceptable alternative in advance. Thus, in an investment decision under assumed certainty this principle might take the form: *Search for alternative investment opportunities until one is discovered which will yield a return of 10 per cent.* In many equipment investment decisions, firms use a minimum acceptable rate of return, which is much the same kind of notion. The level of satisfaction used to distinguish satisfactory alternatives from those which are unsatisfactory is called the "aspiration level."

The whole key to the usefulness of this second principle is, of course, the process of fixing the aspiration level. Ideally, the aspiration level ought to be set so that the marginal cost of finding alternatives, if the level is raised, is just equal to the marginal gain from the alternatives thus obtained. This clearly shares the difficulties of our first principle of search, although in Chapter 16 we will explore an important decision problem in which this is actually done. In all practicality, the best that can ordinarily be done is to strive to see that the following general effects take place. As the alternatives become increasingly expensive to discover, the aspiration level should come down. Contrariwise, as alternatives become easier to discover the aspiration level may be raised. In fact, as the cost of search goes down, the tendency to seek optimal alternatives rather than merely satisfactory alternatives becomes more marked.

It is difficult to say how aspiration levels are determined in general. Some firms fix their aspiration levels on the basis of what appears to be necessary to the survival of the organization. Others may decide on an aspiration level for profit and derive a whole complex of aspiration levels from this. Still others take their clues from their competitors, aspiring to be leaders in the industry, or simply maintain an established competitive position. Even without these influences, there is a gradual tendency for aspiration levels of a firm to rise with time. We are continually discovering that what once satisfied us will no longer do so.

In summary, ignorance seems to prevent the application of a maximizing principle to the search process, and most search activity is thus characterized by the attempt to discover satisfactory alternatives.

TECHNIQUES OF SEARCH

Just how does one go about discovering additional alternative courses of action? Much of the answer to this question is wrapped up in the study of creative thinking, and the development of creative and imaginative approaches to management problems. The psychology of creativity is a fascinating but very specialized topic which cannot be discussed here. Many psychologists believe that creativity can be developed and cultivated and that it flourishes under certain special conditions. It has often been noted that a little conscious reflection of the creative process may be a great help. In the remainder of the chapter a few simple schemes for the development of alternative courses of action which appear to have some general usefulness will be suggested.

MODIFICATION OF ALTERNATIVES

One very well known scheme for generating new courses of action is to start with an existing or known alternative and modify it. Often from this "root" alternative a whole family of modifications will spring. It is often suggested that the key to this modification process is the asking of a series of suggestive questions.

1. Can any part of the alternative be eliminated?
2. Can it be combined with other alternatives?
3. Can any aspects of it be increased? What happens if we maximize some aspect of it?
4. Can any aspects of it be decreased? What happens if we minimize some aspect?
5. Can it be divided into parts? Can the parts be rearranged? Inverted? Permuted?
6. Can it be extended "horizontally" or "vertically"?
7. Can the people involved be changed? Can the location be changed? Can the resources used be changed? Can the time be changed?
8. Can we wait and see what happens to the alternatives in the future?
9. What if some aspect of the decision situation were different?

Clearly, not all of these questions make sense in a given context nor do they exhaust the list of fruitful possibilities. They are intended to be only suggestive. One of the most devastating questions that can be asked in some decision situations is, "Why must any action be taken at all?" This question leads to a more fundamental level of thinking with respect to the alternatives.

Another version of the process of modification involves starting with an ideal root alternative, rather than an existing one. The decision maker attempts to specify the characteristics of the ideal or ultimately desirable alternative course of action for a given decision problem. Such an ideal will not often be attainable, but it may provide the basis for generating some possible new alternatives. One begins to investigate why the ideal is not attainable and as a result discovers restrictions and limitations which prevent its attainment. The ideal is then modified by a process of successively taking into account the restrictions until an alternative is developed which is in fact obtainable.

GROUP PROCESSES

Memory and experience provide a fertile source for ideas which mature into new alternatives. One widely used way to tap the memory and experience available to the firm is through some sort of group process such as the committee, the research team, the design team, or the informal groups which form during a coffee break. This is the province of the sociologist and the study of small groups. Much work has been done on the problems of leadership in small groups, the organization of such groups, and their behavior in problem solving. Very little, however, seems to be known about the small group considered specifically as a mechanism for obtaining alternatives.

There is some current interest in a small group process known as "brainstorming" in which the group members are invited to suggest alternatives without fear of criticism or evaluation. All suggestions are recorded by the group, and no member is allowed to make any remark which is critical or evaluative of a suggestion. This is intended to create an atmosphere of stimulating freedom of thought and expression, and to obviate any inhibitions which the members might otherwise feel. Advocates of brainstorming report its usefulness in obtaining alternatives in a variety of situations, but some research casts reasonable doubt on its effectiveness. Most people seem to agree that the small group cannot create any ideas which are not simply the sum of the contributions of the individuals in it. The group does not think. However, some sort of group process may be effective and economical for eliciting and combining alternatives which have been discovered by its members. It is a device which is being more and more widely used in decision making all the time.

SUGGESTIONS FOR FURTHER STUDY

Box, G. E. P. "Evolutionary Operation: A Method for Increasing Industrial Productivity," *Applied Statistics,* Vol. 6 (1957).

CYERT, RICHARD M., and MARCH, JAMES G. *A Behavioral Theory of the Firm.* Englewood Cliffs, N.J.: Prentice-Hall, Inc., 1963.

HADAMARD, JACQUES. *The Psychology of Invention in the Mathematical Field.* Princeton, N.J.: The Princeton University Press, 1945.

HAYNES, W. WARREN, and SOLOMON, MARTIN B. "A Misplaced Emphasis in Capital Budgeting," *The Quarterly Review of Economics and Business,* Vol. 2, No. 1 (February, 1962).

MARCH, JAMES G., and SIMON, HERBERT A. *Organizations.* New York: John Wiley & Sons, Inc., 1958.

MORRIS, WILLIAM T. *Management Science in Action.* Homewood, Ill.: Richard D. Irwin, Inc., 1963.

PROBLEMS

4-1.   A firm has decided to build a new plant and is about to begin the search for a site. What principles would you suggest the firm keep in mind in order to make the search for alternative sites as effective as possible?

4-2.   The sales volume of a small jobbing machine shop fluctuates considerably. The volume of work has varied from a backlog equivalent to about 40 per cent of the shop's weekly capacity, to a shortage causing idleness of about 50 per cent of capacity. What alternatives might be considered in meeting these fluctuations?

4-3.   It is known that one of 128 samples of steel, each in the form of a small cylinder, is radioactive, but just which one is not known. A radiation detection device is available. Design a program of search which will discover the radioactive sample, and will require the minimum number of readings with the detection device.

4-4.   You are standing on the side of a large mountain in a fog so dense that you can see only the small patch of ground at your feet. How would you find the top of the mountain?

4-5.   Given an unknown function $y = f(x)$, you may select values of x and the corresponding values of y will be reported to you. How would you search for the maximum of the function if there was a cost associated with each x, y combination you explored?

4-6.   Given an unknown function $z = f(x,y)$, you may select pairs of x,y values, and the corresponding first derivatives of the function will be reported to you. That is, if you select a pair of values x_1,y_1, you will be told the values of

$$\frac{dz}{dx} \quad \text{and} \quad \frac{dz}{dy}$$

at that point. Design a program of search to find the maximum of the function. Design a second program given the additional information that the function has a unique maximum.

4–7. A firm wishes to purchase a fork lift truck to handle palletized materials in its warehouse. How would you obtain the alternatives?

4–8. A personnel manager must fill the following positions. How might he obtain alternative candidates for each?

a) Production worker.

b) Time study man.

c) Department foreman.

4–9. Describe two examples from your own decision-making experience which tend to confirm the Simon-March hypothesis. Describe one which tends to deny it.

4–10. Describe a situation from your own experience in which the marginal cost of discovering an additional alternative and the marginal gain to be derived from it might reasonably be estimated.

4–11. List as many methods as you can for the production of a gray iron cylinder of length 2 inches $\pm \frac{1}{32}$ and diameter 1 inch $\pm \frac{1}{32}$.

4–12. List as many methods as you can for transmitting "yes or no" messages between an aircraft and a control tower.

4–13. A community of 50,000 persons wishes to find all the cases of TB which exist among its residents. Suggest a program of search.

4–14. A firm is seeking the solution to an important and troublesome technical problem. It decides to assign four engineers to the task. What would be the advantages of

a) Having the four work as a team?

b) Having them work independently instead of as a team?

c) Having them work as two independent teams of two men each?

4–15. Suppose your company is interested in buying a machine and has so far received two bids from machinery manufacturers. What *principles* might help you decide whether or not to seek additional bids?

4–16. A firm is looking for a new product to manufacture. It wishes to operate as though the following statements were true:

a) The cost of discovering and evaluating each potential product is *c*, a known constant.

b) The present worth of the profit from a potential product (exclusive of costs mentioned in statement (a) is a random variable P with distribution $f(P)$.

How long should they search?

Chapter 5

DATA GATHERING

INTRODUCTION

In this chapter we consider the data-gathering response to a model or conception of a decision situation. The analyst who feels that the doubts and uncertainties in his view of a management decision problem can be attacked by a program of data collection finds himself confronted with a search problem similar in principle with that we have outlined in Chapter 4. He must consider how and where to search for the information he wishes; thus he has what we have called the problem of the pattern of search. Since it generally costs money to collect data, he is concerned about balancing this cost against the value of the data which he obtains, thus encountering the problem of the extent of search. Useful generalizations on these questions are difficult, except perhaps the remark that in practice they are answered on the basis of experience and judgment rather than by precise calculation. Only if the data-collection decision is a rather well-defined statistical problem can we make anything like a careful computation of the best time at which to terminate data gathering. We examine these instances in Chapter 20. Generally useful remarks about where and how to search for data are even more difficult. The variety of sources from which information is obtained for decision making is too great for anything like a complete enumeration. It is important, however, not to give the impression that the information needed to make decisions arises as if by magic, or even that it is relatively easy to obtain. Indeed, it is perhaps true that the most difficult and expensive part of the analysis of most decisions is the information-collection task. In this chapter we will examine briefly the reservoir of information which is to be found within the firm itself, chiefly by way of the accounting and performance recording systems, and suggest a few of the commonly used sources outside of the firm. In the chapter which follows, we go on to suggest some of the ways in which this information is processed for use in decision making.

THE COST ACCOUNTING SYSTEM

All firms carry on certain accounting functions whose chief aim is to record the financial history of the firm and periodically produce a report of the results of past operations. Such a report usually includes a profit and loss statement showing the income and expenses for the period covered, as well as a balance sheet showing the forms and valuations of the firm's assets and liabilities at some moment in time. While this information is essential in many top-level management decisions, such as those having to do with finance and organization, it is somewhat removed both in time and in detail from decisions at the usual project level. A much more useful source of information for the decision analyst is often the cost accounting system which functions in most manufacturing firms.

The basic purpose of a cost accounting system is to trace the expenses incurred by the firm to the areas of responsibility of the decision makers in the firm who have some control over these expenses. It aims to tell the foreman what costs were incurred by his department, the plant manager what costs were incurred in his plant, and so on. Costs are traced to spheres of responsibility so that the decision maker in authority can take action to control costs if such a decision is made. Thus, the main purpose of a cost accounting system is to provide a basis for control decisions. Herein lies both the strength and weakness of most cost accounting systems. The system is usually designed carefully around the organization of decision makers which it serves, thus it becomes ideally suited for the firm's control decisions. Its very suitability for this purpose sometimes tends to limit its usefulness for planning decisions of any other kind. Suppose, for example, we wish to estimate the savings to be obtained from installing a conveyor system in a foundry. We may find that most of the handling is now done by the production workers themselves and that their wages are allocated directly to the various jobs which pass through the foundry. It may not be possible to separate out the cost of materials handling. To make this more explicit we will consider the basic structure of a typical cost accounting system.

CLASSIFICATION OF COSTS

The basic inputs to a cost accounting system consist of records of the expenses incurred by the firm. These expenses are then broken down into various classifications of cost. The particular classification used will be designed to suit the purposes of the firm, but a typical simple classification might include:

Direct Labor: cost of labor expended directly in the production of the product.

Direct Materials: cost of materials which are actually consumed directly in the production of the product.

Indirect Labor: the cost of labor which is not directly associated with the production of any particular unit of output, such as supervision, maintenance labor, storeskeeping, janitorial service, and so on.

Indirect Materials: cost of material which does not enter directly into the product, such as maintenance supplies, cutting oil, light bulbs, and so on.

Overhead: usually includes all other costs not placed in one of the above classes, such as the costs of management, staff services, plant building, and power.

In accumulating and classifying these costs, the system also attempts to preserve their identity in such a way that they may be allocated for control purposes. Thus, when a particular operator's time and wages are recorded and classified as direct labor, it is important perhaps to identify the department in which he worked, the particular job or product on which he worked, and the type of activity in which he was engaged. This information makes possible appropriate cost analyses for the control decisions involved.

BASES FOR ANALYSIS

For control purposes the firm usually assigns responsibility for various segments of its operations to particular decision makers. Thus, a worker may be responsible for a machine, a group leader for several machines, a foreman for a department, and the plant manager for the entire plant. The cost accounting system attempts to provide each of these persons with an estimate of the costs incurred by the portion of operations for which he is responsible. A particular portion of the operations which form a realm of responsibility is often called a cost center. The job of the accounting system is then to break down the costs in terms of cost centers. It will report to a foreman the cost of direct labor, direct materials, indirect labor, and so forth used by his department during some period of time. For most classifications of cost it may be relatively easy to trace costs to such a cost center. Since overhead costs are beyond the control of the department foreman, no attempt would be made to allocate these to his cost center.

The basic control decision at a cost center usually revolves around some kind of standard cost. The function of this standard cost is simply to provide an explicit decision rule for deciding whether or not action is required to control costs. Thus, the firm may establish a standard cost for direct labor on each product within a given cost center. Such a standard cost may specify a given direct labor cost per unit of production. If direct labor costs rise above this standard, the decision must be to take some action to explain or reduce these costs. As long as direct labor costs per unit of production remain below the standard, the decision may be to take no control action.

Two major problems are encountered at this point: how to establish the standard cost, and what particular control action should be taken when the standard is not met. Sometimes standard costs are based on the average of actual past costs, sometimes on an estimate of what costs "should" be under "normal operating conditions," and sometimes on an estimate of what costs would be under ideal or optimal operating conditions. Just what control action should be chosen when standards are not met depends on how standards are set and also upon a great deal of knowledge which is not a part of the cost accounting system itself. Its function in control decisions is to determine the choice between two alternatives: "no control action" and "some control action." It does not usually help much with the decision as to just exactly what control action should be taken.

A second basis for analysis is the tracing of costs to the product itself for purposes of pricing, profit measurement, and inventory valuation. The attempt here is to estimate the cost of a particular unit of product, the cost of a particular job or order, or the unit cost of each of a line of products. The chief problem is how to allocate the indirect costs and overhead. Let us suppose we wish to set up a system which will estimate the cost of production for each order passing through a jobbing machine shop. It is usually possible to preserve the identity of the direct labor and direct materials costs in relation to each order. Overhead, which may include the costs of the accounting department, the engineering department, and the shipping department, as well as the cost of heating the plant, is much more difficult. The method used by most cost accounting systems is to select some more or less arbitrary basis for allocating overhead costs to the product or order. For example, some period of "normal operation" may be selected and the ratio of total overhead expenses to direct labor-hours may be computed. This ratio then becomes the overhead "rate" and overhead expenses are charged against the product by simply multiplying the number of direct labor-hours consumed in the production of a particular order or unit of product by this rate. This simple device suggests that overhead expenses are taken to be proportional to direct labor-hours, and the constant of proportionality is this rate which is based on some period of normal production volume. Other bases for allocating overhead expenses suggest that they should be taken as being proportional to direct labor costs, machine-hours, or direct material costs.

The accounting system is usually designed so that overhead allocation is made in the most realistic manner consistent with reasonable simplicity. Thus there is always a certain amount of arbitrariness in the allocation process, which makes the results of the cost accounting process only approximate estimates of the "actual" costs. This method does, however, give a complete estimate of the costs of production of an order, a job, or a unit of product. Such an estimate is obviously essential not only for the control decisions, but for all decisions involving pricing, profit estimating, and inventory valuation.

In addition to allocating costs to cost centers and to the product itself, most cost accounting systems can be used from time to time for special studies which involve particular bases of allocation. For example, after a new machine is installed, the cost accounting may be modified so as to trace costs directly to this machine. This may permit an evaluation of its individual performance as a prototype for further new equipment. Such detailed analysis might not be routinely necessary for management purposes.

SOME PROBLEMS

For decision-making purposes, the use of cost accounting data raises some problems which must be noted. The first difficulty to be overcome is that of discovering exactly what costs are included in the various cost classifications and what the system rules are for analyzing these costs on various bases. Every system has its own particular rules and definitions which are designed for control and costing purposes within the particular firm. The analyst must take care to discover such things as exactly what costs are included in the indirect materials classification and exactly how overhead is allocated to the product. Without a clear understanding of the cost accounting process, no precise interpretation may be made of the data which it yields.

The method of allocating overhead using a "rate" or proportionality constant is the source of some difficulty. Clearly, if overhead is taken to be proportional to direct labor-hours, the estimated cost of a unit of output may be very different than if it is taken to be proportional to machine-hours or direct labor costs. It is often very difficult to decide which method of allocation is best and one may hope only for consistency and careful interpretation of the cost data resulting. The overhead rate is also based upon some period of normal operations. As some of the costs included in overhead usually are fixed costs, any decision which involves a change in the volume of production must be viewed in terms of the resulting change in overhead rate. Suppose, for example, a firm is considering the possibility of increasing its output from 20,000 units per month to 30,-000. Assuming that this increase in output will involve no increase in sales department expenses, how should selling costs be allocated to the product? If selling expenses are $10,000 per month, then the cost accounting system might simply allocate an equal portion of these expenses to each unit of product. While this may be arbitrary, any other scheme may be excessively complicated. Thus, at a volume of 20,000 units per month, each unit of product would have 50 cents allocated to it as its share of the selling costs. If we then fall into the trap of thinking it costs 50 cents to sell each unit of product, when the volume is increased to 30,000 we may continue to allocate the same amount to each unit. Actually, of course, if selling costs do not change, the proper allocation would be 33⅓ cents at the higher level of production.

Another example of this same difficulty arises with the introduction of automatic machinery. Suppose the firm is considering the introduction of equipment which will reduce the direct labor time for a given operation by 40 man-hours per week. Suppose further that the cost of a direct labor-hour for this operation is $2.50 and that the cost accounting system presently allocates overhead to the product at the rate of 200 per cent of direct labor costs. Now it is tempting to say that if 40 man-hours per week are saved, this results in a cost reduction of $100 per week in direct labor costs and $200 per week in overhead costs. This latter saving is probably not realized at all since it is not likely that *overhead* is actually reduced very much by the introduction of the new equipment.

Still another problem which is continually troublesome is that of allocating costs among several lines of product. Consider a firm which is producing only product *A* at the rate of 5,000 units per week. All of its costs are classified as direct labor, direct materials, or overhead. Its total overhead expense is approximately $25,000 per week and this is allocated uniformly to each unit of product. Thus, the cost as estimated by the accounting system might be:

Direct labor	$ 1.20
Direct materials	6.00
Overhead	5.00
	$12.20

Now suppose the firm discovers that using the scrap material left over from product A and some idle equipment it can produce a new product, called B. Since the material that goes into B is scrap which would have been wasted otherwise, no cost is attached to it. Further, since the overhead expenses are now being absorbed by A, no charges for overhead are made against B. Thus, the only cost attributed to product B might be the direct labor that goes into its production, amounting to, say, $1.00 per unit. This line of thinking leads the firm to offer product B on the market at a very low price. Soon orders pour in for product B and the firm has to cut back its production of A in order to fill these orders. At this point it is clear that the scrap from product A may no longer be sufficient in quantity, and the firm must buy material for the production of B. The decreasing volume of A reduces the amount of overhead expense which is actually charged to production. A prompt revision of the cost accounting system must be made or the firm will begin to lose money. Clearly product B must bear its share of the overhead expenses and the material used in its production must be costed against it. This will lead to a revision of the market price of B which more closely reflects its production costs.

The principle involved is a familiar one. As long as the volume of A is maintained, the firm will make a profit on product B if the marginal revenue from its sale exceeds the marginal cost of production. If A is produced at 5,000 units per week, it may be quite reasonable to say that the marginal production cost for B consists only of direct labor. However, as soon as the volume of production for A changes, either the estimated cost of A or that of B must be changed. Further, if the volume of B exceeds that for which scrap material is available from the production of A, then the marginal cost of B goes up accordingly. These principles are well known, and one must simply guard against losing sight of them through unquestioning reliance upon cost accounting data.

With these cautions about the interpretation and use of cost accounting data, the accounting system can become a useful and important source of information for the analysis of decisions. It can be used to obtain detailed estimates of operating costs, maintenance costs, material costs, and so on.

OTHER SOURCES WITHIN THE FIRM

Every firm contains a vast "memory" filled with information on its past operations. Machine data processing, punched cards, magnetic tape, and microfilm are coming into general use and thus increasing further the capacity of the firm's memory. The cost accounting system is itself a part of this reservoir of information. In the process of studying a decision the first question which the analyst asks as the information requirements begin to emerge is, "Is this information already available within the firm?" The information available varies from firm to firm, but some of the standard and useful sources are typically:

1. General ledger accounts.
2. Sales records, bills, and salesman's reports.
3. Production control records.
4. Inventory records.
5. Quality control records.
6. Purchasing department records.
7. Time study records and the results of other industrial engineering studies.
8. Personnel records.

It is impossible to examine typical instances of these sources in detail; however, their use raises certain general questions which are worth noting:

1. Are the conditions under which the data were recorded clearly understood? For example, productivity data during a period when a new product is first produced may be markedly different from the same measurements made after production has been under way for some time.

2. Can a sample of the information be used in the decision, rather than a complete study of all available data? (The advantages and disadvantages of sampling are discussed in the next chapter.)

3. If the data needed are not available, can a system for recording in the future be established? The answer to this question usually depends on whether the decision involved is to be made repeatedly in the future. If so, it may be economic to establish a system which will routinely furnish the information required for the decision.

4. Are the data being recorded so as to achieve something like a reasonable balance between storage cost and retrieval cost or access time? For example, the data on sales invoices may be stored by preserving the original invoices, by photographing them on microfilm, or perhaps by transferring the information to punched cards. Each of these methods

will result in different storage costs and different costs of getting the information back once it is stored. This question clearly cannot be answered without reference to the larger context of record-keeping methods throughout the firm.

5. If the exact information desired is not available, is there some way of inferring it from what is available? For example, suppose we need an estimate of the time required to perform a certain operation and find that this information is not available. It may be that from job timecards we can obtain the total time devoted to the operation for some period, from production records obtain the number of units processed, and by taking the ratio obtain a crude estimate of the performance time. Such an estimate may have serious shortcomings, but it may well be the only information available for decision-making purposes. At least it may give an idea of the order of magnitude of performance time, which will serve until better information is obtained.

AUTOMATION IN MANAGEMENT INFORMATION SYSTEMS

Automatic data-processing systems are widely available which mechanize the great volume of clerical work necessary to operate and control a business enterprise. These systems may vary from what are now fairly common machine-accounting systems, to the most modern and elaborate data-processing complexes which have as their core a large digital computer. The alternatives open to the firm run this entire gamut, and often include a variety of comparable systems produced by different manufacturers.

Here again the major tangible benefit comes through the reduction in human labor required to accomplish payrolls, billing, production control, management reports, and so on. In this case, the savings may often be realized without a major capital investment, since very often the kind of equipment required is not sold, but is leased or rented by the manufacturer. This provides both advantages and disadvantages over direct purchase, as noted in Chapter 3.

Planning an automatic data-processing system requires considerable time. The firm's operations must be studied in detail, and the data required to operate and control them must be sifted to decide just what will be handled by the proposed system. Thus, one of the major advantages is usually a revision, modification, and ultimately a simplification, of all the data-handling functions carried on within the firm. Useless forms are eliminated, files are disposed of, and reports which are of little interest to management are finally discontinued. The files may be consolidated and reduced to punched cards or tape, or some other form which makes them available as inputs to the automatic systems and simultaneously reduces the necessary storage space. Improved office systems and procedures could be achieved without automatic data handling, but often the decision to automate provides the impetus which is otherwise lacking.

The greatest benefits may be those which are most difficult to evaluate. What is it worth to management to have more detailed and more accurate reports on the activities of the firm than ever before? What is it worth to know the firm's inventory position three or four days earlier than was previously possible? What is the value of having more frequent sales reports, or of having a complete profit and loss statement monthly instead of quarterly? What also is the benefit to the firm of being able to meet its payroll a few days closer to the closing date? All these possibilities may be of significant importance to the firm, but the careful analyst tries to sort out the real benefits from the often compelling glamor of being able to do hundreds of man-hours of clerical work in a few minutes or hours of machine time.

At present, one of the costly aspects of automatic data processing is that of programming the machines. For routine operations the firm will use standard programs or those which, once made, can be used over and over again. For special studies and reports to management, new programs will be required. The current effort to make the programming function itself more and more automatic holds good possibilities for dramatic savings.

For the analyst some particularly difficult questions arise. Can he achieve the necessary foresight to design the management information system so as to capture the data he will need for future analyses? Can he predict the sort of analytical techniques which will become useful in the firm and begin to accumulate the data they will require? Presently, it is often the case that when a new technique or a new decision is studied by the analyst, the data are simply not available. Does an automatic data-processing system really make data more available to him, or does the inflexibility and programming cost make it less readily available? How does one decide what data should be routinely available in the system and what capability the system should have for special studies on a nonroutine basis? As management information systems are now evolving, the trend appears to be toward on-line, real-time systems. An on-line system is one in which every person or location in the company which generates or uses information processed by the system is connected directly to the system. For example, the airline reservation systems now in use permit a direct link between the computer and every reservation agent's counter. Real-time systems are those which post transactions or events as they happen, rather than in batches at the end of an accounting period. One system, now being developed, will give management a balance sheet, profit and loss statement, and a variety of other reports daily, or even hourly if desired. What will be the impact of such systems on management decision making? Have we already swamped some managers with more information than they can handle? How will these systems change the role and problems faced by the analyst? The possibilities are fascinating, but little is generally known at present.

It has been suggested that the biggest payoff in management data processing may come from the study of decision problems which simply could not have been studied otherwise. For example, one production control problem involved the scheduling of 623 parts through 33 machine tool groups so as to maintain adequate inventory levels and to utilize the machine tools effectively This problem was of such magnitude that the paper work for manual scheduling made it almost impossible to keep any schedule at all up to date with changing conditions. Not only could this be done on a digital computing machine, but the machine could actually work out rapidly a large number of possible schedules from which the best one could be selected. Without the computer nothing of the sort could be done, but the tangible benefits are difficult to measure.

One of the problems involved in the selection of an automatic data-processing system is that rapid technological advance quickly makes presently available systems obsolete. If the equipment is to be rented, this is less of a problem than if it is to be purchased. The time required at present to design and build an entirely new data-processing system is estimated at four to five years. This rate of obsolescence can have serious implications for any long-term commitment either to rent or buy the equipment. Coupled with the extended planning period necessary to make the data-processing operations explicit prior to installation of the system, timing may become a difficult aspect of the decision.

SOURCES OF INFORMATION OUTSIDE THE FIRM

It would be futile to attempt to present any sort of a comprehensive description of the variety of sources of information which lie outside the firm. However, the following classification of these sources may provide a useful basis for embarking on the problem of obtaining the information required for a decision:

1. *Published Information.* A useful first step is often to see if the information needed has been published in a book, periodical, or report. Technical directories, trade journals, United States government publications, and the comprehensive reference books available in many fields are especially important in this respect.

2. *Information Available on Request.* The second vast reservoir of information is that which is not published but is available for the asking. Suppliers, customers, banks, government agencies, chambers of commerce, and even competitors are often willing to furnish needed information on the basis of a serious and tactful request.

3. *Research and Development.* If the information is not published and cannot be obtained by consulting someone who knows, the only alternative may be to undertake the process of generating it through research and development. These activities are usually expensive and may not always be successful, thus this final step is taken only in connection with very important decisions and when the two sources mentioned above are known to be inadequate.

EXAMPLE

Suppose a firm is considering the purchase of one of several alternative production machines and that experience and preliminary investigation reveal that the following information is needed for each alternative:

Price	Output
Installation cost	Scrap rate
Operating costs	Service life
Maintenance cost	Salvage value

Assuming this decision is important enough to warrant a rather detailed analysis, we will suggest some of the sources from which basic information might typically be obtained, and in the next chapter illustrate some of the techniques which might be used to process this information for inclusion in the analysis.

The price of each machine would most likely be obtained through a direct quotation from the manufacturer. The installation cost might be the result of a detailed estimate by the plant millwright based upon data obtained from similar jobs done in the past. If the installation is to be performed by the manufacturer or by an outside contractor, quotations might be obtained from these sources. If the major difference in operating costs among the alternatives will arise out of differing direct labor requirements, the firm's time study department might be consulted. Either from performance times observed on similar machines doing similar operations, or from a system of synthetic time values, an estimate of the direct labor requirements might be obtained. From the personnel department or the accounting department an estimate of the wage rates from the skill levels involved could be obtained, which would yield a direct labor cost estimate when combined with the performance time estimates. Maintenance costs might be separated into costs associated with regularly scheduled maintenance activity or preventive maintenance, those costs which result from breakdowns, and repairs which require unscheduled maintenance effort. Once a preventive maintenance program is established, the times, skills, wage rates, and thus the costs may be estimated by recourse to the information available from the time study department, the accounting department, and the records of the maintenance department itself. The frequency and severity of breakdowns are much more difficult to estimate, and are typically obtained either from records of the firm's experience with similar machines or from data furnished by the manufacturer describing the failure patterns of his equipment under operating conditions similar to those which exist within the firm.

The estimated output of each alternative is usually based upon the manufacturer's specifications of feeds, speeds, power, and capacity for his equipment, in combination with estimates from the time study department of human performance times wherever they are involved. The scrap rate of each machine may be difficult to estimate, but some basis may be obtained from the manufacturer's claims as to precision and accuracy and from the records of the quality control department for similar machine and job situations. The service life depends heavily on the firm's policy with respect to machine replacement. How does the firm decide when to replace a machine and when to continue its use? The problems of formulating replacement policy are examined in detail in Chapter 9. Once this policy is clearly established, data from the firm's own records or from those of the manufacturer may provide a basis for estimating service life from the study of similar machines. Salvage value is usually a function of the age of the machine, as well as its condition and degree of obsolescence. Often the best one can do is to obtain data on current and past market prices for used machinery as a basis for estimating the salvage values of the alternatives under consideration.

CONCLUSION

In understanding the data-gathering response to a model of a management decision, several points might be kept in mind.

1. Gathering data implies some rather definite idea as to how the data will be used. While a certain amount of free, unplanned information gathering may be useful at the outset of a study, soon one must begin to match the data with the model. There is little point in gathering data which has no role in the model, just as there is little point in developing models for which the data cannot be obtained. Models which involve concepts that cannot be operationally defined and models which require data that is costly or impossible to obtain are of little use to the analyst.

2. While we cannot answer directly the question of how much data to collect, in a sense the remainder of this book is aimed at helping the analyst form reasonable judgments on this basic point.

3. Perhaps the most difficult problems in the study of decisions are the problems of quantifying probabilities and values of outcomes. These are problems of data gathering and measurement to which we now turn special attention.

SUGGESTIONS FOR FURTHER STUDY

BIERMAN, HAROLD, JR. *Managerial Accounting, an Introduction.* New York: The Macmillan Co., 1959.

SHULTZ, GEORGE P., and WHISLER, THOMAS L. *Management Organization and the Computer.* Glencoe, Ill.: The Free Press, 1960.

SPRAGUE, RICHARD E. *Electronic Business Systems.* New York: The Ronald Press Co., 1962.

VATTER, WILLIAM J. "Contributions of Accounting to Measurement in Management," *Management Science,* Vol. 5, No. 1 (October, 1958).

PROBLEMS

5–1.   A company is considering replacing its conventional trucks with turbine-powered vehicles. What information would you like to have in studying this decision? Where would you expect to get it?

5–2.   How would you obtain the information relevant to a choice between

a) Two makes of engine lathes for general production work in a job shop?

b) Shipping a product by rail or motor freight?

c) Casting or welding a small component part?

d) Making or buying a part?

e) Marketing a home workshop drill press in fully assembled or knocked-down form?

5–3.   How can a small jobbing foundry obtain the data necessary to quote prices to its potential customers?

5–4.   What information could be obtained to estimate the cost of having a production line break down for 30 minutes?

5–5.   A machinery manufacturer operates its own captive foundry for making gray iron castings. When business is good the regular shift capacity of the foundry is insufficient, and the question is raised whether the excess work should be done on overtime or subcontracted to other foundries. Explain why you would or would not consider overhead in the analysis of this decision.

5–6. A firm is considering whether to make or buy a minor component of a new product it is bringing out. The best bid obtained from outside suppliers is $1.00 per unit. The cost accounting system yields estimates (based on similar items made in the past) of $.40 per unit for direct labor and $.32 per unit for direct materials. Explain briefly why they should make or buy under each of the following conditions:

a) The company has the necessary production facilities available for the component and no other use in mind for them. Normal overhead items charged against these facilities would work out to $.60 per unit.

b) The facilities are currently being used for a sideline item which earns just enough to cover direct labor, direct materials, and overhead. This item would be discontinued if the component is made.

Chapter 6

PREDICTION AND JUDGMENT*

INTRODUCTION

OUR PROBLEM HERE is to look briefly at the methods by which we can make statements about the possible futures and the outcomes in a decision. This is a problem simply because decisions have to do with choices among alternatives whose outcomes are future events. We cannot know the future. All we have is information about past events, which we try to use to make guesses about future events. Sometimes this information is relatively complete, sometimes it is fragmentary, and sometimes it is virtually nonexistent. What methods one uses to make guesses about the future depend heavily on how much relevant past information is available. If we have a suitable amount of carefully recorded data about past events, the techniques of statistics may be used to make predictions about the future. Lacking such data, we may be forced to make guesses in a much more literal sense. To help keep track of the variety of processes involved, some simple terminology is in order.

We will refer to all schemes for making statements about the future as forecasting methods. When some explicit method of collecting data on past events and inferring something about the future from these data is used, we will speak of *prediction*. This includes all the techniques of inferential statistics and many simplifications thereof. The important point about prediction is simply that the data are clearly written down and the method of inference is explicitly stated. When we lack data on past events or when we lack an explicit method of making estimates from these data, then we must resort to guesses, expert opinion, and so on. These schemes we will lump under the term *judgment*. The distinction here is that the estimate is produced completely or partially from some person's

---

* This chapter presumes that the reader has had some previous introduction to elementary statistics.

or group's accumulated experience and thinking. This production does not have the same explicit character as a record of past sales which is digested by a computer and yields an estimate of future sales by a process precisely stated in the computer's program. Now, in most decisions, a complex mixture of prediction and judgment is actually used. For purposes of understanding, it is important to separate the two processes as clearly as possible, and to be conscious of the point at which prediction stops and judgment begins. It is also worth saying again that probably every interesting management decision involves judgments to some extent. The major distinction made between judgment and prediction is simply one of explicitness of the measurements and the process of inference. If all this is explicit then it could all be done by a computer. So far, only a relatively small number of very special decisions are being made by a computer.

It is often useful to think of future events as the result in part of factors which have determined these events in the past and the result in part of factors which are new and different. To the extent that, say, future sales are the product of the factors which have determined past sales, the analyst may use explicit prediction techniques to extend the past into forecasts of the future. To the extent that future sales depend on factors which were not active in the past, historical data fails and we must rely on the experience and judgment of management. Recognizing that every forecast requires some mixture of prediction and judgment, the contribution of the analyst is to take over the task of explicit prediction so as to relieve management for the task of making judgments. The analyst, then, tends to be a specialist in prediction techniques and need not have the rich experience of the manager. The manager, on the other hand, relies on his depth of knowledge and experience accumulated over the years but need not be an expert in prediction techniques. Forecasting, perhaps more than any other aspect of decision making, involves the combined skill, experience, and perhaps even the luck of the analyst and the manager.

In this chapter we seek to establish three basic points:

1. We cannot make statements about the future which are free of risk and uncertainty. Yet both analysts, working with prediction techniques, and managers, making judgments, suppress, absorb, or assume away the risk and uncertainty. The analyst sometimes discards all the information which his prediction techniques could produce except a single number, perhaps the mean. The manager, either from psychological need

for certainty or because of the social norms of managerial behavior, also produces single-valued statements about the future. This process of suppressing risk and uncertainty produces what we have already called decisions under assumed certainty. Perhaps the most important fundamental development in the analysis of management decisions has been the trend toward the explicit recognition of risk and uncertainty, rather than their suppression. We shall try to learn in later chapters whether this makes any difference in the way managers decide.

2. There are a great many prediction models which the analyst might use to produce forecasts. He is faced with the same difficult decisions in connection with this response to a decision situation which we have met before. How should one search for a prediction model? When should one stop developing more and more refined prediction models which reduce the risk and uncertainty involved but which increase the cost of data collection and computation? As before, one must rely largely on judgments by the analyst, and the remainder of this book is aimed at helping to develop a reasonable basis for these judgments.

3. In the case of decisions under assumed certainty we did not pretend to know the future, but simply chose to act in a manner consistent with a single possible future. This is in general the position of the analyst. While we cannot know the future, we make recommendations to management by taking a view of the future (explicitly or implicitly) and suggesting the actions which would be consistent with this view. The analyst says, "If you view the future in this way, then the best choice would be. . . ." If the manager accepts this recommendation, we may think of him as *acting as if* the analyst's statements about the future were true. In short, we deal with the future by adopting a view of it and then trying to act consistently with this view.

VIEWS OF THE FUTURE

While we admit we do not know the future, we are free to look ahead, taking whatever view of it we find useful. One's view of the future may take on four basic forms.

1. *Ignorance.* We may see the future as a sort of blank, finding ourselves unwilling or unable to make any useful statements about it. Decisions made under such conditions have been described as "heroic" rather than "rational." This view of the future is approached in many managerial situations where little or no attempt is made to forecast. It is also suggestive of the fundamental management philosophy of avoiding the necessity for forecasts by being able to respond quickly to whatever happens. Cyert and March find this characteristic of many decision processes in industry. (30)

2. *Assumed Certainty.* We choose as if only one possible future could occur. We suppress risk and uncertainty, in favor of single-valued statements about the future.

3. *Probabilistic.* We may admit that we are not able to say exactly what is going to happen in the future, but we are able to say that one of

several possible futures will occur with stated probabilities. The classic example is that of flipping a coin.

4. *Uncertain.* Our view of the future may suggest simply that a variety of futures are possible but we are unable to make any statements about their probabilities.

These possible views of the future lead directly to our formulation of decisions as being made under conditions of assumed certainty, risk, or uncertainty.

There is an intimate relationship between the statements which the analyst attempts to make about the future and the way in which the decision is formulated. If we decide in advance to treat a certain decision as one of these three types, then the data which we obtain and the way in which we organize them will depend upon this choice. If we wish to treat a decision as one under risk, then we will attempt to obtain probability distributions as the result of our predictions; whereas in treating a decision as one under certainty, we will be interested only in single-valued predictions. Things may work the other way also. That is, the data we are able to obtain and the form in which we are able to make predictions will determine the basic formulation of the decision.

This leads to the question, "Which comes first, the conceptualization of the decision, or the form of the relevant predictions?" The answer is usually that neither actually comes first. The process of analysis begins perhaps with an initial formulation of the decision in one of the forms we have suggested. As the data are obtained and the predictions made, it becomes evident that this may have to be changed. As the basic conceptualization is changed, then we may seek predictions in different forms. Thus, the process is a sequential one which is carried on until we eventually find a conceptualization of the decision for which predictions may be made in the appropriate form. The analyst is continually revising his model of the decision in light of the predictions obtained, and continually modifying the form of the predictions sought as the model changes.

IMPROVING PREDICTIONS OR JUDGMENTS

A business firm may be thought of as a "learning" or "adaptive" organism. It can benefit from its past experience and from its mistakes. Perhaps one of the best sources of such learning, and one of the most widely neglected, is past forecasts compared with actual events. The most obvious beginning toward the improvement of forecasts. whether they are produced by explicit prediction techniques, implicit judgment processes, or the usual combination of both, is to record them and compare them with the actual outcomes. This is done by the firm which follows up its capital investment decisions with a "postaudit," designed to see if their investments are performing in accordance with the forecasts on which the decisions were based. It is done by the company president who keeps track of his sales manager's forecasts and then compares them with actual sales data. This is especially useful when forecasts are made repeatedly and the actual events are observable within a reasonable period of time. Consider, for example, the jobbing foundry which forecasts the cost of producing various castings for its customers and then measures the actual costs of production. There are many instances in which firms forecast costs and then are able to observe the actual costs which result. In these situations it may be valuable to keep track of the effectiveness of the forecasts made as a basis for improving the process.

Let us suppose that it is possible in such a situation to obtain data on forecasted and actual costs for various jobs. Let

$$E_i = \text{forecast of the cost for job } i$$
$$A_i = \text{actual cost for job } i$$
$$e_i = \frac{E_i}{A_i} \text{ error ratio for job } i$$

Instead of using the ratio of forecast to actual cost as a measure of error, we might have used some other function such as

$$\frac{E_i - A_i}{A_i}$$

We will, however, proceed using e_i as previously defined. One might expect that, if e_i were obtained for a number of jobs and tabulated, it might be reasonably described by a probability distribution $f(e)$. Some statistical analysis would be necessary to support this supposition, since e_i might differ markedly among jobs of different sizes, types, or degrees of complexity. However, if we are able to obtain an $f(e)$ for the class of jobs under consideration, then it is useful to compute the mean and variance of the error ratio.

$$\bar{e} = \sum ef(e)$$
$$\sigma_e^2 = \sum (e - \bar{e})^2 f(e)$$

The mean of the error ratio, $\bar{e}$, provides a measure of the accuracy, bias, or validity of the forecasts. If the mean is equal to one, then we may say that our forecasts are accurate in the sense that on the average they are equal to the actual cost we are attempting to estimate. If the mean of the error ratio differs from one, the amount of this difference is a measure of the bias in our forecasting process. If, for example, $\bar{e} = 1.05$, then we may say that on the average our predictions are 5 per cent too high. If this is the case then it would be sensible to correct our forecasts in the future to adjust for this bias. We might then work with a corrected forecast, E'_i, computed from the relation

$$E'_i = \frac{E_i}{\bar{e}}$$

The alternative to this method might be to investigate the process in an attempt to trace back the source of this bias and correct it where it originates. This can only be done if the prediction process is explicit.

The variance of the error ratio is a measure of the precision of process. It reflects the pattern of dispersion of our forecasts in terms of the average of their squared deviations from their mean. This is also referred to as the reliability of the process.

There is no simple short-run way to overcome lack of precision. It may be taken directly into account in decision making as will be done with decisions under risk. It may also be possible to review the process, looking for the steps in this process which are the major contributors to the variance of our predictions, and seek to reduce this variance at its source. Time, experience, and the accumulation of larger samples of data should have the effect of improving the precision of our predictions.

The point, however, is that very often the variance of the error is neglected entirely. When this happens, we have a typical example of the suppression of risk and the resulting tendency to assume that the forecasting process is free of error. This, indeed, suggests the way in which many decisions under assumed certainty arise. In later chapters we examine the results of taking explicit account of the risk expressed by the variance of the error ratio in the analysis of decisions.

FUNCTIONS OF SEVERAL VARIABLES

Consider a problem such as that of forecasting the cost of installation for a machine. There are two basic methods of obtaining the total installation cost. One method is to break the installation task down into more elementary tasks, forecast the cost of these elementary tasks, and combine the results into an estimate for the job. Similarly, the job might be broken down into a labor requirement, a materials requirement, and a machine requirement. Costs of each of these three inputs could be forecast and then combined to give a total installation cost. The second basic method is simply to forecast the total installation cost directly, without breaking the task into simpler elements. It is often suggested that the first of these methods will give better results; however, it is worth a little investigation to see why this may or may not be correct.

The problem posed here may be stated in a simple mathematical fashion. It is desired to forecast a quantity B and it is known that B is a function of several variables,

$$b_1, b_2, \ldots \ldots \ldots, b_n$$
$$B = f(b_1, b_2, \ldots, b_n)$$

The problem is to obtain a forecast of B by one of the two following methods:

1. Forecast B directly.
2. Forecast $b_1, b_2, \ldots \ldots, b_n$ and then compute B.

To show the conditions under which one or the other of these two methods will be more effective, we will think of the forecasts as being random variables. This is clearly the case with predictions produced by the methods of inferential statistics as a result of sampling, and it is a model which has been used by psychologists for judgments. Let

$$\hat{B} = \text{a forecast of } B$$
$$\hat{b}_i = \text{a forecast of } b_i$$

To assume that $\hat{B}$ and $\hat{b}_i$ are random variables can simply be interpreted as saying that if the process, whatever it is, were to be repeatedly applied to the estimation of a quantity, the resulting forecasts would be usefully described by a probability distribution. Using these distributions we can speak of the means, $E(\hat{B})$ and $E(\hat{b}_i)$, as well as the standard deviations, $\sigma_{\hat{B}}$ and $\sigma_{\hat{b}_i}$. The standard deviations or variances are measures of the precision or reliability of the methods. One may then ask, "By which of the two methods does one obtain the more precise or reliable forecast of B?" The answer depends upon the functional relationship between B and b_i, as well as upon the standard deviations themselves. If, for example, B is simply the sum of the b_i,

$$B = b_1 + b_2 + \cdots + b_1 + \cdots + b_n$$

then, using method 2, the standard deviation of the result will be (assuming independence of the b_i)

$$\sqrt{\sigma_{\hat{b}_1}^2 + \sigma_{\hat{b}_2}^2 + \cdots + \sigma_{\hat{b}_i}^2 + \cdots \sigma_{\hat{b}_n}^2}$$

Let $\sigma_{\hat{B}}$ be the standard deviation of the forecast using method 1. Clearly if

$$\sigma_{\hat{B}} > \sqrt{\sigma_{\hat{b}_1}^2 + \sigma_{\hat{b}_2}^2 + \cdots + \sigma_{\hat{b}_i}^2 + \cdots + \sigma_{\hat{b}_n}^2}$$

then method 2 will be preferred. Otherwise method 1 will give more precision. Another example which is often encountered is that in which B is the product of two quantities

$$B = b_1 b_2$$

If we again let $\sigma_{\hat{B}}$ stand for the standard deviation of forecasts produced by method 1, it can be shown that method 1 will be preferred if

$$\sigma_{\hat{B}} < \sqrt{b_1^2\, \sigma_{\hat{b}_2}^2 + b_2^2\, \sigma_{\hat{b}_1}^2 + \sigma_{\hat{b}_1}^2\, \sigma_{\hat{b}_2}^2}$$

Otherwise method 2 will be more precise. We are assuming in both of these examples that the b_i are independent in the probability sense. This sort of reasoning may be extended to any sort of functional relationship between B and the b_i.

To illustrate the usefulness of these ideas, suppose that a study of the effectiveness of some process indicates that the standard deviation of the forecasts is about 10 per cent of the quantity being forecast.

$$\sigma_{\hat{B}} = (.10)B$$
$$\sigma_{\hat{b}_i} = (.10)b_i$$

If, given a problem in which $B = b_1 + b_2$, the standard deviation of the result by method 2 will be

$$(.10)\sqrt{b_1^2 + b_2^2}$$

and by method 1

$$(.10)B$$

The latter result may be rewritten as

$$(.10)\sqrt{(b_1 + b_2)^2} = (.10)\sqrt{b_1^2 + b_2^2 + 2b_1 b_2}$$

showing clearly that method 2 will always be preferred in this situation. Alternatively, suppose $B = b_1 b_2$. The standard deviation of the forecast by method 1 will be:

$$(.10)B = (.10)b_1 b_2$$

Using method 2 the standard deviation is given by

$$\sqrt{b_1{}^2(.10)^2 b_2{}^2 + b_2{}^2(.10)^2 b_1{}^2 + (.10)^4 b_1{}^2 b_2{}^2}$$

This may be reduced to

$$(.10) b_1 b_2 \sqrt{2 + (.10)^2}$$

Inspection now reveals that method 1 will always be preferred in this case.

It cannot be assumed that it will be widely possible to measure the standard deviations used in this analysis. However, it appears worth noting that the universal assumption, that forecasts of the elements should first be made and then combined into an over-all result, may not always hold. The foregoing analysis attempts to give some insight into the problem and suggest a method of empirical resolution which could be used to improve the precision of forecasting.

We go on now to review some examples of prediction, not in an attempt to instruct the reader in prediction techniques but to invite him to associate his ideas about prediction with the decision-making process. The techniques of prediction themselves fill many, many books. Some practical suggestions will then be made about judgment. The process of judgment is so little understood that it is difficult to say much about it beyond the usual: "Good judgment is important. Sometimes it can be developed with experience."

PREDICTION

The process of prediction begins with some data which are the results of an experiment. The actual conduct of the experiment may or may not be under our control. When we take data on past events from the records of the firm, the experiment which generated the data is the actual history of the firm. This is clearly beyond our control. If we wish to predict next year's sales on the basis of last year's sales, it is impossible to do a controlled experiment to obtain the data. If we set up an experiment, such as a life test for a product, then the experiment may be largely under our control. The advantage of a controlled experiment is, of course, that we can develop a better idea of the source of variation in the data.

From the data, we move often to the techniques of statistical inference in order to produce the prediction. The basic notions surrounding these techniques are

1. It is usually uneconomic, if not impossible, to obtain data on the entire population or universe of events in which we are interested. Thus,

inevitably we resort to sampling. This means that when we make an inference about a population on the basis of a sample, there will be errors in the inference. These are called "sampling errors."

2. The basic feature of all working statistics is the phenomenon that suggests the larger the sample size, the smaller the sampling errors.

3. Since sampling errors may often be calculated, given a judgment about the acceptable amount of errors, one may decide how large a sample to take.

4. Even the seemingly explicit methods of inferential statistics involve in their application a great deal of judgment and skill.

We will try to suggest some of the points at which such judgments must be made in the examples which follow.

In discussing statistical techniques, especially as they are applied to management decision problems, one is torn between two considerations. The techniques have been rigorously developed by statisticians to be used under carefully specified conditions. These conditions are indicated by such assumptions as independence, normality, and so on. When these assumptions hold, detailed results may be produced using the techniques. If the assumptions do not hold, then the techniques cannot be expected to do what the statistician had promised. It is very important to understand in detail the basis of any technique to be used. On the other hand, in decision-making practice, one sometimes is forced by the pressures of time and money to use these techniques in a very rough and ready manner.

Often one must make strong assumptions about the data in order to use a technique, and frequently he violates some of the required assumptions. In addition, some of the detailed results which are possible using the techniques are unnecessary for the decision problem at hand and are thus overlooked. This is the "quick and dirty" kind of statistics. One wonders about the importance of a detailed understanding of statistics if it is to be used in a quick and dirty fashion in practice. The answer is clearly that if you are going to break the rules, the only way to avoid catastrophe is to know what rules you are breaking and have some idea of the consequences. Rough and ready statistics is like first aid, which, in the hands of the inexperienced, may be fatal. With this note of caution, we offer some rough and ready examples of prediction techniques.

PREDICTING SALES 1

The sales prediction is one of the basic guesses that must be made to provide a basis for a variety of planning decisions. As an example consider the problem of making a short-term sales prediction on the basis of data giving sales monthly for the past 24 months. Such data appear in Table 6–1.

Since numerous prediction models might be tried with such data, the first decision is to select one such model for a trial. One of the best ways to get some feeling for the data is to plot them as has been done in Figure 6–1. Immediately one is faced with several alternatives:

1. Are the data simply a random sample of independent observations?
2. Are there trends up or down? Are there seasonal effects? Are the data cyclical?
3. Is there some other set of observations to which the sales data might be related?

TABLE 6–1

Monthly Sales

Month	Units Sold	Month	Units Sold
1	85	13	80
2	73	14	89
3	83	15	80
4	88	16	86
5	80	17	75
6	74	18	73
7	80	19	90
8	80	20	79
9	79	21	72
10	74	22	80
11	80	23	88
12	79	24	90

These are not really mutually exclusive alternatives, but each suggests an approach to prediction.

For these data, let us try the simplest possible prediction model. Can the data be reasonably viewed as a random sample to independent observations from a single probability distribution? If the answer is in the affirmative, we have what the statistician calls a "stationary time series." More important, we may infer what the probability distribution from which the data came looks like and, if we are willing to assume that the basic features of past sales will extend to future sales, we may use the inferred probability distribution as the prediction.

The first step is to calculate estimates for the means and standard deviation of the probability distribution of the population from

FIGURE 6–1

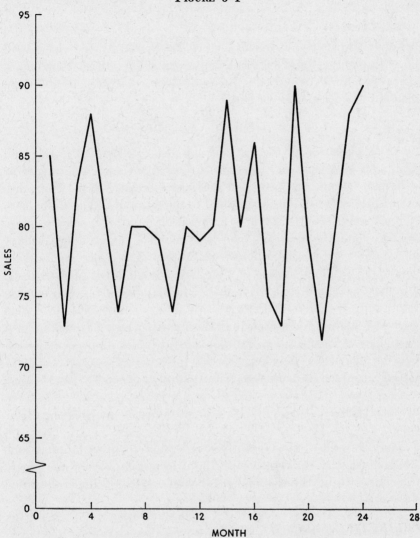

which the data might have come. Letting y_i stand for the sales in month i, we have

$$\bar{y} = \frac{\sum_i y_i}{N} = 80.7$$

as an estimate of the population mean, and

$$\sigma_y = \sqrt{\frac{\sum_i (y_i - \bar{y})^2}{n - 1}} = 5.7$$

as an estimate of the population standard deviation. Using $n - 1$ in the denominator gives us an unbiased estimate.

Now if the data are to be described as a random sample of independent observations, then it is very likely that all the values will lie within three standard deviation units of the mean. This fact is supported by Tchebycheff's Inequality (see Chapter 10). On the basis of the estimates we have

$$\bar{y} + 3\sigma_y = 97.8 \qquad \bar{y} - 3\sigma_y = 63.6$$

An examination of the data reveals that all the values fall well within these limits, and thus, on this count at least, one might be willing to accept the proposed description of the data. There are other tests which might be applied to detect nonrandom influences, such as trends. For example, starting with month 21, sales increase for three months in a row. Does this represent nonrandom behavior? Tables are available which show that this is not an unlikely event in a random sample of numbers. On the basis of such tests, one may conclude that to describe the data as a random sample is not unreasonable. If (and this is a very important "if") one were also willing to assume that the factors which have influenced past sales will continue to influence future sales, then a prediction may be made. We may predict that next month's sales will be a sample from a probability distribution with mean 80.7 and standard deviation 5.7. If necessary we could go on to predict the form of the distribution, but the amount of data is somewhat small for this.

Again however, the point to note is that in many applications the analyst may throw away all the information except the mean, thus suppressing the risk and producing a decision under assumed certainty.

PREDICTING SALES II

To illustrate a different prediction model, suppose that sales figures for the past 24 months are as given in the first two columns of Table 6–2. Plotting these data results in the graph of Figure 6–2. A general rising trend with time is suggested by the data. We might then investigate the notion of viewing sales as being the result of a rising trend with time plus a random element.

One simple method of getting rid of some of the random element in order to get a better view of the trend is to compute a moving average. For example, a four-month moving average at any point

TABLE 6–2

Month (x)	Units Sold (y)	y^2	xy
1	79	6,241	79
2	68	4,624	136
3	78	6,084	234
4	83	6,889	332
5	76	5,776	380
6	70	4,900	420
7	77	5,929	539
8	75	5,625	600
9	77	5,929	693
10	72	5,184	720
11	79	6,241	869
12	78	6,084	936
13	80	6,400	1,040
14	89	7,921	1,246
15	81	6,561	1,215
16	87	7,569	1,392
17	77	5,929	1,309
18	75	5,625	1,350
19	93	8,649	1,767
20	81	6,561	1,620
21	76	5,776	1,596
22	84	7,056	1,848
23	93	8,649	2,139
24	95	9,025	2,280

in time is simply the average of the sales for the previous four months. A four-month moving average for the data in the example is given in Table 6–3.

A six-month or an eight-month moving average would have smoothed the data even more, but the four-month average, plotted in Figure 6–3, gives a somewhat better view of the trend than the original data. The general strategy is to pick a long enough base to cancel out the effects of random fluctuations but a short enough one

TABLE 6–3

Month	Four-Month Average	Month	Four-Month Average
4	77.00	15	82.00
5	76.25	16	84.25
6	76.75	17	83.50
7	76.50	18	80.00
8	74.50	19	83.00
9	74.75	20	81.50
10	75.25	21	81.25
11	75.75	22	83.50
12	76.50	23	83.50
13	77.25	24	87.00
14	81.50		

FIGURE 6–2

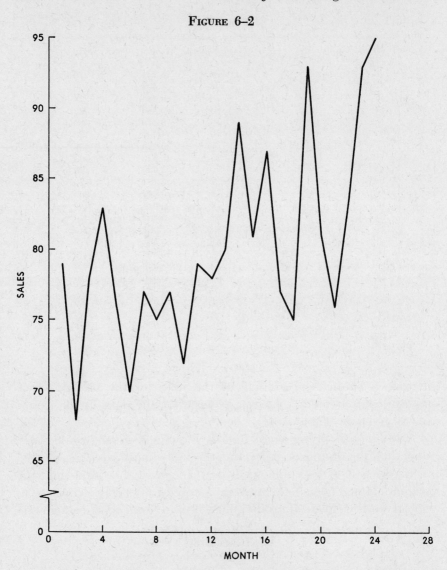

to discard data which is no longer relevant. Thus, in a sense, the analyst must seek the assistance of the manager in making judgments as to the relevance of past data. To what extent do the factors which have influenced sales in the past continue to operate? What new factors are becoming important? Only if we are willing to assume that the trend will continue in the future and that other influences on sales will remain substantially the same, may the moving average prediction be used alone.

FIGURE 6–3

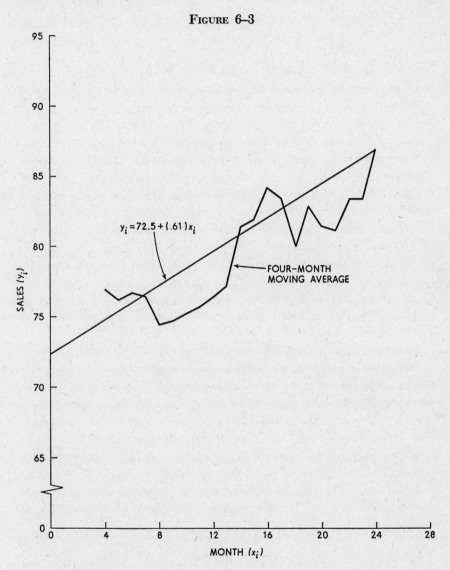

The moving average technique is typical of several in which practical applications find one overlooking the fact that it is an average which is produced. The average is taken as a single valued statement about the future, thus suppressing risk and producing a model of a decision under assumed certainty. An interesting special kind of moving average is called exponential smoothing. The reader may discover the elements of this idea through problem 6–12.

An alternative approach to the investigation of the trend is suggested by the methods of regression analysis. Let us assume that sales are related to time and that our problem is to predict sales (y) on the basis of a knowledge of time (x). We have in hand $n = 24$ pairs of observations, each pair consisting of an x value, say x_i, and a y value, say y_i. It would be useful to have a function relating y to x which could be used as a basis for prediction. The first question is then, "Of all the functions which might be used to express the relation between x and y, which should be selected?" Often one makes this decision by trying the simplest possible relation first, the straight line. If this is acceptable, it is used. If not, more complicated functions are investigated. This is in accord with the scientific principle favoring the simplest possible explanation of phenomena. Acceptable is usually defined here in two ways. First, the relation must be statistically acceptable in the sense that it expresses some fundamental regularity in the data, rather than random influences alone. This is the test of statistical significance. Second, it must be acceptable in the light of the analyst's judgment, based perhaps on his knowledge of the situation from which the data came.

In setting out to discover a straight-line function which acceptably describes the data, we might simply draw a line through the points on Figure 6–2 "by eye." This quick, practical method leaves one with difficulties in deciding which of all such lines is most acceptable. It is useful to decide this on the basis of a well-defined criterion. The one most used suggests that the best-fit line be defined as that line which minimizes the sum of the squared deviations of the data around the line. This is the regression line.

Let y'_i stand for the predicted value of y associated with a particular value of x, say x_i. We wish to establish a regression line of the form

$$y'_i = a + bx_i$$

so as to minimize the quantity

$$\sum e^2 = \sum_i (y_i - y_i')^2$$

The problem then resolves itself into finding the values of a and b which will minimize the sum of the squared deviations. To do this one may simply take the first derivative of Σe^2 with respect to a and with respect to b, set the equations equal to zero, and solve.

$$\sum_i e^2 = \sum_i (y_i - a - bx_i)^2$$

$$\frac{d\sum_i e^2}{da} = -2\sum_i (y_i - a - bx_i) = 0$$

$$= \sum_i y_i - na - b\sum_i x_i = 0$$

$$a = \frac{\sum_i y_i}{n} - \frac{b\sum_i x_i}{n} = \bar{Y} - b\bar{X}$$

$$\frac{d\sum_i e^2}{db} = -2\sum_i (y_i - a - bx_i)x_i = 0$$

$$= \sum_i x_i y_i - a\sum_i x_i - b\sum_i x_i^2 = 0$$

$$b = \frac{\sum_i (x_i - \bar{x})(y_i - \bar{y})}{\sum_i (x_i - \bar{x})^2} = \frac{n\sum_i x_i y_i - \sum_i x_i \sum_i y_i}{n\sum_i x_i^2 - \left(\sum_i x_i\right)^2}$$

The values of a and b which satisfy these relations form the intercept and slope respectively of the regression line. A table such as Table 6–2 is helpful in carrying out the necessary calculations. For computing the slope, b, we require

$$\sum_i x_i = 300 \qquad \sum_i x_i^2 = 4,900 \qquad \sum_i y_i = 1,923$$

$$\sum_i x_i y_i = 24,740$$

From these we have

$$b = \frac{24(24,740) - (300)(1,923)}{24(4,900) - (300)^2} = .61$$

$$a = \frac{1,923}{24} - (.61)\frac{300}{24} = 72.5$$

$$y_i' = 72.5 + (.61)x_i$$

This line is plotted in Figure 6–3.

Again, if we are willing to assume that this trend will extend into the future it may be used for prediction. The tremendous importance of the judgments leading to this willingness cannot be emphasized too often. Our prediction for the coming month ($x_i = 25$) might be, "Sales for the coming month may be viewed as a random variable with mean $72.5 + (.61)(25)$."

An important question at this point is that of the statistical acceptability of the trend line we have just established. The question is, "Suppose there is in fact no trend at all, what is the probability that a sample of sales data would exhibit the kind of behavior we have just described by a trend line?" Another way of putting the question is, "What is the probability that a sample from a population having no trend would by chance exhibit the rising tendencies in our data?" There are a variety of ways of answering this question, but we will choose the correlation coefficient as an example.

The coefficient of correlation between two sets of observations is defined as

$$r = \frac{n\sum_i x_i y_i - \sum_i x_i \sum_i y_i}{\sqrt{\left\{n\sum_i x_i{}^2 - \left(\sum_i x_i\right)^2\right\}\left\{n\sum_i y_i{}^2 - \left(\sum_i y_i\right)^2\right\}}}$$

The correlation coefficient tends toward plus one or minus one as the degree of association between the variables increases. If the regression line has a positive slope and the data are tightly grouped around it, the correlation coefficient will be close to plus one. If the data are tightly grouped around a regression line with a negative slope, the coefficient of correlation will be close to minus one. If the data are widely scattered in the "shotgun" pattern, then the coefficient of correlation will be close to zero. For our data we have

$$r = \frac{593,760 - 567,900}{\sqrt{(27,600)(27,519)}} = .61$$

This we might judge to be a moderately useful relationship. From the appropriate statistical tables we can discover that the probability of a coefficient this large or larger occurring by chance is less than 5 per cent. On this basis we might choose to grant the statistical acceptability of our trend line, and thus its usefulness as a basis for prediction.

An interesting interpretation of the correlation coefficient suggests that its square is the proportion of the variance in y which can be "explained by" or "attributed to" variation in x. In our example this may be taken to mean that 37 per cent of the variance in sales is attributable to the rising trend given by the regression line. The remainder of the variance is what we have called in our model the "random element."

All this, however, depends upon the validity of the assumptions upon which this prediction model is based. These assumptions may be stated as follows:

1. It is assumed that if we could actually examine the population from which the data came we would find that the mean value of y for any x was given by a linear function of x.

2. For any x, y is a random variable with mean as above, but with a standard deviation which is the same for all values of x.

3. The values of y are independent. Knowing one value of y gives no additional information about another.

4. When we wish to investigate statistical significance or acceptability, we usually make the assumption that the probability distribution of y is normal.

It is possible, of course, to conduct investigations which would test the validity of these assumptions in any given application of the prediction model. More often than not, no such investigation is made. We tend to rely on the analyst's judgment that the conditions which characterize the application do not do extraordinary violence to the assumptions.

PREDICTING SALES III

To illustrate yet another prediction model, consider the problem of the firm which manufactures brake shoes for railroad freight cars. For purposes of scheduling production and establishing inventory levels it wishes to make a prediction of sales on a monthly basis. Data are available showing sales for the past 20 months. Sales figures are given in sets of brake shoes. A brake shoe serves the same function for a freight car as the brake lining does for an automobile. The brake shoe is forced directly against the freight car wheel. Brake shoes wear out with considerable frequency, creating a significant replacement business. The data are given in Table 6–4 and are plotted in Figure 6–4.

Since a first examination of the data perhaps does not suggest any marked trends, one might begin by simply investigating the simple probability distribution model. Specifically, can the data be viewed as a random sample of independent observations from a probability distribution? We begin as before by estimating the population mean and standard deviation. The population mean is estimated by

$$\bar{y} = \frac{\sum_i y_i}{n} = \frac{7{,}663}{20} = 383.1$$

and the population standard deviation by the unbiased estimator

$$\hat{\sigma} = \sqrt{\frac{\sum_i (y_i - \bar{y})^2}{n-1}} = \sqrt{\frac{18{,}520}{19}} = 31.2$$

Testing for the variability of the data we may compute

$$\bar{y} + 3\hat{\sigma} = 476.7 \qquad \bar{y} - 3\hat{\sigma} = 289.5$$

TABLE 6–4

Month	Sales	Month	Sales
1	438	11	345
2	345	12	368
3	369	13	380
4	333	14	392
5	405	15	420
6	363	16	420
7	415	17	390
8	383	18	410
9	345	19	340
10	390	20	412

It is readily observed that the data fell well within this range. One may also make various tests for nonrandom influences within these limits. Although there is a long run upward beginning with month 11, this is not statistically significant. That is, it is reasonably likely that a random sample from a given probability distribution might exhibit such a run. We might even at this point be willing to accept the probability distribution model as a basis for prediction. Alternatively, we might search for trends, seasonal effects, and cycles in the data, probably with little success.

Suppose, however, for decision-making purposes it is worthwhile to search for a model which will yield a better prediction. By better, we mean here that the prediction takes the form of a probability distribution with a standard deviation smaller than that which would be obtained by the foregoing method. Let us appeal to some information about the underlying phenomena. To make a long story short, suppose we develop the following hunch. The more a freight

car is used, the more often it is stopped and the greater the wear
on its brake shoes. Thus, periods of high activity for the railroads
will eventually result in high replacement rates for brake shoes,
and contrariwise. The usage of railroad freight cars is revealed by
carloading data which are available on a monthly basis. Increased
carloadings should be reflected in increased brake shoe replacement
at some future time. This hunch will bear considerable investigating
but it suggests the possibility of predicting future sales on the basis
of past carloadings. Just what the best time lag is between monthly

FIGURE 6–4

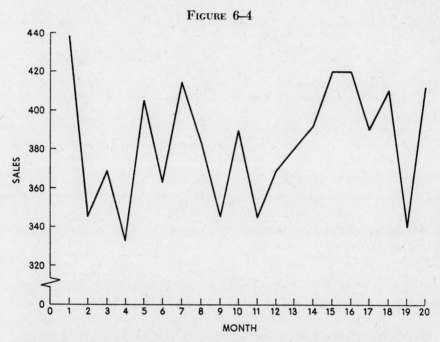

carloadings and monthly sales is also a matter for considerable investigation. However, as an example, we will investigate the possibilities for prediction using a six-month time lag. The necessary
data on carloadings are given in Table 6–5.

When monthly carloadings (six months previous) are plotted
with monthly sales, as in Figure 6–5, the hunch begins to look
rather interesting. The graph suggests strong possibilities of a useful
relationship. To explore this relationship further we develop the
regression line which describes the relationship between monthly
sales (y) and carloadings (x). This is found by the methods presented previously to be

$$y' = 76.8 + .032x$$

The regression line is plotted in Figure 6–5. If we are willing to accept this relationship and to assume that it will continue to hold in the future, then we have a basis for prediction. On the basis of carloadings for the past month, we could predict the sales six months in the future. The question of the acceptability of this relation merits further discussion.

The first question is, "Does this regression line give a prediction with a smaller variance or standard deviation than that obtained using the probability distribution model?" We may estimate the

TABLE 6–5

Month	Carloadings (Six Months Previous)	Month	Carloadings (Six Months Previous)
1	10,840	11	8,600
2	8,400	12	9,700
3	8,480	13	9,900
4	8,560	14	10,000
5	9,600	15	10,200
6	8,900	16	10,400
7	10,300	17	10,480
8	9,160	18	10,500
9	8,860	19	8,200
10	9,500	20	10,900

standard deviation of the y values around the regression line using the relation

$$\hat{\sigma}_y' = \sqrt{\frac{\sum_i (y_i - y_i')^2}{n - 2}}$$

Here we use $n - 2$ in the denominator, instead of $n - 1$, since the deviations whose squares are being averaged are based on two quantities (a and b) computed from the sample, rather than just one ($\bar{y}$) as before. For the data in the example and the computed regression line this yields

$$\hat{\sigma}_y' = \sqrt{\frac{3,615}{18}} = 14.3$$

At this point our prediction using the regression line may take the form, "Given the carloadings for month i, say x_i, our prediction is that sales six months hence may be viewed as a random variable with mean $y' = 376.8 + .032x_i$ and with standard deviation 14.3." Comparison of this prediction with that obtained from the probability distribution model indicates immediately the reduction in the standard deviation which has been achieved.

The foregoing statements suggest that the relation has made an important reduction in the standard deviation and thus is likely to be statistically acceptable. To confirm this we may compute the correlation coefficient which turns out to be $r = .897$. This indicates that we have a good relationship in the sense that the data are

FIGURE 6–5

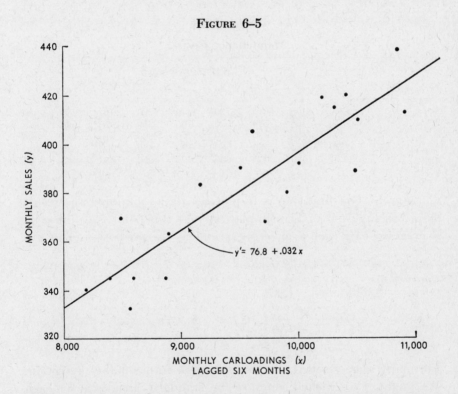

closely grouped around our regression lines. Again by consulting the appropriate statistical tables we will discover that the correlation coefficient is very unlikely to occur by chance.

PREDICTION OF MAINTENANCE COSTS

The particularly difficult problem in estimating maintenance costs is that of estimating the frequency and severity of break-downs, failures, and malfunctions which may occur. These clearly cannot be predicted with absolute precision and the analyst's only hope is to discover some statistical regularities on which to base his prediction. Suppose that, either from the firm's records or from the machinery manufacturer, we can obtain data on the maintenance expenses for a group of five machines in relation to their ages. An example of such data is given in Table 6–6.

These costs will depend also on the maintenance policy employed by the firm. If a preventive maintenance program is used, the costs will differ from those that would arise if repairs were made only after failures. The problem of maintenance policy is discussed in

TABLE 6–6
Maintenance Costs

	Year of Operation								
	1	2	3	4	5	6	7	8	9
1	$263	$400	$610	$720	$840	$780	$910	$960	$ 900
2	310	468	520	630	765	846	920	980	860
3	236	390	630	680	740	865	810	850	960
4	220	482	580	780	759	839	900	830	1,010
5	271	510	635	690	796	850	850	965	935

Chapter 13. Our first step is to plot the data, obtaining the result shown in Figure 6–6. The simplest step at this point is to take the average cost for each year of operations as the prediction. Thus:

Year of Operation	Average Maintenance Cost	Year of Operation	Average Maintenance Cost
1	$260	6	$836
2	450	7	878
3	595	8	917
4	700	9	933
5	780		

For many purposes this will be a sufficient form for the prediction. We might if we wished compute the standard deviations for each year as well.

There may be situations, however, in which one wishes to fit an equation to such data in order to imbed it in an analytical solution to a problem. An examination of Figure 6–6 suggests that the usual straight line will not be satisfactory in this case.

In selecting a type of function which might describe these data, reference may be made to some theories about the underlying phenomena. There is some evidence, both theoretical and empirical, to suggest the following behavior for maintenance costs. Suppose the machines in question are complex and consist of a number of component parts which may fail. When the machine is new, all of the components are new, and very few failures result. As the machine grows older the components begin to fail, and as the years of service go by more and more failures occur. Thus, maintenance costs tend to rise. As the components are replaced or repaired, the distribution of component ages changes. Instead of a machine consisting of mostly new components, we have one made up of components of widely differing ages. When this happens the failures tend to become more or less evenly spread in time, and the rate at which failures occur levels off. It follows then that maintenance costs should also level off. A glance at Figure 6–6 suggests that this may be a

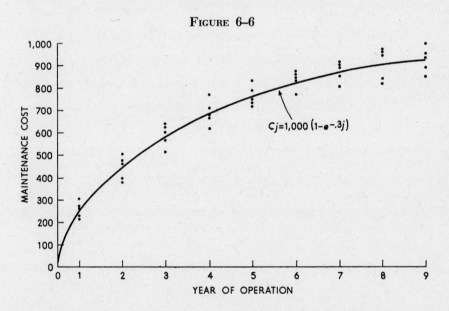

FIGURE 6–6

$$C_j = 1,000 \left(1 - e^{-.3j}\right)$$

fair description of the effects shown by these data. One type of function which would describe such a pattern is of the form

$$Y = A(1 - e^{-Bx})$$

In fitting such a function we may apply the usual ideas of estimating the parameters A and B which will minimize the sum of the squared deviations of the data about the function. The direct approach we have used above creates computational difficulties in solving the normal equations, since A and B will enter in nonlinear fashion. Because of this, and because exponential functions of this type are extremely useful, we will suggest a method of fitting such a function.

We begin by taking the first derivative of the function with respect to x.

$$\frac{dy}{dx} = ABe^{-Bx}$$

We then solve the function itself for the quantity e^{-Bx}

$$e^{-Bx} = 1 - \frac{Y}{A}$$

Substituting this in the expression for the first derivative we have

$$\frac{dy}{dx} = AB - BY$$

Let the derivative be approximated by the first difference of Y,

$$Y(x+1) - Y(x) = \triangle Y = AB - BY$$

This is a linear function which may be fitted to the data by the usual method. Letting the result be

$$\triangle Y = a - bY$$

We may then solve for A and B.

$$B = b \qquad\qquad A = \frac{a}{b}$$

These are the parameters for the original exponential function. Applying this method to our problem, let c_{ij} be the maintenance cost for the jth year of operation for machine i.

$$Y = c_{ij}$$
$$\triangle Y = c_{ij+1} - c_{ij}$$

For example, for $j = 1$ and $i = 1, \ldots, 5$ we have

$\triangle Y$	Y
137	263
158	310
154	236
262	220
239	271

Similarly from the data we obtain a total of 40 pairs of values which yield the regression line:

$$\triangle Y = 284 - (.295)Y$$

From this we obtain

$$B = .295 \qquad\qquad A = \frac{284}{.295} = 963$$

The exponential function for the data is then

$$Y = 963(1 - e^{-.295x})$$

or

$$c_j = 963(1 - e^{-.295x})$$

In this problem the first difference of Y is only the very crudest approximation to its first derivative. Thus the resulting exponential equation suffers from this approximation. Actually the equation

$$c_j = 1,000(1 - e^{-.3x})$$

would be more satisfactory. Our point is, however, to demonstrate the method of fitting the exponential function.

PREDICTING SERVICE LIFE

The service life of an asset may be influenced by several factors:

a) The duration of the firm's requirement for the services of the asset.
b) The physical characteristics of the asset which determine the length of service it will provide before requiring major repairs, replacement because of irreparable failure, or before its declining effectiveness makes it no longer economic to continue operation.
c) The replacement policy of the firm which may take into account not only the foregoing factors but the appearance of new and better equipment on the market.

Thus, service life cannot be predicted without reference to these considerations, which will be discussed in detail in Chapter 9. To illustrate a typical prediction technique which may be used in this connection, let us assume that we wish to predict the length of service that may be expected from an asset before a major overhaul is required. While this prediction may not itself determine service life of the asset to the firm, it may be an important part of the determination.

Often this prediction must be only a judgment based on experience which is roughly related to the asset and the conditions of service under consideration. Sometimes, however, it may be possible to obtain data on the time to major overhaul for assets which are similar or identical. If these data are accumulated in the records of the firm, presumably they will apply to conditions of service which are likely to be met by a new asset. If they are obtained from other sources, care must be taken to see that the conditions of service under which the data were obtained are reasonably similar to those which will be found in the firm. Such data are often displayed in the form of a mortality curve which shows the number of machines in an original sample of N, that have not required a major overhaul at the end of various lengths of service. If we define

$S(t)$ = number of machines which have not yet required overhaul at the end of period t
t = periods of service or the "age" of the machine

we may obtain a mortality curve such as that shown in Figure 6–7.

FIGURE 6–7

Mortality Curve

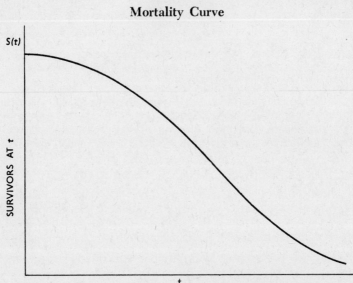

From such data we can compute the probability that a new machine will require overhaul in some future period t

$$p(t) = \frac{S(t-1) - S(t)}{N}$$

The conditional probability that a machine, which has not been overhauled at the end of period t, will be overhauled in period $t + 1$ is given by

$$\frac{S(t) - S(t+1)}{S(t)}$$

Sometimes we will wish to use the average time to major overhaul for such machines which may be predicted from the mortality curve by

$$\sum_{t=1}^{\infty} tp(t)$$

Sometimes, on the other hand, we might wish to use two extreme points on the mortality curve to give some idea of the longest and the shortest time to major overhaul which might be expected. We may, for example, find the values of t which correspond to the service lives which will be exceeded by 95 per cent of such machines and which will be exceeded by only 5 per cent of such machines. These would be the values of t, say $t_{.95}$ and $t_{.05}$ which satisfy the following relations:

$$S(t_{.95}) = (.95)N$$
$$S(t_{.05}) = (.05)N$$

PREDICTION—AN OVERVIEW

Prediction is a tricky business at best. One hopes to identify relationships or regularities which can be assumed to hold, not only in the data comprising the sample, but in the future as well. Sometimes one comes to feel that if these relationships or regularities are clearly obvious, no elaborate statistical techniques will be needed to explore them. On the other hand, if they are not obvious, there is little point in testing them out with prediction techniques. This kind of judgment, usually advanced by the "practical man," seriously undervalues the part that prediction techniques can play in decision making. Some of the broad possibilities are suggested in the following paragraphs.

Given the problem of predicting a variable y, there are a number of alternative possibilities for prediction models.

1. The variable y may be viewed as a known constant, remaining the same in the future as it has in the past.

2. We may use a simple probability distribution as a model for predicting y. The model suggests that y is a random variable with a known probability distribution. This probability distribution is assumed to be the same in the future as it has been in the past.

3. We may look for relations between y and some other variable x. Hopefully it will be discovered that y, which must be predicted, is related to x, which can be observed. Here the regression model is used to establish the relationship.

4. One might use several variables, $X_1, X_2, \ldots, X_m$ to predict y. Thus, in predicting sales, we might observe personal income, unemployment, bank clearings, and so on, using all of these in a relationship to predict y. This is called a multiple regression model.

5. One might explore the relationship between y and the variable time, leading perhaps to the disclosure of long-term trends.

6. Finally, the full-fledged field of time series analysis suggests such models as the view that y is the result not only of a trend, but of seasonal, cyclical, and random influences as well. Seasonal fluctuations are those with a fixed period, such as the "Christmas rush." Cyclical fluctuations are oscillatory movements with neither period nor amplitude constant. This kind of prediction model can become rather complex. The basic point here is, however, that one assumes that the value of y at time t, $y(t)$, is in important ways dependent on past values of y, say the value at time $t - k$. Time series analysis is largely devoted to the establishment of relations of the form

$$y(t) = f\{y(t - k)\}$$

7. All of these models basically assume that there are some more or less useful regularities in data about the past which can be used to predict the future. They do not lend themselves directly to the prediction of such dramatic future events as war, recession, or fire. These kinds of future events are called contingencies. It is difficult to be precise about the meaning of a contingency, but the notion is that of a dramatic discontinuity and opposed to a gradual trend. In engineering decisions it is often important to predict such future contingencies as technological breakthroughs, new laws, political changes, business failures, entrance of new competitors, floods, and so on. The prediction models discussed previously are not particularly suited to this task in many cases. Here are the situations in which judgment must be applied to the greatest extent. This is the area in which subjective probabilities come into great use. It is almost impossible to obtain data relevant to these contingencies, yet they may have a most important influence on the analysis of particular decisions.

JUDGMENT

Judgment forms the major input to many decision processes in actual practice. In spite of this, relatively little can be said about it in a constructive or instructive way. There are books full of admonitions that management is an art requiring good judgment, but so is almost everything else. About the only definite statement that can be made is that judgment improves through experience. There seems to be no effective short cut to it, although the educational process must certainly enhance judgment abilities to some extent. In the sections which follow some suggestions are made which may be of some assistance in the improvement of judgments.

REDUCING THE REQUIRED DISCRIMINATION

It is always well to keep in mind that predictions, however they are made, are inputs to the decision process. The nature of the decision itself may suggest the requirements which the predictions must satisfy. In a decision under certainty among two production machines, we may wish to select the machine which has the lower annual cost. If we know the annual cost of one of the machines, the annual cost of the second machine need only be a prediction of whether this cost is above or below that of the first machine. If the prediction process were one of judgment to a large extent, then it seems reasonable that it would be far easier to judge whether the cost is above or below a given number than to attempt to judge the cost in precise numerical terms. This leads to the principle of reducing the required discrimination, which is especially useful in connection with judgments, but may apply to more objective prediction methods as well.

This principle may be stated as follows: *When the magnitude of one of the variables entering the analysis of a decision must be judged, find the value of the variable for which the choice shifts from one alternative to another. The judgment required is then only whether or not the magnitude of the variable is greater than or less than this critical value.*

Suppose in a decision under certainty, all the outcomes have been evaluated with one exception. That is, $V(\theta_i)$ have been predicted for all $i \neq k$, and $V(\theta_k)$ is as yet unknown but is to be judged. For purposes of determining the decision, the only judgment required is a choice of one of the following statements:

$$a)\ \ V(\theta_k) \geq \max_{i \neq k} V(\theta_i)$$

$$b)\ \ V(\theta_k) < \max_{i \neq k} V(\theta_i)$$

Once one of the statements has been selected, a course of action is clear. This represents a considerable reduction in the level of discrimination required of the judgment process. The only merit claimed for this scheme is that, when judgments must be made, it is far easier to make, or to convince others to make, judgments of the above sort than to judge a specific numerical quantity for $V(\theta_k)$.

A more difficult situation arises when more than one of the outcomes in a decision under certainty must be evaluated by judgment. Perhaps the best method is to make paired comparisons between the outcomes whose values are to be judged until the maximum of this group is obtained. It can then be compared against the maximum of the outcomes which have been evaluated by other means, as was done earlier.

In a decision under risk one often finds that the probabilities can only be obtained from some process of judgment. In the following example, suppose this is the case:

	p_1	p_2
	s_1	s_2
a_1	$V(\theta_{11})$	$V(\theta_{12})$
a_2	$V(\theta_{21})$	$V(\theta_{22})$

As will be explored later, one may make this decision by choosing the alternative which maximizes the expected return. Applying the principle of reducing the required discrimination, we would compute the probability, say p_1, for which the two alternatives have equal expected return.

$$\text{Expected return for } a_1 = V(\theta_{11})p_1 + V(\theta_{12}) \{1 - p_1\}$$
$$\text{Expected return for } a_2 = V(\theta_{21})p_1 + V(\theta_{22}) \{1 - p_1\}$$

Setting these quantities equal and solving for the resulting value of p_1, say $\hat{p}_1$, we have

$$\hat{p}_1 = \frac{V(\theta_{22}) - V(\theta_{12})}{V(\theta_{11}) - V(\theta_{12}) - V(\theta_{21}) + V(\theta_{22})}$$

It is only necessary then to judge whether p_1 is greater than or less than this critical value. This would seem in most cases to be considerably easier than trying to judge the numerical value of p_1.

If we extend the foregoing problem to include three possible futures and two alternatives, then the process of setting expected returns equal yields the following equation after simplification:

$$\hat{p}_1\{V(\theta_{11}) - V(\theta_{13}) - V(\theta_{21}) + V(\theta_{23})\} + \hat{p}_2\{V(\theta_{12}) - V(\theta_{13}) - V(\theta_{22}) + V(\theta_{23})\} = V(\theta_{23}) - V(\theta_{13})$$

The values of p_1 and $\hat{p}_2$ which satisfy this equation will form a straight line when plotted on a graph as in Figure 6–8. This line divides the area below the line $p_1 + p_2 = 1$ into two regions. The judgment necessary to determine the decision is simply in which of these two regions the point corresponding to p_1 and p_2 lies.

Closely related to the reduction of required discrimination is the notion that, after we obtain an idea of which alternative is preferred, we may then show how far our information may be in error without changing our preference. This is often called "sensitivity analysis." An example of sensitivity analysis is presented in Chapter 13.

FIGURE 6–8

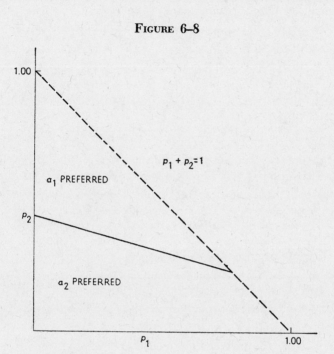

SUGGESTIONS FOR FURTHER STUDY

BROWN, ROBERT G. *Statistical Forecasting for Inventory Control.* New York: McGraw-Hill Book Co., Inc., 1959.

CARTER, C. F., and WILLIAMS, B. R. *Investment in Innovation.* London: Oxford University Press, 1956.

CYERT, RICHARD M., and MARCH, JAMES G. *A Behavioral Theory of the Firm.* Englewood Cliffs, N.J.: Prentice-Hall, Inc., 1963.

HOLT, CHARLES C.; MODIGLIANI, FRANCO; MUTH, JOHN F.; and SIMON, HERBERT A. *Planning Production, Inventories, and Work Force.* Englewood Cliffs, N.J.: Prentice-Hall, Inc., 1960.

KIMBALL, B. F. "A System of Life Tables for Physical Property Based upon the Truncated Normal Distribution," *Econometrica,* Vol. 15, No. 4 (October, 1947).

KURNOW, ERNEST; GLASSER, GERALD J.; and OTTMAN, FREDERICK R. *Statistics for Business Decisions.* Homewood, Ill.: Richard D. Irwin, Inc., 1959.

MORONEY, M. J. *Facts from Figures.* Baltimore: Penguin Books, Inc., 1959.

PROBLEMS

6–1. Suggest an example of a decision to illustrate each of the possible views of the future mentioned in the chapter.

6–2. Machines of a certain type have been used by a firm in the past and have been replaced at various ages with salvage values indicated below.

Machine Number	Age at Replacement, Years	Salvage Value
1	8	$ 620
2	7	650
3	9	510
4	9	480
5	7	690
6	7	720
7	6	950
8	8	590
9	5	1,000
10	9	530

a) What would be your estimate of the salvage value of such a machine if the firm were to keep it 7.5 years?

b) What would be your estimate for 10 years? For 4 years? What sort of dangers do you see in this estimating process?

6–3. The sales records of a firm for the past 24 months indicate the following:

	196x			*196y*	
Month	*Sales in Units*		*Month*	*Sales in Units*	
Jan.	88		Jan.	82	
Feb.	71		Feb.	79	
Mar.	81		Mar.	83	
Apr.	80		Apr.	80	
May	82		May	82	
Jun.	75		Jun.	83	
Jul.	74		Jul.	87	
Aug.	88		Aug.	72	
Sep.	74		Sep.	77	
Oct.	83		Oct.	71	
Nov.	74		Nov.	87	
Dec.	81		Dec.	73	

Make a sales prediction for the next 12 months.

6–4. Two years ago a firm introduced a new product which won immediate acceptance and has been growing slowly but steadily in popularity. In planning the production program for the coming year, a monthly sales prediction is necessary. Based on the following records, make a prediction for the coming 12 months.

Month	Sales (Thousands of Units)	Month	Sales (Thousands of Units)
1	142	13	166
2	154	14	182
3	160	15	171
4	152	16	168
5	163	17	191
6	160	18	170
7	173	19	171
8	173	20	188
9	170	21	191
10	167	22	207
11	173	23	204
12	167	24	209

6–5. In order to fix the proper level for its final inventory, a plant wishes to predict its shipments for the next six weeks. Data are available showing weekly shipments for the last 24 weeks. What sort of prediction can be made from these data?

Week	Units Shipped	Week	Units Shipped
1	547	13	554
2	528	14	578
3	527	15	546
4	556	16	563
5	521	17	594
6	524	18	600
7	520	19	595
8	525	20	607
9	534	21	590
10	542	22	608
11	546	23	599
12	545	24	613

6–6. An electronics firm assembles one of its specialty items only on order. It wishes to estimate the number of man-hours required for assembly on the basis of the size of the order so as to make competitive price quotations. Data on the number of units ordered and the man-hours required for assembly are given below for the last 18 orders. Obtain a relation which could be used to estimate man-hours of assembly time from the size of the order.

Order No.	Units	Man-Hours	Order No.	Units	Man-Hours
1	39	88	10	36	75
2	28	60	11	22	41
3	52	108	12	34	84
4	52	110	13	34	78
5	41	97	14	30	72
6	23	57	15	31	71
7	42	99	16	48	105
8	60	132	17	27	60
9	22	47	18	26	55

6–7. A large trucking firm removes the engines from its vehicles for complete rebuilding when, in the judgment of their chief mechanic, the engines require it. From the maintenance records of the firm, the mileage on the engines at the time of rebuilding is obtained for the past year. Estimate the service life (miles to rebuilding) for the engines (mileage in thousands).

Truck No.	Mileage	Truck No.	Mileage	Truck No.	Mileage
1	108	11	106	21	83
2	102	12	114	22	99
3	80	13	98	23	99
4	83	14	85	24	108
5	89	15	101	25	96
6	95	16	101	26	99
7	88	17	84	27	107
8	102	18	102	28	108
9	103	19	110	29	91
10	97	20	98	30	96

6–8. For the following decisions under risk, plot the regions of probability for which the choice is determined.

a)

	p_1	p_2
	s_1	s_2
a_1	\$50	\$120
a_2	70	90
a_3	90	60

b)

	p_1	p_2	p_3
	s_1	s_2	s_3
a_1	\$50	\$120	\$30
a_2	70	90	50
a_3	90	60	20

In each case the number in the matrix represents profits, and the choice is to be made so as to maximize expected profit.

6–9. The estimating department of a small jobbing machine shop has compared its estimates on twenty recent jobs with the actual production costs. What suggestions could you make for improving the estimates?

Job No.	Estimated Cost	Actual Cost	Job No.	Estimated Cost	Actual Cost
1	\$328	\$395	11	\$ 868	\$ 800
2	519	541	12	699	631
3	476	436	13	932	930
4	209	267	14	681	709
5	662	561	15	1,771	1,818
6	785	770	16	625	621
7	813	854	17	935	913
8	815	962	18	113	105
9	616	684	19	440	411
10	39	35	20	518	560

6–10. Shown below are the maintenance histories of six similar machines used under similar conditions of service. Obtain an exponential function relating maintenance expense to age.

Machine Number

Age	1	2	3	4	5	6
1..............	$ 56	$ 64	$ 54	$ 71	$ 73	$ 66
2..............	96	98	104	108	94	98
3..............	138	122	134	137	119	138
4..............	151	158	154	146	140	145
5..............	175	163	156	167	157	158
6..............	183	186	174	171	180	179
7..............	176	185	186	190	187	191
8..............	206	213	201	200	208	195

6–11. Design an experiment to test the effectiveness of the following methods of estimating total order costs for goods manufactured to customer's order.

a_1: estimate the total order cost directly based on past experience with similar orders.

a_2: estimate direct labor requirements, direct material requirements, wage rates, material costs, and so on; then compute order cost.

6–12. A company uses the following method of making sales predictions: next month's sales are predicted to be this month's sales prediction (E_t), plus a fraction (a) of the difference between this month's actual sales (S_t) and this month's sales prediction (E_t). In symbols

$$E_{t+1} = E_t + a(S_t - E_t)$$

This method is called exponential smoothing.

a) Show that this is equivalent to using a weighted moving average.

b) What happens if $a = 0$?

c) What happens if $a = 1$?

d) What would be the considerations in choosing a value for a?

6–13. A company sells both in the civilian and military markets. It wonders which of the following prediction procedures will prove more precise.

a) Use past data on military sales to predict future military sales. Do the same for civilian sales. Add the predictions to get company sales.

b) Use past data on total company sales to directly predict future company sales.

Which would be more precise if the standard deviation of a sales forecast is independent of its magnitude?

Chapter 7

EVALUATING OUTCOMES—MULTIPLE GOALS

INTRODUCTION

THE ANALYST OF management decisions aims at evaluating outcomes as far as possible in terms of explicit criteria or measures of value such as cost or profit. When the resulting conceptualization of a decision is presented to management, their response is nearly always to modify the analyst's work through the addition of various judgments. Perhaps the most significant and difficult judgments are those pertaining to value. The necessity for these judgments arises in two ways. First, it is usually not possible for the analyst to be fully aware of the objectives of the firm since these are often implicit in the thinking of management, rather than explicitly stated. Second, most outcomes contain aspects which are relevant to the objectives of the firm but cannot be readily evaluated by the analyst in terms of cost, profits, or whatever measures of value are being employed. While it is very useful to use cost or profit as a measure of value for most firms, not all aspects of an outcome can be directly measured in these terms, and most firms have other objectives, such as customer service, good will, community reputation, job satisfaction, safety, employment stability, and so on. These factors, which cannot be directly expressed in cost or profit terms, are called "intangibles" or "irreducibles."

The ultimate aim of the analyst with respect to these intangibles is to develop objective methods of evaluating them, so that a single measure of value may be associated with each outcome in a decision. This measure would have the property of objectively reflecting not only the cost of profit represented by the outcome but also the worth of the intangible values associated with it.

It must be immediately pointed out that the study of decisions

154

and value measurement is a very long way from this goal at the present time. This means that in most instances intangibles must be evaluated by some process of judgment exercised by the decision maker and based upon his perception of the objectives of the firm. (If his personal objectives differ from those of the firm, there may be little to prevent their inclusion in the decisions he makes.) The analyst often finds little opportunity to influence or even gain insight into this judgment process. Nevertheless, it is important to try to understand why it is necessary and to be able to seize whatever opportunities present themselves for improving these judgments.

In attacking the problem of evaluating intangibles it is very easy to get embroiled in questions which could only be answered by lifting the top of the decision maker's head and looking inside. Thus, if management decides to forego profit in return for something rather vaguely called "good will," we cannot ask if they really mean this, or if this really represents the objectives of the firm. If a decision maker indicates that laying off an employee is equivalent in his judgment to a loss of $1,000, little can be done to validate his statement in any ordinary sense. What can be done with respect to the evaluation of intangibles is to make the judgments explicit and consistent.

In terms of our objectives of rationalizing decisions, explicitness and consistency are of basic importance. In this chapter we will explore briefly the origin of intangible values within the firm and some of the attempts to make value judgments both explicit and consistent. The reader should be warned that this is not only the most important part of the analysis of decisions but also the most difficult and most primitive with respect to scientific development. Indeed, some people believe that science can never make much of a contribution to the problem, while others strongly disagree.

VALUES AND OBJECTIVES OF THE FIRM

One way to think about the problem of value measurement is to begin by looking at the objectives or goals of the firm. The outcomes in a decision are then evaluated in terms of how far they advance the firm toward its objectives, or their efficiency for the objectives. Conceptually at least, if the objectives of the firm were explicitly stated, the analyst would attempt to predict how well the outcomes served these goals and the outcomes could be evaluated more or less directly. It is true that for most firms a great deal of useful analysis can be done based upon the assumption that the most important goal is profit maximization. Even this idea has its difficulties when examined closely. There are different ways of defining and computing profit, depending, for example, on what accounting conventions are used. It is also necessary to decide how to choose between profits this year and profits ten years hence. This latter problem is sometimes dealt with in terms of the interest calculations used in Chapter 3. One sometimes finds, however, decisions which are made in direct conflict with the objective of profit maximization. This suggests the presence of other objectives. One finds also that the firm attaches importance to various aspects of the outcomes in a decision beyond simply the cost or profit aspects. Thus, the analyst is confronted with the problem of intangible values.

If it were possible to obtain an exact statement of the objectives of the firm, the problem of evaluation would be practically solved. Several intervening factors make this very difficult.

1. It is often quite difficult to obtain from any manager an explicit statement of the firm's goals. Managers may find themselves unable or unwilling to render such an explicit definition of objectives. Even if we obtain it from one manager, the other members of management may see the objectives differently, and the stockholders may in turn hold still a different view. We have only a primitive understanding of how these differing views of the firm's objectives are, or could be, aggregated into what we might wish to call "the objectives" of the firm. Still another level of difficulty arises when we consider the possibility that each decision maker may from time to time interject his own personal objectives, which may be somewhat different from those of the firm.

2. Generally the firm will have several objectives rather than a single one. Thus, we are confronted with a multiplicity of objectives, some of which may be in conflict with others. The firm may, for example, wish to make as much profit as possible, but at the same time be a "good place to work." When the decision to keep on or lay off some employees who are temporarily not needed is to be made, these goals are seen to be in conflict with each other. In theory this is taken care of by assuming some higher-level objective which subsumes both profit and stability of employment and permits them to be evaluated on a common measuring scale. This is usually rather difficult to do in practice. In general, however, the

firm does have conflicting goals, and evaluation of outcomes which serve more than one objective requires some knowledge of the relationship between them.

3. It is likely that as management, ownership, business conditions, competitive pressures, and so on change, the objectives of the firm may also change. Thus, we must think of the firm's objectives as being dynamic in some vague sense.

Still other features complicate the problem of measuring values in terms of the objectives of the firm. In spite of these difficulties, it is instructive to examine the logical structure of the value measurement problem in these terms. This will help to make clear the steps that would have to be taken to measure intangible values and will indicate those few steps that we know something about as well as the many steps which still present great difficulties.

THE BASIC STRUCTURE OF MULTIPLE OBJECTIVES

Let us assume that a firm has a set of objectives or goals represented by G_1, G_2, ... , G_n. G_1 might represent maximization of this year's profit; G_2, maximization of next year's profit; G_3, the maintenance of favorable employee attitudes; G_4, the maintenance of satisfactory relations with the community; and so on. Now suppose one has the problem of analyzing a decision within the context of this firm, and that several outcomes are connected with the alternatives in the decision. The outcomes are represented by θ_1, θ_2, ... , θ_m. If we were to carry out the full process of value measurement explicitly, it would be necessary first to evaluate each outcome in terms of each objective. To do this we must have complete predictions of all the aspects of each outcome which are related to any of the objectives. For a given outcome it would be necessary to know what it would represent in terms of this year's profit, next year's profit, its effect on employee attitudes and so on. Granting all this, one could then speak of the value of each outcome with respect to each objective. We might symbolize the value of outcome a with respect to objective b by $V_b(\theta_a)$. Our next step would be to define a function which would weight these evaluations according to the relative importance of the various objectives, and combine them into a single measure which would be the value of the outcome with respect to the firm's complex objectives. The result might be expressed as

$$V(\theta_a) = V\{V_1(\theta_a), V_2(\theta_a), \cdots, V_m(\theta_a)\}$$

These final measurements would then appear in the decision matrix and some principle of choice could be applied. This process, carried out in detail, might be called "explicit value measurement."

The antithesis of explicit value measurement is implicit measurement, wherein the outcome is evaluated as a whole by the process of judgment. In most decisions, it is possible to use a value measurement process that is partly explicit and partly implicit. The analysis of management decisions has traditionally attempted to evaluate outcomes in terms of cost or profit explicitly, and then rely on judgments for the implicit determination of the complete evaluation.

METHODS—AN EXAMPLE

In many value measurement problems it is helpful to think in terms of three basic methods of measurement. The most common method used to evaluate outcomes in cost or profit terms is based simply on the accountant's synthesis of values from the expenses of the firms. This method is founded on the exchange value concept, which suggests that something is evaluated in terms of what it will cost to buy, or what it will bring if sold on the market. The accountant merely synthesizes these expenses into a measure of cost or profit for the particular outcomes involved in a decision.

Suppose, for example, an economic lot size decision is to be made of the sort studied in Chapter 3, and that the problem of measuring the cost of setting up for a production run is under consideration. Starting with estimates of the direct labor and machine time involved in setting up, the accountant would apply labor costs and machine costs based directly on expense estimates to produce a measure of this setup cost. This of course assumes that no other considerations are involved, such as the confusion, delays, and administrative problems associated with the setup process. It would also assume that total setup cost over the planning period is linear in the number of setups.

A second method of obtaining this cost is simply to ask someone who presumably is experienced in these matters to make a judgment. This judgment might be in part based on the measurements produced by the accountant; nevertheless it would primarily be a judgment.

The third method involves the study of past decision-making behavior and the inference of values from this behavior. Although this method does not lend itself yet to wide use in the analysis of management decisions, it is suggestive of some interesting possibilities. To illustrate, suppose we ask the decision maker to review his past decisions with respect to economic lot sizes and to select one or several which he feels were satisfactory decisions. We are asking him to make a judgment about the effectiveness of past decisions. From a study of such a satisfactory past decision we might obtain the lot size decided upon, the storage cost, demand, and planning period used. If the decision maker judges this decision to have been satisfactory, we might assume that the lot size was close to optimal. Thus, the factors involved might approximately satisfy the relation

$$L = \sqrt{\frac{2C_1D}{C_2T}}$$

In this relation we have assumed that everything is measured except the set up cost, C_1. We could then solve it for C_1.

$$C_1 = \frac{L^2C_2T}{2D}$$

The result would be a measure of setup cost, inferred from a past decision which was judged to be optimal. Such an inference is filled with possible pitfalls; however, it does provide an approximate evaluation of setup cost which could be used in future decisions. Clearly, if we infer setup costs in this way from a series of decisions, all of which are judged to be satisfactory, and these costs turn out to be markedly different, some questions of importance could be raised. We might, for example, inquire of the decision maker whether or not the setup cost had actually changed in these situations, or if he had simply committed errors of inconsistency. This method is a useful guide to consistent decision making in the sense of our original objectives.

INDIFFERENCE CURVES

Still speaking of the logical structure of the value measurement problem and not necessarily of methods of solution, it is helpful to review the traditional economic approach to the problem. This approach involves an expression of the relationship between goals of objectives by what are called "indifference curves." To interpret this in terms of our problem, let us suppose that we consider for the moment a firm which has but two objectives: immediate profit and customer good will.

Assuming we have a rather definite way of measuring profit, more must be known about the term "good will." To be definite, let us suppose that good will is taken to mean the satisfaction of the customer with the products they purchase from the firm. To provide an operational measure of good will, let us assume that the number of complaints received plus the number of units returned by the customers is an approximate measure of good will. Now the whole range of decisions about product design, raw materials, production methods, inspection methods and policy, and so on will have outcomes which bear upon these two goals.

Suppose we are confronted with two outcomes, the first of which involves x dollars profit, and a mean rate of complaints and returns of y per month. The second outcome may represent a prediction of w dollars profit, and z complaints and returns per month. If $x > w$ and $y < z$, then there is no problem since the first outcome will be clearly preferred to the second. If, however, $x < w$ and $y < z$, then the question arises: "As the choice is shifted from the first outcome to the second, is the loss of good will offset by the increase in profit?" This leads us directly to what is familiarly called the "trade-off" between profit and good will. The trade-off simply expresses the rate at which we would be willing to exchange profit for good will or vice versa. We assume that, given any two outcomes involving different profits and different rates of complaints and returns, we can, either through explicit value measurement or through judgment, determine that the two outcomes are equally valued or that one is preferred. If the two outcomes are of equal value to the firm, then we will say that the firm is indifferent as to which it chooses. Given a large number of preference or indifference statements of this sort, we could construct a series of indifference curves, one of which is shown in Figure 7–1.

On one axis of the indifference graph, profit is plotted; on the other, our measure of good will. An indifference curve on this graph passes through a set of profit–good will combinations which are all of equal value to the firm. An indifference curve might be referred to as an "isovalue line." The slope of an indifference curve at any point is the trade-off between profit and good will at that point. The slope is the rate at which good will may decrease with increasing profit in order to maintain the firm's indifference, or to preserve equality of value. In general, the trade-off changes as one moves along the indifference curve. That is, in general, we cannot be sure that the indifference curves will be straight lines. This means that if we have fairly low good will we would be willing to make a large sacrifice in profits in order to increase it by a given amount. On the other hand, if the firm's good will is already substantial, we would be willing to sacrifice only a small amount of profit in order to increase it by the same amount.

The purpose of indifference curves is the representation of values, rather than their measurement. It is important, however, to have a clear idea of how objectives might be related and the meaning of trade-off between them. Management decision mak-

FIGURE 7–1

An Indifference Curve

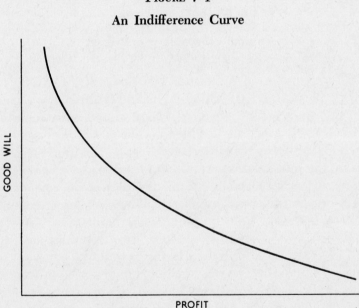

ing is often characterized by trade-off statements involving such things as quality versus price, short-term profit versus long-term profit, volume versus quality, and the like. One of the most useful methods of attacking evaluation problems involving multiple objectives is to go after judgments of the trade-offs.

As a simple example of a family of indifference curves, consider the relation between present and future sums of money. Assume a firm must make a choice between alternatives having outcomes which involve immediate incomes as well as incomes two years hence. The firm finds two of its goals are relevant: maximization of present profits and maximization of profits two years in the future. One interpretation of interest rates is that they provide a method of translating a future income into an equivalent (or indifferent) present income.

Let

$$x = \text{A present profit}$$
$$y = \text{Profit two years hence}$$
$$i = \text{An interest rate}$$

The present and future sums may be assumed to be related by the expression

$$x(1 + i)^2 = y$$

FIGURE 7–2

**An Indifference Curve for Present
and Future Profit**

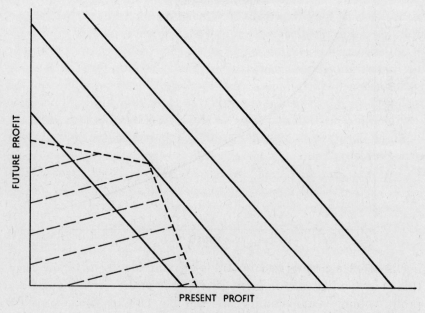

An indifference curve would then be a plot of all values of x and y which had a given present worth, K.

$$K = x + y/(1 + i)^2$$

This is of course a straight line, when plotted in the x, y plane.

The trade-off between present and future profits is constant. If the interest rate is 5 per cent then $(1 + i)^2 = 1.103$. The firm would then be willing to trade off \$1.103 of profit two years hence for \$1.00 of profit at present.

A family of indifference curves, called an "indifference map," is a way of expressing the preferences of a decision maker. It is usually assumed for analytical purposes that indifference curves are continuous, nonintersecting, and downward sloping. Under these assumptions, if the alternatives open to the decision maker are within the shaded area of Figure 7–2, the best choice would be that alternative farthest from the origin in a general northeasterly direction.

SCALES

All problems of measurement, including that of the measurement of values, involve the construction and use of scales. Everyone is familiar with the ordinary scales used in physical measurement, such as length, weight, temperature, and so on. The values of outcomes in most management decisions are measured on a scale of dollars which is so common as to be taken completely for granted. To understand more clearly the problem of value measurement it is necessary to introduce a more general picture of the kinds of scales which might be used and then to show that different decision problems require different types of scales for value measurement.

Three basic types of scales are relevant in the analysis of decision problems.

1. An ordinal scale is simply a ranking. If we rank outcomes according to our preference for them, we have measured them on an ordinal scale. Sometimes we will say that an outcome, A, is "preferred or equivalent to" another outcome, B. This relation defines a partly ordered scale.

2. An interval scale has an arbitrary zero point and a constant unit of measurement. Temperature is often measured on the Fahrenheit or Centigrade scales, which are interval scales.

3. A ratio scale has an absolute zero point and a constant unit of measurement. When we measure weight we use ratio scales, which have absolute zero points. When we evaluate an outcome in dollars of profit, we are also using a ratio scale.

It is easy to see that, in a decision under assumed certainty, if we were able simply to rank all the outcomes in order of preference, then the decision would be determined. Thus, for this class of decisions all that is required is an ordinal scale. In dealing with intangibles in such a decision we need attempt no more than a ranking of the outcomes.

ORDINAL SCALING

The most obvious method of obtaining an ordinal scale is simply
to present the outcomes in a decision to the decision maker and ask
him to rank them in order of preference. There is, however, a
simple device which makes this task easier and provides some
check on the internal consistency of the value judgments obtained.
This is the method of paired comparisons. The decision maker is
asked to consider the outcomes two at a time, and for each pair
indicate which is the preferred outcome. This is then carried on
until all possible pairs of outcomes have been submitted to com-
parative value judgment. From the results of these judgments a
complete ordinal scale may be constructed.

Suppose in a decision there are five outcomes, A,B,C,D,E, each
representing intangible values to some extent. The method of
paired comparisons suggests that these be submitted to the decision maker two at a time for a preference judgment. In general, if
there are n outcomes, $n(n-1)$ $(\frac{1}{2})$ pairs must be judged. Assume
that the results of this process are indicated by the following list
of preference statements (the symbol $>$ should be read "is preferred
to"):

1. $A > B$	6. $B > D$
2. $A > C$	7. $B < E$
3. $A > D$	8. $C > D$
4. $A > E$	9. $C < E$
5. $B < C$	10. $D < E$

The first step in deducing the ordinal scale from these results is
to rearrange the list so that all the "is preferred to" signs point in
the same direction.

1. $A > B$	6. $B > D$
2. $A > C$	7. $E > B$
3. $A > D$	8. $C > D$
4. $A > E$	9. $E > C$
5. $C > B$	10. $E > D$

The outcome which ranks first on our ordinal scale must be preferred to four other outcomes in this problem, and thus should appear four times on the left-hand side of our list. The outcome A
appears four times on the left, and thus ranks at the top of the
ordinal scale. Similarly, the outcome which ranks second must be
preferred to three other outcomes, and should appear three times
on the left-hand side of the list. In general, if there are n outcomes,

the outcome whose rank is r on the resulting ordinal scale will appear $n - r$ times on the left-hand side of a list such as we have just constructed. In this problem the resulting ordinal scale is

Rank	Outcome	$n - r$
1......................A		4
2......................E		3
3......................C		2
4......................B		1
5......................D		0

The reader should convince himself that all this is logically correct.

Now suppose this little scheme of deducing the ordinal scale from the results of paired comparisons does not work out just the way this example suggests it should. Suppose the decision maker in comparison number 7 on our list had judged $B > E$ instead of $B < E$. When we revised the list to make all the symbols point in the same direction, we would find that B, C, and E all appeared twice on the left-hand side of the list. The rule for deducing the ordinal scale would then fail. This event is the clue that there is an inconsistency in the judgments which have been made by the decision maker. Going back over his statements we would find him having said:

B is preferred to E. (7)
E is preferred to C. (9)
C is preferred to B. (5)

Something is wrong here, for these statements seem logically inconsistent. This relationship is called an "intransitivity." While some might argue that the decision maker may really mean these things, we would probably want to invite him to review these statements to see if he had made a mistake. If an ordinal scale is to be obtained it must be that all the value judgments are transitive; if they are not we are inclined to regard the decision maker as inconsistent in a logical sense. Thus, the method of paired comparisons insures this kind of internal consistency of the judgments obtained.

SCALE REQUIREMENTS

For decisions under assumed certainty, we need only evaluate intangibles on an ordinal scale to completely determine choice. This is not generally true with decisions under risk or uncertainty, and for either of these types the scale requirement may depend on the particular principle of choice to be used.

The simplest kind of a decision under risk is one with only two outcomes, which may in general be labeled "success" and "failure." Suppose in making such a decision the principle of maximizing expectation is to be used. For each alternative the probability of success is easily obtained. Let this probability be P_i for alternative a_i. The expectation for alternative a_i may be written

$$E(a_i) = P_i V(S) + (1 - P_i) V(F)$$

where S stands for the outcome success, and F for failure. In such a decision suppose that

$$E(a_I) > E(a_i) \text{ for all } i \neq I$$

This implies

$$P_I V(S) + (1 - P_I) V(F) > P_i V(S) + (1 - P_i) V(F), \text{ for all } i \neq I$$

This reduces to

$$P_I \{ V(S) - V(F) \} > P_i \{ V(S) - V(F) \}$$

This relation will hold if $P_I > P_i$ and if $V(S) > V(F)$. Thus, in this simple decision we need only know that the value of success is greater than the value of failure. This is, of course, an ordinal relationship.

Consider now the general form of a decision under risk wherein we wish to select the alternative which maximizes expectation. The expectation for any alternative is

$$E(a_i) = \sum_j p_j V(\theta_{ij})$$

Assume there is some alternative, I, for which

$$E(a_I) > E(a_i) \text{ for all } i \neq I$$

This implies

$$\sum_j p_j V(\theta_{Ij}) > \sum_j p_j V(\theta_{ij}), \text{ for all } i \neq I$$

which may be written as

$$\sum_j p_j \{ V(\theta_{Ij}) - V(\theta_{ij}) \} > 0$$

Whether or not this relation holds depends clearly on the differences in values. If the relation does hold, we could add a constant to all the values without changing its truth. Thus we could change the zero point on our value scale without influencing the decision. Clearly, also, we could multiply both sides of the inequation by a positive constant without changing its validity. This is the same as saying that we could change the unit of measurement of our value scale without influencing the decision. Thus, the conclusion is that an interval scale, having an arbitrary zero point and a constant unit of measurement, is sufficient to determine a decision under risk when the principle of maximizing expectation is used.

INTERVAL SCALING

As soon as we move beyond the problem of measuring values on an ordinal scale, things begin to get complicated. One method of value measurement has, however, received considerable interest and some application to industrial decision problems. This method has certain limitations but is quite simple. It was developed by Churchman and Ackoff and used by them in connection with the evaluation of the objectives of a firm. We shall discuss it in terms of the evaluation of outcomes, although their use of it may be more plausible in some respects. (25)

Consider a decision in which there are m outcomes, θ, ... , θ_m, to be evaluated. This method requires two rather strong assumptions:

1. It must be possible for the decision maker to think about and judge the value of any combination of outcomes. That is, it must be possible to consider not only the value of θ_1 but also the value of the occurrence of both θ_1 and θ_2.
2. Values are assumed to be additive. Given the value of θ_1 and the value of θ_2, it is assumed that the value of the occurrence of both θ_1 and θ_2 is the sum of their individual values.

The decision maker then undertakes the following steps:

1. Rank the outcomes. Assume that this is accomplished and that the subscripts are reassigned to indicate the rankings. Thus θ_1 is ranked first, θ_2 is ranked second, and so on.

2. Let $V(\theta_1) = 1.00$ and assign values to the other outcomes which reflect a judgment of their values relative to θ_1. This actually completes the judgment process, but the remaining steps serve to refine these initial judgments and strengthen their internal consistency.

3. Compare θ_1 with the combination of $\theta_2 + \theta_3 + \ldots + \theta_m$. The plus sign here is to be read "and." If θ_1 is preferred to the com-

bination of the other outcomes, then the values assigned in step 2 must satisfy the relation

$$V(\theta_1) > V(\theta_2) + V(\theta_3) + \cdots + V(\theta_m)$$

If the assigned values do not satisfy this relation, adjust the value of θ_1 until the statement holds. If θ_1 is not preferred to the combination of other outcomes, the inequality sign will be reversed, and, if necessary, the value of θ_1 may be adjusted to satisfy the relation.

4. Next compare θ_1 with the combination of $\theta_2 + \theta_3 + \cdots + \theta_{m-1}$ and repeat the process of adjusting the value of θ_1 if necessary.

5. The process of comparison and adjustment is carried on according to the following pattern. In any given problem many of these comparisons will be unnecessary, and the process may be considerably shorter.

compare θ_1 with $\theta_2 + \theta_3 + \cdots + \theta_{m-2}$
. . . .
. . . .

compare θ_1 with $\theta_2 + \theta_3$
compare θ_2 with $\theta_3 + \cdots + \theta_m$
compare θ_2 with $\theta_3 + \cdots + \theta_{m-1}$
. . . .
. . . .

compare θ_2 with $\theta_3 + \theta_4$
. . . .
. . . .
. . . .

compare θ_{m-2} with $\theta_{m-1} + \theta_m$

6. We sometimes divide the values which satisfy these relations by the quantity $V(\theta_1)$ which simply has the effect of "normalizing" them to a zero-one scale.

It must be emphasized that this method adds nothing mysterious to the validity of the judgments which it requires. The basic value judgments which are made in steps one and two are, after all, nothing more than judgments. The remainder of the method simply provides a way of checking and improving the internal consistency of the judgments. It provides a way of helping the decision maker detect any errors in his judgments, under the assumption that he wishes to be consistent in the sense of this method. The method does, however, have the advantage of providing a systematic and organized way of checking consistency. This, in practical situations, is not inconsiderable.

In use, the judgments may be made by a group of persons, such as the executive committee of the firm. One method of operation is to have each member of such a group go through the foregoing process independently. The individual values may then be simply averaged or some process of discussion and search for consensus may be undertaken. To weight every person's results equally is democratic, but any number of other methods might be used, perhaps weighting the results of some persons more than those of others. One of the side benefits of such a group process of value judgment is often that the members leave the group satisfied with the values which have been assigned, thus bringing a fundamental measure of agreement to decisions made within the firm.

The method has been applied in several interesting cases. Churchman and Ackoff report its use in the following instances:

a) To establish a priority list for equipment requested by various departments of a firm.

b) To assign values to the criteria used in the selection of public housing sites.

c) To evaluate the relative importance of various product characteristics in a new-product search by a firm.

d) To assign relative weights to the various manufacturing defects which could occur in a product. These weights were multiplied by the number of times a particular type of defect occurred in a sample, and the sum of these products was used as a criterion for accepting or rejecting the lot of product.

e) To evaluate the following objectives of a firm for the purpose of making decisions about long-range plans:

1. Security of existing management.
2. Financial security.
3. Financial opportunity.
4. Security and promotion of key personnel.
5. Labor stability.
6. Technological leadership.
7. Community service.

The following hypothetical example will suggest some of the considerations involved.

AN EXAMPLE

A printing firm has just signed a two-year contract to print a nationally circulated monthly magazine. It anticipates the possibility that the contract might be renewed for another two years at the end of this period. The firm now faces the decision as to whether it should do the printing with its present equipment, which is adequate but not modern, or whether it should install a highly automated press line to do the job. Without becoming too involved in the details, let's suppose that the following oversimplified version of this decision is to be studied:

	s_1 Contract Renewed	s_2 Contract Not Renewed
a_1: Present equipment	$V(\theta_{11})$	$V(\theta_{12})$
a_2: Automatic equipment	$V(\theta_{21})$	$V(\theta_{22})$

A four-year study period is used, and management feels that the important considerations are new capital required, employees hired or laid off, and average annual profit. Assume that analysis produces the following descriptions of the outcomes:

θ_{11} = no new capital required, 20 new men hired and kept on for at least four years, average annual profit \$750,000

θ_{12} = no new capital required, 20 new men hired but laid off at the end of two years, average annual profit \$320,000

θ_{21} = \$1.5 million new capital required, 12 men laid off permanently, average annual profit \$1,100,000

θ_{22} = \$1.5 million new capital required, 12 men laid off permanently, average annual profit \$400,000

Two methods of obtaining judgments might be used. In the first, one obtains directly judgments of the outcomes in the decision and checks the consistency by means of the Churchman-Ackoff method. Suppose that the ranking by the decision maker yields the following results:

$$\theta_{21} > \theta_{11} > \theta_{12} > \theta_{22}$$

The next step is to place these outcomes on a scale. Assume this judgment has the outcome:

$$V(\theta_{21}) = 1.00$$
$$V(\theta_{11}) = .90$$
$$V(\theta_{12}) = .40$$
$$V(\theta_{22}) = .30$$

With only four outcomes, the internal consistency checks are very simple, but serve to illustrate the process. We begin by asking the decision maker to compare θ_{21} with the combination of θ_{11}, θ_{12}, and θ_{22}. In making this comparison the decision maker may imagine the possibility of undertaking four projects, each having an outcome represented by one of these symbols. The comparison is then between a single project on the one hand, and the combination of three separate projects on the other. The usefulness of this kind of a check on internal consistency depends on the decision maker's ability to conceptualize and judge such comparisons.

Suppose the result of the first comparison is

$$\theta_{21} < \theta_{11} + \theta_{12} + \theta_{22}$$

The initial assignment of values agrees with this result.

$$V(\theta_{21}) = 1.00 < V(\theta_{11}) + V(\theta_{12}) + V(\theta_{22}) = .90 + .40 + .30 = 1.60$$

Next, a comparison is made between θ_{21} and the combination of θ_{11} and θ_{12}. Assume the result is

$$\theta_{21} < \theta_{11} + \theta_{12}$$

The original values also agree with this judgment.

$$V(\theta_{21}) = 1.00 < V(\theta_{11}) + V(\theta_{12}) = .90 + .40 = 1.30$$

Finally, a judgment is made between θ_{11} and the combination of θ_{12} and θ_{22}. If this turns out as follows,

$$\theta_{11} > \theta_{12} + \theta_{22}$$

then our original values are still consistent.

It is important to note that even with these checks the results are only approximate since the values obtained are not unique. There are other sets of numbers which could also be shown to satisfy the foregoing judgments. The original decision now takes the following form:

	s_1	s_2
a_1	.90	.40
a_2	1.00	.30

Supposing the decision maker wishes to choose the alternative which maximizes expectation, it is easily seen that, if the probabilities of the possible futures are each one half, then the alternatives are equal. If the probability of s_1 is greater than one half, the automatic equipment will be favored. If the probability of s_1 is less than one half, then the present equipment will have the higher expectation. If instead the results of these comparisons had been

$$\theta_{21} < \theta_{11} + \theta_{12} + \theta_{22}$$
$$\theta_{21} > \theta_{11} + \theta_{12}$$
$$\theta_{11} > \theta_{12} + \theta_{22}$$

then it would have been necessary to adjust the value of θ_{21} so that it fell somewhere in the range

$$1.30 < V(\theta_{21}) < 1.60$$

The method does not suggest a unique value for the adjustment, thus once again judgment must be applied. The decision may itself be sensitive to this judgment, depending of course on the probabilities associated with the possible futures.

It is often convenient to "normalize" the results by dividing them through by the largest value, thus placing all the measurements in the interval zero to one. If, in the above case, we had judged $V(\theta_{21})$ equal to 1.45, then the normalized results would be

$$V(\theta_{21}) = \frac{1.45}{1.45} = 1.00$$

$$V(\theta_{11}) = \frac{.40}{1.45} = .62$$

$$V(\theta_{12}) = \frac{.40}{1.45} = .28$$

$$V(\theta_{22}) = \frac{.30}{1.45} = .21$$

A second approach to evaluation in this problem might be to judge first the relative values of the objectives of the firm and then judge the effectiveness of each outcome with respect to each objective. In this decision three of the firm's objectives appear to be relevant:

G_1: profit, as measured by average annual profit over the four-year study period

G_2: employment security, measured in terms of the layoffs and employment duration provided by the firm

G_3: minimization of new capital requirements

The first step is to judge the relative importance of these objectives. Since there are only three, the Churchman-Ackoff method of checking consistency is hardly necessary. Nevertheless, it would be useful in larger problems where more objectives are involved. Suppose management attaches the following relative weights to the firm's objectives:

$$G_1 = 1.00$$
$$G_2 = .50$$
$$G_3 = .10$$

As before, this is little more than an attempt to organize the judgments.

Now it is necessary to make a second series of judgments as to the degree to which each outcome succeeds in meeting each objective. Suppose these judgments are made in the form of numbers on a scale over the range zero to one. The higher the scale value, the more completely an outcome results in the firm's meeting an objective.

The results of this step might, for example, appear as follows:

Outcome	G_1	G_2	G_3
θ_{11}.................	.70	1.00	1.00
θ_{12}.................	.30	.90	1.00
θ_{21}.................1.00		.60	.50
θ_{22}.................	.40	.60	.50

A value is then attached to an outcome which is the sum of the products of the objective weights times the effectiveness judgments.

$$V(\theta_{11}) = (1.00)(.70) + (.50)(1.00) + (.10)(1.00) = 1.30$$
$$V(\theta_{12}) = (1.00)(.30) + (.50)(.90) + (.10)(1.00) = .85$$
$$V(\theta_{21}) = (1.00)(1.00) + (.50)(.60) + (.10)(.50) = 1.35$$
$$V(\theta_{22}) = (1.00)(.40) + (.50)(.60) + (.10)(.50) = .75$$

The decision may be very sensitive to the judgments involved, as in any such process. If, for example, the weights attached to the objectives had differed slightly and turned out to be

$$G_1 = 1.00$$
$$G_2 = .60$$
$$G_3 = .20$$

then using the same judgments of effectiveness, the evaluations would have been

$$V(\theta_{11}) = 1.50$$
$$V(\theta_{12}) = 1.04$$
$$V(\theta_{21}) = 1.46$$
$$V(\theta_{22}) = .86$$

The ranking of the outcomes has now been changed. In this case the choice would be a_1, the present equipment, regardless of the probability that the contract will be renewed.

When seven or more outcomes are to be evaluated, the present method is somewhat burdensome. A special method, representing a modification of this one, has been developed for use with large numbers of outcomes. (25)

The assumptions which form the basis for this method must be kept in mind. It is assumed that the decision maker will be able to rank all of the outcomes, that the ranking will be transitive, and that he can make meaningful assignments to points on a zero-to-one scale. "Meaningful" must roughly be taken to imply that the scale values do somehow reflect his strength of preference. Most importantly, it is assumed that values thus obtained are additive. That is, the value of the combination of two outcomes is the sum of their individual values.

THE SCIENTIFIC STUDY OF VALUES

One may well ask if there is any real point in doing all this. Are we not going to considerable trouble to learn something of a manager's preferences so that we can tell him what he already knows, namely what his own preferences are? The answer to this is perhaps twofold.

In the first place, it is becoming increasingly clear that managers are not entirely sure what their own preferences are. The assumption that, if an analyst presented a manager with predictions of the outcomes associated with various courses of action, the manager would be clearly able to evaluate the outcomes for himself may not be entirely warranted. Indeed, one of the important tasks of the analyst may be that of helping the manager to clarify his objectives and values. The method of doing this may involve making preferences explicit, checking their self-consistency, and encouraging the explicit and careful consideration of trade-offs. The need for value clarification is, as we have said, the motivation for management to respond to a decision by exploring its goals more carefully before making a choice.

Secondly, the analyst is deeply interested in having the manager accept his recommendation as to the appropriate course of action. Management acceptance is the primary means by which the analyst may demonstrate achievement and thus justify his efforts. Further, with increasing management acceptance, the analyst finds greater opportunities to perform his basic function of relieving the manager of some of the hard work of getting a decision made. If, from the study of a manager's preferences among simple outcomes, one is able to predict his preferences among more complex outcomes, and if these predictions turn out to be correct, then the analyst will be increasingly able to make recommendations which the manager will want to accept and the manager will be increasingly inclined to delegate various aspects of the decision process. If one could ever succeed in completely understanding a manager's preferences, the imaginary ultimate accomplishment in this connection would be to read these preferences into a computing machine. The manager could then rely on the machine to make all his decisions, since the machine would achieve the same results as if he himself had made the choices. While it is hardly likely that such a thing will be accomplished, it illustrates the basic point of the scientific study of values.

One might summarize this program in a form such as that of Figure 7–3. The values of the manager are taken to be the basic

FIGURE 7–3

The Scientific Study of Values

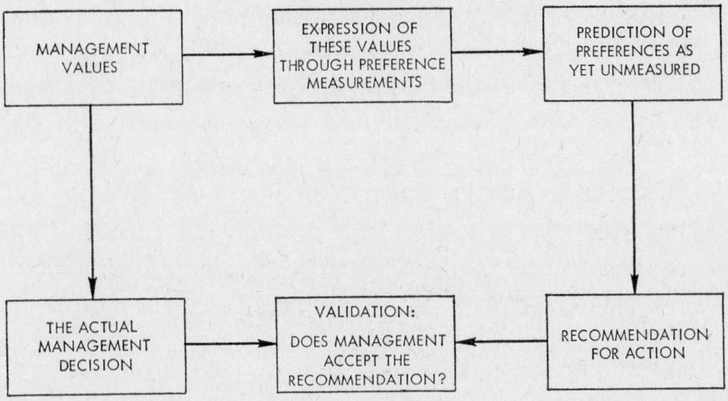

phenomena under study. These values are observed and measured by obtaining preference statements from the manager, using perhaps a method like the method of paired comparisons. The results of this observation program covering some simple preferences are organized into a logical structure, perhaps in the form of an indifference map. This permits the analyst to predict the manager's preferences among outcomes which have not been studied and among outcomes far more complex than those for which the original data were obtained. These predictions of a manager's preferences are then used as a basis for making recommendations with respect to various courses of action. Such a recommendation is interpreted as a prediction of how the manager himself would choose if his preferences were indeed well described by our indifference map, and if he acted in a consistent fashion. Now if the decision actually made by the manager agrees with the recommendation made by the analyst, then the prediction is confirmed. In this sense, one's knowledge of the manager's values may be validated.

CONCLUSION

The problems of the scientific study of values are far from solved. They are at present best considered very difficult problems for research. The analyst may wish, after this brief introduction, to simply take note of the problem and then avoid it. This may mean restricting his activity to the prediction of outcomes, leaving their evaluation to the internalized process of managerial judgment, or restricting evaluations to cost and profit statements. Indeed, for the man who faces the continual pressure of ongoing affairs there is little choice in the matter.

In later sections we will return to this problem, exploring more fully the problem of preferences among risky outcomes and some of the approaches to the evaluation of intangibles which have special usefulness in the understanding of management decision making.

SUGGESTIONS FOR FURTHER STUDY

CHURCHMAN, C. WEST. *Prediction and Optimal Decision.* Englewood Cliffs, N.J.: Prentice-Hall, Inc., 1961.

HEEBINK, DAVID V. "Isoquants and Investment Decisions," *The Engineering Economist,* Vol. 7, No. 4, and Vol. 8, No. 1, 1962.

McKEAN, ROLAND N. *Efficiency in Government Through Systems Analysis.* New York: John Wiley & Sons, Inc., 1958.

PROBLEMS

7–1. Using the method of paired comparisons, find out how one of your associates values ten different makes of automobiles.

7–2. Use the method of paired comparisons to evaluate a number of job opportunities which you have considered.

7–3. Give an example of each of the following:
An ordinal scale.
An interval scale.
A ratio scale.

7–4. How would you go about determining a choice between the two alternatives listed below?

Machine	Equivalent Annual Cost	Flexibility
a_1: Engine lathe	$4,280	Highly flexible
a_2: Turret lathe	3,800	Less flexible

7–5. What is the exchange value concept? What sorts of outcomes may be evaluated using this method?

7–6. In a decision concerning which of several makes of automatic data-processing systems to purchase, what kinds of intangible considerations are likely to be important to the firm?

7–7. In reviewing bids which have been submitted to your firm to supply certain raw materials required in your production process, would you suggest that the contract be awarded on the basis of price alone?

7–8. Draw an indifference curve which roughly portrays your evaluation of salary and job security.

7–9. Draw an indifference curve which suggests your evaluation of price and quality in wrist watches.

7–10. In what ways does the indifference map for present and future profits which appears in the chapter seem unreasonable for a firm which is often short of cash?

7–11. What are the advantages of the method of paired comparisons when used to obtain an ordinal value scale? What troubles would you expect to encounter in its practical application?

$$\text{Let } x = \text{ profit this year (\$)}$$
$$y = \text{ profit this year (\$)}$$

7–12. Suppose a manager's preferences can be represented by indifference lines of the form

$$k = x + \frac{y}{1 + i}$$

The manager may undertake any *two* of the following projects:

Project No.	x	y
1	$ 5,000	$ 5,000
2	0	10,000
3	10,000	0

Show graphically on the manager's indifference map which two he will choose if

a) $i = 0$
b) $i \neq 0$

7–13. The reliability of a weapons system is defined as the probability that it will successfully complete a mission. Suppose you have information on the costs and reliabilities of two competing weapons systems. Discuss the problems involved in deciding which to recommend to the Secretary of Defense.

7–14. Suppose a person's interest in cars centered around purchase price and top speed. Ideally he would like to have the fastest car at the lowest price. Consider the four cars below:

Car	Price	Top Speed (mph)
A	$5000	120
B	4000	125
C	6000	150
D	8000	170

a) Make a rough sketch of the relevant region of the indifference map of a person who ranks the cars as shown below (equal ranks indicate indifference):

Car	A	B	C	D
Rank	2	1	2	3

b) Make a similar sketch for a person who ranks the cars 4,3,1, and 2 for *A,B,C*, and *D* respectively.

7–15. A young man, considering his first job, decides that starting salary and promotion possibilities are of primary importance to him. Faced with an array of job offers, he tries to make an orderly description of his preferences. He decides that promotion possibilities in a company are roughly indicated by the mean time (in years) which it has taken men to become vice-presidents. For several jobs he obtains data on starting salary and mean time to vice-president and, using the method of paired comparisons, ranks them. The results are shown below (equal ranks denote indifference):

Job	Starting Salary	Mean Time to Vice-President (years)	Rank
A	$5000	9	3
B	5500	8	2
C	6000	12	3
D	6500	8	1
E	6500	11	2
F	7000	10	1
G	7500	13	2
H	8000	12	1
I	8000	15	3

a) Sketch a rough approximation to the indifference map of this man in the region for which data are available.

b) Predict his preference between the two jobs below:

Job	Starting Salary	Mean Time to Vice-President (years)
X	$5500	9
Y	7000	11

Chapter 8

EVALUATING OUTCOMES—TAXES

REVIEWING THE PROBLEMS OF EVALUATION

SUPPOSING THAT THE outcomes in a decision have been predicted in the form of dollar costs or profits, one faces the question of whether or not the resulting numbers are those on which a recommendation to management can reasonably be based. Are the cost or profit figures numbers on which management might reasonably base a decision? To what extent do they express the objectives which management seeks? To understand the issues involved in this most difficult question of evaluation, one might consider three ways in which statements of profits (or the present worths of profit streams) might fail to reflect management's values.

1. Management may be interested in its profits after taxes, a consideration we have so far neglected. While the impact of taxes is a matter of some complexity, no serious difficulties of operational definition or measurement arise in transforming our profit predictions into profits after taxes. In the present chapter we will examine the main ideas involved in doing this and the kinds of decisions in which it is worth doing.

2. Management may, as we have noted, have goals other than profits or profits after taxes. They may, for example, be interested in the morale of their employees and the reputation of the firm as a good place to work and as a good neighbor in the community. Thus when one considers the possibility of automating a production process and laying off some employees with substantial seniority, the profit calculations may fail seriously to express the values and goals of management decision makers. This problem was outlined in Chapter 7.

3. So far we have neglected or suppressed risk and uncertainty in the decisions which have been studied. We will see in Chapter 11 that the value of an event and the risk associated with its happen-

ing or not happening are bound together in an inseparable fashion. A manager not only wants to maximize his future profits, but, if he could, he would like to be certain that they will be large. He finds himself, however, most often faced with the choice between a modest but relatively certain future income stream (say a government bond) and a possibly higher but considerably more uncertain future income stream (say a low priced speculative stock).

TAXES

The purpose of this chapter is simply to remind the reader that taxes may be important in the analysis of decisions. The firm may be subject to a variety of federal, state, and local taxes all of which are based on laws of considerable complexity. The federal corporate income tax will be discussed here because of its universal importance. Tax strategy for the firm amounts, largely, to having a clear and detailed understanding of the provisions of the tax laws so that it pays only the tax for which it is legally liable and no more. To do this, most firms employ tax experts who are full-time specialists. Because of the changeableness and complexity of the laws, the only reasonable advice which can be advanced to the analyst is to consult the specialist on any tax considerations which arise in the analysis.

While the firm is obviously interested in the effect of taxes on its operations, the analysis of decisions may require consideration of taxes only if they could make a difference in the choice among the alternatives. If the alternatives are such that considering taxes has the effect of reducing all predicted profits by a constant amount, then the choice could not be influenced and taxes need not be considered for decision-making purposes. Likewise, if consideration of taxes has the effect of multiplying all predicted profits by a constant factor, the decision will presumably be the same before and after the consideration of taxes. Such situations are common, and much perfectly acceptable analysis can be done without any further consideration of taxes. There are, however, other situations in which tax consideration may actually influence choice. The general nature of the federal corporate income tax will be outlined next, followed by some examples of decisions in which taxes might influence the choice among alternatives.

THE FEDERAL CORPORATE INCOME TAX

The federal government requires a firm doing business as a corporation to pay a tax on its earnings each year. The earnings on which the tax is based are usually referred to as "taxable income," and most of the difficulty in tax computation arises from the legal provisions for determining taxable income. It is necessary to use an accounting system which is acceptable to the government and to be consistent in its use. However, the basic computations follow well-established practice. Typically, the determination of taxable income involves the usual pattern of the profit and loss statement:

$$\text{GROSS SALES} - \text{COST OF SALES} = \text{GROSS PROFIT}$$
$$\text{GROSS PROFIT} - \text{EXPENSES} = \text{NET PROFIT}$$

Net profit will be the firm's taxable income, provided the expenses which have been deducted are in accordance with the provisions of

FIGURE 8–1

Profit and Loss Statement
Year Ended December 31, 19XX

Sales (less returns and allowances).............		$80,260
Less: Cost of sales		
Inventory 1/1/xx.........................	$ 8,125	
Purchases................................	59,250	
Goods available for sale..................	$67,375	
Less: Inventory 12/31/xx..................	7,920	
Cost of sales................................		59,455
Gross profit.................................		$20,805
Less: Expenses		
Rent....................................	$ 2,500	
Interest................................	180	
Licenses................................	140	
Bad debts...............................	70	
Depreciation............................	300	
Repairs.................................	50	
Other business expenses.................	2,150	5,390
Net profit from business.....................		$15,415

the tax law. It is these deductions which receive much of the attention, both in the tax strategy of the firm and in the analysis of decisions within the firm. This computation for a small merchandising firm is illustrated in Figure 8–1.

The expenses which are particularly interesting for their tax position in connection with decisions include depreciation, interest, research and development, and depletion. Once taxable income has been computed, the firm's tax is obtained as follows. The income tax is made up of two parts called a normal tax and a surtax. At present, the normal tax is 30 per cent of taxable income and the surtax is 22 per cent of taxable income in excess of $25,000:

$$\text{Total Tax} = (\text{Normal Tax})(\text{Taxable Income})$$
$$+ (\text{Surtax})(\text{Taxable Income} - \$25{,}000)$$
$$= (.30)(\text{Taxable Income})$$
$$+ (.22)(\text{Taxable Income} - \$25{,}000)$$
$$= (.52)(\text{Taxable Income}) - \$5{,}500$$

For the firm whose profit and loss statement is illustrated in Figure 8–1, if we take net profit to be taxable income, only the normal tax must be paid:

$$\text{Total Tax} = (.30)(15{,}415) = \$4{,}624$$

Alternatively, a firm with a taxable income of \$100,000 is liable for

$$\text{Total Tax} = (.52)(\$100{,}000) - \$5{,}500$$
$$= \$46{,}500$$

(The tax bill of 1964 changed the normal tax to 22 per cent and the surtax to 26 per cent on 1965 income.)

INCLUDING TAXES IN DECISIONS

The actual inclusion of tax consideration in decisions regarding alternative projects within the firm poses two difficulties. First, the federal corporate income tax is upon income, thus predictions of the income associated with the project must be made. We have already discussed the problems of trying to associate some part of the income of the firm with a particular machine, for example. Second, the actual rate at which income is taxed depends on the taxable income of the firm as a whole. Thus, to compute the tax associated with a project, one must predict not only the income from the project itself, but that from operations of the entire firm. The effective tax rate for the firm is given by

$$\text{Effective Tax Rate} = \frac{\text{Total Tax}}{\text{Total Taxable Income}}$$

The effective tax rate for the firm is plotted as a function of total taxable income in Figure 8–2. The tax attributable to a project is usually taken to be

$$\text{Project Tax}$$
$$= \text{Total Tax with Project} - \text{Total Tax without Project}$$

The project tax rate is defined as

$$\text{Project Tax Rate} = \frac{\text{Project Tax}}{\text{Project Taxable Income}}$$

If taxable income, both with and without the project, falls below \$25,000, the project tax rate will simply be 30 per cent. Above

$25,000 taxable income for the firm, the project tax rate will be 52 per cent. This will be the case for many firms and is widely used as a project tax rate. If the project takes the firm's taxable income from below $25,000 to some figure above it, then the project tax rate will be the average tax rate over the increment of income derived from the project.

FIGURE 8–2

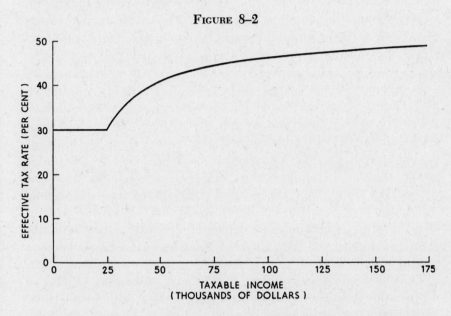

If a firm expects a taxable income of $150,000 before undertaking a project which will yield a taxable income of $10,000, the project tax rate is found as follows: without the project,

$$\begin{aligned}
\text{Taxable Income} &= \$150,000 \\
\text{Total Tax} &= (\$150,000)(.52) - \$5,500 \\
&= \$72,500
\end{aligned}$$

with the project,

$$\begin{aligned}
\text{Taxable Income} &= \$160,000 \\
\text{Total Tax} &= \$77,700 \\
\text{Project Tax Rate} &= \frac{77,700 - 72,500}{10,000} = .52 \text{ or } 52\%
\end{aligned}$$

If the firm expects a taxable income of $20,000 without the same project and $30,000 with it, the project tax rate is

$$\frac{(\$30,000)(.52) - \$5,500 - (\$20,000)(.30)}{\$10,000} = .41 \text{ or } 41\%$$

Another viewpoint often used for rough and ready calculations suggests that the project tax rate simply be taken as the effective tax rate for the firm as a whole.

DEPRECIATION

Under the tax law, permanent tangible property with a useful life of more than one year may be depreciated in computing taxable income. Machinery, equipment, trucks, and so on are typical examples. Some types of intangible property, such as patents and copyrights, may also be depreciated. Land and inventories may not be depreciated for tax purposes.

In computing depreciation deductions the firm must establish a useful life and salvage value for the asset in question, and then select a method of depreciation. For tax purposes, as we shall show presently, it is to the advantage of the firm to select the shortest possible useful life. The life selected, however, must be acceptable to the Internal Revenue Service. There is a possibility that the service life allowed for tax purposes may differ from the actual service life of the asset as employed by the firm. Since the amount of depreciation which may be deducted obviously depends on the salvage value as well, the Internal Revenue Service also keeps a careful watch on it.

The tax law allows the firm to use any reasonable method of depreciation which is consistently employed. The ordinary methods are straight line, fixed percentage of a declining balance, and the sum of the years' digits method. The fixed percentage of a declining balance method is limited to percentages no greater than twice the straight-line rate. Thus, for an asset having a useful life of ten years, the straight-line method would lead to an annual depreciation equal to 10 per cent of the difference between investment and salvage value. The fixed percentage method in this case would be limited to 20 per cent.

Depreciation in year j using the fixed percentage of a declining balance method is given by

$$d(j) = pI(1 - p)^{j-1}$$

Depreciation at the straight line rate would charge a fraction $1/n$ each year, thus the tax laws permit a fixed percentage $p = 2/n$. The depreciation in year j using this percentage will be

$$d(j) = \frac{2}{n} I\left(1 - \frac{2}{n}\right)^{j-1}$$

This is equivalent to assuming a salvage value of

$$I\left(1 - \frac{2}{n}\right)^n$$

Since this plan may not result in full depreciation over the service life of the asset, the Internal Revenue Service permits the firm to switch to straight line depreciation at any time during the service life. Thus the firm may find itself with an asset which has been depreciated using a fixed percentage method with $p = 2/n$ for years $1, 2, \ldots, j-1$. The undepreciated value of the asset at the beginning of year j (the end of year $j-1$) will be

$$I\left(1 - \frac{2}{n}\right)^{j-1}$$

The firm may switch to a straight line method in which the depreciation for the years j, $(j = 1, \ldots, n)$ would be

$$d(j) = \frac{I\left(1 - \frac{2}{n}\right)^{j-1} - S}{n - j + 1} \qquad \text{for } j = 1, \ldots, n$$

The firm will find it advantageous to switch to this method in the first year for which the depreciation thus calculated by the straight line expression is greater than or equal to that calculated by the fixed percentage of the declining balance method. The reader may explore this refinement further in problems 8–12 through 8–15.

The problem of selecting a method of depreciation for tax purposes is often approached on the basis of the following principle. If the firm uses a nonzero interest rate to discount future receipts and disbursements, then any method which will postpone the payment of taxes will be advantageous, in that it will reduce the present worth of the tax payments. This principle does not suggest the possibility of reducing total taxes over a period of time, but simply of postponing the tax outlays and thus reducing their present worth. In decisions where a present worth principle of choice is employed, this principle is of real importance.

Consider a depreciable asset which requires an initial investment of $11,000 and will have a useful life of five years and a salvage value of $1,000 at that time. The asset will earn an annual income, before taxes and depreciation, of $5,000. We will show, first, that no matter what method of depreciation is used, the total tax payments over the life of the asset will remain constant. Assume a project tax rate of 50 per cent.

STRAIGHT-LINE DEPRECIATION

Year	Depreciation	Taxable Income	Tax
1..................	$2,000	$3,000	$1,500
2..................	2,000	3,000	1,500
3..................	2,000	3,000	1,500
4..................	2,000	3,000	1,500
5..................	2,000	3,000	1,500
		Total Tax Outlay.......	$7,500

FIXED PERCENTAGE OF A DECLINING BALANCE (40 per cent)

Year	Depreciation	Taxable Income	Tax
1..................	$4,400	$ 600	$ 300
2..................	2,640	2,360	1,180
3..................	1,584	3,416	1,708
4..................	950	4,050	2,025
5..................	426*	4,574	2,287
		Total Tax Outlay.......	$7,500

* Only $426 depreciation in the fifth year since the total depreciation must not exceed $10,000.

SUM OF YEARS' DIGITS

Year	Depreciation	Taxable Income	Tax
1..................	$3,333	$1,667	$ 833
2..................	2,667	2,333	1,166
3..................	2,000	3,000	1,500
4..................	1,333	3,667	1,835
5..................	667	4,333	2,167
		Total Tax Outlay.......	$7,500

Now suppose the firm uses an interest rate of 10 per cent and bases decisions on present worths. The present worth of the tax outlays in each of the above cases is

Method	Present Worth of Tax Outlays
Straight line............................	$5,686
Fixed percentage of declining balance......	5,225
Sum of years' digits....................	5,443

Thus, from the point of view of present worth, the firm would elect in this case the fixed percentage of a declining balance method. We have used the maximum allowable percentage of 40 per cent in this example. Clearly, the pattern of depreciation can have a significant influence on the present worth of tax outlays over the life of the asset and thus an influence over the present worth of income after taxes. Thus, the pattern of depreciation may be relevant in choices where taxes are to be considered.

Unfortunately there is no one best method of depreciation for tax purposes. The table below shows that the choice between the fixed percentage method (with $p = 2/n$ and switch to straight line where advantageous) and the sum of the years' digits method may depend both upon interest rate and upon service life. The table shows the present worth of depreciation charges for an asset costing $10,000 and having no salvage value. To minimize the present worth of tax payments, one would seek to maximize the present worth of depreciation charges.

Interest Rate	Service Life (years)	Present Worth of Depreciation Charges SYD	FPDB*
.10	5	$8,061	$8,110
.10	10	7,010	6,853
.01	6	9,739	9,736
.10	6	7,832	7,825
.20	6	6,368	6,382
.30	6	5,329	5,370

*Assumes switch to straight line depreciation where advantageous.

It should be noted, also, that in decisions among alternative projects, the mix of depreciable and nondepreciable assets for each of the projects may have a bearing upon choice. Suppose, for instance, we consider the above machine having an investment of $11,000 and a salvage value of $1,000 after a five-year service life as one alternative. This is to be compared with a second alternative which involves the purchase of a plot of land in the center of a city to be operated as a parking lot. The land cannot be depreciated under the tax laws. Suppose the land is purchased for $11,000, is to be used for five years, and then sold. It is expected that its selling price at that time will be $11,000. Assume the net profit before taxes for the parking lot is expected to be $3,600 each year. This will also be the taxable income. We suppose further that the parking lot income will be subject to a project tax rate of 50 per cent, as with the machine.

For the parking lot the taxable income of $3,600 each year will result in a tax of $1,800 and an income after taxes of $1,800. If we neglect interest, this means the total income after taxes over the five-period will be $5(1,800) = \$9,000$. Since the land does not decline in price we need not be concerned with recovering the investment out of income. To simplify the computations, let us consider the machine under a policy of straight-line depreciation. Again neglecting interest, the investment in the machine will yield an income after taxes and depreciation (investment recovery) of $7,500 over the five years. On this basis the parking lot seems advantageous.

However, consider the present worths of the two projects using an interest rate of 10 per cent. The actual receipts an disbursements for the machine, using straight-line depreciation, are:

| Year | Receipts | | Disbursements |
	Depreciation	Income after Taxes	
0	...	.....	$11,000
1	$2,000	$1,500	
2	2,000	1,500	
3	2,000	1,500	
4	2,000	1,500	
5	2,000	1,500 (plus $1,000 salvage)	

The present worth of this series of receipts and disbursements is

$$\{\$2,000 + \$1,500\}(3.791) + 1,000(.6209) - 11,000 = \$2,889.40$$

For the parking lot the actual cash receipts and disbursements are:

Year	Receipts (Income after Taxes)	Disbursements
0	$1,800	$11,000
1	1,800	
2	1,800	
3	1,800	
4	1,800	
5	1,800 (plus $11,000 resale price for land)	

The present worth here is

$$1,800(3.791) + 11,000(.6209) - 11,000 = \$2,653.70$$

The parking lot, on the basis of a present worth criterion, would not be selected in preference to the investment in the machine. The point here is simply that, when taxes are considered and when a present worth principle of choice is used, the proportion of depreciable and nondepreciable assets composing each alternative may influence choice.

BORROWED FUNDS

Interest paid on indebtedness is deductible as a business expense under the present laws. This means that a project which is financed with borrowed capital may have its taxable income reduced by the amount of the interest involved. The reader should carefully distinguish interest used in the analysis of decisions which does not actually represent the cost of borrowed money, from interest which is actually paid for borrowed funds. The former, of course, is not deductible for tax purposes, while the latter is.

Consider, for example, the machine discussed previously. Suppose the machine is financed by means of a loan of $11,000 which is to be repaid at the rate of $2,000 each year for the first four years and $3,000 at the end of the fifth year. Interest is paid at the rate of 10 per cent on the unpaid balance of the loan.

Year	Gross Income	Repayment	Unpaid Balance	Interest	Income before Taxes	Tax
1	$5,000	$2,000	$11,000	$1,100	$1,900	$ 950
2	5,000	2,000	9,000	900	2,100	1,050
3	5,000	2,000	7,000	700	2,300	1,150
4	5,000	2,000	5,000	500	2,500	1,250
5	5,000	3,000	3,000	300	2,700	1,350

Now if we examine the total income over the five years, it will clearly be less using borrowed funds than it would have been if we had used funds that had been considered essentially costless. The point is that, in each year, the deductibility of interest has generated a tax saving. Thus, in the first year, if the machine is financed out of equity capital, the tax will be $1,500, assuming straight-line depreciation. Using borrowed funds the tax is only $950, a saving of $550. This means that the cost of borrowed funds was actually

$$\$1,100 - \$550 = \$550$$

thus cutting the interest rate in half. This ratio carries through for the succeeding years, leaving the firm with an actual interest rate on the loan of only 5 per cent. While the firm might be unwilling to borrow funds at 10 per cent, it might choose to do so in view of the tax savings which reduces the interest rate to 5 per cent.

RESEARCH AND DEVELOPMENT

Expenses for research and development are also deductible for tax computations. By reasoning similar to that used in connection with borrowed funds, it can be shown that any research done by the firm whose effective tax rate is 50 per cent actually costs the firm only 50 cents for each dollar spent. This applies also to research done for the firm by other organizations. This means that research can be a tremendous bargain for the firm, and the government effectively encourages it. This is the basis for the remark, "Research dollars are only 50-cent dollars."

DEPLETION

A firm engaged in mining, oil or gas production, or cutting timber may deduct from its income an allowance for depletion. The firm may choose either the method of cost depletion or the method of percentage depletion. Cost depletion involves simply dividing the total number of recoverable units in the property (tons, barrels, etc.) by the cost of the property. This is then multiplied by the number of units extracted during the tax year in question.

Percentage depletion involves a percentage of the gross income from the property shown in the following table:

Type of Property	*Percentage*
Oil and gas wells	27.5
Sulfur and uranium	23.0
Asbestos, lead, zinc, nickel, and mica (if from deposits in the United States)	23.0
Ball clay, china clay, and rock asphalt	15.0
Coal and sodium chloride	10.0
Brick and tile clay, gravel, clam and oyster shells, shale and sand	5.0

The depletion allowance is limited to 50 per cent of the taxable income from the property.

A variety of other tax provisions may be relevant to any given decision—for example, the provisions for taxing short- and long-term capital gains or losses, the treatment of repairs, replacements, and improvements, and so on. Our point, however, is simply to suggest their possible relevance for decision making and to encourage the analyst to consult the tax specialist.

SUGGESTIONS FOR FURTHER STUDY

BIERMAN, HAROLD, JR., and SMIDT, SEYMOUR. *The Capital Budgeting Decision.* New York: The Macmillan Co., 1960.

DAVIDSON, SIDNEY, and DRAKE, DAVID F. "Capital Budgeting and the Best Tax Depreciation Method," *Journal of Business,* Vol. 34, No. 4 (October, 1961).

ULLMAN, JOHN E. "Investment, Equipment Prices, and Income Tax," *The Engineering Economist,* Vol. 5, No. 3 (Winter, 1960).

WEAVER, JAMES B. "Why Taxes Must Be Considered in Profitability Studies," *The Engineering Economist,* Vol. 3, No. 1 (Summer, 1957).

PROBLEMS

8–1. A $100,000 building can be bought for $20,000 cash with the balance of $80,000 covered by a 20-year mortgage. Payments on the mortgage are $6,000 per year, of which, on the average, $1,800 is considered to be interest. The service life of the building is expected to be 20 years, with a salvage value of $5,000 at the end of that time. It is expected that operating costs for the building will run about $10,000 per year and that rental income will average $20,000 yearly. The building is being considered as an investment by a firm specializing in real estate operation. The firm estimates that a federal income tax rate of 50 per cent would be the rate applicable to the net profits from the building. If the firm wishes to earn 6 per cent on its investment after taxes, should it buy the building?

8–2.   A firm's taxable income for the coming year is estimated to be $22,000. If the firm were to undertake a project which would bring in an additional $6,000 in taxable income, what would be the effective federal income tax rate? What would be the project tax rate?

8–3.   Under what conditions should federal income taxes be considered in the analysis of decisions?

8–4.   An asset which costs $100,000 is ruled by the Internal Revenue Service to have a useful life of 10 years. Its salvage value will be $20,000 at the end of that time. What method of depreciation will be most advantageous from a tax viewpoint? Assume an interest rate of 8 per cent.

8–5.   A loan of $20,000 is to be repaid at 10 per cent interest in five equal annual payments. If the borrower is a firm whose effective tax rate is 50 per cent, what is the actual interest rate after taxes?

8–6.   Explain the effect of the tax laws on a firm's research and development program.

8–7.   A project requiring an investment of $16,000 is expected to have an earning life of 8 years and no salvage value. The estimated annual income from the project is $10,000 with annual operating expenses of $7,000, not including taxes.

   a) Find the rate of return on the project before taxes.

   b) Find the rate of return after taxes, if the effective tax rate is 50 per cent. The project is to be depreciated by the straight-line method over 8 years.

8–8.   The Revenue Act of 1962 permits a tax credit of 7 per cent of the purchase price of some equipment. This, however, reduces the depreciable investment for tax purposes by 7 per cent; thus depreciation is figured on the basis of 93 per cent of the investment in the equipment. (The reduction in depreciation was repealled in 1964.) If the tax credit is taken immediately by a firm, it is equivalent to a 7 per cent reduction in the purchase price of the equipment.

Consider the following equipment which is assumed to fall under the provisions of this law. The initial investment is $16,000; the service life is 8 years; and there is no salvage value. The equipment earns an annual revenue of $10,000 with operating expenses of $7,000 annually.

   a) Assuming straight line depreciation and an effective tax rate of 50 per cent, compute the rate of return after taxes (but without the tax credit).

   b) Compute the rate of return after taxes and tax credit.

8–9.   A firm feels that it can increase its net income before taxes by *K* dollars either by spending *D* dollars on research or by investing *D* dollars in new production equipment. Which will be best after taxes are considered?

8–10. It is proposed that a company use a computer for certain data-processing work for which it now spends $10,000 per year to have done by hand. The cost of operating the computer will be $3,000 per year. The firm may either buy the computer for $12,000 (it will last 3 years and have no salvage value) or rent the computer for $4,500 per year. Assume end-of-year payments. Which would you recommend under each of the following conditions:

a) No interest, no taxes.

b) The firm has internal funds available for investment, but requires at least a 10 per cent return. No taxes to be considered.

c) The firm has internal funds available. Its tax rate is 50 per cent, and it uses straight line depreciation for tax purposes. It requires 10 per cent return on internal funds.

d) The firm would have to borrow money to buy the computer at 10 per cent. Interest and principle repayment would be met with three equal, end-of-year payments. The tax rate is 50 per cent and the firm uses a 40 per cent fixed percentage of a declining balance depreciation method for tax purposes.

8–11. Consider the two machines below:

	Machine A	Machine B
Investment	$20,000	$20,000
Useful life	20 years	20 years
Salvage value	0	$2,000

If equal operating costs and revenues are assumed for each machine with a tax rate of 50 per cent, which machine would be preferred by a firm which uses an interest rate of 10 per cent in computing present worths? Assume straight line depreciation.

8–12. When using the fixed percentage of a declining balance depreciation method for taxes purposes, a firm may switch to straight line depreciation whenever it wishes. When is the best time to make such a switch? Why?

8–13. A machine requires an investment of $11,000 and has a salvage value of $1,000 at the end of five years. A firm begins to depreciate it using a fixed percentage rate of 40 per cent. Will it be advantageous for them to switch to straight line depreciation? If so, when?

8–14. Consider an asset which requires an investment of $10,000 and has a salvage value of $500 after 8 years. The firm wishes to compare two methods of depreciation, sum of the years' digits and fixed percentage of a declining balance using a 25 per cent rate and switching to straight line when advantageous.

a) Which would be preferred using an interest rate of .01?

b) Which would be preferred using an interest rate of .10?

c) If there were no salvage value, which would be preferred if service life were 8 years? If service life were 4 years? Assume 10 per cent interest rate.

Chapter 9

REPLACEMENT POLICY

INTRODUCTION

THE DECISION as to the best time to replace a machine has traditionally occupied a major portion of the attention of analysts in the field of management decisions. This is fundamentally due to the frequency with which this decision must be made by most firms, and the significant consequences of the decision. The formulation of a replacement policy plays a major part in the determination of the basic technological and economic progress of the firm. The aggregate of all such replacement policies in use, in turn, becomes a basic determinant of the level of activity of the entire producer goods segment of the economy, which is engaged in the manufacture of production equipment. Thus, when firms begin to defer the replacement of their equipment, the immediate result is a decline in the production of manufacturing equipment, which in turn leads to unemployment, and is often taken as one of the signals that a business recession is under way.

The consequences of an inadequate replacement policy for the firm are potentially disastrous. If the replacement is postponed beyond a reasonable time, the firm may find that its production costs rise, whereas the costs of its competitors who are using more modern equipment are declining. Thus, the firm is no longer able to meet price competition, and finds it impossible either to earn or borrow the funds with which to replace its machines. This is a technological and economic trap from which escape can be made only through the most drastic means.

A secondary reason for the extensive interest in replacement policy is that there are many fundamental assumptions upon which such a policy might be based. Analysts starting from differing basic assumptions have arrived at conclusions which naturally must differ also. Some basic assumptions lead to policies which are relatively easy to apply in practice, while others require the collection of information which is difficult to obtain and the execution of more complex computations. Thus, there has been an important element of controversy over replacement policy, which has stimulated its development, but has perhaps left those who are not specialists in the field a little mystified. We may best avoid pursuing these exchanges of viewpoint by laying out a range of fundamental assumptions upon which replacement policies may be based, and leaving, as always, the choice of assumptions and thus of policy to the analyst. This choice calls for the exercise of his judgment based on an appreciation of the details of the particular situation which he faces.

We will begin with a basic problem of the economic life of an asset and then introduce a variety of possible assumptions which might be used to enrich the analysis. Although the discussion will be carried on in terms of machine replacement, it is not hard to see that the ideas, in fact, apply to any decision involving the termination of one project in favor of another. It is customary to divide assets into two categories: those subject to gradual deterioration over their lives, such as machine tools, and those which suddenly fail, such as light bulbs. In this chapter we discuss only the first category of assets, leaving the second until Chapter 13.

ECONOMIC SERVICE LIFE

Let us begin with the problem of economic service life, which can be more precisely stated, "Find the service life for an asset which will minimize the average cost per period of service." Once an asset has been purchased, it is clear that the longer it is used, the more periods of service one has over which to spread the first cost of the asset. The problem of economic service life will only be interesting if there are some other costs which tend to rise with the age of the asset. For most machines, operating cost, maintenance cost, and the like tend to go up as the life of the machine progresses. Thus, there is an economic life where the declining capital recovery cost is offset by the increasing operation and maintenance costs, and the total of these costs is minimized. To show this, let

$$TC(n) = \text{total cost over the life of an asset which is}$$
$$\text{replaced after } n \text{ periods}$$
$$AC(n) = TC(n)/n \text{ average cost per period}$$
$$I = \text{initial investment in the asset}$$
$$c_j = \text{sum of operating and maintenance costs in}$$
$$\text{period } j$$

The problem is simply to choose n so as to minimize $AC(n)$. To make it simple we will assume that the interest rate is taken to be zero, that the asset has no salvage value at any time, that minimizing average cost per period is a reasonable objective, and that

$$c_j \geq c_{j-1} \qquad \text{for } j = 2, 3, \cdots\cdots\cdots$$

This last assumption simply indicates that operation and maintenance costs do not decrease with the age of the asset.

In these terms the total cost of an asset kept in service for n years may be written as:

$$TC(n) = I + \sum_{j=1}^{n} c_j$$

and

$$AC(n) = TC(n)/n = \frac{I}{n} + \frac{1}{n} \sum_{j=1}^{n} c_j$$

Now suppose we let N be the value of n which minimizes $AC(n)$. It must be true that

$$AC(N + 1) - AC(N) \geq 0$$

and

$$AC(N - 1) - AC(N) \geq 0$$

Substituting in the first of these conditions for a minimum, the expression for average cost, we have

$$\frac{I}{N + 1} + \frac{1}{N + 1} \sum_{j=1}^{N+1} c_j - \frac{I}{N} - \frac{1}{N} \sum_{j=1}^{N} c_j \geq 0$$

$$NI - (N + 1)I + N \sum_{j=1}^{N+1} c_j - (N + 1) \sum_{j=1}^{N} c_j \geq 0$$

$$-I + Nc_{N+1} - \sum_{j=1}^{N} c_j \geq 0$$

$$c_{N+1} \geq \frac{I + \sum_{j=1}^{N} c_j}{N} = AC(N)$$

Performing similar operations with the second of the conditions for a minimum we may obtain the result

$$c_N \leq AC(N)$$

Putting both of these inequalities together yields

$$c_N \leq AC(N) \leq c_{N+1}$$

The ideal replacement policy model would reflect the complex considerations of a firm's replacement problems in detail and thus approach a "best" or optimal policy. Yet at the same time an ideal model would be simple enough for easy data collection, computation, and understanding. Since these two goals are antithetical, the analyst must seek some compromise between them, balancing as he thinks best the two opposing effects.

In examining the models which follow, we will sometimes obtain both analytical solutions and direct evaluations for a range of alternative policies. The analytical solutions are useful for obtaining insights into the sense of policy deduced from the models, but, in most current applications, direct evaluations like that of Table 9-1 would be done by a computer. Numerous computer programs for these models are already available (74, 105), and the interested reader will find it rather easy to develop his own.

TABLE 9-1

n	I/n	$\sum_{j=1}^{n} c_j$	$\frac{1}{n}\sum_{j=1}^{n} c_j$	$AC(n)$
1.............	$1,000	$ 50	$ 50	$1,050
2.............	500	160	80	580
3.............	333	340	113	446
4.............	250	600	150	400
5.............	200	950	190	390
6.............	167	1,400	233	400
7.............	143	1,960	280	423

On this basis we may then formulate the following policy: *Replace at the end of any period for which the operation and maintenance costs in the next period exceed the average cost up to the time of replacement. Do not replace as long as the operation and maintenance costs in a period do not exceed the average cost to the end of the period.* If we interpret c_j, as the marginal cost of obtaining the service of the machine for period j, given that it has served to the end of period $j - 1$, then this policy will be recognized as an application of a familiar principle obtained in Chapter 2. The average cost will come down as long as marginal cost is below it. When marginal cost exceeds average cost, then average cost will begin to rise.

A simple example will illustrate this policy. Suppose a machine can be obtained for an investment of $1,000 and that the pattern of its operating and maintenance costs is predicted as follows:

j	1	2	3	4	5	6	7
c_j	\$50	\$110	\$180	\$260	\$350	\$450	\$650

Table 9–1 illustrates a complete set of average cost computations for this machine. In general, it would not be necessary to carry out all of these computations, for a good guess at economic life might lead quickly to an answer which could be shown to satisfy our conditions.

Inspection of the right-hand column will show that the average cost is minimum at the end of five years of service. Thus $N = 5$ and $AC(N) = \$390$ and the conditions previously derived are satisfied.

$$c_N = c_5 = \$350 \leq AC(N) = \$390 \leq c_{N+1} = c_6 = \$450$$

To restate the policy: *As long as the marginal cost is below the average cost, do not replace. When marginal cost exceeds average cost, then replace.* This analysis might be useful as a basis for replacement policy under the following conditions. Suppose the machine in question is utilized in an activity which is expected to continue for an indefinite period. When this machine is replaced it will be replaced by another which has been predicted to have identical investment and operating costs, and all future machines will have the same characteristics. Then the economic life calculated previously will be the optimal time of service for each machine in this indefinite sequence of machines. Since we assumed that we are planning for a series of identical machines, the best thing to do is to replace every N periods.

If we now modify this analysis by introducing a series of predicted salvage values for the machine at various points in its life, we obtain a slightly different result. If we take S_j to be the salvage value of the machine at the end of the jth period of service, then it can be shown that N must satisfy the following double inequality:

$$c_N + S_{N-1} - S_N \leq AC(N) \leq c_{N+1} + S_N - S_{N+1}$$

Note here that the marginal cost interpretation also applies since $S_{j+1} - S_j$ is simply the loss in salvage value suffered by extending the life of the asset by one more period. This added to the operating and maintenance costs is the marginal cost.

REPLACEMENT POLICY ASSUMPTIONS

The restrictive assumptions made to simplify the foregoing analysis indicate something of the possibilities for alternative bases upon which replacement policies might be based. We will now attempt to establish several important classes of assumptions and describe some of the alternatives within these classes.

1. *Planning Horizon.* By the planning horizon we simply mean the point in time furthest in the future which is considered in the formulation of policy. In some methods of analysis it is convenient to assume an infinite or indefinitely removed planning horizon. Sometimes, while we may not take this assumption too seriously, it may be convenient to use a mathematical method which is consistent with this view of the planning horizon. This assumption is used when we simply are unable to predict when the activity under consideration will be terminated. In other cases it may be clear that the project will have a definite and predictable duration and that the formulation of replacement policy might more realistically be based upon a finite planning horizon.

2. *Technology.* Assumptions with respect to technology refer to the development of the class of machines which are candidates to replace those under study. If we assume that all future machines will be the same as those now in service, then we are saying that there will be no technological progress in the area. However, we may wish to explicitly recognize that machines which may become available in the future are significantly more efficient, reliable, or productive than those now on the market. This assumption leads to the recognition of the phenomenon of obsolescence. Clearly, if the best available machine gets better and better all the time, our decision to replace the machine we now have may be considerably hastened. The difficulty is, of course, to quantify this phenomenon of obsolescence so that it can be applied analytically to the formulation of bases for policy.

3. *Predictions of Cost Patterns over Asset Life.* An infinite variety of predictions might be made of revenue, cost, salvage value, and so on over the life of an asset. Sometimes one wishes to assume that revenue is constant, that costs are nondecreasing, and that salvage value is nonincreasing over the life of a machine. In other cases it will be necessary to take account of a decline in revenue over life. This will determine whether the analysis is directed toward cost minimization or profit maximization. In the analysis which follows we will generally assume that operating and maintenance costs do not decrease with age and that salvage values do not increase with age. That is

$$c_{j+1} \geq c_j \qquad \text{for } j = 1, 2, \ldots$$
$$S_{n+1} \leq S_n \qquad \text{for } n = 1, 2, \ldots$$

These assumptions have the effect of assuring that most of the functions we will study will have unique minima.

4. *Interest Rate.* One may choose to assume an interest rate equal to a zero or nonzero rate. In analyses which contemplate an infinite planning horizon it is necessary to use a nonzero interest rate in order to obtain finite costs.

5. *Availability of Capital.* One may assume that sufficient capital is available either at no cost or at interest rate, i, to the firm in order to make any investments called for by a replacement policy. On the other hand, one may wish to recognize that capital is limited and must be allocated carefully among alternative investments. Thus, the replacement policy would have to recognize the limited availability of funds. One might wish to introduce explicitly the pattern of capital availability over time, and the costs of obtaining additional capital by various means (see Chapter 3).

This variety of possible assumptions may suggest a large number of possibilities for developing bases for replacement policy. We will not try to exhaust them all, but rather to exhibit a series of different formulations which may serve to introduce the various approaches which might be made. The reader may develop his own skill as a model builder by deducing policies based on assumptions other than those discussed.

IDENTICAL MACHINES, INTEREST, AND SALVAGE VALUE

Suppose we assume that an indefinite sequence of identical machines is contemplated and that the optimum service life is sought. Assume that the salvage value, S_j, is given, that the interest rate, i, is not zero, and that the operating and maintenance cost are nondecreasing with age of the machine. We now let $TC(n)$ stand for the present worth of all future costs associated with an indefinite sequence of identical machines, each of which is replaced after n years (periods).

$$TC(n) = I + \sum_{j=1}^{n} \frac{c_j}{(1+i)^j} - \frac{S_n}{(1+i)^n} + \frac{I}{(1+i)^n} + \sum_{j=1}^{n} \frac{c_j}{(1+i)^{n+j}}$$

$$- \frac{S_n}{(1+i)^{2n}} + \frac{I}{(1+i)^{2n}} + \sum_{j=1}^{n} \frac{c_j}{(1+i)^{2n+j}} - \frac{S_n}{(1+i)^{3n}} + \cdots \cdots$$

$$TC(n) = \left\{ I + \sum_{j=1}^{n} \frac{c_j}{(1+i)^j} - \frac{S_n}{(1+i)^n} \right\}$$

$$\left\{ 1 + \frac{1}{(1+i)^n} + \frac{1}{(1+i)^{2n}} + \cdots \cdots \right\}$$

This is a geometric series of the form ar^m where

$$a = I + \sum_{j=1}^{n} \frac{c_j}{(1+i)^j} - \frac{S_n}{(1+i)^n} \qquad r = \frac{1}{(1+i)^n}$$

and

$$S_\infty = \frac{a}{1-r}$$

Thus

$$TC(n) = S_\infty = \frac{I + \sum_{j=1}^{n} \dfrac{c_j}{(1+i)^j} - \dfrac{S_n}{(1+i)^n}}{\dfrac{(1+i)^n - 1}{(1+i)^n}}$$

Note that this has the following interpretation:

$$P = I + \sum_{j=1}^{n} \frac{c_j}{(1+i)^j} - \frac{S_n}{(1+i)^n}$$

is the present worth of all the expenses associated with the first asset.

$$P(1+i)^n = Q = \text{Future worth of } P \text{ after } n \text{ periods}$$
$$(1+i)^n - 1 = \text{Interest rate for } n \text{ periods}$$

Thus $TC(n)$ is the amount invested now which is equivalent to an indefinite sequence of payments, Q, at the end of every n periods.

If $N = $ optimal service life, then

$$TC(N+1) - TC(N) \geq 0 \qquad TC(N-1) - TC(N) \geq 0$$

Let

$$\frac{1}{1+i} = A$$

$$TC(N+1) = \left\{ I + \sum_{j=1}^{N+1} c_j A^j - S_{N+1} A^{N+1} \right\} \left\{ \frac{1}{1 - A^{N+1}} \right\}$$

$$= \left[\{TC(N)\}\{1 - A^N\} + c_{N+1} A^{N+1} + S_N A^N - S_{N+1} A^{N+1} \right] \left[\frac{1}{1 - A^{N+1}} \right]$$

$$TC(N+1) - TC(N) = \left\{ \frac{1 - A^N}{1 - A^{N+1}} - 1 \right\} \left\{ TC(N) \right\}$$

$$+ \left\{ c_{N+1} A^{N+1} + S_N A^N - S_{N+1} A^{N+1} \right\} \left\{ \frac{1}{1 - A^{N+1}} \right\} \geq 0$$

$$TC(N+1) - TC(N) = \{ A^{N+1} - A^N \}\{ TC(N) \} + c_{N+1} A^{N+1}$$
$$+ S_N A^N - S_{N+1} A^{N+1} \geq 0$$
$$= (A - 1) TC(N) + c_{N+1} A + S_N - S_{N+1} A \geq 0$$

For convenience these may be written

$$c_{N+1}A + S_N - S_{N+1}A \geq \frac{I + \sum_{j=1}^{N} c_j A^j - S_N A^N}{1 + A + A^2 + \cdots + A^{N-1}}$$

$$c_N A + S_{N-1} - S_N A \leq \frac{I + \sum_{j=1}^{N-1} c_j A^j - S_{N-1} A^{N-1}}{1 + A + A^2 + \cdots + A^{N-2}}$$

If, instead of a present worth basis of comparison, we wished to use an equivalent annual cost basis, it is only necessary to recall that if we let $AC(n)$ stand for the equivalent annual cost given replacement every n years, then

$$AC(n) = TC(n)i$$

It can then be easily shown that the foregoing conditions for N may be written as

$$AC(N) \leq c_{N+1} + S_N(1 + i) - S_{N+1}$$
$$AC(N - 1) \geq c_N + S_{N-1}(1 + i) - S_N$$

This may be directly interpreted as follows: *As long as the average cost is greater than the marginal cost of extending the life of the asset by one additional year, do not replace; as soon as the marginal cost of one additional year's service exceeds the average cost, the asset should be replaced.*

While this principle provides the desired insight into the basic considerations of replacement policy, the actual determination of the optimal policy may be easier to compute by the tabular method used previously.

EXAMPLE

Consider an indefinite sequence of machines, each of which requires an initial investment of $10,000. The salvage value at the end of year j in the life of a machine is given by

$$5000 - 500(j - 1)$$

and the operating and maintenance costs are given as follows:

j	1	2	3	4	5	6	7	8	9
c_j	$1,000	1,200	1,600	2,000	2,200	2,600	3,000	3,400	3,800

The computations leading to the optimal replacement policy are illustrated in Table 9–2, using an interest rate of 10 per cent. It should be noted that, having decided that the best time to replace a machine is some 5 or 10 years in the future, one does not simply forget the problem until that time arrives. The replacement policy decision is reviewed and the calculations redone from time to time, as new information becomes available. As one accumulates operating and maintenance history on a machine, as the market for used equipment changes, and as new models come on the market, the time for replacement may be reviewed.

TABLE 9–2

n	Col. 1 $I + \sum_{j=1}^{n} \dfrac{c_j}{(1+i)^j}$	Col. 2 $\dfrac{S_n}{(1+i)^n}$	Col. 3 Col. 1 − Col. 2	Col. 4 $\dfrac{i(1+i)^n}{(1+i)^n - 1}$	Col. 5 $AC(n) =$ Col. 3 · Col. 4
1	\$10,909	\$4,545	\$ 6,364	1.10000	\$7,000
2	11,901	3,719	8,182	.57619	4,714
3	13,103	3,005	10,098	.40211	4,060
4	14,469	2,391	12,078	.31547	3,810
5	15,835	1,863	13,972	.26380	3,686
6	17,303	1,411	15,892	.22961	3,649
7	18,842	1,026	17,816	.20541	3,660
8	20,428	700	19,728	.18744	3,698
9	22,040	424	21,616	.17364	3,753

IMPROVED CANDIDATE FOR REPLACEMENT, FINITE PLANNING HORIZON

So far we have assumed that all assets under consideration were identical. It is perhaps more realistic to recognize that often the replacement decision involves an asset now in use and a candidate for replacement which is in some ways better than the present asset. This, of course, reflects the technological progress which is continually under way. The current model of a machine is likely to be more effective than the past models, and one would expect it to be less effective than future models. In most areas this technological progress appears as a combination of gradual advances in effectiveness, together with the occasional technological "breakthrough" which revolutionizes the character of the machines. Similarly, the decision to replace a given asset may involve consideration of a candidate for replacement which is of an entirely different nature altogether. Thus, in considering replacement policy for a fleet of forklift trucks, the decision might involve replacement with conveyors rather than simply newer fork lifts.

Let us begin by supposing that a firm now has a machine in use on a process which is expected to terminate at some definite point, T, in the future. After T, the process will be discontinued and the requirement for a machine will cease to exist. Thus we have a finite planning horizon. There is presently on the market a newer machine which is in some ways more effective for the application being considered than the present machine. The problem then is, in view of the finite planning horizon, when, if at all, should the present machine be replaced with the newer one. To simplify the problem, let us further assume that the planning horizon is such that if the newer machine is obtained at any time, it will be retained until time T. Assume also that machines will now be appearing on the market prior to T which are significantly more effective than the one now on the market.

Recalling the discussion of sunk costs in Chapter 2, let the investment in the present machine, I_o, be taken as its realizable value on the used-machinery market at the present time. Let

c_{oj} = operating and maintenance costs for the present machine during the jth additional year of use

s_{oj} = salvage value of the present machine at the end of the jth additional year of use

I_1 = investment required to obtain the newer machine

c_{1j} = operating and maintenance cost for the newer machine during the jth year of use

s_{1j} = salvage value of the newer machine at the end of the jth year of use

Assume that the operating and maintenance costs for both machines are nondecreasing with time and that an interest rate, i, is to be used. The problem may then be posed as that of finding the number of additional years of service, n, from the present machine which will minimize the present worth of all costs over the planning period T. Clearly, if n turns out to be zero, the new machine should be introduced immediately; if it turns out to be T, the newer machine should not be used at all.

We may write the present worth of all costs as a function of n:

$$TC(n) = I_o + \sum_{j=1}^{n} \frac{c_{oj}}{(1+i)^j} - \frac{S_o}{(1+i)^n} + \frac{I_1}{(1+i)^n}$$

$$+ \sum_{j=1}^{T-n} \frac{c_{1j}}{(1+i)^{n+j}} - \frac{S_{1T-n}}{(1+j)^T}$$

If we let N stand for the optimal value of n, then as usual N must satisfy the following conditions:

$$TC(N + 1) - TC(N) \geq 0 \qquad TC(N - 1) - TC(N) \geq 0$$

These conditions lead to the following results:

$$c_{oN+1} + (1 + i)S_{oN} - S_{oN+1} \geq I_1 i - \frac{S_{1T-N} - S_{1T-N-1}}{(1 + i)^{T-N-1}}$$

$$+ \sum_{j=1}^{T-N} \frac{c_{1j}}{(1 + i)^{j-1}} - \sum_{j=1}^{T-N-1} \frac{c_{1j}}{(1 + i)^j}$$

and

$$c_{oN} + (1 + i)S_{oN-1} - S_{oN} \leq I_1 i - \frac{S_{1T-N+1} - S_{1T-N}}{(1 + i)^{T-N}}$$

$$+ \sum_{j=1}^{T-N} \frac{c_{1j}}{(1 + i)^j} - \sum_{j=1}^{T-N+1} \frac{c_{1j}}{(1 + i)^{j+1}}$$

Interpretation of these leads directly to the following principle: *As long as the cost of one additional year of use for the present machine is less than the savings resulting from postponing the purchase of the new machine one year, do not replace; when the cost of extending the use of the present machine for an additional year exceeds the savings resulting from postponing the purchase of the new machine, then the new machine should be purchased.*

EXAMPLE

Consider a firm which expects to engage in a certain production activity for eight more years, after which time the activity is to be discontinued. Presently used equipment could be sold immediately for $4,000 ($I_o$). Predicted salvage values and operating costs for this equipment are given in the following table.

j	c_{oj}	S_{oj}
1	$1,600	$3,500
2	2,000	3,000
3	2,200	2,500
4	2,600	2,000
5	3,000	1,500

New equipment is available with the following characteristics: $I_1 = \$8,000$

j	c_{1j}	S_{1j}
1	$ 800	$3,800
2	1,000	3,600
3	1,400	3,400
4	1,800	3,200
5	2,000	3,000
6	2,400	2,800
7	2,800	2,600
8	3,200	2,400

Now suppose we assume that the best pattern of replacement will be to retire the present equipment after n additional years, using the new equipment to complete the eight-year period. In general, one would want to investigate the possibility of using more than one of the new machines within the eight-year period, but we will assume that, for the moment, at most one new machine will be used.

Solving the problem, first using an interest rate of zero, we obtain Table 9–3. If interest is taken at 5 per cent, the results are as shown in Table 9–4.

TABLE 9–3

Col. 1	*Col. 2*	*Col. 3*	*Col. 4*
n	$I_o + \sum\limits_{j=i}^{n} c_{oj} - S_{oj}$	$I_1 + \sum\limits_{j=1}^{T-n} c_{1j} - S_{1T-n}$	*Col. 2 + Col. 3*
0	0	\$21,000	\$21,000
1	\$ 2,100	17,600	19,700
2	4,600	14,600	19,200
3	7,300	12,000	19,300
4	10,400	9,800	20,200
5	13,900	7,800	21,700

IMPROVED CANDIDATE FOR REPLACEMENT, INDEFINITE PLANNING HORIZON

Now let us reformulate the previous problem with somewhat different assumptions. Consider a present machine in use as before and a newer machine which is taken as the first of an indefinite sequence of identical machines. The problem now falls into two parts: finding the best time to replace the present machine, and determining the economic life of the newer machine once it has been placed in service. Let

n = number of years of additional service required of the present machine

N_1 = optimal service life for the newer machine

$AC(N_1)$ = annual cost of the newer machine based upon replacement with an identical machine every N_1 years

We may then write the present worth of all costs as a function of n in the following form:

$$TC(n) = I_o + \sum_{j=1}^{n} \frac{c_{oj}}{(1+i)^j} - \frac{S_{on}}{(1+i)^n} + \frac{AC_1(N_1)}{i(1+i)^n}$$

Table 9-4

n	Col. 1 $I_o + \sum_{j=1}^{n} \dfrac{c_{oj}}{(1+i)^j}$	Col. 2 $\dfrac{S_{on}}{(1+i)^n}$	Col. 3 Col. 1 − Col. 2	Col. 4 $\dfrac{I_1}{(1+i)^n}$	Col. 5 $\sum_{j=1}^{T-n} \dfrac{c_{1j}}{(1+i)^{n+j}}$	Col. 6 $\dfrac{S_{1T-n}}{(1+i)^T}$	Col. 7 Col. 4 + Col. 5 − Col. 6	Col. 8 Col. 3 + Col. 7
0	0	0	0	$8,000	$11,866	$1,624	$18,242	$18,242
1	$ 5,524	$3,333	$ 2,191	7,619	9,238	1,760	15,097	17,288
2	7,338	2,721	4,617	7,256	6,999	1,895	12,360	16,977
3	9,238	2,159	7,079	6,910	5,119	2,030	9,999	17,078
4	11,377	1,645	9,732	6,581	3,586	2,165	8,002	17,734
5	13,728	1,175	12,553	6,268	2,254	2,301	6,221	18,774

where

$$AC_1(N_1) = \left\{ I_1 + \sum_{j=1}^{N_1} \frac{c_{ij}}{(1+i)^j} - \frac{S_{1N_1}}{(1+i)^{N_1}} \right\} \frac{i(1+i)^{N_1}}{(1+i)^{N_1} - 1}$$

The optimal service life for the new machine, N_1, may be found by the method presented previously and thus the value of $AC_1(N_1)$ may be computed.

Letting N be the optimal value of n, and using the conditions

$$TC(N+1) - TC(N) \geq 0 \qquad TC(N-1) - TC(N) \geq 0$$

we obtain the following results:

$$c_{oN} + S_{oN-1}(1+i) - S_{oN} \leq AC_1(N_1) \leq c_{oN+1} + S_{oN}(1+i) - S_{oN+1}$$

This then suggests that the present machine should be kept as long as the marginal cost of one additional year of service is less than the annual cost for the newer machine. The present machine should be replaced when the marginal cost of one additional year of service exceeds the average annual cost of the newer machine.

EXAMPLE

Taking the same problem which was formulated in the previous section, let us now assume an infinite planning horizon. Using an interest rate of 0 per cent, Table 9–5 shows that the newer machine

TABLE 9–5

Col. 1	Col. 2	Col. 3
n	$I_1 + \sum_{j=1}^{n} c_{ij} - S_{1n}$	$AC_1(n) = $ Col. 2/n
1....................	$ 5,000	$5,000
2....................	6,200	3,100
3....................	7,800	2,600
4....................	9,800	2,450
5....................	12,000	2,400
6....................	14,600	2,433
7....................	17,600	2,514
8....................	21,000	2,625

should be kept five years. Thus we consider that when the newer machine is installed, it is the first of an indefinite sequence of such machines where a replacement is made every five years. The average annual cost for such a chain of machines is $2,400. In Table 9–6 it is shown that the marginal cost for one year of additional

service from the present machine is \$2,100. Since this is less than
\$2,400, it would be wise to keep the present machine for at least
one more year. The marginal cost of a second year of additional
service from the present machine is, however, \$2,500. This leads to

TABLE 9–6

n	$AC_o(n)$	$C_{on} + S_{on-1} - S_{on}$
1...................	\$2,100	\$2,100
2...................	2,300	2,500
3...................	2,433	2,700
4...................	2,600	3,100
5...................	2,780	3,500

TABLE 9–7

n	Col. 1 $\displaystyle\sum_{j=1}^{n} \frac{c_{1j}}{(1+i)^j}$	Col. 2 $\dfrac{S_{1n}}{(1+i)^n}$	Col. 3 $I_1 + $ Col. 1 $-$ Col. 2	Col. 4 $AC_1(n)$
1..............	\$ 762	\$3,619	\$ 5,143	\$5,400
2..............	1,669	3,265	6,404	3,444
3..............	2,878	2,937	7,941	2,914
4..............	4,359	2,632	9,727	2,743
5..............	5,926	2,350	11,576	2,674
6..............	7,717	2,089	13,628	2,685
7..............	9,700	1,848	15,852	2,742
8..............	11,866	1,624	18,242	2,828

TABLE 9–8

n	c_{on}	S_{on}	$c_{on} + S_{on-1}(1+i) - S_{on}$
0.................	0	\$4,000	0
1.................	\$1,600	3,500	\$2,300
2.................	2,000	3,000	2,675
3.................	2,200	2,500	2,850
4.................	2,600	2,000	3,450
5.................	3,000	1,500	3,600

the conclusion that the present machine should be kept for only one
more year. The average cost for the present machine is also included
in Table 9–6 to show that it is *not* relevant in the decision.

Tables 9–7 and 9–8 show the corresponding calculations when an
interest rate of 5 per cent is used.

OBSOLESCENCE

The previous analysis suggests immediately the following generalization. In actuality, the newer machine under consideration is not the first in an indefinite sequence of identical machines. More likely, continuation of technological progress will place upon the market a whole sequence of machines, each one in some ways more effective than its predecessor. The automobile industry with its custom of yearly model changes is the outstanding example of this phenomenon. If one compares one's automobile with the new models each year, the comparison is less and less favorable as the years pass, for two reasons. The car itself is growing older and thus its operating and maintenance costs are rising in comparison to those of a new car. The new cars may be getting better each year in the sense of having lower operating and maintenance costs than the previous year's model. Thus, the car looks worse and worse, partly because it is getting older and partly because the new models are getting better as time passes. It seems only reasonable that this latter phenomenon, usually called "obsolescence," should be taken into consideration in developing a replacement policy.

The greatest obstacle to be overcome here is that of predicting the economic effects of future technological progress in a particular field. As we have suggested, this progress often involves both a gradual long-run improvement of future machines and infrequent dramatic advances which have a revolutionary effect on the technology. The latter class of events is believed by many to be virtually impossible to predict very far in advance. As we shall see in an example which follows, predictions can be made of the more gradual type of technological advance, but only with great difficulty in some areas. Recognizing the underlying obstacles here, let us illustrate the kind of analysis which would result for a very simple linear prediction of technological improvement. It must be emphasized that such a linear prediction is only illustrative, and it is in no sense argued that technological progress in any particular area proceeds in this way. Of course, one would expect that a linear prediction would lead to a relatively simple problem of analysis, and this is in fact the case. Analyses of this general nature have been developed and widely advocated by the Machinery and Allied Products Institute. (129,130)

To make the analysis very simple, let us ask the question, "What is the economic life of a machine which is one of a technologically developing sequence having a constant rate of improvement over time?" Suppose we assume that any machine in the sequence will require the same initial investment and that no salvage values are involved at any time. We also assume that for any machine its operating and maintenance costs increase linearly with age. For example:

Year of Use	Operating Cost
1	First-year cost
2	First-year cost $+ a$
3	First-year cost $+ 2a$
4	First-year cost $+ 3a$
.	. . .
j	First-year cost $+ (j - 1)a$

We may now reflect on the assumptions about obsolescence in the statement that the first-year operating cost of a machine decreases in a linear fashion with calendar time (years). Thus:

Time of Purchase (Manufacture)	First-Year Operating Cost
Beginning of year 1	c
Beginning of year 2	$c - b$
Beginning of year 3	$c - 2b$
Beginning of year 4	$c - 3b$
.	. . .
Beginning of year k	$c - (k - 1)b$

In general, then, the operating cost for the jth year of use of a machine which was purchased new at the beginning of year k is given by

$$c + (j - 1)a - (k - 1)b$$

It should be emphasized again that this prediction is only illustrative.

Suppose we wish to establish a policy of replacing this class of machines every n years with the best model that is then available on the market. It should be noted that it is not necessarily clear at the outset that it will be optimal in any sense to have n be a constant; however, this will be established as the analysis goes on. We seek the value of n, say N, which will minimize the following present worth:

$$TC(n) = I + \sum_{j=1}^{n} \frac{c + (j - 1)a}{(1 + i)^j} + \frac{I}{(1 + i)^n} + \sum_{j=1}^{n} \frac{c + (j - 1)a - nb}{(1 + i)^{n+j}}$$

$$+ \frac{I}{(1 + i)^{2n}} + \sum_{j=1}^{n} \frac{c + (j - 1)a - 2nb}{(1 + i)^{2n+j}} + \frac{I}{(1 + i)^{3n}} + \cdots .$$

This reduces to

$$TC(n) = \left\{ I + \sum_{j=1}^{n} \frac{c + (j-1)a}{(1+i)^j} \right\} \frac{(1+i)^n}{(1+i)^n - 1} - \sum_{k=1}^{\infty} \sum_{j=1}^{n} \frac{knb}{(1+i)^{kn+j}}$$

This may be expressed as an annual cost using the relation

$$TC(n)i = AC(n)$$

yielding

$$AC(n) = \left\{ I + \sum_{j=1}^{n} \frac{c + (j-1)a}{(1+i)^j} \right\} \frac{i(1+i)^n}{(1+i)^n - 1} - \left\{ \sum_{k=1}^{\infty} \sum_{j=1}^{n} \frac{knb}{(1+i)^{kn+j}} \right\} i$$

The usual method of solving this problem is to substitute for it another problem which can be shown to have the same solution. The basis for this substitution is the following argument. The annual operating cost of a machine may be thought of as being composed of two parts. The first part is what we have already designated as annual operating cost in the usual sense, using the expression

$$c + (j-1)a$$

for the first machine. In addition one might argue that by keeping a machine, rather than replacing it with the best model then available, one is in fact giving up the opportunity to realize the savings in operating cost which result from technological advance. Thus it is argued that the operating costs of the first machine increase not only with age, but in terms of opportunities foregone for the realization of lower operating costs through replacement. On the basis of this opportunity cost argument, the operating costs and the opportunity (obsolescence) costs for the first machine may be expressed as

$$c + (j-1)(a+b)$$

It is further argued that the problem of finding the economic service life for an indefinite sequence of identical machines, whose costs behave in this way, will have a solution which is also the solution to the original problem which we posed. The truth of this assertion is established by means of a proof given in Appendix B.

Thus we are led to pose the substitute problem of finding the value of n, say N, which will minimize the present worth given by

$$TC(n) = \left\{ I + \sum_{j=1}^{n} \frac{c + (j-1)(a+b)}{(1+i)^j} \right\} \frac{(1+i)^n}{(1+i)^n - 1}$$

This may be expressed in annual cost form as

$$AC(n) = \left\{ I + \sum_{j=1}^{n} \frac{c + (j-1)(a+b)}{(1+i)^j} \right\} \frac{i(1+i)^n}{(1+i)^n - 1}$$

Based upon our previous analysis, we can state immediately that the value of n we seek must satisfy the relations

$$AC(N) \le c + N(a+b) \qquad AC(N-1) \ge c + (N-1)(a+b)$$

This value of N is thus the basis for an optimal replacement policy under the conditions of linearly increasing operating costs and linear technological advancement. Note that, in the substitute problem, the optimality of a constant N has been previously established. Given that the substitute problem yields a solution to the original problem, then it follows that constant N is optimal for the original problem also.

EXAMPLE

Consider a technologically developing sequence of machines, each of which will require an initial investment of \$10,000, and will have no salvage value at any time. Suppose that the operating and maintenance costs for the jth year of a machine purchased at the beginning of year k are given by

$$1,000 + (j-1)(190) - (k-1)(10)$$

That is: $a = \$190$ and $b = \$10$. We are interested in finding an optimal replacement policy. Let us make the additional simplifying assumption that the interest rate is zero.

As suggested previously, we formulate the substitute problem of finding the economic life for an indefinite sequence of machines for which

$$
\begin{aligned}
I &= \$10,000 \\
c_j &= 1,000 + (j-1)(200) \\
S_j &= 0, \text{ for all } j
\end{aligned}
$$

Solving the substitute problem by the usual tabular method we obtain Table 9–9. For a solution we have $N = 10$ years, which is also taken to be the solution to the original problem. It should be noted that the annual cost for 10 years does not apply to the original problem.

As a check on the validity of the substitute problem let us compute the answer directly. Consider a planning horizon of 30 years. Suppose we were to replace every five years, thus utilizing six machines over the 30-year period. The first of these machines would have operating costs of \$1,000, \$1,190, \$1,380, \$1,570, and \$1,760 respectively in the five years of its use. The average of these costs is \$1,380, and the annual cost of investment recovery is \$2,000, yielding an average annual cost of \$3,380. The second machine which is purchased at the beginning of year six, has operating costs of \$950, \$1,140, \$1,330, \$1,520, and \$1,710 in the respective years of its use. For the second machine the average annual cost turns out to be

TABLE 9–9

n	I/n	c_i	$\sum_{j=1}^{n} \dfrac{c_i}{n}$	$AC(n)$
1............	\$10,000	\$1,000	\$1,000	\$11,000
2............	5,000	1,200	1,100	6,100
3............	3,333	1,400	1,200	4,533
4............	2,500	1,600	1,300	3,800
5............	2,000	1,800	1,400	3,400
6............	1,667	2,000	1,500	3,167
7............	1,429	2,200	1,600	3,029
8............	1,250	2,400	1,700	2,950
9............	1,111	2,600	1,800	2,911
10............	1,000	2,800	1,900	2,900
11............	909	3,000	2,000	2,909
12............	833	3,200	2,100	2,933
13............	770	3,400	2,200	2,970
14............	714	3,600	2,300	3,014
15............	667	3,800	2,400	3,067

\$3,330. The average annual cost for each of the six machines is as follows:

Machine Number	Purchased at Beginning of Year	Average Annual Cost
1.........................	1	\$3,380
2.........................	6	3,330
3.........................	11	3,280
4.........................	16	3,230
5.........................	21	3,180
6.........................	26	3,130

Now the grand average of these annual costs can easily be shown to be \$3,255.

Now consider exactly the same computations based on a 10-year replacement period. The results are

Machine Number	Purchased at Beginning of Year	Average Annual Cost
1.........................	1	\$2,855
2.........................	11	2,755
3.........................	21	2,655

The grand average of these costs is \$2,755.

TABLE 9–10

Col. 1	Col. 2	Col. 3	Col. 4	Col. 5	Col. 6	Col. 7
n	$\dfrac{c_i}{(1+i)^i}$	$\displaystyle\sum_{i=1}^{n} \dfrac{c_i}{(1+i)^i}$	$\dfrac{i(1+i)^n}{(1+i)^n - 1}$	Col. 3 · Col. 4	I · Col. 4	$AC(n) =$ Col. 5 + Col. 6
1	$ 943.40	$ 943.40	1.06000	$1,000.00	$10,600.00	$11,600.00
2	1,068.00	2,011.40	.54544	1,097.10	5,454.40	6,551.50
3	1,175.44	3,186.84	.37411	1,192.23	3,741.10	4,933.33
4	1,267.36	4,454.20	.28859	1,285.44	2,885.90	4,171.34
5	1,345.14	5,799.34	.23740	1,376.76	2,374.00	3,750.76
6	1,410.00	7,209.34	.20336	1,466.09	2,033.60	3,499.69
7	1,463.22	8,672.56	.17914	1,553.60	1,791.40	3,345.00
8	1,505.76	10,178.32	.16104	1,639.12	1,610.40	3,249.52
9	1,538.94	11,717.26	.14702	1,722.67	1,470.20	3,192.87
10	1,563.52	13,280.78	.13587	1,804.46	1,358.70	3,163.16
11	1,580.40	14,861.18	.12679	1,884.25	1,267.90	3,152.15
12	1,590.40	16,451.58	.11928	1,962.34	1,192.80	3,155.14
13	1,593.92	18,045.50	.11296	2,038.42	1,129.60	3,168.02

Repeating the process for a 15-year replacement period we obtain:

Machine Number	Purchased at Beginning of Year	Average Annual Cost
1........................ 1		$2,997
2........................16		2,847

Here the grand average is $2,922.

Let us now compare the annual costs obtained in the solution of the original problem, with those obtained in the solution of the substitute problem.

Replacement Period	Annual Cost from Substitute Problem	Annual Cost from Original Problem	Difference
5 yrs..................	$3,400	$3,255	$145
10.....................	2,900	2,755	145
15.....................	3,067	2,922	145

These computations are perhaps sufficient to suggest that we are dealing with two functions of n which differ only by a constant. It follows then that both functions must take a minimum for the same value of n. Thus, the solution of the substitute problem must also be the solution to the original problem.

The solution to the substitute problem using an interest rate of 6 per cent is shown in Table 9–10.

EXAMPLE

To illustrate an actual application of this analysis to replacement policy we will describe briefly an investigation carried on by Smith (121) leading to a replacement policy for a fleet of motor trucks. For a motor freight line it is possible to estimate the revenue earned by a truck, thus the study was formulated with the objective of profit maximizing rather than cost minimizing. It was desired also to include specifically the considerations of obsolescence and interest in the analysis.

Suppose that the profit earned annually by a truck depends both on the age of the truck and on the year of its manufacture. Let

$$P(kn, j) = \text{profit earned by a truck manufactured at the}$$
$$\text{end of year } kn \text{ during the } j\text{th year of its life}$$
$$\text{(revenue less operating costs)}$$

Then the present worth of the income from such a truck which is kept in service for n years is given by

$$\left\{ \sum_{j=1}^{n} \frac{P(kn, j)}{(1+i)^j} - I + \frac{S^n}{(1+i)^n} \right\} \frac{1}{(1+i)^{kn}}$$

For an indefinite sequence of trucks replaced every n years, the present worth of the future income stream is given by

$$\sum_{k=0}^{\infty} \left[\left\{ \sum_{j=1}^{n} \frac{P(kn, j)}{(1+i)^j} - I + \frac{S_n}{(1+i)^n} \right\} \frac{1}{(1+i)^{kn}} \right]$$

The problem is then to find the value of n, say N, which will maximize this quantity. (In the original formulation, n was treated as a continuous variable. We have made n discrete in order to be consistent with our previous analysis.)

On the basis of a very careful study of technological developments in motor trucks during the period from 1943 to 1952, it was suggested that two important kinds of progress had been made. First, through the use of lighter equipment, more axles, and longer trailers combined with shorter tractors, it had been possible to increase the payloads without violating the legal restrictions on weight and size. Using data from the Interstate Commerce Commission, it was shown that average load had risen significantly over this period. The rise in average load was successfully approximated by a linear function of the form

$$A + BT$$

where T denotes the year. Clearly, this increase in average load might be traced to factors such as increases in legal weight limits; however, it seemed reasonable to ascribe a major portion of it to the technological developments mentioned previously. Thus, it was assumed that the average load carried by a vehicle manufactured at the end of year kn was given by

$$A + Bkn$$

From the data used, a value of $B = .09$ resulted. The average annual mileage for a truck in the firm studies was 105,000 miles and the average revenue was $\$.0183$ per ton-mile. Thus it may be said that technological progress of this particular sort increases the annual profit available from the newest model trucks at the rate of

$$(.09)(105,000)(.0183) = \$173 \text{ each year}$$

The second type of technological progress in the motor truck field stemmed from developments in engines. These developments took the form of decreased fuel consumption for a given set of operating conditions and an increase in engine horsepower. With respect to fuel consumption the data revealed that most of the decrease in this area had been wiped out by the increase in average load. It was also clear that some of the decrease was due to improvements in the fuel itself, rather than in the engines. For these reasons the net decrease in fuel consumption was shown to be negligible.

On the other hand, it was to be expected that horsepower increases would permit increases in speed and thus an increase in the productivity of a truck. It was shown that the travel time of a truck measured in minutes per mile was related to the ratio of gross weight to net horsepower in the following simple manner:

$$\text{Travel time} = A_1 + B_1 \text{ (gross wt/net HP)}$$

In this relation the coefficients depend on the rate of rise and fall for the roads traveled. It could also be shown that, as the technology progressed over time, the weight-horsepower ratio did in fact fall linearly:

$$\text{(Gross wt/net HP)} = A_2 + B_2 T$$

It could then be established that each year the technology of engines developed to the extent that a new truck had an annual profit of \$39 more than the previous year's model, as a direct result.

From these two sources it was estimated that obsolescence for motor trucks increases at the rate of approximately \$200 per year. It is important to note that, during the period studied, the technology made gradual progress. No dramatic advances occurred, thus the linear prediction of technological development seemed appropriate.

A study of the records of operating expenses for the truck fleet revealed that two costs increased with the age of a truck: fuel costs and maintenance costs. It was possible to show that fuel consumption in gallons per mile depended on cumulative mileage in the following way:

$$\text{Fuel consumption} = A_3 + B_3 \text{ (cumulative mileage)}$$

For the fleet under study, cumulative mileage depended only on the age of the truck. Each truck averaged 105,000 miles per year, thus cumulative mileage at the end of year j was simply $105,000(j)$.

Repair costs under the particular maintenance policies in use by the firm tended to rise at a decreasing rate with cumulative mileage. Eventually, repair costs tended to level off. Repair costs in dollars per mile could be adequately described by the relation

$$\text{Repair cost} = A_4(1 - e^{-B_4 M})$$

where M is cumulative mileage.

The salvage value predictions were obtained from a study of the used-truck market. This study showed that the resale value of a truck dropped dramatically during the first year, and then tended to decline at a constant rate with age. The salvage value after the initial drop is approximated by the function

$$S_j = (A_5 - B_5 j)I$$

Considering the obsolescence effects and the fuel and repair costs, it can be shown that the profit for the jth year of use of a truck manufactured at the end of year kn takes the form

$$P(kn,j) = K + knb - c_j$$

From the foregoing relations it may be deduced that b is of the order of \$200. The operating and maintenance costs for year j, c_j, are taken to be the sum of the fuel costs and the repair costs for year j. Thus,

$$c_j = \int_{j-1}^{j} \{A_3 + B_3 M + A_4(1 - e^{-B_4 M})\}dj$$

Recalling that M stands for cumulative mileage, and is given in this case simply by the relation

$$M = mj = (105{,}000)j$$

we may write

$$c_j = \int_{j-1}^{j} \{A_3 + B_3 mj + A_4(1 - e^{-B_4 mj})\}dj$$

Based upon Smith's data, we obtain from this equation the following predictions for the annual operating and maintenance costs:

Year

1	$c + \$38$
2	$c + \$1{,}178$
3	$c + \$1{,}495$
4	$c + \$1{,}598$
5	$c + \$1{,}662$

where c is a constant which will not influence the solution.

The salvage values, as a function of the initial investment, are given approximately by the following table:

Year	Salvage Value
1	$.5444 I$
2	$.4738 I$
3	$.4032 I$
4	$.3326 I$
5	$.2620 I$

In order to find the optimal replacement policy for the trucks, we substitute the problem of finding the economic life for an infinite sequence of trucks, each of which requires an initial investment I, has salvage values as shown previously, and has years profits as follows:

Year	Profit
1	$K - (c + 38)$
2	$K - 200 - (c + 1178)$
3	$K - 400 - (c + 1495)$
4	$K - 600 - (c + 1598)$
5	$K - 800 - (c + 1662)$

Since neither K nor c will influence the solution, we may omit both constants and proceed to solve a cost-minimization problem. If we assume that interest is neglected, the calculations leading to a minimum average annual cost are as shown in the following table:

n	$\dfrac{I - S_n}{n}$	c_j	$AC(n) = \dfrac{I}{n} + \dfrac{1}{n}\sum_{j=1}^{n} c_j$
1	$2,787	$ 38	$3,025
2	1,725	1,378	2,483
3	1,304	1,895	2,408
4	1,094	2,198	2,471
5	968	2,462	2,562

Since we have taken time to be discrete, we may then suggest that the trucks should be replaced at the end of three years of service. The problem is solved, again using an interest rate of 8 per cent, in Table 9–11.

TABLE 9–11

n	Col. 1 $\dfrac{S_n}{(1 + i)^n}$	Col. 2 $\sum_{j=1}^{n} \dfrac{c_j}{(1 + i)^i}$	Col. 3 $I - $ Col. 2 $+$ Col. 3	Col. 4 $AC(n)$
1	$3,401	$ 35	$ 3,190	$3,445
2	2,663	1,217	5,110	2,865
3	2,098	2,721	7,178	2,785
4	1,602	4,336	9,290	2,805
5	1,169	6,012	11,399	2,855

Examination of Table 9–11 shows one of the interesting considerations which emerge in the practical development of replacement policy. Under the assumptions which have been made it is clear that the optimum replacement interval is three years. Note, however, that if a truck is kept for four years, or even five, the increase in annual cost is moderate. Thus, the firm might postpone replacement from three years to four years and in doing so incur additional costs amounting to only $20 per year per vehicle. This possibility leads to several interesting thoughts.

It seems reasonable that, even if the firm uses relatively crude methods for determining a replacement policy, they are unlikely to suffer serious financial loss from so doing. Though it clearly matters when replacement is made, it might be said that, if the firm misses the optimum interval by a year or so in either direction, the extra costs will be relatively small. If this phenomenon is widespread, then we may be quite satisfied with simple and approximate replacement theories.

Futher, it seems clear that, if the firm finds it increasingly expensive to obtain capital or encounters serious problems in budgeting limited amounts of capital, then one source of funds is simply to delay replacement. In fact, this may be a relatively inexpensive and readily accessible source of capital as long as replacement is not postponed too far beyond the flat portion of the equivalent annual cost function.

GENERAL REPLACEMENT MODEL

At this point it is possible to generalize our replacement model to include technological changes which might be reflected not only in the pattern of operating and maintenance costs but also in changes in initial investment and the pattern of salvage values. Under these conditions it may be that the replacement interval would change as well.

Let

I_t = initial investment in a machine purchased at the end of period t

c_{tj} = operation and maintenance costs for the jth year of a machine purchased at the end of period t

S_{tj} = salvage value at the end of the jth year of use for a machine purchased at the end of period t

N_k = life of the kth machine in the sequence of replacements

We would then have a generalized present worth function which might be written

$$TC(N_1, N_2, \cdots, N_k, \cdots) = I_0 + \sum_{j=1}^{N_1} \frac{c_{0j}}{(1+i)^j}$$

$$- \frac{S_{0N_1}}{(1+i)^{N_1}} + \frac{I_{N_1}}{(1+i)^{N_1}} + \sum_{j=1}^{N_2} \frac{c_{N_1 j}}{(1+i)^{N_1+j}}$$

$$- \frac{S_{N_1 N_2}}{(1+i)^{N_1+N_2}} + \frac{I_{N_2}}{(1+i)^{N_1+N_2}} + \sum_{j=1}^{N_3} \frac{c_{N_2 j}}{(1+i)^{N_1+N_2+j}} - \cdots$$

This function may be the sum of an infinite series if the planning horizon is infinite, otherwise it may be carried out to a finite planning horizon. While it is perfectly general, it suffers from the usual difficulty of requiring some very troublesome predictions. It is not possible to write a general solution for it in any interesting form. Further, there are good practical reasons suggested by the previous example for questioning the advantage of the additional detail and expense it would require. It does, however, suggest some of the range of possible bases which one might use in developing a replacement policy. One might do well, however, to keep in mind that the data for many complex replacement models are highly speculative. A detailed, refined replacement model may be little better than a simple one if the major source of error is unreliable data.

SUGGESTIONS FOR FURTHER STUDY

DEAN, BURTON V. "Replacement Theory," *Progress in Operations Research* ed. R. L. ACKOFF), Vol. I. New York: John Wiley and Sons, Inc., 1961.

MAYER, RAYMOND R. "Problems in the Application of Replacement Theory," *Management Science*, Vol. 6, No. 3 (April, 1960).

REISMAN, ARNOLD, and BUFFA, ELLWOOD S. "A General Model for Investment Policy," *Management Science*, Vol. 8, No. 3 (April, 1962).

TERBORGH, GEORGE. *Dynamic Equipment Policy.* New York: McGraw-Hill Book Co., 1949.

PROBLEMS

9–1. Find the optimal time to replace a machine which cost $2.000 initially and has the following estimated operating costs and salvage values:

Year	Operating Cost	Salvage Value
1	$400	$500
2	500	450
3	600	400
4	700	350
5	800	300
6	900	200

Use interest at 0 per cent. State explicitly any assumptions you make.

9–2. Find the economic service life of a machine that requires an initial investment of $4,000, has no salvage value at any time, and has operating and maintenance costs of

Year	1	2	3	4	5	6
Cost	$300	$500	$800	$1,200	$1,800	$2,300

Assume zero interest rate.

9–3. A firm expects to enter into an activity which will last 13 years. It has no suitable equipment available but can purchase a machine requiring an investment of $3,000. The machine will have no salvage value at any time, and its annual operating costs are as follows:

Year	1	2	3	4	5	6
Annual operating costs	$500	$900	$1,300	$1,300	$1,500	$2,000

If interest is at zero per cent, what is the best pattern of replacements?

9–4. A firm uses a large hydraulic press which was purchased some years ago at a cost of $25,000. It has been offered a chance to have the work now done on this press performed by an outside contractor at a cost of $5,800 per year. The firm learns that the present market value of the press is $15,000. The operating cost and salvage value for the next five years of use are predicted in the table below.

Year	Operating Cost	End-of-Year Salvage Value
1	$2,000	$12,000
2	3,000	9,000
3	4,000	6,000
4	6,000	4,000
5	8,000	2,000

If the interest rate is zero, what should the firm do over the next five years?

9–5. Show that the limit of the equivalent annual cost as the interest rate approaches zero is the present worth divided by the replacement interval. (Hint: use l'Hospital's rule.)

9–6. Consider a machine requiring an initial investment of $10,000 with operating costs given by

$$C_j = 2000 + 200(j - 1)$$

and salvage values given by

$$S_n = 8000 - 1000(n - 1) \quad \text{for } n \leq 9$$

Assuming an infinite planning horizon, static technology, future machines identical to present machine, interest rate of 1 per cent, and no capital limitation, find the optimum replacement interval.

9–7. Which of the two machines described below would you recommend a firm purchase if the firm requires 10 per cent on its investments?

	Machine A	Machine B
Investment	$29,000	$18,500
Operating costs	$4,000 per year for the first 4 years increasing by $1,000 per year after that	$6,000 per year for the first 5 years increasing by $1,000 per year after that
Salvage value	None at any time	None at any time

9–8. A mine is expected to produce for 15 more years. A major item of equipment is needed which requires an investment of $50,000. The equipment will have no salvage value (nor can it be removed when the mine ceases to produce), and its annual operating costs are as follows:

Year	1	2	3	4	5	6
Annual operating costs	$8,000	$11,000	$18,000	$18,000	$20,000	$24,000

If interest is at zero per cent, what is the best pattern of replacements?

9–9. A firm estimates it can save $50,000 per year in handling costs by purchasing a fleet of ten forklift trucks. Each truck will cost $5,000, will last ten years, and will be financed with funds on which the firm requires at least 5 per cent interest. Should the fleet be purchased if the cost and salvage value histories are as indicated below?

Year	Net Realizable Value at Year End	Operating Costs during Year
1	$2,200	$2,500
2	1,500	2,700
3	1,000	3,100
4	600	3,600
5	400	3,900
6	200	4,100
7	100	4,250
8	0	4,400
9	0	4,500
10	0	4,600

9–10. One class of machines used in large numbers by a manufacturer has a purchase price of $10,000 and cost and salvage value histories shown below.

Year	Salvage Value	Operating Cost
1	$7,000	$10,000
2	5,000	10,000
3	4,000	10,000
4	3,000	14,000
5	2,000	16,000

When a machine is installed there are costs of $2,000, and when one is removed the cost is $1,000. What replacement policy would you recommend if interest is 10 per cent?

9–11. A particular boring machine may be purchased for $25,000. Its salvage value is expected to decline at a constant rate to a level of $5,000 at the end of ten years. Annual operating costs are

Direct labor	$4,000
Indirect labor	500
Power consumption	600
Maintenance	$1,500 + 150(j - 1)$

Here j denotes the age of the machine. With interest of 10 per cent, what is the economic life of the machine?

9–12. Find the economic life of the machine described in problem 9–11, if the salvage values, direct and indirect labor costs, and power consumption are as given, but the maintenance cost prediction is

$$\$1,500 + 200(j - 1)$$

9–13. An asset can be purchased for \$50,000 which is expected to earn a revenue of

$$R_j = 45,000 - 3,000j$$

in the jth year of operation. Operating costs for the jth year will be

$$c_j = 7,000j$$

It will have no salvage value at any time. If interest is taken to be 5 per cent, find the service life which will maximize the equivalent annual profit.

9–14. What will be the effect of the federal corporate income tax on the decision of problem 9–13 above?

9–15. Find the optimal replacement interval for a type of machine for which the following data is given:

Initial Cost = \$90,000

Year	Annual Operating Cost
1	\$36,000
2	36,000
3	39,000
4	42,000
5	45,000
6	51,000
7	60,000
8	60,000
9	61,000
10	62,000

Salvage Value = $\$45,000 - 3,000(j - 1)$ $j \leq 10$

a) If $i = .10$
b) If $i = .05$
c) If $i = 0$
d) If $i = .10$ and all operating costs are increased by 10 per cent.
e) If $i = .10$ and all operating costs are decreased by 10 per cent.
f) If $i = .10$ and all salvage values are increased by 10 per cent.
g) If $i = .10$ and all salvage values are decreased by 10 per cent.
h) If $i = .10$ and the investment is reduced by 7 per cent.

9–16. By installing a mechanized handling system in a part of its production process, a firm estimates that it can replace several manual operations now costing about \$12,000 per year. The mechanized system will cost \$10,000, and it will have no salvage value. Its operating costs will be \$1,000 for the first year and will increase by \$300 each year after that. Assuming an interest rate of 6 per cent, what replacement interval would you recommend for the system?

9–17. A firm is presently using a machine which has a market value of $8,000 to do a specialized production job. The requirement for this operation is expected to last only six more years after which it will no longer be done. The predicted costs and salvage values for the present machine are

Year	1	2	3	4	5
Operating cost	$1,000	$1,200	$1,400	$1,800	$2,300
Salvage value	$5,000	$4,500	$4,000	$3,300	$2,500

A new machine has been developed which can be purchased for $12,-000 and has the following predicted cost performance:

Year	1	2	3	4	5	6
Operating cost	$ 500	$ 700	$ 900	$1,200	$1,500	$1,900
Salvage value	$11,000	$10,500	$10,000	$9,500	$8,500	$7,500

a) If interest is at 0 per cent, when should the new machine be purchased?

b) When, if interest is at 5 per cent?

9–18. A manufacturer moves the materials in his production operations using a fleet of forklift trucks. He has consistently used the same make and model of forklift over the past several years. Their purchase price is about $8,000 each, and the records of operation and repair indicate the following average annual expenses as a function of the age of the vehicle:

Year	1	2	3	4	5	6	7	8
Operating costs	$3,000	$3,000	$3,500	$4,000	$4,500	$5,250	$6,250	$7,750

Assuming that these costs can be reasonably used as a basis for prediction, find the best time to replace the fork lifts under each of the following conditions:

a) Interest at 0 per cent and no salvage value at any time.

b) Interest at 7 per cent and no salvage value.

c) Interest at 0 per cent and year-end salvage values as follows:

Year	1	2	3	4	5	6	7	8
Salvage value	$4,700	$3,200	$2,200	$1,450	$950	$600	$300	0

d) Interest at 7 per cent and salvage value as in part (*c*).

9–19. Consider an indefinite sequence of machines, each requiring an initial investment of $20,000. Assume no salvage value at any time, and an interest rate of zero. Operation and maintenance costs are predicted by the function

$$C_j = 2,000 + 4,000(j - 1) - 120(j - 1)^2$$

a) What is the best replacement policy if a given machine will last for at most ten years?

b) What would be your guess as to the best replacement policy if a machine would last up to twenty years?

9–20. A new machine is available which requires an investment of $20,000 and for which the following predictions have been made.

Year	Operating Cost	Salvage Value
1	$11,000	$15,000
2	11,500	11,000
3	12,000	8,000
4	13,000	6,000
5	15,000	4,000

a) What is the economic life of the machine if interest is 10 per cent?

b) When (if at all) should the old machine below be replaced with the new machine?

Present market value = $5,000

Year	Operating Cost	Salvage Value
1	$12,000	$4,000
2	14,000	3,000
3	16,000	2,000
4	17,000	1,500
5	18,000	1,000

9–21. For heavy milling jobs a firm uses two mills which were purchased in 1920 at a cost of $2,500 each. They may be sold on the present market for $1,500 each, and their resale value is expected to decline at the rate of about 10 per cent per year in the future. The firm is considering replacing these with a single modern machine which will cost $150,-000 (installed) and will last up to 20 years. The salvage value of this machine is expected to decline by an equal amount each year to a level of $30,000 at the end of 20 years. Other relevant costs are as follows:

Annual Costs	Old Machines (Total for both)	New Machine
Direct labor	$33,000	$13,000
Indirect labor	4,000	1,200
Maintenance	5,000	2,000
Tooling costs	0	4,000
Power consumption	3,000	4,500

If the firm uses an interest rate of 6 per cent, what is its best choice at this point?

9–22. Consider a machine costing $18,000 with the predicted operating costs and salvage values indicated below.

Year	Operating Cost	Salvage Value
1	$ 3,000	$9,000
2	3,600	4,500
3	4,200	2,250
4	5,400	1,125
5	6,900	600
6	8,400	600
7	10,200	600
8	12,000	600

Interest may be neglected.

a) Find the economic life of such a machine.

b) A company is now using three of these machines, one of which is one year old and two are two years old. It is considering the proper time to replace the three old machines with two new machines which have just become available. Each of the new machines costs $24,000 but has a capacity 50 per cent greater than one of the old machines. Data for the new machines are shown below:

Year	Operating Cost	Salvage Value
1	$ 3,600	$12,000
2	4,500	6,000
3	5,400	3,000
4	7,200	1,500
5	9,300	900
6	12,000	900
7	15,000	900
8	18,300	900

When should the three old machines be replaced with the two new ones?

9–23. Plot operating cost as a function of time for a sequence of machines which are replaced every n years and subject to obsolescence at a constant rate. The operating cost in the jth year of use of a machine produced in year k is given by

$$c + a(j - 1) - b(k - 1)$$

9–24. Find the optimal replacement interval for machines which require an initial investment of $5,000, have no salvage value, and have annual operating costs given by

$$c_j = 800 + 80(j - 1)$$

The effects of obsolescence are reflected in a decline in the first year operating cost of each year's new model by $120. Interest is 8 per cent.

9–25. Consider a machine which requires an investment of $10,000 but has no salvage value. Operating costs are given by

$$c_j = 1000 + 600(j - 1)$$

Obsolescence reflected in declining operating costs is equivalent to $400 per year. Find the optimal replacement policy if

a) $i = .01$
b) $i = .10$

9–26. A trucking firm wishes to establish a replacement policy for its vehicles. The initial investment in a truck is $10,000 and is expected to change little in the future. The salvage value is given by

$$S_n = 5000 - 500(n - 1)$$

The first year operating cost of the current model is $1,000. As trucks grow older their operating costs are expected to increase each year by $600. As new models are introduced, technological developments are expected to lower operating costs by $400 each model year. If you consider an indefinite planning horizon with interest at two per cent, what policy would you suggest?

9–27.   Consider an indefinite sequence of machines, each having a purchase price of $15,000 but no salvage value at any time. Operating costs are given by

$$c_j = 1500 + 200(j - 1) - 100T$$

where

$$j = \text{age } (j = 1, 2, \dots)$$
$$T = \text{year of manufacture } (T = 0,1,2, \dots)$$

Using an interest rate of 6 per cent find the optimal replacement policy.

9–28.   A firm is presently using a machine which has a market value of $6,000 to do a specialized production job. The requirement for this operation is expected to last only eight more years after which it will no longer be done. The predicted costs and salvage values for the present machine are

Year	1	2	3	4	5
Operating cost	$1,800	$2,200	$2,400	$2,800	$3,200
Salvage value	$4,500	$4,000	$3,500	$3,000	$2,500

A new machine has been developed which can be purchased for $10,000 and has the following predicted cost performance:

Year	1	2	3	4	5	6	7	8
Operating cost	$1,000	$1,200	$1,600	$2,000	$2,200	$2,600	$3,000	$3,400
Salvage value	$9,600	$9,200	$8,800	$8,400	$8,000	$7,600	$7,200	$6,800

a) If interest is at 0 per cent, when should the new machine be purchased?

b) When, if interest is at 5 per cent?

9–29.   Show mathematically how you would develop a replacement policy based upon the following assumptions:

a) Infinite planning horizon.

b) Technological progress reflected in declining operating costs over the next k years, ceasing after that time.

c) Nonzero salvage values.

d) Nonzero interest rate.

9–30.   Show mathematically how you would develop a replacement policy based on the following assumptions:

a) Infinite planning horizon.

b) Technological progress reflected in a "breakthrough" which is expected to bring a significant reduction in operating costs three years hence.

c) No salvage values.

d) Nonzero interest rate.

9–31. What is the general effect on the analysis of this chapter if the assumption that operating costs do not decrease with age is dropped?

9–32. Construct a replacement model based on the following assumptions:

a) Infinite planning horizon.

b) Investment in new machines increases linearly with time.

c) Salvage value declines with age at the rate of 10 per cent of initial investment per year.

d) For all machines

$$c_j = a + b(j - 1)$$

e) No capital limitation.

9–33. Formulate a replacement model which reflects the following conditions:

a) Annual model changes reduce investment at a constant rate.

b) Operating costs increase at a constant rate with age.

c) Salvage value declines by 10 per cent of the original investment each year.

d) Nonzero interest rate.

e) No capital limitation.

9–34. Convert the identical-machine, no-salvage-value, non-zero-interest-rate model into a profit maximizing model by including a predicted revenue R_j which depends on the age of the machine.

9–35. Production of a certain product is planned at a steady annual rate of 20,000 units for the indefinite future. Two machines are being considered for which the following data are available.

	Machine A	Machine B
Investment	$20,000	$30,000
Annual operating cost	$8,000 + 500(j - 1)$	$6,000 + 1,000(j - 1)$
Salvage value	$18,000 - 2,000\,n$	$25,000 - 1,000\,n$
Set-up cost per run	100	400
Annual capacity	30,000 units	40,000 units

Storage costs for the product are $1.00 per unit per year, based on the average amount stored. Machine capacity not used for the product in question can be used for other work at a profit of $.10 per unit equivalent. If you take interest at zero per cent, what would be your advice to management? Support your advice with quantitative evidence.

Chapter 10

A REVIEW OF PROBABILITY THEORY

INTRODUCTION

FOR THE MATHEMATICIAN, the theory of probability is a branch of abstract mathematics which deals with relationships between numbers called probabilities. These probabilities arise out of primitive and uninterpreted notions, and lead to a formal structure, of interest in itself. For those interested in the analysis of decisions, the importance of probability theory stems from the possibility of interpreting its statements in terms of some of the events which arise in connection with decisions. As soon as one recognizes that many interesting decisions must be made with something less than perfect and complete information, the need arises for a method of dealing with decisions which fall somewhere between perfect information and complete ignorance. These decisions we have called "decisions under conditions of risk." Probability theory provides a way of measuring and talking about the risk involved in a decision. Decision makers traditionally have spoken about running the calculated risk, without exhibiting any very explicit calculation. Probability theory simply provides a logical structure which, if interpreted in terms of observed happenings, can be used to calculate the risk.

The well-worn example of flipping a coin serves best to illustrate. One feels quite sure that if such a coin were flipped a very large number of times, it would come up heads roughly half of the time and tails the other half. When a decision must be made as to which way to wager, heads or tails, on a single flip of a coin, we interpret these events in terms of probabilities. Although we do not carry out the flipping experiment, we are usually willing to say that the probability of heads is one half. We are saying that we do not have perfect information as to the outcome of the next flip, nor are we willing to be called completely ignorant in the matter. We do claim that

230

if we wager heads repeatedly, approximately one half of the time we will be right and one half of the time, wrong. This becomes the expression of the calculated risk. The theory then provides theorems which permit the computation of probabilities for more complicated events, such as the probability of heads three times in a row, or the probability of heads coming up five times in eight flips.

This interpretation of probability theory is called the "relative frequency interpretation." To be more precise, the relative frequency interpretation requires one to think in terms of an experiment which can be repeated. If the experiment is repeated indefinitely, the relative frequency of an outcome is called its probability. In fact, probability is defined as the limit of the relative frequency of an outcome as the number of replications goes to infinity. In applying this definition, the notion of experiments has to be taken quite broadly to include those experiments which yield observations as a result of our manipulations (coin flipping), and those experiments from which we get observations without actually manipulating things ourselves (astronomy, birth rates). All sorts of repeated observations have the possibility of being linked with the theory of probability.

The relative frequency definition has a significant difficulty for one breed of practical decision makers, who may be called "the empiricists." If in fact, probabilities are defined as the limits of relative frequencies, and if we take this definition seriously, how will they ever be measured? Nothing could be more inconvenient than having to flip a coin an infinite number of times in order to get the probability of a head. Even if we are willing to take a guess at what the limit would be, of what use is the result if we are going to make only a small number of decisions involving risk? Probabilities tell us about long-run behavior, whereas we are often clearly interested in the short run. This creates some important problems in connection with decisions under risk, which we shall investigate in Chapter 11.

If, instead of wagering on the flip of a coin, one wished to wager on a football game, a new problem arises. The decision maker with an abiding interest in football will neither admit that he feels completely ignorant of the outcome of the game, nor will he claim that he has complete information as to the winner. If the wager is to be viewed as a decision under risk, the relative frequency definition of probability hardly fits. It is difficult to imagine an appropriate experiment which could be repeated a number of times. Even if one could arrange to have the teams play several games, the results would be questionable. The teams would learn each other's strategies and capabilities, and injuries would perhaps change the composition of their forces. In such situations, the decision maker may still wish to speak of the probability that his team will win, but in doing so we think of him as stating a personalistic or subjective probability. Personalistic probabilities may be very roughly defined as the decision maker's judgments, guesses, or feelings about the likelihood of a future event. There are real difficulties at present with defining the notion of personalistic probability more clearly, measuring it, and then discovering whether or not the results behave in the way the theorems of probability theory suggest. More will be said of this in Chapter 20. For simplicity, we will proceed with the relative frequency interpretation in mind.

ORGANIZING THE DATA

We begin by considering an experiment which can have a finite number of possible outcomes, $S_1, S_2, \ldots, S_j, \ldots, S_m$. This is the sort of thing we find when we study a newsboy's business, and find that he sells 23 or 24 or 25 or . . . or 32 papers each day. (He wonders how many papers to buy; see Chapter 14.) If the experiment were repeated N times, the number of times each of the outcomes occurred could be counted. The results might be summarized in a graph, or histogram, such as that in Figure 10–1.

If we take the frequency of S_j and divide it by N, we have an estimate of the probability of S_j. To get the actual probability of S_j, under a serious interpretation of the relative frequency definition, we would have to find

$$\text{Probability of } S_j = p(S_j) = \lim_{N \to \infty} \frac{\text{frequency of } S_j}{N}$$

Nevertheless, using the observed relative frequency as our best estimate of the probability, we can go on as though we knew $p(S_j)$.

If S_j is a number, as in the newsboy example, we may compute the mean of the S_j (also called the average or expected value) which measures the central tendency of the data.

$$\text{Mean of the } S_j = E(S) = \sum_{j=1}^{m} S_j p(S_j)$$

The mean has the property that the sum of the deviations of the data around it is zero.

$$\sum_{j=1}^{m} \{S_j - E(S)\} p(S_j) = 0$$

The variability of the data may be expressed by the variance, σ^2.

$$\sigma^2 = \sum_{j=1}^{m} \{S_j - E(S)\}^2 p(S_j)$$

The square root of the variance is called the standard deviation. We will also be interested in the probability that the outcome, S, will be less than or equal to some S_k. This is given by

$$P(S \leq S_k) = \sum_{j=1}^{k} p(S_j)$$

(See the Addition Theorem, p. 239.)

In an experiment which can have an infinity of possible outcomes, each expressible by a number, we represent the outcomes by a con-

FIGURE 10–1

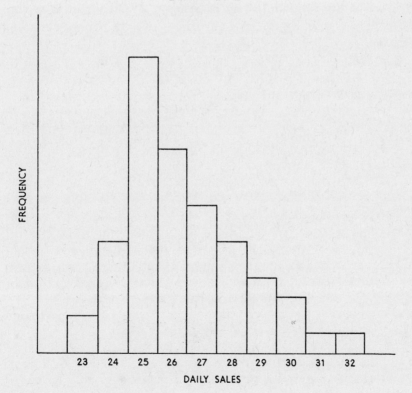

tinuous variable, S. The histogram above them becomes a function of S, which yields the probability distribution, $p(S)$. We then have:

$$\text{Mean of } S = E(S) = \int_{S} Sp(S)dS$$

$$\text{Variance of } S = \sigma^2 = \int_{S} \{S - E(S)\}^2 p(S)dS$$

$$P(S \leq S_k) = \int_{S=-\infty}^{S_k} p(S)dS$$

$p(S)$ is often referred to as the "probability density function," or simply the "density function." The function $P(S \leq S_k)$ is sometimes called the "cumulative function" or simply the "distribution function."

SOME USEFUL DISCRETE DISTRIBUTIONS

Below are three frequently encountered probability distributions, each of which is based on the assumption that the outcomes of an experiment are represented by a variable, x, which can take on a finite number of values. Such a variable is called a "discrete random variable."

UNIFORM DISTRIBUTION

$$p(x) = \frac{1}{n+1}$$

$$\text{for } x = a, a+1, a+2, \ldots, a+n-1, a+n$$

$$E(x) = a + \frac{n}{2}$$

$$\sigma^2 = \frac{n^2}{12} + \frac{n}{6}$$

This applies to experiments in which all outcomes are equally likely. For example, when a single die is rolled, the numbers 1, 2, 3, 4, 5, 6 occur with equal probability. The probability is $\frac{1}{6}$. The numbers in a table of random numbers have a uniform distribution.

BINOMIAL DISTRIBUTION

$$p(x) = \frac{n!}{x!(n-x)!} p^x (1-p)^{n-x}$$

$$\text{for } x = 0, 1, 2, \ldots, n$$

$$E(x) = np$$

$$\sigma^2 = np(1-p)$$

If a coin is flipped n times, the probability of obtaining x heads is given by the binomial. If we have a batch of castings, a proportion p of which are defective, the probability of finding x bad castings, if we take a random sample of n of them from the batch, is also given by the binomial distribution.

Assuming that the probability of obtaining oil when a well is drilled is .10, and that this probability applies to all wells, one may compute the probability of bringing in one well in five drillings.

$$x = 1 \qquad n = 5 \qquad p = .10$$

$$p(1) = \frac{5!}{1!4!}\,(.10)^1(.90)^4 = .328$$

This is the probability of finding oil exactly once in five drillings. It might be interesting to know also the probability of finding oil at least once in five attempts.

$$p(x \geq 1) = 1 - p(x = 0) = 1 - \frac{5!}{0!5!}\,(.10)^0(.90)^5 = 1 - .59 = .41$$

POISSON DISTRIBUTION

$$p(x) = e^{-m}\frac{m^x}{x!}$$

$$\text{for } x = 0, 1, 2, \ldots, \infty$$

$$E(x) = m$$

$$\sigma^2 = m$$

If we have a telephone switchboard serving a large number of subscribers, we might find that the number of incoming calls in an interval of time of length t was a random variable having a Poisson distribution. The mean might well be proportional to t. Thus

$$\text{Probability of } x \text{ calls in an interval } t = e^{-kt}\frac{(kt)^x}{x!}$$

Figure 10–2 shows the cumulative probability curves for the Poisson distribution. These curves may be used to evaluate the probability that x will be c or less.

$$P(x \leq c) = \sum_{x=0}^{c} e^{-m}\frac{m^x}{x!}$$

To use the chart, let pn equal m, the mean of the distribution. The chart is entered on the horizontal axis at the mean of the probability distribution in question. The intersection of the ordinate at this point with the curve for the desired value of c will yield the cumulative probability of the vertical axis.

FIGURE 10-2

Cumulative Probability Curves—Poisson Exponential*

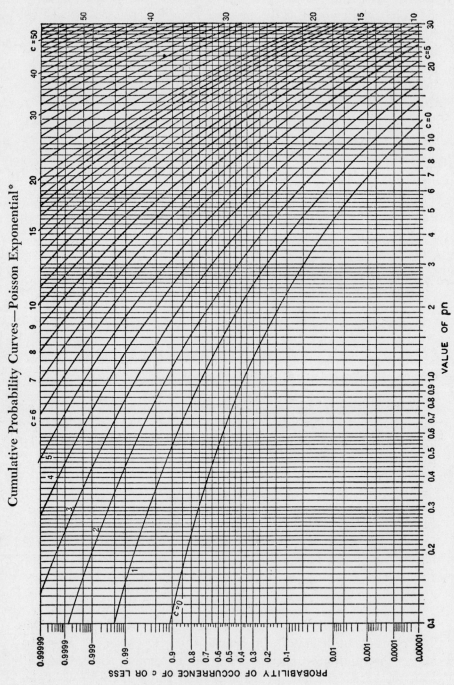

* For determining probability of occurrence of *c* or less defects in a sample of *n* pieces selected from an infinite universe in which the fraction defective is *p*. (A modification of a chart given by Miss F. Thorndike *B.S.T.J.*, October, 1926). Reprinted with permission from H. F. Dodge and H. G.

SOME CONTINUOUS DISTRIBUTIONS

If the outcome of an experiment is a continuous variable and if the values taken by this variable can be described by a probability distribution, then it may be called a "continuous random variable." The following are three of the more useful continuous probability distributions:

FIGURE 10–3

Uniform Distribution

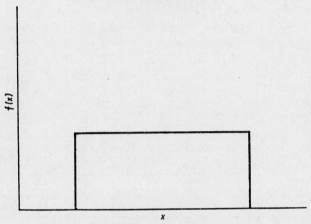

UNIFORM DISTRIBUTION

$$f(x) = \frac{1}{b - a} \qquad \text{for } a \leq x \leq b$$

$$E(x) = \frac{a + b}{2}$$

$$\sigma^2 = \frac{(b - a)^2}{12}$$

FIGURE 10–4

Normal Distribution

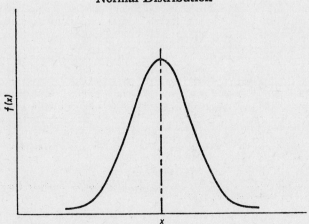

$$f(x) = \frac{1}{\sqrt{2\pi}\sigma} e^{-\frac{(x-\mu)^2}{2\sigma^2}} \quad \text{for } -\infty \leq x \leq \infty$$

$$E(x) = \mu$$

$$\sigma^2 = \sigma^2$$

Table 10–1 gives cumulative probabilities for the standard normal distribution.

Table 10–1

Cumulative Probabilities for the Standard Normal Distribution*

Normal Deviate z	.00	.01	.02	.03	.04	.05	.06	.07	.08	.09
0.0	.5000	.4960	.4920	.4880	.4840	.4801	.4761	.4721	.4681	.4641
0.1	.4602	.4562	.4522	.4483	.4443	.4404	.4364	.4325	.4286	.4247
0.2	.4207	.4168	.4129	.4090	.4052	.4013	.3974	.3936	.3897	.3859
0.3	.3821	.3783	.3745	.3707	.3669	.3632	.3594	.3557	.3520	.3483
0.4	.3446	.3409	.3372	.3336	.3300	.3264	.3228	.3192	.3156	.3121
0.5	.3085	.3050	.3015	.2981	.2946	.2912	.2877	.2843	.2810	.2776
0.6	.2743	.2709	.2676	.2643	.2611	.2578	.2546	.2514	.2483	.2451
0.7	.2420	.2389	.2358	.2327	.2296	.2266	.2236	.2206	.2177	.2148
0.8	.2119	.2090	.2061	.2033	.2005	.1977	.1949	.1922	.1894	.1867
0.9	.1841	.1814	.1788	.1762	.1736	.1711	.1685	.1660	.1635	.1611
1.0	.1587	.1562	.1539	.1515	.1492	.1469	.1446	.1423	.1401	.1379
1.1	.1357	.1335	.1314	.1292	.1271	.1251	.1230	.1210	.1190	.1170
1.2	.1151	.1131	.1112	.1093	.1075	.1056	.1038	.1020	.1003	.0985
1.3	.0968	.0951	.0934	.0918	.0901	.0885	.0869	.0853	.0838	.0823
1.4	.0808	.0793	.0778	.0764	.0749	.0735	.0721	.0708	.0694	.0681
1.5	.0668	.0655	.0643	.0630	.0618	.0606	.0594	.0582	.0571	.0559
1.6	.0548	.0537	.0526	.0516	.0505	.0495	.0485	.0475	.0465	.0455
1.7	.0446	.0436	.0427	.0418	.0409	.0401	.0392	.0384	.0375	.0367
1.8	.0359	.0351	.0344	.0336	.0329	.0322	.0314	.0307	.0301	.0294
1.9	.0287	.0281	.0274	.0268	.0262	.0256	.0250	.0244	.0239	.0233
2.0	.0228	.0222	.0217	.0212	.0207	.0202	.0197	.0192	.0188	.0183
2.1	.0179	.0174	.0170	.0166	.0162	.0158	.0154	.0150	.0146	.0143
2.2	.0139	.0136	.0132	.0129	.0125	.0122	.0119	.0116	.0113	.0110
2.3	.0107	.0104	.0102	.0099	.0096	.0094	.0091	.0089	.0087	.0084
2.4	.0082	.0080	.0078	.0075	.0073	.0071	.0069	.0068	.0066	.0064
2.5	.0062	.0060	.0059	.0057	.0055	.0054	.0052	.0051	.0049	.0048
2.6	.0047	.0045	.0044	.0043	.0041	.0040	.0039	.0038	.0037	.0036
2.7	.0035	.0034	.0033	.0032	.0031	.0030	.0029	.0028	.0027	.0026
2.8	.0026	.0025	.0024	.0023	.0023	.0022	.0021	.0021	.0020	.0019
2.9	.0019	.0018	.0018	.0017	.0016	.0016	.0015	.0015	.0014	.0014
3.0	.0013	.0013	.0013	.0012	.0012	.0011	.0011	.0011	.0010	.0010

* The normal deviate z has $\mu = 0$ and $\sigma = 1$. The table gives the integrals from z up to infinity. For example, the probability that z will be equal to or greater than 1.52 is .0643. To transform a normal variable x, having mean μ and standard deviation σ, to z, the following relation is used:

$$z = \frac{x - \mu}{\sigma}$$

Reproduced from Kurnow, Glasser, and Ottman, *Statistics for Business Decisions* (Homewood, Ill.: Richard D. Irwin, Inc., 1959).

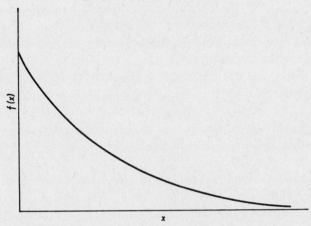

FIGURE 10–5

Exponential Distribution

EXPONENTIAL DISTRIBUTION

$$f(x) = m \, e^{-mx} \qquad \text{for } 0 \leq x \leq \infty$$
$$E(x) = \frac{1}{m} \qquad m > 0$$
$$\sigma^2 = \frac{1}{m^2}$$

SOME USEFUL THEOREMS

Some of the theorems of probability theory which will be especially useful in the remaining sections of this book are discussed in the following paragraphs. This should not be taken as an orderly or complete exposition of the theory, but simply as a basis for recollection of its most pertinent parts.

THEOREM I—THE ADDITION THEOREM

The simplest form of the addition theorem applies to mutually exclusive events or outcomes. Two outcomes are said to be mutually exclusive if they cannot both occur on a single trial or experiment.

If S_1 and S_2 are any two mutually exclusive outcomes, the probability that either S_1 or S_2 occurs is $p(S_1 + S_2) = p(S_1) + p(S_2)$.

If the newsboy sells 23 papers with probability .05 and 24 papers with probability .10, then the probability that he will sell either 23 or 24 papers is .15. As long as these numbers refer to, say, total daily sales, then they are clearly mutually exclusive.

A more general version of the addition theorem is not restricted to mutually exclusive outcomes.

If S_1 and S_2 are any two outcomes, the probability that either S_1 occurs or that S_2 occurs or that they both occur is $p(S_1 + S_2) = p(S_1) + p(S_2) - p(S_1 \cdot S_2)$ *where* $p(S_1 \cdot S_2)$ *stands for the probability that both S_1 and S_2 occur.*

A consumer survey investigating the ownership of automatic washers and dryers for a sample of 100 families finds the following results:

	Washer	No Washer
Dryer.....................18		34
No dryer................. 2		46

The numbers in the table represent numbers of families. Suppose we are willing to accept these data as the basis for estimating some probabilities. (Actually we would want to make some statistical tests.)

Probability that a family has a washer $= p(W) \quad = \dfrac{18 + 2}{100} = \dfrac{20}{100}$

Probability that a family has a dryer $\quad = p(D) \quad = \dfrac{18 + 34}{100} = \dfrac{52}{100}$

Probability that the family has both $\quad = p(W \cdot D) = \dfrac{18}{100}$

If we are interested in the probability that a family has either a washer or a dryer or both, the theorem suggests.

$$p(W + D) = p(W) + p(D) - p(W \cdot D) = \frac{20}{100} + \frac{52}{100} - \frac{18}{100} = \frac{54}{100}$$

This may be confirmed by noting that

$$p(W + D) = p(W \cdot D) + p(NW \cdot D) + p(W \cdot ND)$$

$$= \frac{18}{100} + \frac{34}{100} + \frac{2}{100} = \frac{54}{100}$$

THEOREM II—THE MULTIPLICATION THEOREM

If S_1 and S_2 are two independent outcomes, then the probability that both S_1 and S_2 occur is $p(S_1 S_2) = p(S_1)p(S_2)$.

If a coin is flipped twice, clearly there is no way in which the outcome of the first flip can influence the outcome of the second. The two flips are independent events in the sense of the multiplication theorem. Thus, the probability that the first flip will result in heads and that the second flip will result in heads is

$$p(H \cdot H) = (1/2)(1/2) = 1/4$$

Independence in this sense, which is called "independence in the probability sense," must be distinguished from independence in the functional sense. In speaking of functions such as $y = f(x)$ we are interested in the functional dependence of y, the dependent variable, on x, the independent variable. Independence in the probability sense means that the occurrence of an outcome, S_1, in no way adds to our knowledge of the occurrence of S_2, or its nonoccurrence. That is, the probability of S_2 is in no way changed if we are given the information that S_1 has occurred, or that it has not occurred. In terms of conditional probabilities this means

$$p(S_2|S_1) = p(S_2)$$

If $S_1, S_2, \ldots, S_j, \ldots, S_m$ form a set of mutually exclusive and collectively exhaustive events, then

$$\sum_{j=1}^{m} p(S_j) = 1$$

If $S_1 \ldots S_m$ represent the outcomes in a decision under risk, if no more than one of them can occur on any decision, and if they together exhaust all the possible outcomes, then clearly their probabilities must sum to one. Some outcome must occur, and it must be one or another of those listed, thus, by the addition theorem, their probabilities should total one.

A certain electronic system consists of a number of basic components which function in series. The reliability of a component is defined as the probability that it will function satisfactorily during the performance of a mission. If, for example, the system is a part of a missile, then the mission might be defined as the flight of the missile. Suppose the electronic system consists of five stages or components with reliabilities R_1, R_2, R_3, R_4, R_5 respectively. If the system is to function satisfactorily for the mission, every component must function satisfactorily. The probability that the system will function is called the "system reliability" and we will assume this is given by the product of the component reliabilities.

$$R_s = R_1 R_2 R_3 R_4 R_5$$

For a system consisting of n stages in series, this may be written

$$R_s = \prod_{j=1}^{n} R_j$$

This is equivalent to assuming that the performances of the components are independent. Suppose, further, that various systems are

to be constructed out of components, each of which has an individual reliability of .90. The system reliability as the system grows
more complex is as follows:

Numbers of stages in series....	1	2	3	4	5	6	7
R_s...............	.90	.81	.73	.65	.59	.53	.48

This illustrates something of the reliability problems encountered
by the designers of complex systems.

One way to improve system reliability is to put duplicate or
"redundant" components in parallel. If, for example, we put two
stage-one components in the system with a switching device which
brings the second into operation when the first fails, this would improve the reliability of stage 1 and thus of the system as a whole. If
each of these components, a and b, has a reliability of .90, then the
over-all reliability of the first stage will be

$$R_1 = R_{1a} + R_{1b} - R_{1a}R_{1b}$$
$$= .90 + .90 - .81 = .99$$

THEOREM III—CONDITIONAL PROBABILITY

$$p(S_2|S_1) = \frac{p(S_1 \cdot S_2)}{p(S_1)}$$

Returning to the previous consumer survey example, we could
say that, given the knowledge that a family has a washer, the probability that it has a dryer is

$$p(D|W) = \frac{p(D \cdot W)}{p(W)} = \frac{18}{20}$$

It follows that

$$p(S_1|S_2) = \frac{p(S_1 \cdot S_2)}{p(S_2)}$$

and also that

$$p(S_1 \cdot S_2) = p(S_1)p(S_2|S_1) = p(S_2)p(S_1|S_2)$$

From this last relation we obtain what is known as Bayes' rule:

$$p(S_1|S_2) = \frac{p(S_2|S_1)p(S_1)}{(pS_2)}$$

In a somewhat more general form Bayes' rule may be written

$$p(S_j|S_k) = \frac{p(S_k|S_j)p(S_j)}{\sum_{i=1}^{m} p(S_k|S_i)p(S_i)}$$

THEOREM IV

If x *and* y *are random variables with means* E(x) *and* E(y) *respectively, then the mean of their sum is the sum of their means.*

$$E(x + y) = E(x) + E(y)$$

A firm makes two major product lines, X and Y. The predicted dollar sales of line X is a random variable x with mean $E(x)$, and the predicted dollar sales of Y is a random variable y with mean $E(y)$. Then we may say that, if the sales of X and the sales of Y are independent, the total sales for the firm will be a random variable $x + y$ with mean $E(x) + E(y)$. If the products in lines X and Y are substitutes for each other, independence may be questionable. If, however, X consists of consumer products and Y consists of industrial products, independence may be a reasonable assumption.

THEOREM V

If x *and* y *are independent random variables with means* E(x) *and* E(y) *respectively, then the mean of their product is equal to the product of their means.*

$$E(xy) = E(x)E(y)$$

Suppose x is the unit price of a commodity purchased by a firm and y is the quantity which will be required to fill a certain order. If it can be assumed that whatever quantity is purchased will be too small to influence the market price of the commodity, and that the quantity purchased is dictated by the requirements of the production process and not by price, then x and y might be assumed to be independent. Then, in estimating the cost of performing the production for the order, one might include the total cost of the commodity, predicted by its mean. The mean of the total cost would simply be the product of the mean of the unit cost and the mean of the quantity purchased.

THEOREM VI

If x *and* y *are independent random variables with variances* σ_x^2 *and* σ_y^2 *respectively, then the variance of their sum is equal to the sum of their variances.*

$$\sigma_{x+y}^2 = \sigma_x^2 + \sigma_y^2$$

Suppose a product is assembled from three basic components: A, B, and C. These components are assembled end to end so that the length of the final product is the sum of the lengths of the individual components. Since this over-all length is critical, the designer sets tolerances on the lengths of the components. Suppose the tolerances have been set as follows:

$$T_A = \pm .001$$
$$T_B = \pm .002$$
$$T_C = \pm .001$$

These tolerances are the allowable range of variation around the nominal lengths. Now suppose that when the components go into production each is produced on a separate machine. The length of component A is subject to variation from a variety of factors which influence the machine and the operator. Suppose, however, we may reasonably think of the length of A as a random variable with mean equal to the nominal length and variance σ_A^2. Suppose that when this machine is controlled with reasonable care, $3\sigma_A = .001$.

This means of course that only a relatively small proportion will fall outside the tolerance limits. If the length of A is normally distributed with mean equal to the nominal length, then only about 3 pieces in 1,000 will be outside the tolerance limits.

Assuming this situation is equivalent to assuming

$$\sigma_A = \frac{.001}{3} = 33 \times 10^{-5}$$

If we make the corresponding set of assumptions for B and C we obtain

$$\sigma_B = 67 \times 10^{-5}$$
$$\sigma_C = 33 \times 10^{-5}$$

Now the theorem suggests that the variance of the length of the final product is given by

$$\sigma_{A+B+C}^2 = \sigma_A^2 + \sigma_B^2 + \sigma_C^2$$

Substituting the assumed values we have

$$\sigma_{A+B+C}^2 = (33 \times 10^{-5})^2 + (67 \times 10^{-5})^2 + (33 \times 10^{-5})^2 = 6,667 \times 10^{-10}$$
$$\sigma_{A+B+C} = 82 \times 10^{-5}$$

Assuming all the lengths are normally distributed, about 99.7 per cent of the final assembly units will lie in the range of $\pm 3\sigma_{A+B+C}$ about the nominal dimension.

$$3\sigma_{A+B+C} = .00246$$

The point here is simply that if we add the original tolerances,

$$T_A + T_B + T_C = \pm .004$$

we obtain an inflated idea of the range in which most of the final assemblies lie. The original tolerances for the components are consistent with an over-all tolerance for the final assembly of

$$T_{A+B+C} = .00246$$

THEOREM VII

If x *is a random variable with variance* σ^2, *then the variance of the variable* a $+$ bx *is* $b^2\sigma^2$.

This theorem is important because it tells the effect of a change of scale on the variance of a set of numbers. Suppose we have the numbers 250, 350, 450, 200, 400. Calculations of the mean and variance of these numbers may be simplified by coding or changing scale. We might subtract 200 from each of them and divide the results by 50. This is the same as forming a new variable

$$-200 + (1/50)x$$

This results in the numbers 1, 3, 5, 0, 4. The mean of these is $1\frac{3}{5}$. The mean of the original data is clearly

$$200 + (50)(13/5) = 330$$
$$(1/5)\{(1 - 13/5)^2 + (3 - 13/5)^2 + (5 - 13/5)^2 + (0 - 13/5)^2$$
$$+ (4 - 13/5)^2\} = \frac{86}{25}$$

We may then obtain the variance of the original data by taking

$$(50)^2 \frac{86}{25} = 8600$$

THEOREM VIII

If x *and* y *are normally distributed, independent random variables with means* $E(x)$ *and* $E(y)$, *and variances* σ_x^2 *and* σ_y^2 *respectively, the probability distribution of the variable* ax $+$ by *is also normal, the mean of* ax $+$ by *is* $aE(x) + bE(y)$, *and its variance is* $a^2\sigma_x^2 + b^2\sigma_y^2$.

THEOREM IX (TCHEBYSHEV'S INEQUALITY)

If x *is a random variable with mean* $E(x)$ *and variance* σ^2, *then, for any* k > 0, *the probability that* x *differs from its mean in absolute value by more than some positive quantity,* k, *is less than or equal to the variance of* x *divided by* k^2.

$$\text{Probability } \{|x - E(x)| \geq k\} \leq \frac{\sigma^2}{k^2}$$

This "limit theorem" is useful if we know the mean and variance of x, but know nothing more about its probability distribution. The theorem is true for any probability distribution whatsoever. What it promises in generality, it pays for in weakness, since it tells only the upper limit or upper bound of a probability. It does not give the probability itself.

Suppose we have a production quota of k units per day to meet, and that it is considered very important to meet this quota. There is a choice between two machines, a_1 and a_2. It is known that the daily production of a_1 is a random variable, x, with mean $E(x)$ and variance σ_x^2. Likewise, the daily production of a_2 is a random variable, y, with mean $E(y)$ and variance σ_y^2. Nothing further is known about these probability distributions. We wish to choose the machine which will minimize the *upper limit of the probability* that we fail to meet the production quota. Let:

$$\begin{aligned}
\text{Production quota} &= 100 \text{ units per day} \\
E(x) &= 120 \text{ units per day} \\
\sigma_x^2 &= 100 \\
E(y) &= 130 \text{ units per day} \\
\sigma_y^2 &= 350
\end{aligned}$$

With machine a_1 the probability that the production quota will not be met is the probability that x falls below 100 units per day, or the probability that

$$x - E(x) = x - 120 \leq -20$$

Thus, for a_1, k equals 20. Since the theorem speaks only of the absolute value of $x - E(x)$, we will be able only to compute the upper limit of the probability that x differs from its mean by more than 20 in either direction. Actually we are only interested in the probability that x will be less than its mean by more than 20.

$$\text{Probability } \{|x - 120| \geq 20\} \leq \frac{100}{400} = .25$$

Similar analysis for a_2 yields $K = 30$, and

$$\text{Probability } \{|y - 130| \geq 30\} \leq \frac{350}{900} = .315$$

Thus, to minimize the *upper limit* of the probability that the production quota will not be met, we might best choose machine a_1.

THEOREM X—THE CENTRAL LIMIT THEOREM

If the mean, μ, and variance, σ^2, of any probability distribution are finite, the distribution of the mean of samples from it ap-

proaches the normal distribution with mean μ, and variance σ^2/n as the sample size n increases.

SUGGESTIONS FOR FURTHER STUDY

KURNOW, ERNEST; GLASSER, GERALD, and OTTMAN, FREDERICK R. *Statistics for Business Decisions*. Homewood, Ill.: Richard D. Irwin, Inc., 1959.

MORONEY, M. J. *Facts From Figures*. Baltimore: Penguin Books, Inc., 1951.

WALLIS, W. ALLEN, and ROBERTS, HARRY V. *Statistics—A New Approach*. Glencoe, Ill.: The Free Press, 1956.

Chapter 11

DECISIONS UNDER RISK

INTRODUCTION

WHEN A DECISION MAKER does not suppress his ignorance of the future but makes it explicit in the form of probabilities, then he faces what we are calling a decision under risk. When the analyst works with a model of a decision in which several possible futures are recognized and the probabilities of these are explicitly stated, then the model is one of a decision under risk. The presence of probabilities is the key to our definition of risk. They may be based on explicit historical or experimental evidence, or on implicit managerial experience, or, most often, on some combination of the two. Whether or not the probabilities are stated and how they are arrived at are matters of judgment and tactics on the part of the analyst, and it is the purpose of the next few chapters to clarify the issues involved. If the probabilities are not stated, then the decision is one under conditions of uncertainty. We will postpone the discussion of responses to uncertainty until Chapter 17, assuming for the present that probabilities are available in the model of the decision with which the analyst works.

Suppose, for example, that a firm is considering whether or not to bid on a government contract. To prepare the proposal will require an expenditure of some $20,000. If the award is won, a profit of $100,000 will result. We will suppose that the analyst estimates the probability of winning is about .50 and that the manager whom he advises agrees with this estimate. To make the decision explicit, we return to our basic model. There are two alternatives, to bid or not to bid, and two possible futures, win and lose. Using profit as a measure of value for the outcomes, the matrix appears below.

	$p_1 = .50$ S_1:*Win*	$p_2 = .50$ S_2:*Lose*
a_1: Bid	$100,000	−$20,000
a_2: Do not bid	0	0

Generally, the model of a decision under risk will include the following elements:

a_i = ith alternative course of action $(i = 1, \ldots , n)$
S_j = jth possible future $(j = 1, \ldots , m)$
θ_{ij} = outcome resulting from selecting action a_i when
     the future turns out to be S_j
$V(\theta_{ij})$ = value of outcome θ_{ij} to the decision maker
p_j = probability that future S_j will occur

The general form of such a decision is then represented by the matrix notation:

	p_1 S_1	p_2 S_2	p_3 S_3	p_4 S_4
a_1	$V(\theta_{11})$	$V(\theta_{12})$	$V(\theta_{13})$	$V(\theta_{14})$
a_2	$V(\theta_{21})$	$V(\theta_{22})$	$V(\theta_{23})$	$V(\theta_{24})$
a_3	$V(\theta_{31})$	$V(\theta_{32})$	$V(\theta_{33})$	$V(\theta_{34})$

Here

$$n = 3 \quad \text{and} \quad m = 4$$

For convenience we have written the probabilities immediately above the futures with which they are associated. When such a decision has been made explicit, the next question is how to process the data into a recommendation or explanation for management action. In the bidding decision introduced previously, a natural and conventional response is to compute the expected profit associated with each alternative and recommend to management the action having the largest expected profit. If the outcomes have been evaluated in terms of profit, then $E(a_i)$ will stand for the expected profit for the ith action.

$$E(a_i) = \sum_j V(\theta_{ij}) p_j$$

In the example we have

$$E(a_1) = \$100,000(.50) - \$20,000(.50)$$
$$= \$40,000$$
$$E(a_2) = 0$$

We might then recommend a_1, bid, to the manager, since it has the higher expected profit. We might, however, find that the manager rejects this advice and does not bid. Yet several other firms (operating, we will assume, from essentially the same model of the decision) do bid on the contract. Can it be that all of the firms have acted reasonably? Can we offer an explanation which is consistent with these differing conclusions? Clearly, we must look further into the matter for more is involved than we have so far made explicit in the decision matrix.

RESPONSES TO RISK

The variety of responses which decision makers exhibit in risky situations is sometimes bewildering. Some people have life, health, accident, and collision insurance, and some do not. Those who have these types of insurance have them in greatly varying amounts. Some investors own "growth" stocks, some prefer bonds, and perhaps the majority invest in a diversified portfolio of securities. Young men with neither obligations nor experience go into business for themselves, while older men with experience but with family obligations as well, do not. Some people are willing to enter hazardous occupations in return for higher monetary rewards; some are not. Some will take every opportunity to gamble; some will never gamble commercially; and many gamble sometimes. Can we understand all of these decisions in a way which will make them seem reasonable and in the best interests of the decision maker?

The reader might gain more direct insight by asking himself how he would choose in the following risky situations:

1. Suppose you are stranded in Las Vegas with $20 and no immediate source of further funds. It is very important to you to get to Los Angeles, but you must have at least $40 to pay your fare. Would you be willing to bet your $20 on "red" at the roulette table? See Chapter 1 for a model of the roulette decision showing that the expected dollar profit is negative.

2. Suppose you have just arrived in Monte Carlo with enough money to make a long-anticipated tour of Europe, providing you budget carefully. A friend suggests that you put all your money on red at the roulette table, pointing out that if you win you can make the trip in style. Would you take his advice?

3. You go to your boss with a new idea for a major change in company policy. You feel that the idea has a fifty-fifty chance of succeeding. Your boss is dubious but agrees to give it a trial if you will show your confidence in the plan. He will double your salary if it succeeds but expects you to resign if it fails. You feel that your present salary is rather good, and it is your guess that you would be able to find another job paying at most three fourths of your present salary. What would you do?

4. You have won, during an evening of poker, x dollars. As the game concludes, one of the other players asks if you will bet the x dollars on a single flip of a fair coin. Your profits for the evening are shown below.

	.50 *Win*	.50 *Lose*
Bet	$2x$	0
Do not bet	x	x

What would be your decision for various values of x?

People often choose to bet in situation 1, not to bet in situation 2, but in situation 3 it may be difficult to find a clear majority opinion. In the fourth case, many people will accept the bet if x is small, but as x grows larger they become unwilling to bet. Thus it would seem that the expected profit, 0 in this case, does not explain their choices, but rather the value of x itself is involved. Our task is to provide an explanation or theory which will make these choices appear consistent with the objectives and beliefs of the decision makers from which they came. We must understand something of what is going on here before we can make recommendations to management in risky decisions.

MANAGEMENT RESPONSES TO RISK

We seek a principle of choice which will use the data in a model of a decision under risk to determine a preferred course of action. One may approach the understanding of a manager's attitude toward risk in much the same way as the understanding of his preferences was approached in Chapter 7. The discussion of the scientific study of values led to the following program. If the analyst could get data on the manager's preferences, than perhaps a model could be developed which would "explain" or agree with the observations and serve as a basis for predicting his preferences among outcomes beyond those observed. The analyst could then use the model as a basis for making recommendations which he predicts are consistent with the manager's values. If the analyst and the manager agree as to the alternatives, futures, and outcomes involved in the decision, and if the analyst's model of the manager's preferences is successful, then presumably the recommendation will be accepted. In this sense the recommendation would be consistent with the manager's own attitudes. He would want to accept the result because it is the same conclusion he himself would have reached had he taken the time to do the analysis which has been done for him. The manager might then be willing to delegate (perhaps with only perfunctory approval) those routine decisions for which the alternatives and outcomes can be determined by routine methods and for which the analyst's model of his preferences is applicable. This relieves the manager to devote more of his time to those difficult decisions which really require his experience and judgment. The manager may further become willing to accept the assistance of the analyst in finding consistent preferences among complex outcomes which are perhaps beyond his immediate experience. The analyst, beginning with simple expressions of preferences reflecting the manager's experience, reasons with the aid of the model to reach deductively consistent preference statements for complex outcomes. The manager may find that this relieves him of many hours of difficult study in complicated decision problems.

The study of management responses to risk may be approached with a program similar in principle to this. Now, however, it will be useful to study a manager's attitudes toward actions which involve probabilistic combinations of outcomes rather than sure outcomes as before. As will become evident, it is difficult to divorce a manager's attitude toward profit from his attitude toward the chances of making various amounts of profit. By studying his preferences in risky situations we will try to capture in a model his attitudes toward risk, profit, and loss. As before, we will try to make some observations which will serve as a basis for such a model of how he responds in the face of risk. Assuming the manager wishes to be consistent in the sense of not contradicting himself, he would be interested in accepting recommendations based on such a model. For the analyst, the model becomes a principle of choice which he uses to process the data describing a decision under risk into a recommendation for management action.

DEVELOPING A MODEL OF ATTITUDES TOWARD RISK

Let us begin with some data indicating the responses of a particular manager to some risky alternatives. Suppose we confront this manager with two contracts (or gambles, or business opportunities) which are very simply described so as to make it reasonably easy for him to state his preferences. Contract A requires an investment of $100,000 the results of which depend on three possible future events. Possible future S_1 will bring the manager a profit of $200,000 if he accepts contract A, while possible futures S_2 and S_3 result in a complete loss of the original $100,000. Contract B requires an investment of $40,000 which will be lost in the event of S_2, but which will yield a profit of $70,000 in the case of either S_1 or

S_2. The manager's decision is whether to accept contract A or contract B (but not both), or to accept neither. For convenience we will label the action "accept neither contract" with the name, contract C. We will suppose that the analyst and the manager agree that the probabilities (whatever their basis) are

$$p_1 = .50 \qquad p_2 = .10 \qquad p_3 = .40$$

The decision is summarized in the matrix below;

	$p_1 = .50$ S_1	$p_2 = .10$ S_2	$p_3 = .40$ S_3
Contract A	\$200,000	−\$100,000	−\$100,000
Contract B	\$ 70,000	\$ 70,000	−\$ 40,000
Contract C	0	0	0

Now we will suppose that the manager, confronted with these three mutually exclusive actions, is able after due consideration to express his preferences. Suppose, for example, he reports that he would most prefer contract B and would choose contract C (accept neither) in preference to contract A. Thus he ranks these actions

1. Contract B
2. Contract C
3. Contract A

Considering this statement as our empirical evidence, can we develop a model or principle of choice which will agree with it or "explain" it? Conventionally in decisions under risk it is suggested that we compute the average or expected profit associated with each action, and choose so as to maximize this quantity. Does this principle provide a model consistent with the results of our experiment?
Let

$$E(a_i) = \text{expected profit for alternative } i \text{ (dollars)}$$

For contract A

$$E(A) = (.50)(\$200,000) + (.10)(-\$100,000) + (.40)(-\$100,000)$$
$$= \$50,000$$

For contract B

$$E(B) = (.50)(\$70,000) + (.10)(\$70,000) + (.40)(-\$40,000)$$
$$= \$26,000$$

For contract C

$$E(C) = 0$$

Summarizing these results and comparing them with the manager's reported preferences we have

Action	Expected Profit	Manager's Ranking
Contract A	$50,000	3
Contract B	26,000	1
Contract C	0	2

Clearly maximizing expected profit fails as a model of this manager's preferences in this experiment. Seeking further clues, perhaps we discuss the matter with him. Possibly he suggests something like this; "I would rather do nothing than accept contract A because, with the limited working capital we now have, the loss of $100,000 would put the firm in very serious trouble. A 50 per cent chance of making $200,000 is not good enough to offset the 50 per cent chance that we will lose the $100,000. On the other hand, contract B is acceptable because we could weather the loss of $40,000 well enough, and the chances of a profit are better." This manager seems averse to risk in a rather reasonable way. To understand his behavior, we will have to consider the actions available to him not simply in terms of expected profit, but in terms of the possible profits and losses, together with the probabilities of each. However, the expected profit principle would have been satisfactory if the choice had involved only contracts B and C. We will return to this point later.

Suppose we had been able to arrange three new contracts labelled A', B', and C' whose conditions were

A': a loss of $200,000 with probability .35
a profit of $400,000 with probability .65
B': a loss of $200,000 with probability .28
a profit of $400,000 with probability .72
C': a loss of $200,000 with probability .30
a profit of $400,000 with probability .70

If we had asked him to rank these three mutually exclusive actions, the decision would have been both easy for him to make and easy for us to explain. The dollar amounts of profit and loss are the same for each contract, and surely a reasonable man would choose the contract which maximizes the probability of a $400,000 profit and minimizes the probability of a $200,000 loss. Thus we would expect the contracts to be ranked

Contract	Manager's Rank
A'	3
B'	1
C'	2

Now we will show a rather remarkable thing. The original decision among contracts *A, B,* and *C* can be reduced to the easy one among contracts *A′, B′,* and *C′* in a way which makes them equivalent in the opinion of a logically consistent manager. Such a manager would find himself indifferent between contract *A* and contract *A′* and thus consider the two equivalent. He would hold similar opinions about *B* and *B′*, as well as *C* and *C′*. Thus if he were consistent he would prefer contract *B′* in the easy, reduced decision and contract *B* in the original decision. This scheme for reducing decisions to equivalent ones, in which the manager would choose so as to maximize the probability of a given amount of profit (or the probability of "success"), provides the basis for our model of his preferences.

To do this, we approach risky decisions from a somewhat different viewpoint. Suppose we may eventually be interested in the manager's attitudes toward contracts involving losses as great as $200,000 and profits up to $400,000. We take these two extreme amounts and form a basic contract or "reference" contract which we will use as a sort of measuring device. The basic contract is one which promises a profit of $400,000 with probability *p,* and a loss of $200,000 with probability $1 - p$.

We then approach the manager with the following question, "If you had already incurred a debt of $100,000, and someone offered to take over your obligation if you would enter into a contract which promised $400,000 with probability *p* and $200,000 loss with probability $1 - p$, what would the value of *p* have to be before you would just be willing to do this?" We suppose that after considerable reflection the manager is able to say that he would be indifferent if *p* were .40. We will interpret this result by saying, "He is indifferent between a sure loss of $100,000 and our basic contract with *p,* the probability of making $400,000, equal to .40." Let us call *p* the probability of success in the basic contract, for short.

Next, we ask him to suppose that he is offered the basic contract and he must choose between it and doing nothing. We wish to learn what the probability of success in the basic contract would have to be, before he would just be willing to accept it. We will suppose that he is able to say that if *p* were .70 he would just be indifferent between the basic contract and doing nothing. We repeat precisely the same sort of question for a loss of $40,000 and profits of $70,000 and $200,000. In each case we ask him to compare the amount in question for sure, against the reference or basic contract, and to report the value of p for which he would be indifferent. Let us imagine the results are those summarized below.

Outcome	*Value of p in Equivalent Basic Contract*
−$100,000	.40
− 40,000	.60
0	.70
70,000	.80
200,000	.90

Using this scheme it would be reasonable to expect indifference between a loss of $200,000 and the basic gamble with $p = 0$. Similarly, we would expect indifference between the basic contract with probability of success 1 and a sure $400,000 profit.

Consider now the matrix in which we summarized the original decision together with the preference statements we have subsequently obtained. The manager has indicated that he is indifferent between our basic contract with probability of success .90 and a sure profit of $200,000. We now suppose that if we alter the original decision by removing the $200,000 and replacing it with our basic contract having a probability of success of .90, we do not alter the value of alternative A in the opinion of the manager. That is, we assume that if the $200,000 profit in contract A is replaced by the basic contract with $p = .90$, then the manager's attitude toward alternative A remains unchanged. If, after all, he is indifferent in the way in which he has reported, then we should be able to make this change without altering his view of alternative A. Using this important assumption, we continue substituting for the outcomes in the original matrix, the various basic contracts for which he has indicated indifference. The transformed matrix now contains the alternatives A', B', and C'. It appears below.

	$p_1 = .50$ S_1	$p_2 = .10$ S_2	$p_3 = .40$ S_3
A'	Basic contract with $p = .90$	Basic contract with $p = .40$	Basic contract with $p = .40$
B'	Basic contract with $p = .80$	Basic contract with $p = .80$	Basic contract with $p = .60$
C'	Basic contract with $p = .70$	Basic contract with $p = .70$	Basic contract with $p = .70$

We suppose, it is to be emphasized, that the values of the alternatives A', B', and C' in the transformed matrix are the same for the manager as the values of the contracts A, B, and C in the original matrix. This supposition defines in part what we mean by a reasonable and consistent manager.

Now if he chooses contract A', he will receive a profit of $400,000 with probability given by

$$(.50)(.90) + (.10)(.40) + (.40)(.40) = .65$$

and suffer a loss of $200,000 with probability:

$$(.50)(.10) + (.10)(.60) + (.40)(.60) = .35$$

This is equivalent to saying that if he chooses contract A it is quite the same as choosing the basic contract with a probability of success equal to .65. If he chooses alternative B' it is the same as choosing to receive $400,000 with probability .72 and lose $200,000 with probability .28. That is

$$(.50)(.80) + (.10)(.80) + (.40)(.60) = .72$$
$$(.50)(.20) + (.10)(.20) + (.40)(.40) = .28$$

Again this is equivalent to saying that choosing alternative B' is quite the same as choosing our basic contract with probability of success equal to .72. This, in turn, we take to be equivalent in the manager's opinion to choosing the original contract B. He has already stated that accepting neither contract A nor contract B is equivalent to accepting our basic contract with probability of success equal to .70. As before alternative C' in the transformed matrix is taken to be indifferent with respect to the original contract C (accept neither).

Now the decision represented by the transformed matrix appears quite obvious to the manager. He chooses alternative B' in preference to A' or C' since this maximizes his probability of success in the basic contract, or gives him the largest probability of making $400,000 and thus the smallest probability of losing $200,000. If he is consistent with his own basic expressions of preference, he will also choose contract B in the original decision. This is, in fact, what we observed.

What we have done is to reduce the original decision to an equivalent one involving only our basic alternative. Having done this, it seemed reasonable that the manager would choose so as to maximize the probability of success. If we wish to, we may assign this probability of success the name utility. The utility of any alternative is thus the probability of success in the equivalent or indifferent basic alternative.

Our results so far are summarized below.

Contract	Expected Dollar Profit	Manager's Rank	Utility
A	$50,000	3	.65
B	26,000	1	.72
C	0	2	.70

Put another way, he already indicated that he would prefer to do nothing rather than accept our basic contract unless the probability of success is at least .70. For contract A we were able to substitute an equivalent basic contract with a probability of success of only .65. Thus, if he were consistent he would do nothing rather than accept contract A. Contract B however, could be reduced to an equivalent basic contract with a probability of success equal to .72. Thus consistency would suggest that he would choose contract B in preference to no contract at all. Since maximizing the probability of success in the basic alternative seems to describe or explain his behavior rather well, we can if we wish call this probability a utility and say that the manager chooses so as to maximize his utility.

It turns out thus that the zero point on our utility scale corresponds to a loss of $200,000, while a profit of $400,000 has a utility of 1.00. We shall see shortly that it makes no difference where we take the zero point and what we take to be one unit of utility. We are developing an interval scale which will perform satisfactorily with an arbitrary zero point and with an arbitrary but constant unit of measurement. In this respect it is like temperature measurement with Fahrenheit or Centigrade scales.

We discover then that, although a model based on maximizing expected dollar return does not seem to describe his attitudes, a model which attaches utilities to outcomes and contracts in the way we have described does indeed agree with his preferences (so far as we have observed them).

UTILITY

Now let us make some general statements about this method of assigning numbers, called utilities, to outcomes and contracts. Notice that we have assigned numbers or utilities to sure outcomes, say a profit of $200,000 for certain, as well as to contracts which were in fact risky alternatives, such as contract A. Now let us adopt the term "prospect" to stand for either of these, and use the symbol $U(P)$ to stand for the utility of a prospect P. Generalizing for our work so far, we could suggest that our method of assigning utilities has the property

$$U(P_1) > U(P_2)$$

if and only if the manager prefers the prospect P_1 to the prospect P_2. This is true on the basis of our observations so far, and if he acts in a consistent fashion, it will be true in general. Thus our model predicts that if he acts consistently, he will always choose the prospect which maximizes his utility.

Notice also a second property of this scheme. We have assigned the following utilities:

$$U(-\$100,000) = .40$$
$$U(\$200,000) = .90$$
$$U(\text{Contract } A) = .65$$

Now suppose instead of computing the expected dollar return for contract A, we compute the *expected utility*.

Expected Utility of Contract A = $(.50)U(-\$100,000) + (.50)U(\$200,000)$
$= (.50)(.40) + (.50)(.90)$
$= .65$

Thus, under this scheme for assigning utilities, the utility of a risky alternative is equal to its expected utility. While our expected dollar return model did not work, an expected utility model does. Thus we may reach the following important conclusion about decisions under risk: *A manager who wishes to act in a logically consistent way in any decision under risk will choose the alternative which maximizes his expected utility.*

If we could measure a manager's utilities in this way, then the problem of a principle of choice for decisions under risk would be solved. Before examining the possibilities of applying this scheme in actual management situations, let us sharpen our understanding of it.

First let us show that the zero point and the unit of measurement on the utility scale make no difference in the results. We chose $-\$200,000$ as the zero point and $\$400,000$ as the unit point because it was convenient. They represented the extremes of the range in which we expected to deal. Now suppose we change the unit of measurement by multiplying all the utilities by a positive constant and change the zero point on the scale by adding a constant to all the utilities. Under this transformation the utility of a prospect $U(P)$ becomes $a + bU(P)$. Under our method of assigning utilities, the utility of a prospect is equal to its expected utility. Thus

$$U(A) = (.50)U(-\$100,000) + (.50)U(\$200,000) = .65$$
$$U(B) = (.40)U(-\$\ 40,000) + (.60)U(\$\ 70,000) = .72$$

For the manager whom we studied we might transform the utility scale by multiplying by a positive constant b and adding a constant a. Calling the transformed utility scale U', we have

$$U'(A) = (.50)\{a + bU(-\$100,000)\} + (.50)\{a + bU(\$200,000)\}$$
$$= a + bU(A)$$

and similarly

$$U'(B) = a + bU(B)$$

Thus any decision consistent with the original utility scale will also be consistent with the transformed utility scale.

GRAPHICAL REPRESENTATION

We can get a further look at this manager's attitudes toward risk by plotting the utilities of the various amounts of money we have measured. This is done in Figure 11–1 where we have also taken the liberty of passing a smooth curve through the points. It is now clear that the value of money for this man, as we have measured it, is not proportional to the amount of money. His utility function exhibits a diminishing marginal utility for money. That is, the more money he has, the less the utility of an additional dollar.

Now consider contract A which involves a profit of \$200,000 with utility .90 (point a on the utility function) and a loss of \$100,-000 with utility .40 (point b). Now let q be the probability with which the profit of \$200,000 is received. For any q we could compute the expected dollar return from contract A:

$$q(\$200,000) + (1 - q)(-\$100,000)$$

and the expected utility for contract A:

$$q(.90) + (1 - q)(.40)$$

The utility of the contract is, as we have shown, equal to its expected utility. We now plot the points whose coordinates are the expected dollar returns and the expected utilities for values of q from zero to one. These points will fall on a straight line between a and b. The reader who is not convinced of this should explore the matter through problem 11–2. The original value of q, which was .50, results in a point half way between a and b, marked A. The coordinates of this point A are the expected dollar return for contract *A*, $50,000, and its utility (or expected utility), .65. Contract *B* is represented in similar fashion by point *B;* and accepting neither contract, assuring a net gain of zero dollars, is represented by point *C* lying right on the utility function. Now the diagram shows what we have already discovered: The dollar expectation for *A* is greater than that for *B*, and both are greater than zero. The utility for *A* is less than the utility of *C*, while the utility of *B* is greater than that of *C*.

FIGURE 11-1

The Manager's Utility Function

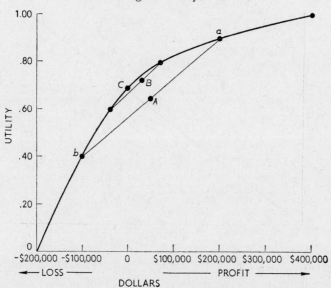

Notice also that if we consider prospects of the form:

a profit of *K* with probability .50
a loss of *K* with probability .50

these prospects have zero expected dollar return. As the value of *K* is increased from zero, the utility of the resulting prospect decreases. Notice also that as *K* increases the variance of the dollar return increases. Thus we could say that for a given expected dollar return, the manager would prefer the prospect with the smallest variance of the dollar return. This is another characteristic which is described by the term risk aversion. This manager does not like to take chances if he can avoid it, and he seeks certainty in his undertakings.

OTHER TYPES OF ATTITUDES

Suppose the results of our utility measuring effort had been different. The utility function in Figure 11–2 describes the attitudes of a manager who does not feel that the amounts of loss involved in the contracts are such as to put his firm in serious difficulties; thus he is not averse to taking risks if the expected dollar return is positive. For this manager the utility of money is proportional to the amount, and the expected utility is proportional to the expected

FIGURE 11–2

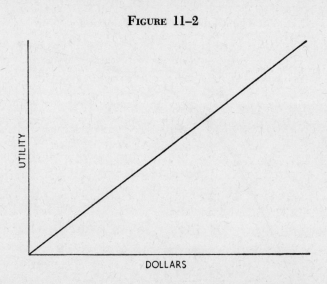

dollar return. Such a man, if he acts consistently will want to choose so as to maximize expected dollar return. The analyst need not be concerned about establishing a utility scale, since it will differ from the dollar scale only by multiplication by a positive constant and addition of a constant.

The manager whose utility function appears in Figure 11–3 is a different man entirely. He very much wants to make large profits but is somewhat unconcerned about large losses. He welcomes opportunities to take risks, loves to gamble, and is willing to play long shots. Notice that a prospect promising a profit of D dollars certain, has a lower utility than a prospect having an expected dollar profit of D. For a given expected dollar return, this man prefers the prospect with the highest variance of dollar return.

Finally, Figure 11–4 suggests a sort of utility function for which there is some experimental confirmation. This manager is willing to take gambles involving small amounts of money but not those involving large dollar amounts.

FIGURE 11–3

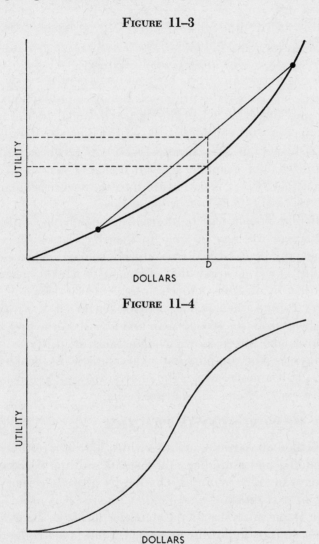

FIGURE 11–4

MISTAKES

The utility model we have outlined is subtle in its implications, and sometimes mistakes are made in using it. For example:

1. We do not want to fall into the habit of saying that P_1 is preferred to P_2 because $U(P_1) > U(P_2)$. Indeed, it is just the other way around: utilities represent and predict preferences; they do not cause them. See Figure 7–3.

2. We cannot generally say that

$$U(P_1 \text{ and } P_2) = U(P_1) + U(P_2)$$

This will be true only if the utility function is linear. Note that in Figure 11–1

$$U(\$400,000) = 1.00$$

while

$$U(\$200,000) + U(\$200,000) = .90 + .90 = 1.80$$

3. We have so far considered the utility function for particular types of risky actions. We cannot be sure how far these results may be generalized. For example a given manager may be willing to accept contract *B* if it is a venture into the securities market but not if it represents a bet on a horse race.

4. Different people will be described by different utility functions, although we may be able to identify classes of people or firms that may be described by similarly shaped utility functions. We cannot, however, argue that if a gain of $1,000 increases one man's utility by .3 units, while a loss of $1,000 decreases another man's by .2 units, then society will be better off if we take this amount away from the second man and give it to the first. That is, we cannot make interpersonal comparisons of utility.

5. Utility is not an inherent characteristic of people nor of prospects. It is a model which the analyst uses to describe people's preferences or decisions among prospects.

UTILITY MEASUREMENT IN PRACTICE

The method of assigning utilities which has been outlined is useful for gaining understanding and insights into the decisions made by managers in the face of risk. One can "explain" decision-making behavior in past decisions and predict consistent choices in future decisions. If the analyst and the manager have the same image or model of a decision and if the manager wishes to act consistently in the sense of the model of his preferences, then the predictions would presumably turn out to be correct. The manager would want to accept the analyst's recommendations. In this sense, the problem of the analyst in dealing with decisions under risk would be "solved." He could provide the manager with consistent recommendations for action in complex decisions, thus relieving the manager for more troublesome problems.

If one could, within the limitations of time and effort imposed by the ongoing affairs of business, measure the manager's utilities, one would clearly find it useful to do so. But what of the difficulties of dealing with an actual managerial situation in this way? Could this actually be done? At best it would appear difficult. (57)

The axioms which lead to this method may be very roughly stated as follows:

1. The decision maker can make a complete and transitive ranking of the outcomes.
2. Any prospect or gamble involving equally desirable outcomes is just as desirable as either outcome by itself.
3. If outcomes A, B, and C are ranked so that A is preferred to B, B is preferred to C, and A is preferred to C, then a gamble exists involving A and C which is just as desirable as B.
4. If A and B are equally desirable then the gamble $pA + (1 - p)C$ is just as desirable as the gamble $pB + (1 - p)C$.

If these axioms hold, then the existence of the utility scale can be shown. The question of interest is whether these axioms do hold in the firm and whether the decision maker can answer questions of the sort indicated previously.

Would the manager be willing to answer the rather large number of questions one would have to ask? Could one put the questions in a meaningful way? Would the manager try to put the analyst off with casual responses, rather than serious consideration? Could he correct the intransitivities and other inconsistencies in his answers? Would his responses be reliable or would distractions lead to errors in the sense of different responses to the same question on different occasions?

Note also that, in presenting the method, we have assumed that the profit and loss aspect of the outcomes alone was relevant. Are there other aspects beside money which have value for him? We have not considered the problem of multiple goals which was raised earlier. If there are other aspects of the outcomes which concern him, then we would have to identify these in order to predict future choices.

Without prejudging whether it is possible to obtain a manager's utility to a useful degree of approximation with a reasonable expenditure of time and effort, we will suggest some "practical" approximations to this procedure. These approximations are in the form of principles of choice which are related to utility maximization in various ways, but which substitute the judgment of the analyst for the detailed construction of a utility function. These principles reflect practice in the sense that they describe the ways in which analysts often deal with decisions under risk. Like utility maximization itself, they have two important uses. On the one hand they may be thought of as suggestions as to how one might proceed to make a decision under conditions of risk. That is, each principle may be interpreted as a recommendation which a decision maker is invited to follow. On the other hand they may offer some assistance in explaining or understanding the decisions which we see people making around us.

DOMINANCE

The first step in making a decision under risk is to eliminate from consideration any alternatives which are clearly not to be chosen no matter what principle of choice is used. The relation of dominance is useful in formulating our common sense in this respect. In the following simple decision, the profits for three alternatives and three possible futures are shown.

	p_1 S_1	p_2 S_2	p_3 S_3
a_1	$5	$1	$8
a_2	$9	$4	$2
a_3	$6	$8	$10

Inspection reveals immediately that no matter what possible future is considered, more profit is to be obtained from a_3 than from a_1. Thus a_1 would never be chosen in preference to a_3, and a_1 may be eliminated from further consideration. In such a case we say that a_3 dominates a_1, or that a_1 is dominated by a_3. To state the dominance relation more explicitly we might say, "If there are two alternatives a_g and a_h, such that

$$V(\theta_{gj}) \leq V(\theta_{hj}), \text{ for all } j$$

then a_g is dominated by a_h, and a_g may be eliminated from further consideration." Our first step is thus always to dispose of any dominated alternatives. If, after repeated applications of the principle of dominance, we are left with only one alternative, then it is clearly the preferred course of action. In general, this will not be the case, and other principles of choice may be brought to bear. All one needs to know to apply the relation of dominance is that the manager in this decision prefers more money to less of it. Dominance really requires only a ranking of the outcomes and is thus rather easy to discover. It is usually a more or less automatic simplification of the decision which is made in the preliminary stages of developing the model.

EXPECTED PROFIT

Possibly the most common principle of choice in practice suggests that the manager choose the action which maximizes expected profit or minimizes expected loss. We have already seen a case in which this was not satisfactory, but arguments can be given to justify its use in certain other situations. We assume for the present that the dollar consequences of outcomes are the only consequences of concern to the manager.

Suppose we are concerned with a routine decision under risk in a large corporation. The maximum possible profit in the decision is $100 and the maximum possible loss is $50. We are thus interested in the manager's utility function for money in the range from a loss of $50 to a profit of $100. We hypothesize that whatever the shape of his utility function (see Figures 11–1 to 11–4) we will make only negligible errors if we approximate it by a straight line in this range. The smaller the range between minimum and maximum profits in a decision, the better will be a straight line approximation to the utility function. Thus it is argued that over a small range, maximizing expected profit will yield much the same decisions as maximizing utility or expected utility. For this reason, decisions involving moderate dollar consequences can be well understood by maximizing expected profit. As long as the analyst deals with such "small" decisions, he can deal with expected profits and be freed of the necessity for measuring the manager's utility function. The manager in turn is freed from small routine decisions, so that he may bring his judgment to bear on large important decisions. Just how to divide decisions into classes such that some may usefully be treated as expected profit maximizing problems while others require utilities, cannot be indicated precisely. The judgment and experience of the analyst together with the behavior of the manager must resolve this question in each business situation.

In future discussions we will generally assume that the term "expectation principle" refers to maximizing expected profits or minimizing expected losses. The symbol $E(a_i)$ will be used to refer to the expected profits or expected losses associated with the ith action.

Let us pause briefly to consider one of the arguments which sometimes arises in connection with any principle of choice which suggests that expectation maximizing is a reasonable guide for decision making. To be specific, consider a class of decisions in which dollar amounts are not large and the analyst suggests maximizing expected dollar return as a guide for behavior. Suppose a person had not arrived at this point by conceiving of it as an approximation to utility maximization as we have but simply encounters the suggestion that he "ought" to choose in decisions under risk so as to maximize dollar expectation. He may well confront us with the basic objection that the expectation or average has empirical meaning only if a very large number of decisions are involved. If one or a small number of decisions are made, the actual or sample average of the outcomes may differ widely from the expectation as defined above. Thus, if we begin flipping a fair coin we know the expected number of heads is one half of the number of flips, but we would have to perform a very large number of flips to consistently observe approximately this result. This notion is also familiar in the context of sampling. We know that the larger sample we observe, the more likely it is that the sample average will be close to the population average. The best way to make this clear is to return to the statistician's definition of this property of the average, one form of which is called the weak law of large numbers.

The Weak Law of Large Numbers. Suppose x is a random variable with expected value $E(x)$ and that we observe successive values of x, say $x_1, x_2, x_3, \ldots, x_n$, where these values of x are independent. Then for every $e > 0$ as $n \to \infty$

$$\text{Probability} \left\{ \left| \frac{x_1 + x_2 + x_3 + \ldots + x_n}{n} - E(x) \right| > e \right\} \to 0$$

In words, this says that the probability of the observed average differing from the expectation by any amount, e, approaches zero as the number of observations increases toward infinity. Notice that even this does not say the sample average will certainly be close to the expectation, but only that the probability of it being otherwise is very small for large n. Now this can be applied directly to a sequence of identical decisions whose outcomes are independent. Suppose on each of these decisions we choose a_i and that the value of the outcome of this choice is a random variable $V(\theta_{ij})$. The law would then say, for every $e > 0$ as $n \to \infty$

$$\text{Probability} \left\{ \left| \frac{V_1(\theta_{ij}) + V_2(\theta_{ij}) + \ldots + V_n(\theta_{ij})}{n} - E(a_i) \right| > e \right\} \to 0$$

where $V_1(\theta_{ij})$ is the value of the outcome of the first decision, $V_2(\theta_{ij})$ is the value of the outcome of the second, and so forth. Thus we could say that the average of the outcomes of our decisions on which we choose a_i is very likely to be close to $E(a_i)$ in the long run. Unfortunately this says nothing about what will happen in the short run if we make only one or a few decisions. Note also that the law applies, as we have given it, only to decisions whose outcomes are independent.

If a decision maker is making a large number of decisions or is willing to behave as though this were the case, then maximizing expectation has much appeal. Using the weak law of large numbers, we can establish the following result.

Law of Long-Run Success. Consider a sequence of identical decisions whose outcomes are independent. Let S_n' be the sum of the values of the outcomes of the first n decisions when the principle of maximizing expectation is used, and let S_n be the sum of the values of the outcomes of the first n decisions when *any other* principle of choice is used. Then as $n \to \infty$

$$\text{Probability } \{S_n' > S_n\} \to 1$$

In words this means that the sum of the values of the outcomes of a series of decisions is greatest if we maximize expectation, with probability approaching one as the number of decisions increases. Clearly this is a very powerful result if one is confronted with a large number of decisions. The proof of this law is given in Appendix C.

On the basis of these two results one can argue that maximizing expectation is clearly advantageous in the long run, but means nothing over the short run, or with one or a few decisions. To this common argument we might respond in the following ways:

1. In measuring the manager's attitudes toward risk we did not ask him how he would behave in the long run, but rather what his preferences were in one-time decisions under risk. We were able to assign utilities so that his preferences were reflected by numbers which happened to be equal to expected utilities. All this was done with no reference whatsoever to long-run effects. Thus expected utility is a guide, an index, or an indicator which he will maximize if he acts in one-time decisions consistently with his own stated preferences. In so far as we consider dollar expectation maximizing as an approximation to utility maximizing, the same statements hold. Dollar expectation is a guide to behavior, an index number,

or indicator which he will want to maximize if he is to be consistent with himself.

2. When we report to a manager that he should choose a particular risky action and the expected dollar return associated with that action is $1,000, we should be careful to avoid having him get the impression that he will soon receive exactly $1,000. If the decision is to be repeated a large number of times, then he may, if he wishes, interpret the $1,000 as a limit approached by the average profit per decision; but in the short run it is not necessarily the amount of any transaction which he will experience. For example, if we recommend to a manager that he undertake a risky action which promises a loss of $200 with probability .50 and a profit of $2,200 with probability of .50, then on no instance on which he takes such an action will he receive $1,000. Furthermore, it is important for the manager to understand that if he takes the recommended action once and loses $200, or even loses $200 several times in succession, this does not necessarily prove that our recommendation was "wrong." It may remain the action which is logically consistent with his own preferences.

3. If, however, a decision is to be repeated a large number of times, then the Law of Long-Run Success suggests that with probability approaching one his total profit will be greatest if he chooses so as to maximize expected profit. But this is equivalent to saying that in the long run there is increasingly little risk associated with his total profit. Thus maximizing total profit by means of an expected profit principle will have the effect of maximizing the manager's utility. Thus we could argue that whether a decision is to be made once or whether it is to be made many times, *the consistent principle* is utility maximization. Further, in the long run maximizing expected profit results in maximizing utility.

THE MOST PROBABLE FUTURE PRINCIPLE

The utility maximizing principle provides a way of simplifying the complex elements of a decision under risk to a single number for each alternative, the largest of which indicates the consistent choice. Maximizing dollar expectation is likewise a scheme for simplifying the complex fabric of real decision situations. The key, as we have said, to understanding management decision making is to understand what simplifications are involved. There are many other modes of simplification, three examples of which we shall illustrate. One response to a decision under risk is, of course, to suppress the risk entirely, transforming it into a decision under assumed certainty. Indeed it may be useful to think of this mode of simplification of risk as the way (explicitly or implicitly) in which decisions under assumed certainty arise. In a decision under assumed certainty, we are not troubled about the nonlinearity of a manager's utility function. If the outcomes are expressed in dollars, maximizing dollars will have the same result as maximizing utility as long as the utility function has a nonnegative slope. This of course does not free us from the problems of multiple goals discussed in Chapter 7.

This principle suggests that, as the decision maker confronts the various possible futures in a decision under risk, he simply overlooks all except the most probable one and behaves as though it were certain. More explicitly, find the S_j for which p_j is maximum, and for this possible future select the alternative i which will maximize $V(\theta_{ij})$. This principle is not very appealing if the analyst has already obtained estimates of the probabilities of a number of possible futures. It is usually more satisfactory in that case to use them all with the expectation principle, rather than throwing them out except for the largest and setting it equal to one. However, many decisions are based upon this principle since in fact only the most probable future is really studied. For example, many decisions to embark on new ventures are made only on the basis of what will happen if the venture succeeds, although there is almost always some nonzero probability that the venture will fail. Again, most decision makers would agree that there is some nonzero probability of a war in any given year, although they may make all their decisions as though peace were assured. In almost all decisions there are possible futures which we choose to neglect because they seem to have small probability. The most probable future principle clearly seems most appealing where there is some future whose probability far exceeds that of all the others, and where the outcomes of all possible futures are of roughly the same order of magnitude. In decisions where the possibility of catastrophe is present though with small probability, the order of magnitude of the loss might be so large that we could not neglect it. Thus, the firm may make such decisions as to insure itself against fire.

On the other hand it may be used to explain a man's decision to drive to work in the morning. He knows that there is some nonzero probability that he will meet death in a fatal accident on the way, yet he does not consider this possibility every time he gets into his car. He considers only the most probable future, that he will make

the trip safely. Thus he is freed from the anguish of considering
the value of his own life and how the probabilities of preserving it
depend on his driving habits and the like.

We hypothesize that much of the suppression of risk which occurs
in decision making can be understood in terms of the most probable
future principle. Sometimes we will deal with a variant of this principle which suggests that only the expected outcome or average
outcome be considered and the decision again be treated as a decision under assumed certainty. For example, a manager planning
production for the coming year might plan as though sales were
going to be a single known quantity, perhaps equal to the expected
value of past sales. We saw some examples of this method of suppressing risks in Chapter 6. Since it will often be the case that the
most probable future is the same as the average or expected future,
the distinction may be of minor importance. We shall see, more
importantly, in Chapters 12 and 13 that there are some cases in
which dealing with risk in terms of an expected future principle is
the same effectively as maximizing expected profit, but also that
there are some cases in which the two principles are quite different.

THE ASPIRATION LEVEL PRINCIPLE

The dollar expectation principle simplifies risky decisions by
making a linear approximation to the manager's utility function.
The most probable future principle suppresses the risk entirely. Now
instead of making a linear approximation to the utility function,
we might simplify it even further by representing it by a function
which took on only two values. We might for example use the function

$$U(x) = K \qquad \text{for } x \geqslant A$$
$$U(x) = k \qquad \text{for } x < A$$

where x is the amount of a dollar profit or loss and $K > k$. The number A receives the name aspiration level. Since we have shown that
we can do no harm by changing the zero point and unit point on our
utility scale, we can let

$$K = 1 \text{ and } k = 0$$

Now for any risky action which promises a value of $x \geqslant A$ with probability p and a value of $x < A$ with probability p, the utility (or
expected utility) will be given by

$$p(1) + (1 - p)(0) = p$$

and maximizing utility will become equivalent to maximizing the probability of achieving or exceeding the aspiration level A.

Just what value of A to use in any decision situation is a matter which can only be answered by attempting to learn about a manager's preferences. One might hypothesize, however, that in a wide variety of situations it would be far easier to get a manager to classify outcomes as "acceptable" or "not acceptable," than it would be to obtain his utility function. Psychologists exploring decision-making behavior have found the concept of aspiration level a very useful one (116). One proposal, which has had some confirmation,

FIGURE 11–5

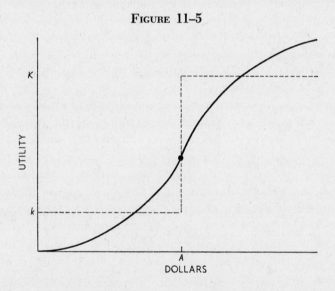

is that the aspiration level be taken to be the point of inflection on a utility function of the sort shown in Figure 11–4. The resulting approximation is suggested by Figure 11–5.

It is possibly true that some form of aspiration level principle is the most widely used of all principles in management decision making. An aspiration level is simply some level of profit which the decision maker desires to attain, or some level of cost which he desires not to exceed. The aspiration level may also be stated in terms of other criteria which are more or less related to cost or profit, as, for example, the firm which attempts to keep its facilities operating at a level of 70 per cent capacity at least. For a decision under risk, an aspiration level policy might be expressed as follows. For a given aspiration level, A, select the alternative which maximizes the probability that the outcome will be equal to or greater than A.

The Simon-March hypothesis which was introduced in Chapter 4 suggests that, in most decision making, one was likely to be concerned with selecting acceptable alternatives, rather than optimal alternatives. This is in direct agreement with the aspiration level principle, since the criterion for dividing acceptable alternatives from those which are not acceptable is simply an aspiration level. To the extent that the Simon-March hypothesis is true, the aspiration level principle provides a useful understanding of how many decisions are made.

Many decisions which fall into the general class of control decisions utilize standards against which actual performance is judged. If the actual performance meets the standard, we decide not to take any action, but if not, some control action may be taken. In designing and operating the system which is thus controlled, one tries to select alternatives which will maximize the probability of having the system meet the standard. The whole idea of a standard which plays such an important part in these decisions is, of course, simply an aspiration level. Management uses standards for almost everything. Thus we have standard costs, standards for output, standards for quality, standards for personnel selection, standards for the performance of salesmen, and so forth. When the standard is met, we are satisfied; when it is not, we decide to take some sort of corrective action. This is the fundamental principle of management by exception.

There are several situations in which an aspiration level is appealing.

1. When it is costly or difficult to discover what the alternative courses of action are, we may wish to search for alternatives only until one is found which gives a reasonable probability of achieving the aspiration level. This may be more economical than an extensive search for the alternative which can be shown to maximize expectation, for example.

2. Sometimes it is difficult or impossible to evaluate the outcomes in a decision. It may be possible, however, to classify the outcomes into two groups, those which meet the aspiration level of the decision maker, and those which do not. Then the reasonable choice becomes the alternative which maximizes the probability of achieving the aspiration level. Thus, we may classify the outcomes of a decision into the categories "success" and "failure" and attempt to maximize the probability of success.

3. Sometimes the alternatives are of a transient nature and may

not in fact be accumulated until one is ready to make a maximizing choice. Thus, when a person sells a house he may obtain a number of offers spread over a period of time, but each offer must be accepted within, say a 24-hour limit or it lapses. Here an aspiration level is almost essential. This problem is closely related to those presented later in the chapter on purchasing policy.

EXPECTATION-VARIANCE PRINCIPLES

We noticed earlier that for a decision maker whose utility function for money exhibited decreasing marginal utility (Figure 11–1) the utility of a prospect was related in part to the variance of profit. In particular, if one considered several prospects, all having the same expected profit, the utility would be greatest for the prospect having the smallest variance of profit. Thus, if one believed that a decision-maker's utility function for money did increase at a decreasing rate, one could make the following predictions without actually quantifying the utility function more precisely:

1. If two actions have the same expected profit, the one having the smaller variance of profit will be preferred.
2. If two actions have the same variance of profit, the one having the larger expected profit will be preferred.

We can generalize this notion in the following interesting way. Consider an action which will produce a profit x with probability $f(x)$. Let

$U(a)$ = the utility of this action
$E(a)$ = the expected profit associated with this action

$$= \int_x xf(x)dx$$

σ^2 = the variance of the profit

$$= \int_x [\{x - E(a)\}^2]f(x)dx$$

The utility function, $U(a)$ could be expanded as a Taylor series giving

$$U(a) = U(c) + (x - c)\frac{dU(c)}{dx} + \frac{1}{2}(x - c)^2\frac{d^2U(c)}{dx^2} + \cdots \cdots \cdots$$

where c is a constant. Now let $c = E(x)$ and take the expected value of both sides of the foregoing equation.

$$U(a) = \text{Expected utility of } a$$
$$= U[E(x)] + \tfrac{1}{2}\sigma^2 \frac{d^2 U[E(x)]}{dx^2} + \cdots \cdots \cdots$$

This gives the utility of any probability distribution of money returns, in terms of the mean and variance of the distribution. If the phenomenon of diminishing marginal utility of money is present, then the second derivative of the utility function will be negative. Thus, for equal expectations, the firm would attempt to minimize the variance of the money return.

Now clearly one cannot compute $U(a)$ by this method unless the utility function is known to the extent that its second derivative at the point $E(x)$ can be estimated. However, the following expedients may be helpful. In decisions involving consequences of sufficient magnitude that the analyst does not wish to base his recommendation on expected profit alone, the variance of profit might be computed. Perhaps some actions can be eliminated on the basis of two simple situations noted above. Beyond this, the computation and reporting of profit variances may serve to sharpen the insights of both the analyst and manager and provide another descriptive parameter of the actions on which judgment may be focussed.

CONCLUSION

These four principles, together with the dominance relation, suggest "practical" and expedient ways of dealing with decisions in the face of risk. They may be considered methods of simplifying the complexity of reality, methods of suppressing risk, or methods of approximating a decision-maker's utility function. One cannot decide in general which will provide the most useful description of decision-making behavior or the most useful basic for making recommendations for management action. This is a matter about which the analyst must develop some judgment. In the next several chapters we explore the results of using these principles in connection with a variety of management decisions under risk. It is hoped that these examples will help to cultivate the sort of judgment required.

SUGGESTIONS FOR FURTHER STUDY

CHERNOFF, HERMAN, and MOSES, LINCOLN E. *Elementary Decision Theory*. New York: John Wiley & Sons, Inc., 1959.

Luce, R. Duncan, and Raiffa, Howard. *Games and Decisions.* New York: John Wiley & Sons, Inc., 1957.

Schlaifer, Robert. *Introduction to Statistics for Business Decisions.* New York: McGraw-Hill Book Co., Inc., 1961.

Green, Paul. "Risk Attitudes and Chemical Investment Decisions," *Chemical Engineering Progress*, Vol. 59, No. 1 (January, 1963).

PROBLEMS

11–1. By using the utility assignment scheme described in the chapter, it is determined that for a given decision maker

$$U(-\$1{,}000) = .10 \qquad U(\$3{,}000) = .50$$

The decision maker reports that he is indifferent between the two alternatives shown below:

	$p_1 = .40$ S_1	$p_2 = .60$ S_2
a_1	$1,000	$1,000
a_2	−$1,000	$3,000

What is $U(\$1{,}000)$?

Suppose the utility scale had been set up so that $U(-\$1{,}000) = B$ and $U(\$3{,}000) = A$, where $1.00 \geqslant A > B \geqslant 0$. Show that this would make no difference in application.

11–2. Consider two points on a plane whose rectangular coordinates are x_1, y_1 and x_2, y_2. Let the coordinates of a third point be

$$x_3 = px_1 + (1 - p)x_2$$
$$y_3 = py_1 + (1 - p)y_2$$

where $0 \leqslant p \leqslant 1$. Show that the third point lies on a straight line joining the first two points.

11–3. Consider the following decision under risk. The matrix values are dollar losses.

	$p_1 = .999$ S_1	$p_2 = .001$ S_2
a_1	−1	−1
a_2	0	−500

What could be said about the utility function of a subject who
  a) prefers a_1?
  b) prefers a_2?

11–4. Suppose you have just $20 in cash which you consider ample for an important social engagement scheduled for this evening. Would you be willing to bet your $20 on a flip of a fair coin?

Suppose again that you have just $20 in cash and want very much to leave immediately for a vacation. The bus fare is $35. Would you be willing to bet your $20 on a flip of a fair coin?

11-5. What can be said about the shape of the utility function of a person who is willing to accept risky investments promising a chance of large gains in return for a chance of modest losses, even though the dollar expectation may be negative?

11-6. Suppose a person refuses to insure his home using a commercial fire insurance policy. What can be said about the shape of his utility function?

11-7. Psychologists have discovered that some persons have a utility function for money which first increases at an increasing rate and then at a decreasing rate. Suppose such a person shows increasing marginal utility from 0 up to $A and decreasing marginal utility from $A up to $B. Show graphically the region in which the expected utility of all fair bets involving outcomes between 0 and B dollars will fall. Show the region of the expected utility of all bets which a person would accept if he chose so as to maximize expected utility.

11-8. As a small business man (the net worth of your business is $100,000) you are offered the following contracts:

a) Contract A promises a profit of $1,000 with probability $\frac{1}{2}$ and a loss of $500 with probability $\frac{1}{2}$.

b) Contract B promises a profit of $200,000 with probability $\frac{1}{2}$ and a loss of $100,000 with probability $\frac{1}{2}$.

Would you accept contract A? What about B? Explain your decisions in terms of

a) Your utility function.

b) The aspiration level principle.

c) The expectation-variance principle.

11-9. Suppose you offer a person a series of fair bets involving a .50 probability of winning x dollars and a .50 probability of losing x dollars. What can be said about a person's utility function if

a) He is willing to bet for all values of x?

b) He is not willing to bet for any value of x greater than zero?

c) He is willing to bet for small values of x but not for large ones?

11-10. In her daily paper a mother reads probabilistic weather forecasts which say, "The chance of rain tomorrow is x." $(0 \leqslant x \leqslant 1.00)$ She asks you how to use the number x in deciding how to dress her children for school. How would you proceed?

11-11. Consider a manager who does insure his plant against fire. Assume the premium is P, the loss if a fire occurs is L, and the probability of a fire is q. Show graphically that this increases his utility and that of the insurance company as well.

11-12. A man is offered the chance to enroll in one or both of the following health insurance plans:

Plan A pays all medical expenses up to a maximum of $1,000 for each illness.

Plan *B* pays only those expenses in excess of $1,000 for each illness. How would you explain a decision to take both plans? To take only plan *B*?

11–13.   A man is considering the purchase of collision insurance for his automobile. He wonders whether to buy "$50 deductible," "$100 deductible," or "$200 deductible." What advice could you give him?

11–14.   A man has just sketched out his own utility function and that of his employer. He notes that if his income were increased by $1,000, his utility would increase by .100. If his employer's income were reduced by $1,000, it appears that the employer's utility would decrease by .010. Thus he asks his employer for a $1,000 raise, pointing out that this amount is 10 times more valuable to him than to the employer and that the utility of the community (or society) will be increased as a result. Comment on this. What advice would you give the employer?

11–15.   The manager whose utility function is shown in Figure 11–1 (see table below) must choose between contract *B* which promises a loss of $40,000 with probability .40 and a profit of $70,000 with probability .60, and a new contract called *D*. Contract *D* actually consists of two contracts, each of which promises a loss of $20,000 with probability .40 and a profit of $35,000 with probability .60. The outcomes of these two contracts making up *D* are independent. What choice would you recommend for the manager?

Utility Table
(Based on Figure 11–1)

Dollars	Utility
−200,000	0
−100,000	.40
− 50,000	.58
− 40,000	.60
− 25,000	.64
0	.70
15,000	.73
50,000	.78
70,000	.80
100,000	.83
200,000	.90
400,000	1.00

11–16.   Consider contract *A* of the example in the chapter, which promised a loss of $100,000 with probability .50 and a profit of $200.000 with a probability .50. Suppose four people, each with utility functions like that of Figure 11–1, decide to enter into this contract sharing equally in profits or losses. Suppose further they all use the above probabilities in considering the contract. Show that under these conditions each person's utility will increase. (See table, problem 11–15.)

11–17.   The manager whose utility function is pictured in Figure 11–1 feels that, although he would not choose contract *A* in the decision discussed in the chapter, if he had the opportunity to accept contract *A* many, many times, it might be more desirable. Show that the utility of taking contract A twice is greater than the utility of taking it once. (See table, problem 11–15.)

11–18. From your own experience suggest examples of decisions for which each of the four principles of choice seems appropriate. Suggest examples also to illustrate the conditions under which each of the principles seems to be unsatisfactory.

11–19. Apply each of the principles of choice to the following decision. The values in the matrix are profits.

	$p_1 = .20$ S_1	$p_2 = .70$ S_2	$p_3 = .10$ S_3
a_1.................	\$ 20	\$100	\$1,200
a_2.................	190	190	190
a_3.................	500	120	100

11–20. Select four actual business decisions with which you are familiar, either through reading or experience. What principle of choice best explains what was done in each case?

11–21. Two men, A and B, are offered tickets in a lottery in which the prize is an automobile worth some \$4,000. The price of a ticket is \$1.00, and they estimate that some 10,000 tickets will be sold. A buys a ticket but B refuses. What explanations can be offered for their behavior in terms of utility functions and the principles of choice discussed in the chapter?

11–22. Which alternative would you select in the decision below? The numbers in the matrix represent profits.

	p_1 S_1	p_2 S_2	p_3 S_3	p_4 S_4
a_1...............	2	12	0	19
a_2...............	5	17	11	16
a_3...............	10	18	12	21
a_4...............	9	8	9	6
a_5...............	3	13	4	20

11–23. Make up a principle of choice of your own for decisions under risk. Show how it would be used in an example. What can be said for and against it?

11–24. A young man is attempting to choose between a career in management with a large corporation and going into business for himself. After considerable study he is able to estimate the probability distributions of the present worths of his future earnings for each alternative (figures are in thousands of dollars).

Corporation Management		*Own Business*	
Earnings	*Probability*	*Earnings*	*Probability*
200–250.............	.60	50–100.............	.50
250–300.............	.30	100–200.............	.30
300–350.............	.10	200–400.............	.15
		400–600.............	.05

Discuss the application of the four principles of choice to this decision.

11–25. Large governmental organizations often carry no fire insurance; large firms often do not insure against small fire losses; but home owners are usually fully insured against fire. Can an explanation be offered which shows that all are acting reasonably?

11–26. What explanation could you suggest for the following observations?

a) During World War II a government faced the choice between two air raid shelter programs for a large city. One program involved many small shelters, while the other proposed a smaller number of large shelters. An analysis showed that the expected number of deaths per raid was smaller if a few large shelters were used, yet the government chose the other program.

b) Many people are far more disturbed by a single air crash involving say forty deaths than they are by a far greater number of deaths on the highways during a summer week end.

11–27. Would you advise a person to gamble in a commercial gambling house? Explain your advice. Suppose a person is known to be an occasional player of slot machines. How would you explain his decision to gamble in the terms of this chapter?

11–28. How would you analyze the decision to buy or not to buy a life insurance policy? What sort of a person buys such a policy?

11–29. What principle of choice might be used by management in selecting among alternative plant safety programs.

11–30. Under the Korean G.I. Bill, a $10,000, five-year term life insurance policy could be obtained. For a veteran of age 25, the annual premium amounted to approximately $30. This policy promises to pay the beneficiary the face amount if the insured dies within the five-year period. It has no other benefits, no cash value, no value as paid-up insurance, and no value at the end of the term. A section of a current mortality table is shown below:

Age	Deaths per 1,000 Persons
25	1.53
26	1.55
27	1.59
28	1.64
29	1.71

Compute the expected return for such a policy. Is this a good basis for deciding whether or not to buy the policy?

11–31. A manufacturer of seasonal goods must produce in advance. His profit from the production of x units when the demand is D is given by

Profit $(x) = (\$1.00)x$ for $0 \leq x \leq D$

$\qquad\quad = (\$1.00)D - (\$.50)(x - D)$ for $x > D$

To simplify the problem suppose that only four values of D are possible: 1,000, 2,000, 3,000, and 6,000 units. Assume that each of these values had probability .25. The manufacturer wishes to choose among four production quantities also equal to 1,000, 2,000, 3,000, and 6,000 units. What would be his choice if

   a) He chose to produce for the expected demand?

   b) He chose so as to maximize expected profit?

   c) He chose so as to minimize the probability of a loss?

   d) He chose so as to maximize the probability of a profit of $3,000 or more?

   e) He chose so as to minimize the variance of his profit?

11–32. Consider the decision to propose or not to propose on a contract which is summarized below.

	p	$1 - p$
Propose	$90,000	−$10,000
Do not propose	0	0

   a) For what value of p would the expected dollar returns be equal for the two actions?

   b) If the expected dollar returns were equal, which action would you recommend to a manager whose utility function was of the same general shape as that of Figure 11–1? Figure 11–2? Figure 11–3?

   c) What action would you recommend on the basis of an aspiration level principle? Show your recommendation for various values of A.

11–33. What explanation could be given for each of the following decisions:

   a) A public utility establishes its capacity so as to keep the probability of being unable to meet customer demand below a level p.

   b) An airline designs its passenger terminal so that the probability of a passenger having to wait in line at the counter more than 20 minutes is less than or equal to q.

   c) A trucking company advertises one-day service between two large cities and is satisfied if the proportion of shipments which take more than one day is kept below r.

11–34. It has been proposed that the problem of multiple goals discussed in Chapter 7 could be explained and understood in terms of multiple aspiration levels rather than in terms of a single complex utility surface. Suggest an example of such an explanation.

11–35. Assuming the decisions involved to be decisions in the face of risk, and using the principles of choice we have studied, explain *briefly* each of the following behaviors:

   a) The board of directors which states that it is company policy *never* to run out of finished goods inventory.

   b) The plant manager in the same company who is more than satisfied if he runs out of finished goods inventory no more than once a week, on the average.

   c) The steel user who is carrying no more than his usual steel inventories in spite of the talk about a possible steel strike.

   d) The big company which conducts an elaborate market research program before launching a new product and their small competitor which does no formal market research at all before bringing out a new product.

e) The man who regularly bets two dollars a week on the horses but keeps his personal savings in government bonds.

f) The manager who assigns two groups of engineers to work separately and independently to solve the same important technical problem.

g) The big company which lets a computer decide whether or not a customer is a good credit risk, while a smaller company spends more money per customer to have an experienced credit manager make the same decision.

11–36. In an equipment selection problem, the following data are given for each of two machines:

Initial investment

$f_j(C)$ = probability distribution of operating costs during j^{th} year of operation

$g(S)$ = probability distribution of salvage value

Interest rate

Service life

Set up a model for comparing the two machines.

11–37. A study of trade association statistics on small business profits suggests that the rate of return on investment for drugstores is a normally distributed random variable with a mean of 16.1 per cent and a standard deviation of 4.2 per cent. A similar study of gas stations shows that the return on investment is also normally distributed with mean equal to 11.8 per cent and standard deviation equal to 3.5 per cent. Discuss the question of which business is the preferred investment.

11–38. A company is considering the installation of a plant to process one of its by-products from the main process into a marketable item. The major consideration is whether the plant is to be an automated, special-purpose installation, or whether it is to be made up of general-purpose equipment. In studying this decision the company finds that future profits will depend heavily on business conditions. It develops three views of the future which may be called boom-inflation (*BI*), recession (*R*), and stable-growth (*SG*). The plant is to be used for the next ten years in any case. The present worths of the future profits are given in the matrix below (in millions of dollars).

	BI	R	SG
Automated plant	$4	−$1	$2
General-purpose equipment	2	.5	1

The probability of *SG* is estimated to be .30. If the expectation principle is to be used, what must be the probability of *R* in order to make the automated plant the better choice? If both alternatives have equal expectations, what principle of choice would you suggest?

11–39. Make explicit the decision to install or not to install seat belts in your car. What principle of choice would you use? Why?

11–40. In explaining why the budget of the sales department has been cut and the budget of the industrial engineering department has been increased, a manager reports, "The chances of a successful cost reduction program are greater than the chances for a successful sales expansion program, for a given expenditure of money." How would you explain his decision in terms of the ideas of this chapter?

11–41. You are invited to play the following gambling game. You flip a fair coin until a head appears. The payoff is 2^n cents if the first head occurs on the nth flip. The probability that the first head will occur on the nth flip is simply $(1/2)^n$.

Show that your expected dollar return is infinite. How much would you be willing to pay in order to play? (The St. Petersburg Paradox)

Suppose the person who invites you to play is not infinitely wealthy, but has 2^{20} cents ($10,485.76). What is your expected dollar return?

11–42. The reliability of a weapons system is defined as the probability that it will successfully complete a mission. Given estimates of the cost and reliability of two weapons systems, how would you advise the Secretary of Defense on which to approve for production?

Chapter 12

THE RECOGNITION OF RISK VS. ASSUMED CERTAINTY

INTRODUCTION

AT THIS POINT it is worthwhile to pause and consider in some detail the basic problem of whether a decision is to be treated as one under risk or as one under assumed certainty. In many cases the answer is clear, but there are also many in which the choice between the two basic approaches is a real one. In this chapter we shall attempt to present some of the strategic and tactical considerations involved in the selection of one of these two modes of analysis. An example will be used which involves a planning decision having to do with the production facilities of the firm. Specifically, the question of the appropriate number of machines for a production department will be analyzed, first as a decision under assumed certainty, and then as a decision under risk. Current practice indicates that one confronts an important strategic choice among these two basic methods of analysis. We will attempt to make clear the factors relevant to this choice, which might be called strategic factors, and the tactical considerations involved in the successful execution of whichever method is chosen.

BASIC CONSIDERATIONS

Like most decision problems, the decision as to how many machines should be planned for a certain production department must be approached with three questions in mind. What data are available, or obtainable at reasonable cost (both in time and in money), which are relevant to the planning decision? What sort of model or logical structure can be constructed to predict the consequences and value of various policy choices? What can be "sold" to management? It is surely a platitude to assert that any strategy which is

285

not compatible with realistic answers to these questions is of limited value to the analyst. Yet how often do we find people amassing reams of data for which they can develop no model or logical structure? How often do we come upon complicated mathematical models for which we could never obtain the necessary measurements in an industrial situation? How often do we suffer that frustrating experience of seeing a reasonable piece of analysis find its way into a file, never to be retrieved? These are the problems of strategy to be examined in this chapter.

THE PROBLEM

A typical and important problem in the planning of production facilities is to decide on how many machines will be needed by a plant, or in this case, by a department. We have in mind a typical processing department which will contain similar machines and through which a variety of products may pass. The considerations involved in this decision are obvious. One wants to know the capacity of the type of machine being considered and the production which will be programmed for the department. Then the decision is a simple matter of planning enough machines to carry out the program, or simply matching "supply" and "demand," "capacity" and "load." The trick is to accurately predict the capacity of the machines and the magnitude of the production program. For purposes of discussion let us suggest two rather different approaches or strategies in rationalizing this decision. The approach which may typify much actual practice today treats the decision as one under assumed certainty. We will compare this with an analysis of the decision as one under conditions of risk.

In this example the reader may wish to imagine two groups of analysts studying the problem independently. One group suppresses the risk and deals with the problem as one under assumed certainty. They do this, we will suppose, using a variant of the most probable future principle. Their behavior might be described as suppressing all the variability in their data and using only the mean or average values.

The other group, one might imagine, treats the risk explicitly but assumes for analytical purposes that the utility function of their firm is approximately linear in the relevant region.

Since managerial judgment would undoubtedly enter the decision after each group had made their recommendations to their respective managements, it is difficult to say what the ultimate decision might be in either case. We can, however, show that the analysts themselves reach rather different recommendations.

ASSUMED CERTAINTY

Perhaps it is typical of many instances of this problem that the analyst looks for the following kind of information:

$\bar{T}_{ij}$ = mean performance time for operation i on product j, measured in hours per unit of product

$\bar{D}_j$ = mean demand for product j measured in units per production period

H = number of hours in a production period

$\bar{E}$ = mean effectiveness factor; a decimal taking into account the usual personal allowances, machine downtime, material shortages, scrapped production, etc.

Having consulted the time study department, the sales department, and various other sources for these average values, the analyst then performs the following simple calculation. The mean number of machines required by the department is given by

$$\bar{M} = \sum_i \sum_j \frac{\bar{T}_{ij}\bar{D}_j}{\bar{E}H}$$

where the summation is over products and operations within the department.

This is a fairly typical approach. Note, however, that even the data required here may be difficult to get in an actual situation, and additional simplifications may have to be made, leading eventually to nothing much more than a professional guess. The mathematical model is simple enough for everyone to use and understand. It represents the kind of calculation which most managements seem to find acceptable. The analyst inevitably feels a certain uneasiness at the gross oversimplifications which it involves. He well knows that performance times vary considerably, as any time study sheet clearly shows. Estimates of production demand in most instances are subject to important errors. The events represented by the effectiveness factor also exhibit wide variation. For example, the scrap rate for a process, even when it is in control in the statistical sense, varies to an important extent. Let us assume for the moment that we can obtain data on all these kinds of variation. These data provide the basis for treating the problem as a decision under risk.

RISK

The basic notions associated with this approach are as follows. If the performance times, demands, and effectiveness factors are subject to variation, then the actual number of machines required will itself be subject to variation. Realistically then, the management problem is to decide what number of machines should be installed to best meet this varying requirement. The result will be that, in general, there will be periods in which more machines are available than are required, and also periods in which fewer machines are available than are required. To the analyst developing a model for this decision it may be tactically important to note the analogy to certain inventory decisions which are studied in Chapter 14. The manager must weigh these consequences, recognizing that, as the number of machines is increased, the chance of having insufficient facilities will decrease, but the chance of having excess capacity increases. This leads to the tactical problem of measuring the costs of these events.

Tactically, also, the problem of describing the variation in the data must be faced. In order to exhibit an initial model let us assume that performance times, demands, and effectiveness factors are random variables which may be described by probability distributions. Thus let

$$f(T_{ij}) = \text{probability distribution of } T_{ij}$$
$$g(D_j) = \text{probability distribution of } D_j$$
$$h(E) = \text{probability distribution of } E$$

We assume that H is fixed by policy and is not subject to important variation. The validity of these assumptions is the subject of much familiar debate. For example, there has been extensive discussion as to whether performance times on man-paced operations can be described by simple probability distributions. As we have seen in Chapter 6, if one uses the techniques of inferential statistics to forecast demand, then the resulting forecasts are subject to errors which may be modeled by probability distributions. The effectiveness factor may include such items as machine delays and scrap production, which are often described by the analyst in probabilistic terms. Clearly, if these variables are taken to be random variables, then the required number of machines, m, will itself be a random variable. Thus

$$f(m) = \propto [f(T_{ij}), g(D_j), h(E)]$$

The tactical problem of finding the probability distribution of m may be approached in several ways. If the foregoing distributions are taken to be of analytically known form, then there are analytic methods for obtaining the distribution of m. If, however, the forms are not obtained, one might use the Monte Carlo method for obtaining an estimate of the distribution of m. (98) This step can be a very difficult one in actual practice. To develop a model for the decision one might proceed somewhat as follows. Suppose the following data are on hand:

$$f(m) = \text{probability distribution of actual}$$
$$\text{number of machines required in a}$$
$$\text{period}$$
$$C_1 = \text{fixed charges per machine per period}$$

Considerable simplification of the model results if we assume that any production which cannot be completed during the regular production period is completed on overtime or by subcontracting. This avoids the mathematically difficult problem of accounting for production requirements which are carried forward from one period to the next. Assume for the moment that overtime is chosen. Let

$$C_2 = \text{cost penalty (excess over regular time) per}$$
$$\text{machine-period of overtime production}$$

If we assume that management wishes to formulate a policy which will minimize expected costs, the criterion function may be written as

$$C(M) = C_1 M + C_2 \int_M^\infty (m - M) f(m) dm$$

where $C(M)$ is the expected cost of a policy of providing M machines.

With the aid of the theorem given below we compute the optimal policy by setting

$$\frac{dC(M)}{dM} = 0$$

Theorem: Let

$$g(y) = \int_{u_0(y)}^{u_1(y)} f(x,y) dx$$

then

$$\frac{dg(y)}{dy} = \int_{u_0(y)}^{u_1(y)} \frac{\partial f(x,y)}{\partial y} dx - f(u_0,y) \frac{du_0}{dy} + f(u_1,y) \frac{du_1}{dy}$$

We let

$$y = M \qquad\qquad u_0 = M$$
$$x = m \qquad\qquad u_1 = \bar{m} = \text{maximum value of } m$$
$$f(x,y) = (m - M)f(m)$$

Then

$$\frac{\partial f(x,y)}{\partial y} = -f(m) \qquad f(u_0,y) = (M - M)f(M) = 0$$

$$\frac{du_0}{dy} = 1 \qquad\qquad f(u_1,y) = (\bar{m} - M)f(\bar{m})$$

$$\frac{du_1}{dy} = 0$$

Using these results as indicated by the theorem, it follows that

$$\frac{dC(M)}{dM} = C_1 + C_2 \int_{M}^{\bar{m}} -f(m)dm - (0)(1) + (\bar{m} - M)f(\bar{m})(0)$$

Finally we set this derivative equal to zero and let the value of M which satisfies the resulting equation be M^*. The result turns out to be the value of M, say M^* which satisfies the following relation.

$$\int_{0}^{M^*} f(m)dm = F(M^*) = \frac{C_2 - C_1}{C_2}$$

(We have assumed that M is a continuous variable, but this is easily corrected.)

Whether this model actually fits the real decision to a useful extent depends on a number of crucial assumptions, some of which have been mentioned previously. In addition we have assumed a linear cost structure, and implicitly a number of assumptions would be involved in the computation of the effectiveness factor. Fitting the model is, of course, a tremendous tactical problem.

STRATEGIC CONSIDERATIONS

Let us assume that the tactical problem of the model could be dealt with and examine some of the strategic questions suggested earlier. Clearly the risk approach requires a large amount of data that may be difficult, if not impossible, to obtain in an actual situation. For example, it may not be possible to obtain performance time distributions for operations in the planning stage. If similar operations are already under way, the data may be available. If not, however, the only recourse may be to a synthetic time system which will roughly give the mean performance time. There may easily be such a large degree of uncertainty connected with the future production program that no forecast can be made. One must also recognize those situations in which the data could be obtained but limitations of time and expense prevent it. It must be emphasized, however, that even if the data are not completely available, the model itself may be of real value, as we will indicate.

The model itself presents a number of difficulties which we have outlined, but these may be overcome by anyone familiar with probability theory and the calculus. Actually there are some hidden difficulties of model construction underlying the effectiveness factor which has been used. Suppose, for example, that we have an operation that is under statistical control with respect to a particular quality attribute, and its mean scrap rate is p. One wants to know how many pieces to make in order to get, say, D good pieces. Here again one may resort to averages and say that the average number of pieces to be made to yield D good ones is given by

$$\frac{D}{1 - p}$$

Alternatively, one might wish to be more accurate and say that the probability of having to produce $D + k$ pieces in order to obtain D good pieces is given by

$$\phi(D, k, p) = \frac{(D + k - 1)!}{k!(D - 1)!} \, p^k (1 - p)^D$$

This is obtained by noting that the probability of having to produce $D + k$ pieces in order to obtain D good pieces is the product of the probability of k defectives in $D + k - 1$ pieces times the probability that the last piece produced (piece number $D + k$) will be good.

Probability of k defectives in $D + k - 1$ pieces =
$$\frac{(D + k - 1)!}{k!(D - 1)!} \, p^k (1 - p)^{D-1}$$

Probability that the last piece is good = $1 - p$

FIGURE 12–1

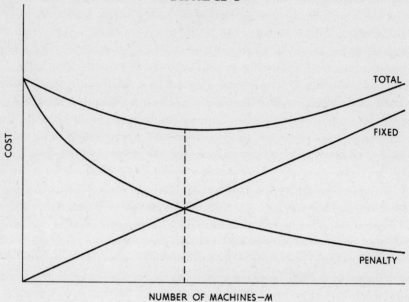

FIGURE 12–2

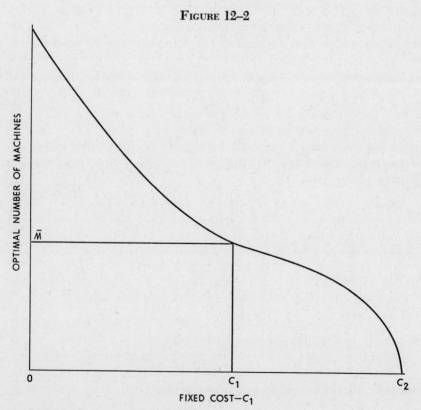

Thus, the model itself may become quite complicated. Experience seems to indicate that it is worthwhile introducing probability distributions as we have done, but that very complicated distributions may perhaps go too far. The step from assumed certainty to risk is nearly always warranted even if the data are not fully available. This step introduces the entire notion of establishing a fixed number of machines in the department, against a requirement which is actually subject to variation. Many feel that if the analyst makes explicit for management the sort of cost function just given, this is itself of considerable value as a basis for management decisions.

The final strategic consideration which was suggested was that of the acceptance by management. This depends heavily on personalities and local factors of course, but something can be said about the benefits of recognizing risk. Let us suppose that the variables in our model are in fact subject to variation, as they are in many situations. The important question then is "How costly will be the errors in our plans if we base them on the assumed certainty approach?"

Figure 12–1 shows the form of a typical cost function and indicates the property of the optimal number of machines. That is, if we plan for any other number of machines, total expected cost will increase. Figure 12–2 indicates the relation between the costs and the optimal number of machines. As C_1 becomes small relative to C_2, more and more machines should be planned for, and contrariwise. If we neglect these costs completely and select a number of machines equal to the average requirement, this is equivalent to assuming values for C_1 and C_2. To the extent that these values are in error, the number of machines will be in error, and thus the cost will be increased.

Figure 12–3 indicates the result of failing to recognize the variation in the required number of machines. As the variation increases, the optimal number of machines increases, and thus the error made by planning for the average machine requirement also increases, if

$$\frac{C_2 - C_1}{C_2} > F(\bar{M}).$$

Finally, Figure 12–4 indicates the difference in total expected costs for the two methods as a function of the variation. Clearly, the more variation present in the machine requirement, the more costly it becomes to overlook variation and plan by using average values. While the exact calculations which these curves suggest

FIGURE 12–3

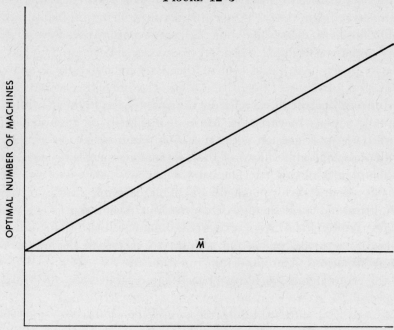

FIGURE 12–4

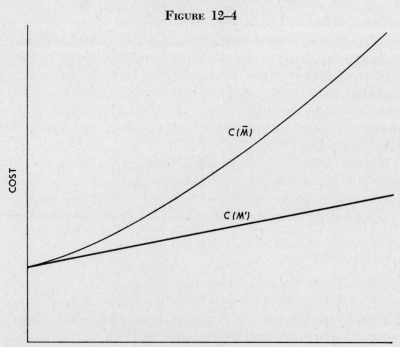

may not be actually carried out, it would seem that the general effects which they portray might well convince management of the importance of somewhat more advanced techniques in studying planning decisions.

CERTAINTY EQUIVALENCE

In some decisions one may move from assumed certainty to risk in a very simple fashion. If, for example, one could minimize expected cost in a decision under risk by minimizing cost in a decision under assumed certainty and then substituting expected values of random variables in place of variables which had been treated as certain, then the decision under assumed certainty may be called the certainty equivalent of the decision under risk.

In Chapter 3 the problem of the economic size of production lots was studied as a decision under certainty. Recalling the symbolism used there, let

$$T = \text{the length of a planning period}$$
$$D = \text{demand to be satisfied over } T$$
$$L = \text{lot size}$$
$$C_1 = \text{setup cost per lot}$$
$$C_2 = \text{storage cost per piece per unit time,}$$
$$\qquad \text{based on average number of units in}$$
$$\qquad \text{storage}$$
$$C(L) = \text{total cost}$$

If all these quantities except L are assumed to be known, then total cost is given by

$$C(L) = C_1 \frac{D}{L} + C_2 \frac{LT}{2}$$

and the lot size which minimizes total cost is

$$L = \sqrt{\frac{2C_1 D}{C_2 T}}$$

Now suppose that our prediction of the storage cost, C_2, is in terms of a probability distribution. The decision may then be treated as one under conditions of risk. Let

$$f(C_2) = \text{probability distribution of } C_2$$
$$E(C_2) = \text{expected value of } C_2$$
$$E(L) = \text{expected cost for a lot size of } L$$

The use of the expectation principle would simply require an expression for $E(L)$ which would then be minimized with respect to L.

$$E(L) = C_1 \frac{D}{L} + E(C_2) \frac{LT}{2}$$

The economic lot size is then

$$L = \sqrt{\frac{2C_1 D}{E(C_2)T}}$$

This is simply the result obtained in the case of assumed certainty, with the expected storage cost substituted for the previously assumed known value.

This is an instance of certainty equivalence. If we have a cost function in which one or more random variables enter in linear fashion, then the expected cost will simply be the linear function of the expected values. Suppose for example that x is a random variable with density function $f(x)$, and mean $E(x)$. Given a cost function of the form

$$c = a + bx$$

the expected cost will be

$$E(c) = \int_x (a + bx)f(x)dx = a + b \int_x xf(x)dx$$
$$= a + bE(x)$$

If, however, the cost function is of the form

$$c = a + bx + ex^2$$

then

$$E(c) = a + bE(x) + eE(x^2)$$

PROBLEMS

12–1. Discuss the following notion: "We do not work with real or absolutely objective decisions, but rather with our own perceptions of decisions. Thus it is critically important in approaching a decision to consider alternative conceptions of it."

12–2. Summarize in your own terms the major differences which arise when the decision discussed in the chapter is viewed as one under risk rather than certainty. Can you formulate any rough principles suggesting when a decision should be treated as one under risk?

12–3. Is it true that if $f(m)$ is symetric around its mean and $C_2 = 2C_1$, then the decision will be the same whether treated as one under risk or one under assumed certainty?

12–4. Referring to the theorem in the chapter, compute the first derivative of $C(M)$ with respect to M, and show that

$$F(M^*) = \frac{C_2 - C_1}{C_2}$$

12–5. Suppose the required number of machines, m, is a normally* distributed random variable with a mean of 100 and a standard deviation of 12. The fixed charges per machine per day are \$30 and the over-time penalty cost per machine-day is \$50. Find the number of machines which will minimize total expected cost.

12–6. Assume the required number of machines is given by

$$m = \sum_i \sum_j \frac{T_{ij} D_j}{E H}$$

Suppose E, H, and the D_j are assumed to be certainly known. The T_{ij} are, however, normally distributed with means μ_{ij} and standard deviations σ_{ij}. What is the probability distribution of m?

12–7. Assume the probability distribution of m is a uniform distribution over the range $90 < m \leqslant 110$.

a) If $C_1 = \$20$ and $C_2 = \$25$, find the number of machines which will minimize total expected cost.

b) Find the number of machines which will fix the probability of working overtime at .10.

c) Find the number of machines which will make the probability of any machines being idle during regular production time equal to .05.

12–8. Using the data of problem 12–7, and keeping the mean of the required number of machines constant, plot the optimal number of machines as a function of the standard deviation of m. Plot the difference in total cost between the optimal number of machines and the average number required, as a function of the standard deviation of m.

12–9. Prepare a short explanation for management's reasons for treating the decision in 12–8 as one under risk. What additional difficulties does this treatment present?

12–10. Explain the principle, "The more variation that is present in the required number of machines, the more costly it becomes to overlook this variation and plan on the basis of averages."

12–11. Consider a plant in which $f(m)$ is normally distributed with a mean of 100 machines. For values of the standard deviation of m equal to 10, 20, and 30 machines, and for values of

$$\frac{C_2 - C_1}{C_2}$$

---

* In Problems 12–5, 12–6, and 12–11, neglect the fact that it would be more realistic to deal with truncated normal distributions since the variables cannot meaningfully be negative.

equal to .50, .60, .80, and .90, find the number of machines which minimizes expected cost.

12–12. Reformulate the model of this chapter recognizing that the number of machines chosen by management should be considered a discrete rather than a continuous variable.

12–13. Sketch Figure 12–3 for the case in which

$$\frac{C_2 - C_1}{C_2} < \int_0^{\overline{M}} f(m)\ dm$$

12–14. How would you respond to an analyst who solves the problem discussed in this chapter as one under assumed certainty but claims that risk is actually considered in the final actions taken by management. It is considered, he claims, by managers using their long experience to supplement his calculations with judgments.

12–15. How would you proceed in a case where management found it extremely difficult to associate a dollar value with having fewer machines than required?

12–16. Suppose you had computed the number of machines which would minimize expected costs in a given situation. Now suppose you wish to take account of the fact that the decision maker's utility function increases at a decreasing rate. Would this increase or decrease the number of machines previously computed?

12–17. In which of the following decisions under risk do certainty equivalents exist?

a) Choosing between two machines so as to minimize the expected value of the present worth when salvage values are predicted in the form of probability distributions.

b) Choosing between two machines so as to minimize equivalent annual cost when service lives are predicted in the form of probability distributions.

c) Choosing the number of machines so as to minimize fixed charges plus expected penalty costs, as discussed in this chapter.

12–18. A firm is attempting to decide between two types of trucks, one a conventional gasoline-powered vehicle and the other diesel powered. The following information has been obtained:

	Gasoline Truck	Diesel Truck
Purchase price.............	$9,000	$7,000
Service life................	4 years	3 years
Salvage value.............	$3,000	$2,000
Operating cost per mile.....	$.14	$.12

Interest is charged at 5 per cent. Which type would be preferred if the annual mileage is predicted to be normally distributed with a mean of 5,000 and a standard deviation of 100?

Chapter 13

DECISIONS UNDER RISK—EXAMPLES

REPRESENTING DECISIONS BY MODELS

To STUDY A management decision we begin by making it explicit in the form of a model. The model is not the actual situation but simply a representation of it. The function of the model is to bring conceptual order out of the perceptual confusion with which experience comes to us. The model is an abstraction or simplification of reality. The creation of a useful model involves difficult compromises between complex models which reflect the rich detail of reality and thus give a more comprehensive basis for choice on one hand, and, on the other, simple models which can be understood, can readily be manipulated, and require reasonable amounts of data and computation. It is difficult, perhaps impossible, to give general directions as to how to create a model of a given decision situation which will turn out to be useful. Rather, the development of models must be regarded as an art. In the next few chapters we undertake one way of communicating this art, that is, to invite the reader to examine a number of examples of models of decisions under risk. This art is learned by experience and experiment, and these examples attempt to begin this process. Let us begin with a typical decision problem and note the ways in which the model abstracts and simplifies.

A machinery manufacturer is concerned about the quality of a casting which goes into his machines. In particular, he asks an analyst to investigate the precautions which might be taken to prevent castings having certain types of internal defects from finding their way into finished machines. After considerable study he concludes that a choice must be made between three inspection policies:

a_1: Do not inspect the castings at all. Castings which fail in service will have to be replaced by a service representative sent out from a regional sales office.

a_2: Adopt an inspection device which detects the defects about 90 per

cent of the time if they are present. Use the device on every casting.

  a_3: Adopt a more modern and foolproof inspection method which always detects the defects. Use this method on every casting.

At the expense of considerable effort he is able to obtain the following information upon which to base the choice. The cost of sending
out a service representative to replace a casting which has failed in
service is estimated to be $20 on the average. The cost of inspect-
ing a casting using the device in a_2 is 40 cents. The inspection device contemplated in a_3 will cost an estimated $1.20 per casting
inspected. Records of inspection for past lots of these castings indicate that it is rather consistently true that one casting in ten has
these troublesome defects.

  Now suppose we consider a particular casting which (unknown
to us) has these internal defects. Under policy a_1 it will not be inspected but will eventually fail in service and cost the manufacturer $20 to replace it. Under policy a_2 the manufacturer incurs
a cost of 40 cents for inspection, but there is a chance of 10 per cent
that the inspection will not detect the defects, and thus the casting
will be used in a machine. It will later fail in service and an additional charge of $20 will be the result. Using policy a_3 the manu-
facturer simply spends $1.20 for inspection which invariably
catches the defects. Consider, on the other hand, what happens
when a perfectly good casting is encountered. Policy a_1 results in no
expense; policy a_2 results in an inspection cost of 40 cents; and
policy a_3, a cost of $1.20. If we add to this the idea that the prob-
ability of a defective casting is .10, the choice may be summarized
in the familiar notation:

S_1 = a defective casting detected by the inspection device of a_2
S_2 = a defective casting not detected by the inspection device of a_2
S_3 = a perfect casting
p_1 = (Probability of a defective casting) (Probability of detecting with a_2)
  = $(.10)(.90) = .09$
p_2 = (Probability of a defective casting) (Probability of not detecting
  with a_2)
  = $(.10)(.10) = .01$
p_3 = .90

	$p_1 = .09$ S_1	$p_2 = .01$ S_2	$p_3 = .90$ S_3
a_1	$20.00	$20.00	0
a_2	.40	20.40	$ .40
a_3	1.20	1.20	1.20

Now if we consider the amounts of money in this matrix small in terms of the resources of the manufacturer, we might reasonably recommend the action which minimizes the expected cost. This would be equivalent to approximating his utility function by a straight line in the region of interest in this decision. The result would be

$$E(a_1) = (.09)(\$20.00) + (.01)(\$20.00) + (.90)(0)$$
$$= \$2.00$$

Similarly

$$E(a_2) = \$ \ .60$$
$$E(a_3) = \$1.20$$

Thus policy a_2 would be recommended as the action which minimizes expected costs. Several comments might be made about this analysis of a decision under risk.

1. The basic decision model may help to organize the data which is relevant to the decision and make it more readily understandable.

2. Somehow a conclusion has been reached to terminate the search for alternatives and consider only three. Others may have been briefly examined and discarded previously, perhaps on the basis of some rough aspiration level principle. When the analysis is completed, none of the three may be "acceptable" to the manager, and we may be asked to search further. If the actions studied do not lend themselves to satisfactory predictions or evaluations of outcomes, we may also decide to search further.

3. Risk enters in two ways: by way of the probabilistic performance of the inspection device in a_2, and by way of the probabilistic occurrence of defective castings. The probabilities were obtained in the first case by accepting the manufacturer's data, and in the second case through the fortunate presence of past data in the firm. If these had not been available we would have had to get judgments of the probabilities or treat the decision as one under uncertainty.

4. In dealing with the costs we suppressed uncertainty or risk and used average values as, for example, in the case of the cost of sending out a service representative. If there is a possibility that this cost may on occasion be very large, our linear approximation to the manufacturer's utility function may be in danger.

5. We have exhibited money outcomes only, neglecting such other value considerations as the manufacturer's reputation for

quality or the customers' ill will when failures occur. The difficulty of evaluating these outcomes leads typically to a situation in which an aspiration level principle is useful. For example, the analyst might recommend the action which minimizes the probability that a casting will fail in service.

6. If the probability of a defective casting had been much smaller, the decision might never have arisen, or it might have been treated with a most probable future principle.

These are but a few of the ways in which, by using a model to represent the decision, we simplify it and abstract from the complexity of reality. Whether it is a useful model is initially a matter of the analyst's judgment and finally a matter of the results observed when the manager undertakes some action. In the examples which follow, it will be left to the reader to raise such points as these in contexts of his own experience and interests. We will simply present a variety of examples of decisions under risk, showing how the various principles of choice might be applied.

INSURANCE DECISIONS

A number of decisions are of the same general form as the decision to insure or not to insure against some loss. Many of these may be usefully treated as decisions under conditions of risk. The general form of these decisions is roughly as follows. On payment of a premium, P, one will be insured against a loss of amount L. The loss L may itself be a random variable which depends on the nature of the catastrophe which generates the loss; however, we will treat it simply as a constant. The basic decision is then whether or not to insure against this loss. Let

$$a_1 = \text{insure}$$
$$a_2 = \text{do not insure}$$
$$S_1 = \text{the catastrophe occurs}$$
$$S_2 = \text{catastrophe does not occur}$$

Assuming that we have evidence indicating the probabilities of the possible future, the decision is one under conditions of risk.

COST MATRIX

	p_1 S_1	$1 - p_1$ S_2
a_1	P	P
a_2	L	0

Examining this decision in the light of the expectation principle, it is clear that a_1 will be preferred if

$$E(a_1) = P < E(a_2) = p_1 L$$

The interesting thing about this decision is that in many applications the expectation principle does not lead to the decision to insure. If we are considering actual insurance decisions such as fire, accident, life, or health insurance, it would be reasonable to suppose that the insurance company wishes to make a profit, or at least cover its costs of operation. If the insurance company itself uses the expectation principle, as it well might, in fixing the premium, then to make a profit of average amount k on each policy it must be that

$$P = p_1 L + k$$

If this is the case then it follows that $E(a_1) > E(a_2)$ and the expectation principle will suggest that one not insure.

This type of decision seems clearly the place to apply some form of the aspiration level principle. Much of our thinking about insurance follows the line that we are willing to pay the premium and accept a small but certain loss in order to be protected against the possibility of a large loss. This might be expressed by suggesting that we have an aspiration level A which lies in the interval

$$P < A < L$$

and thus minimize the probability of having our loss exceed the level A by insuring.

In actuality this decision may be complicated by other factors. It might be that the probabilities used by the decision maker are different from those used by the insurance company. For example, the man whose family seems to incur more than the average amount of illness will consider health insurance a good buy. The family which has a history of less than the average amount of illness might decide not to insure. It may also be that the insurance company returns some of its investment profits to its policyholders and thus effectively reduces the premiums. Insurance statistics indicate that for a given type of industrial plant the probability of a fire in a one-year period is .003. Given that a fire occurs, the loss, y, is a random variable with an exponential distribution:

$$f(y) = .00001 \, e^{-(.00001)y}$$

The expected loss L is

$$L = \int_y y\, f(y)\, dy = \frac{1}{.00001} = \$100,000$$

If a given plant is insured. the expected liability of the insurance company is simply the probability of a fire times the expected loss, given that there is a fire.

$$(.003)(100,000) = \$300$$

If the insurance company charges a premium of $300 it will just break even in the long run. It must, however, cover its operating expenses and perhaps make a profit. Suppose it does this by increasing the premium by 10 per cent to $330 per year.

Now the manufacturer who wishes to buy fire insurance finds that, if he does insure, his expected cost is simply the premium of $330, but if he does not insure, the expected cost is only $300. In most cases, however, he will be willing to pay the premium as a guarantee against the large losses which might result from a fire. If he wishes to maximize the probability that his cost will be less than A, he will insure for any $A > \$330$.

Examples of other decisions of roughly the same form as this are indicated in the following list. It should be noted that in some of these the expectation principle will appear more reasonable than in others.

1. Equipping a fleet of trucks with spare tires.
2. Investment in flood control structures.
3. Installation of safety and fire prevention devices.
4. Provision of spare machines.
5. Provision of spare parts.
6. Cross-training workers for critical jobs.
7. Provision of safety banks of material along a production line.

To apply the expectation principle to decisions having outcomes involving human life, such as safety programs, fire prevention, and flood control, requires the placing of a value on a human life. One usually tries to avoid this problem and reach some acceptable level of risk of loss of life.

WAITING LINES

One interesting and well-developed class of operational decisions has to do with the management of waiting line or queuing processes. There are a wide variety of physical processes involving interrupted flow which may be viewed as waiting lines. When customers go into a cafeteria their flow is interrupted while food is served and thus a waiting line (or queue) is formed. When automobiles move up to an intersection their flow may be interrupted by a traffic signal and again a line is formed. The same general phenomenon of interrupted flow may be seen in aircraft waiting to land, in telephone messages waiting to be put through an exchange, and in material flowing through a job shop. Decision problems involving these processes are interesting both because of the way in which risk arises and because of the limited freedom of choice open to the decision maker.

Consider a specific example in which orders flow from customers to a manufacturing plant, the plant produces to order, and the product then flows to the customers. To be specific let us assume

1. Orders arrive at the plant in an independent random manner which can be described by a Poisson distribution. That is, the probability that the plant will receive exactly x orders in a time interval of length t is

$$f(x, t) = \frac{e^{-\lambda t}(\lambda t)^x}{x!}$$

Here it will be noted that the mean of the Poisson distribution is λt. This is the mean number of orders received by the plant in an interval of length t. The mean rate at which orders arrive is

$$\frac{\lambda t}{t} = \lambda$$

2. Orders are produced in the same sequence in which they are received.
3. The production time for an order is a random variable, r, having a negative exponential distribution.

$$g(r) = \mu e^{-\mu r}$$

It can be shown here that μ turns out to be the mean production rate of the plant (orders per unit time).

4. It will be assumed that the plant works on only one order at a time and that $\lambda < \mu$. Some violence is done here since the plant may, in fact, work on more than one order at a time. Actually, however, it is usually some "bottleneck" operation which effectively fixes the production rate of a plant, and this operation may work on only one order at a time. In understanding the requirement that λ be less than μ, it is necessary to recall that these represent the mean rate at which orders arrive and the mean rate at which they are produced, respectively. If, in the long run, the average arrival rate exceeds the average production rate, then orders will pile up indefinitely. In the limit we would have an infinite waiting line. In practice a plant may actually operate successfully with $\lambda > \mu$ by working overtime to catch up.

The reader will rightly suspect that many of these assumptions are made on the basis of technical considerations, rather than in an attempt to capture reality. While it is not our purpose to elaborate on the mathematics involved in making deductions from these assumptions, it is important to examine the results which provide some important insights. (98) Under these assumptions it is possible to derive the following interesting results. Let

n = number of orders in production and waiting to be produced at the plant. (The backlog is $n - 1$ since we have assumed that the plant works on one order at a time.)

$p(n)$ = the probability distribution of n

Now it seems reasonable that if orders are received in a random manner, and if the production time is random, then the number of orders, n, will itself be a random variable. Thus, in making decisions which will influence the size of its backlog, the firm will be confronted with decisions involving risk.

It is possible to show that this probability distribution depends only on λ and μ.

$$p(n) = \left(1 - \frac{\lambda}{\mu}\right)\left(\frac{\lambda}{\mu}\right)^n$$

This provides the basic expression of risk from which it is possible to derive the following additional results:

$p(0) = 1 - \dfrac{\lambda}{\mu}$ the probability that the plant will be idle

$E(n) = \dfrac{\lambda}{\mu - \lambda}$ the expected number of orders awaiting completion at the plant

$E(w) = \dfrac{1}{\mu - \lambda}$ the average time elapsing between the receipt of the order and its shipment to the customer, or the average time in the system

$P(n) = 1 - \left(\dfrac{\lambda}{\mu}\right)^{n+1}$ the cumulative distribution of n

Assume that on the basis of a study of past operations it is estimated that the number of orders, x, received by the plant in a day is a random variable with a Poisson distribution having a mean of 24 orders per day.

$$t = 1, \lambda = 24 \qquad\qquad f(x) = e^{-24}\frac{24^x}{x!}$$

Suppose further that the production time for an order is a random variable having an exponential distribution with a mean of $\frac{1}{25}$ day per order. The mean production rate is then 25 orders per day.

$$\mu = 25 \qquad\qquad g(r) = 25e^{-25r}$$

The probability distribution of the number of orders on hand is

$$p(n) = \left\{1 - \frac{24}{25}\right\}\left\{\frac{24}{25}\right\}^n = \frac{1}{25}\left\{\frac{24}{25}\right\}^n$$

The proportion of idle time is

$$p(0) = 1 - \frac{24}{25} = \frac{1}{25}$$

The expected number of orders on hand is

$$E(n) = \frac{24}{25 - 24} = 24 \text{ orders}$$

The expected time an order spends in the production system is

$$E(w) = \frac{1}{25 - 24} = 1 \text{ day}$$

By various (costly) changes in plant equipment and work force, the *mean* production rate may be changed. Note that it is probably possible for the production manager to choose only the mean production rate for he is unlikely to be able to influence the instantaneous production rate. Suppose the mean rate at which orders arrive is taken to be beyond the control of the production manager. The decision which he faces is one of fixing the mean production rate of the plant.

The equations set forth previously may be seen to confirm one's intuition about the results of changes in the mean production rate. If the mean production rate is increased, the average number of orders waiting will decrease, the average time between receipt and shipment will decrease, but the probability that the plant will be idle will increase. Thus, the decision may be roughly characterized as one of balancing idle time for the plant against good service for the customers.

Now suppose that as is usually the case, the production rate cannot be fixed at *any* average level in the short run, but rather a choice must be made among several distinct levels. Assume that the production manager's decision involves three alternatives:

a_1: continue with present equipment which achieves a mean production rate of $\mu_1 = 25$

a_2: purchase new machine A which will increase the mean production rate of the plant to $\mu_2 = 27$ but will require an equivalent annual cost of $AC(A)$

a_3: purchase new machine B which will increase the mean production rate of the plant to a level $\mu_3 = 28$ but will require an equivalent annual cost of $AC(B)$

To apply the expectation principle, it is necessary to define

H = number of days per year of plant operation
λH = expected number of orders received per year
C_w = cost per order day of waiting or delay time
C_{Ii} = cost of having the plant idle for one day under alternative i
$E(a_i)$ = expected annual cost increment (or decrement) relative to alternative i

The expected increment annual costs are then

$$E(a_1) = 0$$

$$E(a_2) = AC(A) + C_{I2}H\left(1 - \frac{\lambda}{\mu_2}\right) - C_{I1}H\left(1 - \frac{\lambda}{\mu_1}\right)$$
$$+ C_w(\lambda H)\left(\frac{1}{\mu_2 - \lambda} - \frac{1}{\mu_1 - \lambda}\right)$$

$$E(a_3) = AC(B) + C_{I3}H\left(1 - \frac{\lambda}{\mu_3}\right) - C_{I1}H\left(1 - \frac{\lambda}{\mu_1}\right)$$
$$+ C_w(\lambda H)\left(\frac{1}{\mu_3 - \lambda} - \frac{1}{\mu_1 - \lambda}\right)$$

Assume

$$AC(A) = \$6,000$$
$$AC(B) = \$8,000$$
$$C_{Ii} = \$1,000, \text{ for all } i$$
$$H = 250 \text{ days}$$
$$C_w = \$8.00$$

Then

$$E(a_1) = 0$$

$$E(a_2) = 6,000 + 1,000(250)\left(1 - \frac{24}{27}\right) - 1000(250)\left(1 - \frac{24}{25}\right)$$
$$+ (8)(24)(250)\left\{\frac{1}{27 - 24} - \frac{1}{25 - 24}\right\}$$

$$= -\$8,223$$

$$E(a_3) = 8,000 + 1,000(250)\left(1 - \frac{24}{28}\right) - 1000(250)\left(1 - \frac{24}{25}\right)$$
$$+ (8)(24)(250)\left\{\frac{1}{28 - 24} - \frac{1}{25 - 24}\right\}$$

$$= -\$2,286$$

Negative expectation in the cases of a_2 and a_3 indicate a decrement in expected cost relative to a_1. Thus, both of the latter would reduce costs, but a_2, involving the purchase of machine A, would appear to be the most advantageous. While these equations provide a suitable statement of the expectations involved, often the cost coefficients, C_{li} and C_w, will present serious difficulties of measurement. Typically, the cost of having an order delayed between its arrival at the plant and shipment to the customer may be realized largely in terms of customers' attitudes and satisfactions which may be virtually impossible to evaluate. Such a situation often leads to the use of an aspiration level principle as a means of circumventing this value measurement problem. Instead of attempting to obtain from management some indication of the costs, one tries to discover what level of plant idleness, waiting time, or average backlog the firm is willing to tolerate. A variety of aspiration level statements are possible.

1. The average proportion of plant idle time should be kept below some level A_1.

$$1 - \frac{\lambda}{\mu} < A_1$$

2. The average time in the system for an order should not exceed a level A_2.

$$\frac{1}{\mu - \lambda} < A_2$$

3. The probability that the number of orders in the backlog exceeds some number A_3 must be kept below some value P.

$$P(A_3) = 1 - \left(\frac{\lambda}{\mu}\right)^{A_3 + 1} > 1 - P$$

4. The average number of orders in the backlog should be kept below some level A_4.

$$\frac{\lambda}{\mu - \lambda} < A_4$$

One might select one or more of these statements and then apply a principle of the form: *Select the alternative which satisfies the aspiration level statements with a minimum equivalent annual cost.* Clearly, difficulties may arise in that no alternative may satisfy the aspiration levels selected, or the cost of satisfying them may be excessive in management's view. Such difficulties may lead to a reformulation of the principle of choice or simply to the application of judgment in the choice without the use of an explicit principle.

In many situations one must be content to prepare a description of the outcomes and let management apply judgment to determine a choice. Thus one might simply confront management with a table such as the following:

Alternative	Annual Cost of Additional Investment	Expected Plant Idle Time	Expected Order Waiting Time, Days
a_1	0	4.0%	1
a_2	$6,000	11.1	.33
a_3	8,000	14.3	.25

The problem may be reformulated to suggest the point of view of the sales manager who might have some control over the mean rate at which orders are received by the plant. Such a reformulation would probably need to take account of changes in the firm's revenue, the cost of changing levels of sales effort, as well as whatever price changes might be required.

The waiting line model suggested here in its most elementary form turns out to be applicable to a variety of interesting decision problems in which risk arises because of some random process of interrupted flow.

MAINTENANCE POLICY

Decisions involving policy for preventive maintenance or replacement of machines and machine components are often treated as decisions under risk. The source of risk in this case is usually the difficulty of predicting exactly when a machine is going to break down or require maintenance. If one could predict exactly when the fuel pump of a truck was going to fail it would be easy to replace the pump just before failure. While this would be the best possible maintenance policy, it is not generally possible to make such predictions.

Let us take as a simple specific example of such a decision, the case of a large automatic transfer machine which contains a number of cutting tools. The decision involves the time at which these tools should be replaced. The basic values involved include the very high cost of having a tool fail during the production period, shutting down the machine and the entire production line of which it is a part, and replacing the tool as quickly as possible. Here the major costs are in terms of lost production and enforced idleness of the facilities. On the other hand, there is the possibility that all the tools might be replaced during some time when the machine is idle anyway in the hope that the new tools will reduce the incidence of failures during the production period. Since tools are expensive and the cost of installing them is not trivial, one does not wish to recklessly replace all the tools in a machine every day. The first decision is whether to replace tools only when they fail, or to adopt some policy of preventive replacement of all tools at periodic times. While this decision may itself be studied as one under conditions of risk, let us assume that it has been decided that some preventive replacement policy will be used. The problem then is how often to perform this preventive replacement.

Let us further suppose that it is possible to describe the risk involved by studying the lives of a large sample of such tools. To further simplify the problem assume that all tools behave in nearly the same way with respect to service life. As was suggested in Chapter 6, a mortality curve might be used to describe the behavior observed. Let

$p(t)$ = the probability that a new tool will fail after t periods of service

Assume further that time is to be measured in discrete intervals and that all failures and replacements may be thought of as occurring at the end of an interval. The problem might then be to choose a policy of the following form:

1. All tools which fail are replaced immediately.
2. After T periods, all tools, whether they have failed or not are removed and replaced. This is what is meant by preventive replacement.

The problem of choice is that of selecting the best value of T in the light of two costs:

C_1 = cost per tool of preventive replacement
C_2 = cost per tool of replacement when failure occurs during the production period

Now suppose under our policy we begin with N new tools installed. The first question to be answered is, "How many tools will fail in some period t?" It is simplest and perhaps most natural to answer this question in terms of the expected number of tools which will fail, and thus at the very outset we are led toward the use of an expectation principle. In period t, some tools will fail after having served successfully for the intervening periods. The expected number behaving in this way is (see Chapter 6)

$$Np(t)$$

Some tools will also fail in some period x prior to t, they will be replaced, and their replacements will then fail in period t. The number of tools on the average behaving in this way will be

$$Np(x)p(t - x)$$

This can happen for any period x up to $x = t - 1$. Thus, the number of "second failures" in period t will be on the average

$$N\sum_{x=1}^{t-1}p(x)\,p(t - x)$$

There will be "third failures" and "fourth failures" and so on to be computed and summed to get the expected number of failures in period t. If we let $f(t)$ stand for this number, then

$$f(t) = N\left\{ p(t) + \sum_{x=1}^{t-1}p(x)\,p(t - x) \right.$$

$$\left. + \sum_{y=2}^{t-1}\sum_{x=1}^{y-1}p(x)\,p(y - x)\,p(t - y) + \cdots \right\}$$

As an example, $f(3)$ would be computed as follows:

$$f(3) = N\{p(3) + p(1)p(2) + p(2)p(1) + p(1)p(1)p(1)\}$$

We are now in a position to apply the expectation principle to the choice of T. At the end of T periods we plan to replace all tools. The cost of doing this will be NC_1. Up to this time we will replace only the tools which fail. The expected cost of these replacements is given by

$$C_2\sum_{t=1}^{T-1}f(t)$$

Using T-1 for the upper limit of this summation corresponds to the assumption that failures which occur in period T are not replaced immediately (at cost C_2), but are replaced as a part of the preventive replacement program at the end of period T (at a cost C_1). If failures in period T are not replaced in this way, but must be taken care of immediately, then the upper limit of the summation should be T. Finally the expected cost for a given T is

$$E(T) = NC_1 + C_2 \sum_{t=1}^{T-1} f(t)$$

Since this is nondecreasing with T, we will actually wish to base the choice on the expected per-period cost, $E(T)/T$.

For T to minimize expected costs it must be that

$$\frac{E(T+1)}{T+1} - \frac{E(T)}{T} \geqslant 0$$

and

$$\frac{E(T-1)}{T-1} - \frac{E(T)}{T} \geqslant 0$$

The reader may verify that the results of applying these conditions are

$$C_2 f(T) \geqslant \frac{NC_1 + C_2 \sum_{t=1}^{T-1} f(t)}{T}$$

$$C_2 f(T-1) \leqslant \frac{NC_1 + \sum_{t=1}^{T-2} f(t)}{T-1}$$

The value of T which satisfies these relations will be that which yields a unique minimum as long as $f(t)$ behaves in an ordinary way, which need not concern us at the moment. These relations may be rewritten as

$$C_2 f(T) \geqslant \frac{E(T)}{T}$$

$$C_2 f(T-1) \leqslant \frac{E(T-1)}{T-1}$$

We may now make a familiar interpretation of the result. Preventive replacement should be made at the end of a period T for which the cost of replacing failures during the period is greater than the average per-period cost through the end of the period. This is the marginal cost–average cost relation which has been encountered previously. As long as the marginal cost for the period is less than the average cost through the end of the period, then preventive replacement is not made. This latter statement follows directly from the second relation above.

As we have suggested previously, the nature of this decision leads quite naturally to treatment with the expectation principle.

It is, however, possible to formulate other principles which have appeal. Especially if it is difficult to measure the cost coefficients which enter the expectations, one might wish to appeal to some sort of aspiration level principle. For example, we might decide to do preventive replacement at the end of some period T during which the expected number of failures first exceeds some predetermined level A. That is, perform preventive replacement as soon as $f(t) > A$. In considering such things as light bulbs, we might decide not to replace failures at all, but to replace all bulbs as soon as the number which have failed reaches some predetermined level.

To illustrate numerically the use of the expectation principle, suppose we start with 100 tools with known mortality distribution. From this we derive $f(t)$ with the following assumed results:

t	1	2	3	4	5	6	7	8	9	10
$f(t)$	3	8	14	15	15	14	12	18	15	17

In fact, we would have to be concerned with the behavior of $f(t)$ beyond ten periods, but to simplify the problem we will truncate the data at this point. Suppose it is also known that the cost of changing a tool when preventive replacement is undertaken is \$10. The cost of replacing a tool and other resulting costs when failure occurs during the production period is \$50. Table 13–1 indicates

TABLE 13–1

Col. 1	Col. 2	Col. 3	Col. 4	Col. 5
T	$C_2 f(T)$	$C_2 \sum_{t=1}^{T} f(t)$	$NC_1 + C_2 \sum_{t=1}^{T-1} f(t)$	Col. 4 ÷ T
1.............	\$150	\$ 150	\$1,000	\$1,000
2.............	400	550	1,150	575
3.............	700	1,250	1,550	517
4.............	750	2,000	2,250	562
5.............	750	2,750	3,000	600
6.............	700	3,450	3,750	625
7.............	600	4,050	4,450	636
8.............	900	4,950	5,050	631
9.............	750	5,700	5,950	650
10.............	850	6,550	6,700	670

the usual method of solution. From this table it is evident that preventive replacement should be undertaken at the end of three periods. It may also be confirmed that the conditions for optimality derived previously are satisfied for both $T = 3$ and $T = 8$, although the absolute minimum occurs at $T = 3$.

RECTIFYING INSPECTION

One of the basic decisions in quality management is the decision to accept or reject a lot of a product received from a supplier. The decision hangs basically on the quality of the product in question, which we will suppose can be described simply in terms of good or bad, effective or defective. This decision is often handled by determining in advance an acceptance sampling plan which specifies the exact routine for making the choice. When a lot consisting of S units is submitted by the supplier, the purchaser takes a sample of N pieces at random from the lot. These pieces are classified by inspection as either effective or defective. In any given instance let the number of defective units discovered in the sample be x. The acceptance sampling plan contains a decision rule which states that if x is less than or equal to some acceptance number c, the lot is to be accepted, otherwise the lot is rejected. Risk arises in this decision because the purchaser does not, in general, know in advance how many defectives are in a lot, and because the decision about the lot is based on inference from a sample rather than an examination of the entire lot.

The decision problem is usually treated as one of choosing an acceptance sampling plan. To make the analysis of this decision especially simple we add one additional assumption. Whenever a lot is rejected, it is then inspected 100 per cent and all defective units are repaired or replaced. This process is called "rectifying inspection."

The basic expression of risk in such a decision is the probability that a sampling plan will lead the purchaser to accept a lot which has some proportion of defectives p'. In general p' is unknown, but one may suppose a value for it and then calculate the probability of acceptance. The binomial distribution is often used to calculate this probability, Pa.

$$Pa = \sum_{x=o}^{c} \frac{N!}{x!(N-x)!}(p')^x(1-p')^{N-x}$$

In choosing a plan the relevant values often include the cost of performing the inspection and the cost associated with accepting a defective product. The more inspection done, the less bad product will be accepted on the average, and contrariwise. Here again expectations appear immediately as the most manageable and natural quantities with which to deal.

Any such acceptance sampling plan may be characterized simply by stating the sample size, N, and the acceptance number, c. The average amount of inspection per lot may be obtained as follows. Every lot will be sampled, and thus N items will be inspected. Whenever a lot is rejected, the remaining $S - N$ items will be inspected under our assumption of rectifying inspection. Thus the average number of items inspected per lot will be (average total inspection)

$$ATI = N + (1 - Pa)(S - N)$$

where $1 - Pa$ is the probability of rejecting a lot. Since Pa depends upon p', so does ATI.

The number of bad items accepted will be zero whenever a lot is rejected. However, when a lot is accepted there is the possibility of accepting some bad items in it. If the supplier furnishes a lot with a proportion of defectives p', the probability of acceptance may be computed as indicated previously. If the lot is accepted, $S - N$ items will not be inspected. These will contain an average of $p'(S - N)$ defective units. Thus the average number of defective units accepted per lot is

$$ADA = Pap'(S - N)$$

Now if we let C_1 be the unit cost of inspection and C_2 be the unit cost of accepting defectives, the expected cost per lot for a given sampling plan will be

$$E(N,c) = C_1\{N + (1 - Pa)(S - N)\} + C_2Pap'(S - N)$$

This expectation depends on p', the proportion of defectives in the incoming lots. In most interesting decisions this quantity is not known in advance nor is a probabilistic prediction of it available. The decision is then one under conditions of uncertainty. For purposes of illustration let us suppose that, although p' may not be known in advance, we are able to make a probabilistic prediction on the basis of past experience with the supplier in question. If this is the case, we will be able to select a sampling plan which will minimize expected costs. This is best suggested by way of a numerical example.

Let us suppose that our experience with the supplier suggests that when his process is operating satisfactorily the lots which he sends average about 1 per cent defective. His process runs satisfactorily about 60 per cent of the time. There are occasions when something goes wrong in his plant, and the fraction defective of the lots he sends rises to 2 per cent. This happens about 30 per cent of the time. Further, about 10 per cent of the time his process goes seriously awry and the fraction defective jumps to an average of 4 per cent. Thus, the decision will involve three possible futures which may be tabulated as follows:

$$S_1 : p' = .01 \qquad p_1 = .60$$
$$S_2 : p' = .02 \qquad p_2 = .30$$
$$S_3 : p' = .04 \qquad p_3 = .10$$

Actually there are a very large number of possible sampling plans among which to choose, since any suitable sample size and acceptance number determine a plan. To make things simple, however, suppose we have somehow narrowed the choice down to three plans which now form the alternatives in the decision.

$$a_1 : c = 1 \qquad N = 100$$
$$a_2 : c = 1 \qquad N = 200$$
$$a_3 : c = 3 \qquad N = 100$$

In going forward toward the computation of the expected costs for each alternative it is necessary first to obtain the probabilities of acceptance. These may be obtained by means of various statistical short cuts, with the following results:

PROBABILITY OF ACCEPTANCE

	S_1	S_2	S_3
a_1	.74	.42	.09
a_2	.42	.09	.003
a_3	.98	.85	.45

The reader should examine these to see if they agree with his intuitions about the problems.

Assuming that the product is shipped in lots of 1,000 units, the average amount of inspection per lot (ATI) and the average number of defectives accepted per lot (ADA) may be computed.

	S_1		S_2		S_3	
	ATI	ADA	ATI	ADA	ATI	ADA
a_1	334	6.7	622	7.6	919	3.2
a_2	664	3.3	928	1.6	998	.01
a_3	118	8.8	235	15.3	595	16.2

Again the reader should check these results against his intuition.

Now let us assume that the cost of inspection is $1.00 per unit and that the unit cost of accepting a defective item is $10.00. The expected costs for each of the alternative sampling plans under each of the possible lot fraction defectives are as follows:

	S_1	S_2	S_3
a_1	$401	$698	$951
a_2	697	944	999
a_3	206	388	999

Here there is little need to compute the expectations associated with each alternative since a_3 clearly minimizes expected cost. In general, however, it will be necessary to use the probabilities of the possible futures to actually compute the expected cost for each alternative. To show this suppose we alter the cost involved so that we now have

$$C_1 = \$.30 \qquad C_2 = \$10.00$$

The expected cost matrix then turns out as follows:

| | $p_1 = .60$ | $p_2 = .30$ | $p_3 = .10$ |
	S_1	S_2	S_3
a_1	$167	$163	$308
a_2	232	294	300
a_3	123	223	340

Here the expectations must be computed.

$$E(a_1) = \$180 \qquad E(a_2) = \$257 \qquad E(a_3) = \$175$$

With this set of costs, a_3 is to be preferred if the expectation principle is used, although there is relatively little difference in the expected cost per lot between a_1 and a_3.

Once again there may be difficulty in measuring the costs required for the application of the expectation principle in the foregoing form. Various aspiration level principles might be developed; however, in practice, the decision is usually treated as one under conditions of uncertainty anyway. This will be discussed further in Chapter 18 and thus is not pursued here.

SETTING THE PROCESS AVERAGE

One of the interesting problems which arises in connection with decisions to control the quality of output of a production process is variation in the process which is taken to be economically and practically uncontrollable. If, for example, one is concerned with controlling the diameter of a cylinder turned on a lathe, it is common to find that even under reasonably careful conditions of control, some variation will be discovered in the diameters produced. Often this variation can be described in terms of a probability distribution. Thus, if x is the diameter, when the process is "under control" the variation in x can be satisfactorily described by some density function, $f(x)$. The density function forms the basis for a control chart which is a decision-making device for deciding whether or not the process is "under control." We wish to consider a different but related problem.

Let us suppose that the designer of the cylinder has placed tolerance limits on it. These specify the largest and smallest diameters which are acceptable from the viewpoint of the function of the final product. Let these tolerance limits be S_u and S_L, the upper and lower tolerance limits respectively. Pieces whose diameters fall outside these limits are scrap. If a piece has a diameter which falls above S_u, it may be reworked to acceptable size at a unit cost, C_u. If a piece falls below S_L, it must be scrapped completely, which results in a unit of C_L. In order to be specific, let us suppose that, when the process is "under control," $f(x)$ is given by a normal distribution with mean μ and standard deviation σ.

$$f(x) = \frac{1}{\sqrt{2\pi}\,\sigma} e^{\frac{-(x-\mu)^2}{2\sigma^2}}$$

Now in setting up the machine and controlling it, let us further assume that we can adjust the mean μ of the process but cannot further control it. Thus, for any given setting of the process mean we have a situation pictured in Figure 13–1.

FIGURE 13–1

Setting the Process Average

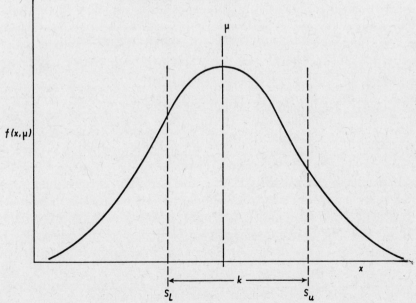

The area under $f(x)$ above S_u represents the proportion of the output that is too large and can be reworked at a unit cost C_u. The area under $f(x)$ below S_L represents the proportion of the output which is too small and must be scrapped at a unit cost C_L. Thus, for any setting of the process mean we can compute the expected cost of the bad material produced.

$$E(\mu) = C_L \int_{-\infty}^{S_L} f(x,\mu)dx + C_u \int_{S_u}^{\infty} f(x,\mu)dx$$

The decision is that of choosing a process average which will minimize this expected cost. This is accomplished, of course, by taking the first derivative of the expected cost with respect to μ and setting it equal to zero. The reader may verify that the result obtained is

$$\mu = S_L + \frac{S_u - S_L}{2} + \frac{\sigma^2}{S_u - S_L} \, ln \, \frac{C_L}{C_u}$$

As one would suspect, the result depends on the ratio of C_L to C_u. The following example will give some feeling for the manner in which the process mean should be set. Let

$$S_u = S_L + k = S_L + 2\sigma$$

$\dfrac{C_L}{C_u}$	$ln \, \dfrac{C_L}{C_u}$	μ
1	0	$S_L + \sigma$
2	.6931	$S_L + 1.3465\sigma$
4	1.3863	$S_L + 1.6931\sigma$
.5	$-$ .6931	$S_L + .6535\sigma$
.25	-1.3863	$S_L + .3069\sigma$

As the ratio of C_L to C_u increases, the process mean is moved up, placing a larger portion of the output above the upper tolerance limit, and a smaller portion below the lower tolerance limit. As the ratio of C_L to C_u decreases, the process average is moved down, placing a larger portion of the output below the lower tolerance limit and a smaller portion above the upper tolerance limit.

EQUIPMENT INVESTMENT

Having devoted considerable attention to the problem of choosing among alternative investments in productive equipment, it is of interest to investigate the possibilities for treating the problem as a decision under risk rather than certainty. Basic to the computations involved when the problem is treated under conditions of certainty are the calculations of present worths of the following form.

$$TC(n) = I + \sum_{j=1}^{n} \frac{c_j}{(1 + i)^j} - \frac{S_n}{(1 + i)^n}$$

In any particular problem this may be modified to include a sequence of machines or it may be converted to an equivalent annual cost. Nevertheless, calculations of the above form underlie the various decision techniques which have been suggested. Thus, it will be important to examine what happens to such present worth computations when the decision is treated as one under risk.

Common sense leads to consideration here of two lines of thought, which depend on the source and magnitude of the risk involved. We will distinguish one case wherein the risk arises primarily out of a process of predicting future receipts and disbursements on the basis of historical studies of such data. In contrast we will consider the case where the risk enters by way of some more or less dramatic contingency in the future which will influence the profitability of the investment but is something more than the result of the extrapolation of past data.

Treating the first case, let us assume that risk arises because our predictions of future operating costs and salvage values are in the form of probability distributions obtained from past data. Thus, we might suppose that we have

$f(S_n)$ = density function of the salvage value at the end of n periods of service

$\bar{S}_n$ = expected value of S_n

$g(c_j)$ = density function for the operating cost during the jth period of use

$\bar{c}_j$ = expected value of c_j

It will be noted immediately that since $TC(n)$ is a linear function of these random variables, the expected value of the present worth will be given simply by

$$\overline{TC(n)} = I + \sum_{j=1}^{n} \frac{\bar{c}_j}{(1 + i)^j} - \frac{\bar{S}_n}{(1 + i)^n}$$

This implies clearly that if we wish to use the expectation principle, then we need not be concerned about the density functions involved, but require only the expected costs and salvage values. In statistical terms this suggests that we use unbiased estimates of the quantities involved. Now common sense and practicality strongly suggest that this is about as far as we may profitably go in elaborating the analysis of the equipment investment problem. Especially when indefinite planning horizons are being used the expectation principle appears quite compatible.

We could, however, go further, and how this might be done in one instance is suggested in the following example. Suppose we have

$f(S_n)$ = normal with mean $\bar{S}_n$ and standard deviation $\sigma(S_n)$
$g(c_j)$ = normal with mean $\bar{c}_j$ and standard deviation $\sigma(c_j)$

Let us assume for simplicity that the operating costs and salvage values are statistically independent. In actuality it might well be that the operating cost in period j might depend on the operating cost in previous periods. Likewise, the salvage value might depend on the operating cost history of a machine. We may then apply a well-known theorem from statistics to obtain the following result (see Chapter 10). The density function of $TC(n)$ will itself be normal with mean equal to $\overline{TC(n)}$ and with variance given by

$$\sum_{j=1}^{n} \frac{\sigma(c_j)^2}{(1+i)^{2j}} + \frac{\sigma(S_n)^2}{(1+i)^{2n}}$$

With the density function of the present worth in hand one might proceed to various aspiration level principles or expectation variance principles. It should be pointed out here that, in general, this density function might be difficult to obtain. Common industrial practice seems to suggest that this is somewhat too detailed and that a more useful approach might be by way of a sensitivity analysis.

By a sensitivity analysis we simply mean in this case a determination of the effect on the present worth of a change or an error in one of the variables used to compute it. We might expect to find that some variables may change by substantial amounts without greatly changing the present worth. We need have little concern for risk arising from such sources. On the other hand, there may be other variables to which the present worth is highly sensitive and it would be important to consider the risk arising from these.

For example, suppose we ask how sensitive the present worth is to changes or errors in the salvage value. If we keep the other variables fixed we may explore this by computing the first derivative.

$$\frac{\partial TC(n)}{\partial S_n} = - \frac{1}{(1+i)^n}$$

Clearly, if n and i are large, then the present worth will not be particularly sensitive to salvage value and perhaps we need have little concern for the density function of S_n. On the other hand, when i

and n are small, changes in salvage value may have a more important influence on the present worth. Then it might be important to examine the density function of the salvage value, paying particular attention to the effect of its extreme values on the decision involved.

Similarly, we can examine the sensitivity of the present worth to the operating costs.

$$\frac{\partial TC(n)}{\partial c_j} = \frac{1}{(1+i)^j}$$

Here again it is clear that the higher the interest rate and the further into the future one goes, the less important are the associated operating costs. The reader will find it instructive to investigate the sensitivity of the present worth to changes in the interest rate.

It is difficult to give an interesting example of the use of sensitivity analysis because it is used primarily as a supplement to judgments about risky decisions. For example, it suggests such useful questions as, "If machine A is preferred to machine B using the expectation principle, then will the choice be the same if the salvage value of B has been underestimated by an amount x and the salvage value of A overestimated by an amount y?" Similar questions may be formulated to include judgments about the risk involved in operating cost estimates and so on. One hopes that the answer to such questions will be that, within the range where any given variable will fall say 90 per cent of the time, machine A is always preferred to machine B. If the answer is not such, then we move further into the realm of judgment and it becomes impossible to set down explicit rules. In the example which follows, some of the ways of setting up an equipment investment decision for the application of these judgments are illustrated.

EXAMPLE

A decision is to be made between two machines. The initial predictions of the relevant expenditures are given in the following table:

	Machine A	Machine B
Initial investment (I)	$20,000	$16,000
Operating and maintenance costs for		
year j $\quad$ $a + b(j-1)$	$2,000 + 500(j-1)$	$3,000 + 400(j-1)$
Salvage value at end of		
year j $\quad$ $I(s)(k)^{j-1}$	$I(.60)(.90)^{j-1}$	$I(.55)(.90)^{j-1}$

To simplify the calculations the interest rate will be taken equal to zero. An indefinite planning horizon is to be used in the analysis and average annual cost as the basis of choice. One might begin by examining the decision as one under conditions of certainty using the foregoing estimates. The first task is to find the optimal service life which will minimize the average annual cost for each of the machines. The calculations are shown in Tables 13–2 and 13–3.

TABLE 13–2

Machine A

N	S_N	$\dfrac{I - S_N}{N}$	c_j	$\dfrac{1}{N}\displaystyle\sum_{j=1}^{N} c_j$	$AC(N) = \dfrac{I - S_N}{N}$ $+ \dfrac{1}{N}\displaystyle\sum_{j=1}^{N} c_j$
1.............	$12,000	$8,000	$2,000	$2,000	$10,000
2.............	10,800	4,600	2,500	2,250	6,850
3.............	9,720	3,427	3,000	2,500	5,927
4.............	8,748	2,813	3,500	2,750	5,563
5.............	7,873	2,425	4,000	3,000	5,425
6.............	7,086	2,152	4,500	3,250	5,402
7.............	6,377	1,946	5,000	3,500	5,446
8.............	5,739	1,783	5,500	3,750	5,533

TABLE 13–3

Machine B

N	S_N	$\dfrac{I - S_N}{N}$	c_j	$\dfrac{1}{N}\displaystyle\sum_{j=1}^{N} c_j$	$AC(N) = \dfrac{I - S_N}{N}$ $+ \dfrac{1}{N}\displaystyle\sum_{j=1}^{N} c_j$
1.............	$8,800	$7,200	$3,000	$3,000	$10,200
2.............	7,920	4,040	3,400	3,200	7,240
3.............	7,128	2,957	3,800	3,400	6,357
4.............	6,415	2,396	4,200	3,600	5,996
5.............	5,774	2,045	4,600	3,800	5,845
6.............	5,197	1,800	5,000	4,000	5,800
7.............	4,677	1,618	5,400	4,200	5,818
8.............	4,209	1,474	5,800	4,400	5,874

These computations lead to the conclusion that the optimal service life for machine A is six years, resulting in an average annual cost of $5,402, and the optimal service life for machine B is also six years, giving an average annual cost of $5,800. Thus, considered as a problem of choice under certainty the preferred alternative is machine A.

At this point let us suppose that some judgment based upon experience with such equipment is brought to bear on the problem.

Perhaps it will be suggested that the estimates used in computing these annual costs might vary to an extent which could throw the choice in favor of machine B. If good evidence were available on the probability distributions of the costs used, the decision might immediately be treated as one under conditions of risk. Let us suppose we do not have sufficient data to predict these probability distributions but that judgment strongly indicates some variation could be present. What is required is simply a way of exploring how the decision would go as these costs vary. This will help in the application of judgment although it will not itself determine the choice.

We will begin by exploring the choice under variation in the operating and maintenance costs. For machine A it has been estimated initially that these costs for year j are given by

$$c_j = a + b(j - 1) = 2{,}000 + 500(j - 1)$$

What will happen to the average annual cost of machine A as the coefficient b in the above equation varies? If, for example, b were to take the value 400, what would be the average annual cost for machine A? This requires the computation of another table, such as Table 13–2. The result of such computations will indicate that if $B = 400$, then the optimal service life would be seven years and the average annual cost would be \$5,146. If this happens and all other variables remain as before, then machine A will still be preferred to machine B. It might, however, be interesting to explore the choice for other values of b.

In this example we may make this exploration most efficiently by recalling the relations which must hold if N is the optimal service life, resulting in a minimum average annual cost, $AC(N)$.

$$AC(N + 1) - AC(N) \geq 0$$
$$AC(N - 1) - AC(N) \geq 0$$

The first of these relations may be written as:

$$AC(N + 1) - AC(N) = \frac{I - S_{N+1}}{N + 1} + \frac{1}{N + 1} \sum_{j=1}^{N+1} c_j - \frac{I - S_N}{N}$$

$$- \frac{1}{N} \sum_{j=1}^{N} c_j > 0 = \frac{I - S_{N+1}}{N + 1} - \frac{I - S_N}{N} + \frac{1}{N + 1} \sum_{j=1}^{N+1} \{a + b(j - 1)\}$$

$$- \frac{1}{N} \sum_{j=1}^{N} \{a + b(j - 1)\} > 0 = \frac{I - S_{N+1}}{N + 1} - \frac{I - S_N}{N}$$

$$+ \frac{1}{N + 1} \sum_{j=1}^{N+1} b(j - 1) - \frac{1}{N} \sum_{j=1}^{N} b(j - 1) > 0$$

The expression

$$\frac{1}{N}\sum_{j=1}^{N}b(j-1)$$

may be simplified to

$$\frac{N-1}{2}b$$

Figure 13–2
Machine A

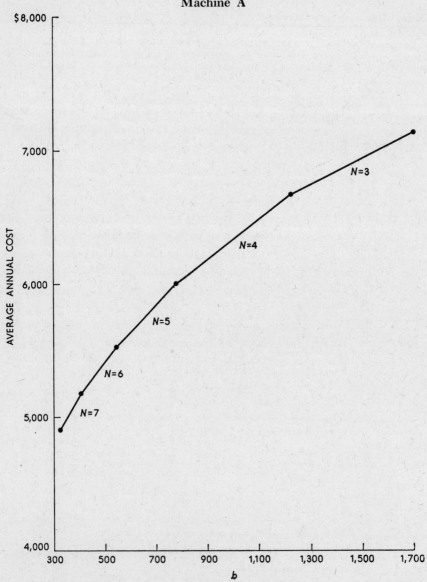

Substituting this in the above,

$$AC(N + 1) - AC(N) = \frac{I - S_{N+1}}{N + 1} - \frac{I - S_{N'}}{N} + \frac{N}{2}b - \frac{N - 1}{2}b > 0$$

$$b > 2\left\{\frac{I - S_N}{N} - \frac{I - S_{N+1}}{N + 1}\right\}$$

This gives the lower bound on b for which N will be the optimal service life. For $N = 6$, we obtain from Table 13–2:

$$b > 2\{2,152 - 1,946\} = 412$$

From the relation

$$AC(N - 1) - AC(N) \geq 0$$

we obtain by similar means

$$b \leq 2\left\{\frac{I - S_{N-1}}{N - 1} - \frac{I - S_N}{N}\right\}$$

This gives the upper bound on b for which N will be the optimal service life. Again for $N = 6$ we obtain from Table 13–2,

$$b \leq 2\{2,425 - 2,152\} = 546$$

The average annual cost may be easily calculated for the extremes of this range for b.

$$b = 412 \quad N = 7 \quad AC(N) = \$5,182$$
$$b = 546 \quad N = 6 \quad AC(N) = \$5,517$$

It may further be seen that for any value of b in this range, machine A will be preferred to machine B, all other things remaining equal.

By similar calculations one may explore additional values of b, as shown in Table 13–4. These results are shown graphically in Fig-

TABLE 13–4

Machine A

Range of b	Optimal Service Life	Range of Annual Cost
$326 < b \leq 412$	7	$\$4,924 < AC(N) \leq \$5,182$
$412 < b \leq 546$	6	$5,182 < AC(N) \leq 5,517$
$546 < b \leq 776$	5	$5,517 < AC(N) \leq 5,977$
$776 < b \leq 1,228$	4	$5,977 < AC(N) \leq 6,655$
$1,228 < b \leq 2,346$	3	$6,655 < AC(N) \leq 7,773$

ure 13–2. If the original estimates for machine B are held constant, then it may be seen that for machine A the value $b = 687$ is critical. If b is above this value machine B will be preferred, otherwise machine A will be preferred.

There is, of course, little reason to suppose that the coefficient b may vary for machine A alone. Similar variation for machine B may be investigated by the same means. The results are shown in Table 13–5.

TABLE 13–5

Machine B

Range of b	Optimal Service Life	Range of Annual Cost
$288 < b \leq 364$	7	$5,482 < AC(N) \leq \$5,710$
$364 < b \leq 490$	6	$5,710 < AC(N) \leq 6,025$
$490 < b \leq 702$	5	$6,025 < AC(N) \leq 6,449$
$702 < b \leq 1,122$	4	$6,449 < AC(N) \leq 7,079$
$1,122 < b \leq 3,166$	3	$7,079 < AC(N) \leq 9,123$

These last two tables provide the basis for exercising judgment about possible variation in the coefficient b and the resulting choice. Let

FIGURE 13–3

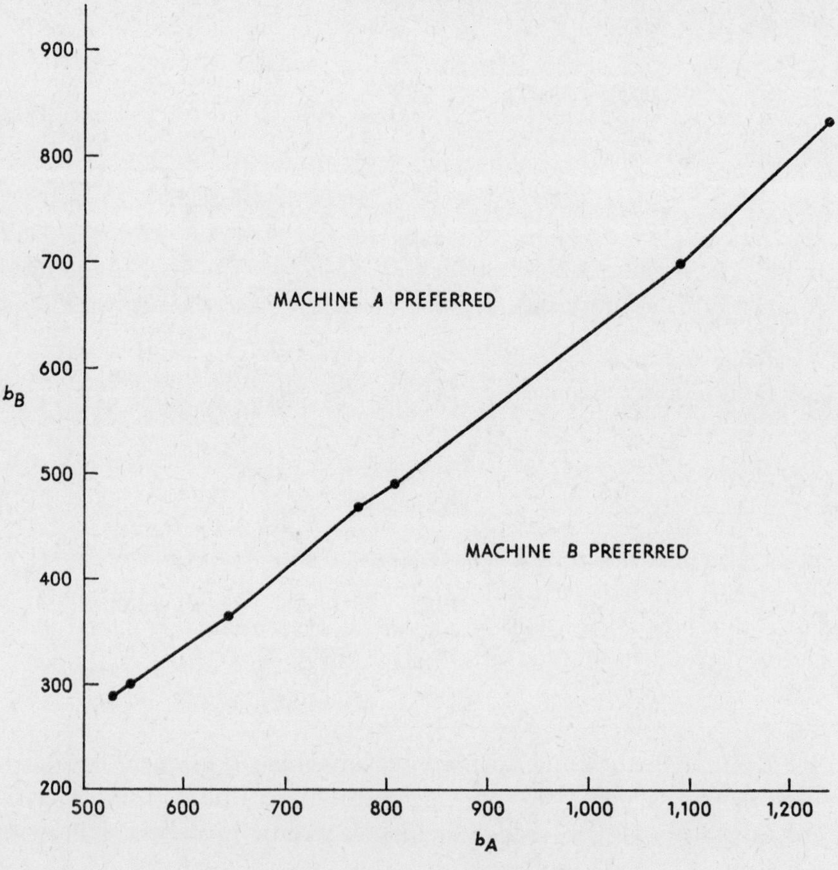

b_A refer to the value of the coefficient for machine A, and b_B apply similarly to machine B. For any pair of values, b_A and b_B, with the help of the tables, one may see which machine would be preferred. Expressing this graphically often helps. In Figure 13–3 a line passing through pairs of values, b_A and b_B, for which the two machines have equal average annual costs has been drawn. For any point

TABLE 13–6

Machine A

k	Range of b	Optimal Service Life N	Range of Annual Cost
.95	$330 < b \leq 386$	7	$\$4,630 < AC(N) \leq \$4,798$
.95	$386 < b \leq 574$	6	$4,798 < AC(N) \leq 5,268$
.95	$574 < b \leq 760$	5	$5,268 < AC(N) \leq 5,640$
.95	$760 < b \leq 1,400$	4	$5,640 < AC(N) \leq 6,600$
.95	$1,400 < b \leq 2,200$	3	$6,600 < AC(N) \leq 7,400$
.90	$326 < b \leq 412$	7	$4,924 < AC(N) \leq 5,182$
.90	$412 < b \leq 546$	6	$5,182 < AC(N) \leq 5,517$
.90	$546 < b \leq 776$	5	$5,517 < AC(N) \leq 5,977$
.90	$776 < b \leq 1,228$	4	$5,977 < AC(N) \leq 6,655$
.90	$1,228 < b \leq 2,346$	3	$6,655 < AC(N) \leq 7,773$
.85	$346 < b \leq 500$	7	$5,238 < AC(N) \leq 5,700$
.85	$500 < b \leq 620$	6	$5,700 < AC(N) \leq 6,000$
.85	$620 < b \leq 820$	5	$6,000 < AC(N) \leq 6,400$
.85	$820 < b \leq 1,260$	4	$6,400 < AC(N) \leq 7,060$
.85	$1,260 < b \leq 2,200$	3	$7,060 < AC(N) \leq 8,000$
.80	$252 < b \leq 512$	7	$5,167 < AC(N) \leq 5,947$
.80	$512 < b \leq 666$	6	$5,947 < AC(N) \leq 6,332$
.80	$666 < b \leq 900$	5	$6,332 < AC(N) \leq 6,800$
.80	$900 < b \leq 1,368$	4	$6,800 < AC(N) \leq 7,502$
.80	$1,368 < b \leq 2,132$	3	$7,502 < AC(N) \leq 8,266$
.70	$542 < b \leq 684$	7	$6,277 < AC(N) \leq 6,703$
.70	$684 < b \leq 862$	6	$6,703 < AC(N) \leq 7,148$
.70	$862 < b \leq 1,112$	5	$7,148 < AC(N) \leq 7,648$
.70	$1,112 < b \leq 1,454$	4	$7,648 < AC(N) \leq 8,161$
.70	$1,454 < b \leq 2,186$	3	$8,161 < AC(N) \leq 8,893$

below this line, machine B will be preferred. For any point above it, the choice will fall on machine A. As we have previously emphasized, this type of graph does not itself determine the choice. It is merely intended to furnish a background over which judgments about the probabilities of various values or ranges of the coefficients may be placed.

There is no reason why this kind of exploration should be confined to one variable alone. If, for example, we suspect variation in the salvage value as well as in the coefficient b, they may be in-

vestigated together. It has been assumed that the salvage value for
machine A is given by

$$S_N = I(s)(k)^{i-1} = I(.60)(.90)^{i-1}$$

and for machine B by

$$S_N = I(.55)(.90)^{i-1}$$

Suppose one is interested in the effects of letting k take on the
values .95, .85, .80, .70. For each value of k one may then explore the
effects of variation in b. This analysis results in the data given in
Table 13–6 for machine A and Table 13–7 for machine B.

TABLE 13–7

Machine B

k	Range of b	Optimal Service Life N	Range of Annual Cost
.95	$234 < b \leq 392$	7	$\$5,079 < AC(N) \leq \$5,553$
.95	$392 < b \leq 502$	6	$5,553 < AC(N) \leq 5,828$
.95	$502 < b \leq 672$	5	$5,828 < AC(N) \leq 6,168$
.95	$672 < b \leq 1,226$	4	$6,168 < AC(N) \leq 6,999$
.95	$1,226 < b \leq 2,134$	3	$6,999 < AC(N) \leq 7,907$
.90	$288 < b \leq 364$	7	$5,482 < AC(N) \leq 5,710$
.90	$364 < b \leq 490$	6	$5,710 < AC(N) \leq 6,025$
.90	$490 < b \leq 702$	5	$6,025 < AC(N) \leq 6,449$
.90	$702 < b \leq 1,122$	4	$6,449 < AC(N) \leq 7,079$
.90	$1,122 < b \leq 3,166$	3	$7,079 < AC(N) \leq 7,123$
.85	$270 < b \leq 488$	7	$5,593 < AC(N) \leq 6,247$
.85	$488 < b \leq 490$	6	$6,247 < AC(N) \leq 6,252$
.85	$490 < b \leq 772$	5	$6,252 < AC(N) \leq 6,816$
.85	$772 < b \leq 1,084$	4	$6,816 < AC(N) \leq 7,284$
.85	$1,084 < b \leq 2,080$	3	$7,284 < AC(N) \leq 8,280$
.80	$344 < b \leq 492$	7	$5,973 < AC(N) \leq 6,417$
.80	$492 < b \leq 554$	6	$6,417 < AC(N) \leq 6,572$
.80	$554 < b \leq 832$	5	$6,572 < AC(N) \leq 7,128$
.80	$832 < b \leq 1,172$	4	$7,128 < AC(N) \leq 7,638$
.80	$1,172 < b \leq 2,028$	3	$7,638 < AC(N) \leq 8,494$
.70	$392 < b \leq 638$	7	$5,984 < AC(N) \leq 7,022$
.70	$638 < b \leq 714$	6	$7,022 < AC(N) \leq 7,212$
.70	$714 < b \leq 936$	5	$7,212 < AC(N) \leq 7,656$
.70	$936 < b \leq 1,282$	4	$7,656 < AC(N) \leq 8,175$
.70	$1,282 < b \leq 2,054$	3	$8,175 < AC(N) \leq 8,947$

From these tables one may construct graphs similar to Figure
13–3 showing the regions for which each machine is preferred.
These tables represent variation in four variables. Graphic presentation is limited to the effects of two or at most three variables at a

time. Thus several graphs may be made as the requirements of judgment dictate.

CONTINGENCIES

The second general source of risk in equipment investment decisions is by way of some future contingency which will perhaps have important effects on the cost or profit associated with a given investment. In connection with machinery investments we might wish to consider contingencies such as

1. Destruction of the machine by some accident or malfunction.
2. Change in product line or activity which would bring an end to the requirement for the machine's services.
3. Technological "breakthrough" making the machine suddenly obsolete.
4. Success or failure of a new product.
5. Conversion to war production or the loss of government contracts.

While we have suggested previously that risk arising through predictions from past data might perhaps be neglected, it is suggested that risk generated by contingencies such as those just indicated might very well be included in the analysis. It is true that the probabilities associated with the sorts of events suggested will at best be personalistic or subjective. However, perhaps much can be gained by their explicit inclusion in the analysis.

SUGGESTIONS FOR FURTHER STUDY

MORRIS, WILLIAM T. *Analysis for Materials Handling Management.* Homewood, Ill.: Richard D. Irwin, Inc., 1962.

SASIENI, MAURICE; YASPAN, ARTHUR; and FRIEDMAN, LAWRENCE. *Operations Research—Methods and Problems.* New York: John Wiley & Sons, Inc., 1959.

PROBLEMS

13–1. A manufacturer of very heavy, custom-designed industrial equipment is planning the casting of a large housing. The housing is a part of a unique end item, for which no future orders can be expected. When the casting is poured, there is some probability p that it will be defective. The defects, however, would not be discovered until much later during the machining process. If he makes one casting and it is later discovered to be defective, he must then incur expensive delay and setup costs to make another. If he makes two at the outset he is protected against this, but is left with a useless casting if the first one is good. If both are bad, he must make a third casting. For simplicity, assume that the probability of the second casting being defective is p also, and that the probability of the third casting being defective is zero. The manufacturer wonders whether he should make one or two at the outset. Let C_1 be the cost of setting up to make either one or two, and C_2 be the other variable costs of producing a casting whether one or two are made.

a) If $p = .50$ which plan will minimize expected cost?

b) If $p = .10$ which plan will minimize expected cost?

c) Under what conditions would you advise the manufacturer to do something other than minimize expected cost?

d) How much would he be willing to pay for a nondestructive testing service which would tell him whether or not a casting was defective immediately after it was poured?

13–2. Show that, in the search decision outlined below, the policy which maximizes the expected value of the present worth involves finding an aspiration level which is used in deciding whether to stop or continue search. A company is searching for investment opportunities. They have already found several, the best of which promises a present worth of future profits estimated at P_B. The company is willing to make decisions on the basis of the following assumptions:

a) The cost of discovering each additional investment opportunity is a known constant C.

b) The present worths of the profits for the population of all investment opportunities which exist (including those not yet discovered) can be represented by a probability density function, $f(P)$.

How should the company decide when to stop searching if they can invest in only one opportunity? (Note that investment opportunities are not transitory like stock or commodity prices. Once discovered, an opportunity remains available to the firm for a reasonable length of time.)

13–3. A small manufacturer hires a market research organization to do a test marketing of three versions of a new product. He receives a report which contains essentially three results:

Version	Est. Sales in One Year (Units)
A	300,000
B	310,000
C	400,000

The product has a market life of one year, with total profits given by

$$
\begin{aligned}
&-\$100,000 + .40 \text{ (units sold)} &&\text{for } A \\
&-\ 150,000 + .55 \text{ (units sold)} &&\text{for } B \\
&-\ 160,000 + .50 \text{ (units sold)} &&\text{for } C
\end{aligned}
$$

The manufacturer is dissatisfied with the market research report, finding it of little assistance in choosing the version to market. What explanation might be offered for his dissatisfaction? What data would be helpful?

13–4. By adjusting the size of the billet which goes into a rolling mill, the mean length of the bars rolled, m, may be controlled. The length of a bar, x, is a random variable with probability distribution $f(m,x)$. If there is a cost C_1 associated with a bar which falls below the lower specification limit L_1, and a cost C_2 associated with a bar which falls above the upper specification limit L_2, show how one might *a*) Find *m* so as to minimize expected cost.

b) Find *m* so as to minimize the proportion of bars which fall outside the specification limits.

13–5. If the probability distribution of bar lengths in problem 13–4 is uniform, obtain an expression for the optimal mean bar length. What principle of choice would you suggest if it were not possible to measure the costs involved?

13–6. During an especially cold winter a large metropolitan gas company was forced on two occasions to ask its large industrial customers to switch to alternate fuels for heating in order that sufficient gas could be assured for private homes. In the face of considerable public pressure the gas company argued that it did not need extra capacity and did in fact have adequate capacity for its demand. What sort of arguments could the gas company give to support its position?

13–7. The designer of a three-stage electronic system wishes to improve the reliability of the system. The first design consists of three stages or components in series. The reliability of a component is defined as the probability that it will function successfully during a given mission or task. The system reliability, defined in a corresponding way, is taken to be the product of the stage reliabilities. He may improve reliability by placing components in parallel at any stage with a switching device which brings in the next component when one fails. The designer is limited in what he may do by a budget restriction which requires that the system cost less than $15,000. Also, space and weight restrictions limit the number of components in parallel at any stage to three. Using the following data, design a system which will have maximum reliability within these restrictions.

Stage	Number of Components in Parallel	Stage Reliability	Total Stage Cost
1	1	.80	$2,000
1	2	.90	4,000
1	3	.95	7,000
2	1	.70	2,000
2	2	.90	5,000
2	3	.92	9,000
3	1	.90	1,000
3	2	.98	3,000
3	3	.99	6,000

13–8. Suppose you enter a gambling casino to play roulette with $700 and you wish to maximize the probability of leaving with a profit of $100. If you limit your alternatives to bets on red or black (see Chapter 1), what would be your betting strategy?

13–9. Is it reasonable for the federal government not to insure its buildings against fire?

13–10. In investigating fire insurance for its plant, a firm obtains the following facts:

Probability of a fire during a year = .003

Given that a fire occurs, the density function of the dollar loss is given by

$$f(y) = me^{-my} \qquad \text{where } m = .0001$$

Annual premium $= \$40$

The policy will cover 90 per cent of the actual dollar value of any fire loss.

In terms of the principles of choice presented in Chapter 11, what explanations could be given for the firm's decision to insure? For a decision not to insure?

13–11. A motor truck firm operates a fleet of 125 vehicles. The firm is considering two policies for handling tire failures.

a_1: Equip each vehicle with a spare tire. This will require a total of 140 spare tires because of the repair time. The annual cost for a tire is estimated to be $25. The cost of repairing a tire failure under this policy is $6.00.

a_2: Enter into service contracts with a number of garages along the routes traveled by the firm's vehicles. These contracts specify that the firm will supply the tires and the garage will handle all tire failures at a flat rate of $10 each. Under this policy the firm will need only 60 spare tires distributed among the garages.

The number of tire failures per 100,000 vehicle miles is a random variable having a Poisson distribution with a mean of 2. The trucks travel an average of 100,000 miles per year each. Which policy would you recommend?

13–12. The probability of a fatal accident is 40 times greater if a person travels one mile by motorcycle than if he travels by automobile. If a person chooses to travel by motorcycle with a total cost of $.03 per mile instead of driving a car at a total cost of $.10 per mile, what can be said about the value which he places on his life?

13–13. A manufacturing firm is considering the purchase of a spare machine for standby service at a crucial point in its production process. The machine will cost $18,000 and will have a salvage value of $3,000 after 15 years of standby service. The machine will be called into service whenever a breakdown occurs. The number of breakdowns per year is predicted on the basis of past experience to be a random variable having a Poisson distribution with a mean of 2. When a breakdown does occur, the costs which would result from lost production and enforced idleness would be a random variable y, if no standby equipment were available. It is estimated that y is equally likely to fall anywhere in the range from $300 up to $2,100. (Neglect interest.)

a) On the basis of the expectation principle, does the standby machine appear to be a good investment?

b) If the firm wishes to maximize the probability that the annual cost of dealing with breakdowns will be below some level A, show which alternative will be preferred as a function of A.

13–14. A machine is designed and built to special order for a manufacturing firm. The machine builder offers to furnish a spare for a major part at the time the machine is built for an additional cost of $1,200.

He also indicates that, if the spare is ordered later on, it will cost approximately $14,000 because of special setups and delays. Let the probability that a spare will be required during the life of the machine be p. The probability that more than one spare will be needed is so small that it may be neglected. For what value of p will the two alternatives be equally costly? Would you suggest an aspiration level principle for such a decision?

13–15. A firm has purchased a large complex machine and is now offered a service contract by the manufacturer of the machine. The service contract guarantees all repairs and adjustments on the machine for a period of one year at a flat rate of $2,000. Two other alternatives are being considered. The firm might use its own technicians to service the machines. The incremental labor cost per breakdown is estimated to be $50 for this alternative. Parts must be purchased which are expected to average $240 per breakdown.

The firm may also call in the manufacturer's technicians as the breakdowns occur. The manufacturer will bill for labor costs at the flat rate of $75 per call, and for parts at a price 10 per cent below that at which the firm could otherwise obtain them.

The number of breakdowns per year is a random variable having a Poisson distribution with a mean of 5. What policy will minimize expected costs? For each policy compute the probability that it will be best.

13–16. A firm is considering the purchase of some major equipment from either supplier A or supplier B. It is felt that A is capable of delivering the equipment on time to meet a desired deadline. The price of A's equipment is, however, considerably higher than that of B. It was felt that B might deliver on time, but there was some possibility that B might deliver late. Further, it is suspected that B may never be able to deliver the equipment according to specifications. The firm feels that if it waited several months, much better information on B's capabilities would be available. Three alternative courses of action are under consideration:

a_1: Order from A. If it later becomes clear that B could deliver, this order can be canceled on payment of certain cancellation charges. Further delay would be encountered while B produces the equipment.

a_2: Order from B. If it later becomes clear that B cannot deliver, the order can be switched at a cost for cancellation and additional delay.

a_3: Wait until B's capabilities are known. This would involve delay in any case.

The firm uses the present worths of profit over a six-year study period as a measure of value for each outcome. The results are shown in the following matrix:

	B Fails to Deliver	B Delivers Late	B Delivers on Time
a_1	100	100	100
a_2	40	50	250
a_3	80	120	180

Clearly, the probabilities of the possible futures can be obtained only on the basis of judgments. Construct a graph showing the values of p_1 and p_2 for which each alternative will be preferred using the expectation principle. Discuss the use of other principles of choice. (Adapted from Isaac, *Operations Research*, Vol. 4, No. 3, 1956.)

13–17. The sales department of a large firm has a list of N prospects which it hopes to obtain as accounts. The sales manager wishes to establish a limit on the number of calls which will be made on a prospect in the attempt to obtain the account. On the basis of past sales activity he obtains the following data showing the probability that a prospect will be sold and the probability that he will be dropped as a function of the number of calls. These are simple probabilities, not conditional probabilities.

Call Number	Probability of Obtaining	Probability of Dropping
1	.06	.44
2	.04	.16
3	.03	.05
4	.01	.05
5	.004	.04
6	.002	.02

What policy with respect to the maximum number of calls will maximize the average number of accounts obtained per call? What other principles of choice might be appropriate for this decision?

13–18. The intervals between ship arrivals at an unloading terminal are distributed according to the following probability distribution:

$$f(x) = me^{-mx}$$

where x is the interval between arrivals in days and m is .5.

It is desired to establish terminal unloading capacity sufficient to make the probability that a ship will have to wait to unload less than k. The terminal can handle only one ship at a time. Once the capacity has been established, the time required to unload a ship does not vary appreciably. Capacity is measured in unloading time.

Management is not quite sure how to select k and wishes to see a graph depicting capacity as a function of k for probabilities greater than .20. Plot such a graph.

13–19. Military aircraft are sent to a certain maintenance depot in such a way that their arrivals appear to be random. The time to overhaul an aircraft is found to be random also. Under these conditions a study reveals that the probability distribution of the number of aircraft at the depot is given by

$$p(n) = \left\{1 - \frac{\lambda}{\mu}\right\}\left\{\frac{\lambda}{\mu}\right\}^n$$

The average time spent at the depot by an aircraft is

$$E(w) = \frac{1}{\mu - \lambda}$$

where

λ = the mean number of aircraft arriving per day
μ = the mean number of aircraft overhauled per day

The commander of the depot wishes to fix its capacity (measured by μ) at a level which will minimize the sum of the average daily costs defined as follows:

μC_1 = average daily operating cost for a depot with capacity μ
C_2 = cost of having an aircraft at the depot for one hour
C_3 = penalty cost for each hour the depot facilities are idle

What is the best capacity for the depot? What other principles of choice might be reasonable for the commander in this decision?

13–20. Consider the milling machine department of a plant organized on a departmental basis. Material arrives at the department at random with an average arrival rate of 20 pieces per hour. The time required by the department to process material is also a random variable, and the average output rate is 25 pieces per hour. Assume that the assumptions underlying the usual queuing model are satisfied.

a) Find the probability that the milling department will run out of work.

b) Find the expected amount of material that will be waiting for processing by the department.

c) Find the probability that the department will have a backlog of between 10 and 13 pieces.

d) Find the expected backlog and the probability of running out of work if the mean production rate is increased by 10 per cent. If the mean arrival rate is raised to 25 pieces per hour.

e) What should be the capacity of the in-process storage area ahead of the milling department if the risk of exceeding this capacity is to be no more than 10 per cent?

13–21. Consider a two-stage production process such that units are produced by the first stage at random points in time, and flow into the second stage at random points in time. The mean output rate of the first stage is ten units per hour, and the mean consumption rate of the second stage is 10.1 units per hour. Assume the assumptions for the usual queuing model are satisfied. The process runs eight hours per day.

a) Find the average bank size between stages.

b) Find the daily time lost by stage two while waiting for material from stage one.

c) If the storage costs (based on average bank size) are $20 per piece per day, and if downtime for the second stage costs $200 per hour, what is the optimum production rate for stage one? Use the expectation principle and leave the answer in symbolic form.

13–22. Material arrives at a plant at an average rate of x loads per hour. It is handled by a fleet of fork lift trucks, each of which has a capacity of y loads per hour. Assuming the input is Poisson and the service time is negative exponential, find the mean delay time for incoming material, the utilization of the fork truck fleet, and the necessary relationship between x and y.

13–23. Telephone calls arrive at an exchange at random with a mean rate x. The mean duration of a call is y. Under the usual assumptions of the queuing model, what must be the capacity of the exchange so that no call will be delayed. Plot the capacity of the exchange as a function of the probability that a call will be delayed.

13–24. Refer to the waiting line example discussed in the text. Assume that the mean rate at which orders arrive, λ, is 20 orders per day. The mean production rate, μ, is 25 orders per day. Find:

  a) Probability distribution of the number of orders received in a five-day workweek.
  b) Proportion of idle time.
  c) Mean time which an order waits.
  d) Plot $p(o)$, $E(n)$, and $E(w)$ as a function of λ for $\mu = 25$.
  e) Plot the same quantities as a function of μ for $\lambda = 20$.

13–25. A firm operates a group of automatic machines which require only intermittent attention from a crew of machine tenders. When a machine requires attention it is serviced by one man, and the service time is a random variable with a negative exponential distribution. The mean service time is 10 minutes. The calls for service occur at random at a mean rate of two per machine per day. If the cost of lost production is taken to be $20 per machine-hour and the wage rate for machine tenders is $3.50 per hour, find the optimum number of machine tenders to service a group of 100 machines. Use the expectation principle.

13–26. Referring to the replacement policy model, let

$$q(t) = \frac{f(t)}{N}$$

Show that

$$a(t) = p(t) + p(1)q(t - 1) + p(2)q(t - 2) + \cdots + p(t - 1)q(1)$$

$$= p(t) + \sum_{j=1}^{t-1} p(j)q(t - j)$$

13–27. The probability of failure for the lining of a tank used in a chemical process is given below as a function of age.

Age in months	1	2	3	4
Probability of failure	.05	.10	.40	.45

If the tank lining fails in service, the tank must be drained immediately, causing a variety of losses and interruptions in the production process. The costs associated with such a failure are estimated to be $10,000. On the other hand, the production schedule provides for emptying the tank at the end of each month and relining may be done at that time. If the tank is relined on schedule, the costs total about $2,000. In no case may the tank run more than four months without relining. Find the relining policy which will minimize expected costs. Assume that the firm operates a large number of such tanks. If a policy T is specified, it means that all tanks are relined when they fail as well as at the end of T months. A tank which fails during month T is repaired on schedule at the end of that month.

13–28. A plant adopts a policy of replacing the fluorescent tubes over the production area whenever they fail. Failure data on 1,000 tubes indicate the following:

Time in months (t)	1	2	3	4	5	6	7
Number of failures $f(t)$	5	17	22	39	78	97	123

t	8	9	10	11	12	13	14	15
$f(t)$	131	138	140	141	143	149	150	151

The plant is considering a policy of simultaneously replacing all the tubes at the end of some period T. If this is done the replacement cost per tube is estimated to be $.67. Under present conditions the replacement of tubes individually costs about $2.20 each. Find the value of T which will minimize expected costs. If the plant can tolerate at most a maintenance expense for tubes of A per month, what would be the best policy?

13–29. The probability that a certain aircraft component will last t hours is given by

t	100	200	300	400	500
$\dfrac{S(t)}{N}$	.90	.80	.60	.45	.15

If the component fails in flight, the aircraft must land for immediate repairs. The cost of such repairs is estimated to be $500 when all associated losses are included. Preventive replacement of the component costs approximately $50. Find the replacement policy which will minimize the total expected costs.

13–30. Derive the conditions for the optimum replacement interval.

13–31. Given

$$N = 1,000$$
$$f(t) = 10 + 20t$$
$$C_1 = \$.20$$
$$C_2 = \$1.00$$

Find T.

13–32. In setting up a replacement policy for fuel pumps on taxicabs, what sort of a principle of choice would you suggest? What would you suggest for the tubes in your television set?

13–33. A firm is considering two possible acceptance sampling plans to form the basis of a rectifying inspection scheme.

$$a_1: c = 2, N = 50$$
$$a_2: c = 1, N = 100$$

Lot size $= 1,000$

The possible futures and their probabilities are

$$S_1: p' = .01, \quad p_1 = .50$$
$$S_2: p' = .03, \quad p_2 = .50$$

If the cost of inspection is \$1.00 per unit and the cost of accepting a defective item is \$50, which plan would you suggest?

13–34. How can one estimate the probabilities of the possible futures in a problem such as 13–33? Would you expect this to be generally possible in actual situations? If these probabilities cannot be estimated, how can the decision be approached?

13–35. What principles of choice are ordinarily used by a firm in selecting an acceptance sampling plan?

13–36. Derive the expression for the optimum setting of the process mean.

13–37. Find the best setting for the process mean given

$$S_u = 1.010 \qquad S_L = .990$$
$$f(x, \mu) = \text{normal with standard deviation } .004$$
$$C_L = \$1.25 \qquad C_u = \$.80$$

13–38. Using the data of problem 13–37, plot the optimum setting of the process mean as a function of the ratio of C_L to C_u.

13–39. If it were not possible to measure the costs in problem 13–37, what sort of a principle of choice would you suggest?

13–40. A large computer manufacturer furnishes a program for capital equipment selection based on the following assumptions:
  i. Purchase prices known.
  ii. Operating costs known functions of machine age.
  iii. Salvage values known functions of service life.
  iv. Interest rate known.
  v. Service lives predicted in the form of probability distributions.

  a) Write a symbolic model for the expected equivalent annual cost of a machine.

  b) Does a certainty equivalent exist?

  c) Under what conditions might the expected equivalent annual cost be a poor basis for choice?

13–41. Perform a sensitivity analysis of the decision in problem 9–3.

13–42. Perform a sensitivity analysis on the decision of problem 9–21.

13–43. Perform a sensitivity analysis on the decision of problem 9–27.

13–44. A firm is developing plans for plant expansion over the next five years. The basis for this planning is a prediction of demand for the firm's product. Demand is viewed as a random variable with a normal probability distribution having a mean which is a function of time. For year t, the expected demand is given by

$$20,000 + 2,000t \text{ units}$$

and the standard deviation is

$$1,000 + 100t + 10t^2$$

where t takes the values 0,1,2,3,4. Expansion is carried out through the purchase of machines, each of which will have an annual capacity of 1,500 units. Because of the cost of capital, the firm does not wish to expand any sooner than necessary.

a) Develop an expansion program if the firm is willing to run a risk of 50 per cent of having the capacity of its plant at the beginning of any year fall short of the demand during that year.

b) Develop an expansion program if the acceptable risk is reduced to 25 per cent.

13–45. In designing an airport it is important to fix the directions of the runways so that as often as possible there will be a runway in the direction of the wind. A study of detailed weather records for a proposed airport site indicate that the wind direction, x, may be described by a probability distribution $f(x)$. Here x is defined over the range 0 to 360 degrees. The designer wishes to place two runways so as to maximize the probability that there will be a runway having a direction within 20 degrees of that of the wind.

Write an expression for this probability and suggest how it might be maximized.

Chapter 14

INVENTORY POLICY

INVENTORY MANAGEMENT

A VERY COMMON field of management decision making, and one which is crucial in many businesses, is the area of inventory management. The decisions involved include those of deciding what stock levels to maintain, when to replenish stock, in what quantities to order, and so on. This is also a field in which analytical techniques for aiding these decisions are well developed and quite successful in practice. In many inventory situations, the primary factor in the decision to establish a stock level policy is the demand which is anticipated against the inventory. This problem of predicting future demand is often best solved by the methods of inferential statistics which will yield a prediction in the form of a probability distribution of demand. The decision then becomes an example of a decision under risk, wherein several possible future demand quantities are recognized and their probabilities are estimated. A simple example of this type will serve to further illustrate the ideas of decision making under conditions of risk.

AN EXAMPLE

To take a simple specific inventory decision, let us consider the problem of the small-boat builder who builds pleasure cruisers. He decides that it is economical for him to build a number of boats during the autumn and winter in order to have them ready for sale during the spring. This permits him to utilize his facilities during periods when he is not occupied with boats for which he has a definite order, and it permits him to reduce costs by building several at a time. His decision then is, "How many boats should be produced for stock?" One of the relevant considerations is the demand for boats which he can expect during the coming season. An analysis of sales over past years using appropriate statistical techniques reveals that there are no significant trends or other identifiable effects which influence sales. In fact, it is concluded that past sales could be described satisfactorily by a probability distribution. It is then decided that the best prediction of sales for the coming year is that they will be much like those in the past. The prediction is then made in the form of the probability distribution of demand. Using D to stand for number of boats sold and $p(D)$ for the probability distribution of demand, the results might be:

D	$p(D)$
1	.10
2	.20
3	.30
4	.20
5	.10
6	.10

These possible demands would correspond to the possible futures in our model for a decision under risk. Let us suppose that the other considerations which enter into the decision are the loss which will be suffered if more boats are built than sold and the loss in profit which will be suffered if more orders come in than can be filled with the boats in stock. The first of these losses arises from such things as keeping money tied up in unsold boats for a long period, the necessity of lowering the price in order to move the boats, and so on. The second kind of loss arises when a customer orders a boat, but because the order cannot be filled from stock, the customer goes elsewhere and the profit that would have been realized on the sale is lost.

STRUCTURING THE DECISION

This decision problem may now be structured in terms of the model for decisions under risk in order to clarify it somewhat.

Alternatives	= number of boats to be built	= I
Possible futures	= number of boats demanded	= D
Probabilities	= density function of D	= $p(D)$
Outcomes	= number of boats in excess of demand (overage)	= $I - D$
	= demand in excess of stock (shortage)	= $D - I$
Evaluation of outcomes	= cost of overage at C_1 dollars per boat	= $C_1(I - D)$
	= cost of shortage at C_2 dollars per boat	= $C_2(D - I)$

We have assumed that the cost of being over by one boat can be measured and that overage costs are simply linear in the number of boats over. Like assumptions have been made for shortages. For the present let us assume that the expectation principle is to be used. Specifically, we wish to select the alternative which will minimize the total expected cost. Total expected cost will be the sum of the expected costs due to overages and the expected cost due to shortages. Computing the expectations in the usual way, we have for the total expected cost associated with the choice of a stock level I:

$$E(I) = \text{expected overage cost given } I + \text{expected shortage cost given } I$$

If an overage occurs, its amount will be given by $I - D$, and the cost of such an outcome will be $C_1(I - D)$. The probability of this outcome is $p(D)$ for values of D which will yield an overage, namely $0 \leqq D \leqq I$. The expected overage cost would then be

$$\sum_{D=0}^{I} C_1(I - D)p(D)$$

By similar reasoning the expected shortage cost turns out to be

$$\sum_{D=I+1}^{\infty} C_2(D - I)p(D)$$

and the total expected cost then is

$$E(I) = \sum_{D=0}^{I} C_1(I - D)p(D) + \sum_{D=I+1}^{\infty} C_2(D - I)p(D)$$

The task of computing $E(I)$ for each possible value of I in order to discover the best choice, may be greatly shortened by appealing to mathematical techniques which will do exactly this for us. If the function $E(I)$ were a continuous function, we would take its first derivative with respect to I, set it equal to zero and the solution of the resulting equation could be shown to be the minimizing choice. Since the number of boats is in fact a discrete variable, as is demand, we must move from the infinitesimal calculus to the calculus of finite differences. The corresponding theorem there suggests that if we knew the optimal I, call it I_0, then if we were foolish enough to build $I_0 + 1$ boats, this would clearly increase (or at least not decrease) expected costs. Likewise, if we were foolish enough to stock $I_0 - 1$ boats, this would also increase (or at least not decrease) expected costs. Mathematically we could write this as

(1) $E(I_0 + 1) - E(I_0) \geq 0$
(2) $E(I_0 - 1) - E(I_0) \geq 0$

The inequations are called the first forward difference and the first backward difference, and they represent the conditions which must hold at the optimal choice of I namely I_0. The situation is pictured in Figure 14–1.

FIGURE 14–1

Total Expected Cost

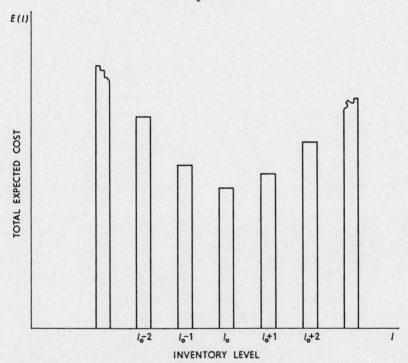

$E(I)$

TOTAL EXPECTED COST

I_0-2 I_0-1 I_0 I_0+1 I_0+2 I

INVENTORY LEVEL

COMPUTING THE OPTIMAL STOCK LEVEL

We can now use conditions (1) and (2) above to compute I_0. We first write $E(I_0 + 1)$ which will be required for use in condition (1).

$$E(I_0 + 1) = \sum_{D=0}^{I_0+1} C_1(I_0 + 1 - D)p(D) + \sum_{D=I_0+2}^{\infty} C_2(D - I_0 - 1)p(D)$$

$$= C_1\sum_{D=0}^{I_0}(I_0 + 1 - D)p(D) + C_2\sum_{D=I_0+1}^{\infty}(D - I_0 - 1)p(D)$$

$$= C_1\sum_{D=0}^{I_0}(I_0 - D)p(D) + C_1\sum_{D=0}^{I_0}p(D)$$

$$+ C_2\sum_{D=I_0+1}^{\infty}(D - I_0) - C_2\sum_{D=I_0+1}^{\infty}p(D)$$

Subtracting from this the quantity

$$E(I_0) = C_1 \sum_{D=0}^{I_0} (I_0 - D)p(D) + C_2 \sum_{D=I_0+1}^{\infty} (D - I_0)p(D)$$

we obtain

$$E(I_0 + 1) - E(I_0) = C_1 \sum_{D=0}^{I_0} p(D) - C_2 \sum_{D=I_0+1}^{\infty} p(D) \geq 0$$

Defining the cumulative distribution function as

$$\sum_{D=0}^{D_1} p(D) = P(D_1)$$

we can write this result as

$$C_1 P(I_0) - C_2\{1 - P(I_0)\} \geq 0$$

or

$$P(I_0) \geq \frac{C_2}{C_1 + C_2}$$

This is of little help by itself, but by a similar process of deduction from the second condition we obtain

$$P(I_0 - 1) \leq \frac{C_2}{C_1 + C_2}$$

If we put these two inequations together we get a key to the best decision:

$$P(I_0 - 1) \leq \frac{C_2}{C_1 + C_2} \leq P(I_0)$$

If we can find the value of I which satisfies this double inequality we will have the optimal choice, I_0.

SOLUTION OF THE EXAMPLE

Returning to our original decision, suppose the cost of being over by one boat is \$100 and the cost of being short by one boat is \$300. Then

$$\frac{C_2}{C_1 + C_2} = \frac{300}{300 + 100} = .75$$

The cumulative distribution function for demand may be computed as

D	p(D)	P(D)
1....................	.10	.10
2....................	.20	.30
3....................	.30	.60
4....................	.20	.80
5....................	.10	.90
6....................	.10	1.00

Inspection reveals that the critical ratio .75 falls between $P(3) = .60$ and $P(4) = .80$. Thus

$$P(I_0 - 1 = 3) = .60 \leq .75 \leq P(I_0 = 4) = .80$$

The best choice is to produce four boats, and this choice has the property of minimizing total expected costs.

THE CONTINUOUS CASE

The continuous case for this type of decision differs not in principle but in mathematical procedure from the discrete case. Suppose that the alternatives are no longer restricted to integral values of I, and that demand is a continuous variable D, with probability distribution $p(D)$. Total expected costs would then be given by the function

$$E(I) = C_1 \int_{D=0}^{I} (I - D)p(D)dD + C_2 \int_{D=I}^{\infty} (D - I)p(D)dD$$

Here one may take the first derivative of $E(I)$, set it equal to zero, and solve for I_0. The result is

$$P(I_0) = \frac{C_2}{C_1 + C_2}$$

The theorem given in Chapter 12 is used in taking the derivative of this function.

Figure 14–2 shows the density function of demand and the notion that any choice I may be represented by a vertical line at the appropriate point of the D scale. The probabilities of being understocked and overstocked are represented by the areas to the right and left of this line respectively. Note also that the foregoing equation may be written in the form:

$$\frac{P(I_0)}{1 - P(I_0)} = \frac{C_2}{C_1}$$

This suggests the following decision rule: *To minimize expected costs, establish the inventory level at the point where the ratio of the probability of an overage to the probability of a shortage is equal to the ratio of shortage cost to overage cost.*

As an example of the continuous case, suppose we are to fix an inventory level of a commodity which is measured and stocked in quantities which can be treated as a continuous variable, such as

FIGURE 14–2

Inventory Level and Demand Distribution

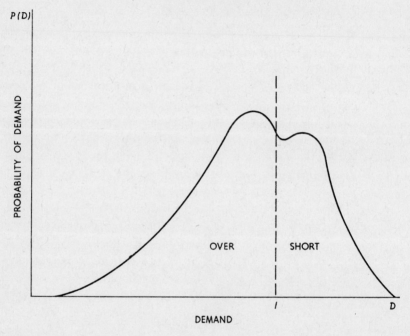

liquid fuel. Suppose the demand distribution is given by the normal distribution with mean of 10,000 gallons per week and standard deviation of 500. Assuming that it is possible to quantify the costs of being understocked and overstocked, let us take

$$C_1 = \$.01 \text{ per gallon}$$
$$C_2 = \$.19 \text{ per gallon}$$

As was shown previously, I_0 must satisfy the relation

$$P(I_0) = \frac{C_2}{C_1 + C_2} = \frac{.19}{.01 + .19} = .95$$

If Z is a standard normal variable, we can read from a table of the normal distribution the value of Z such that $P(Z) = .95$. This value turns out to be $Z = 1.645$. The relationship between Z and D is given by the transformation

$$Z = \frac{D - 10{,}000}{500}$$

Solving for D we obtain

$$D = 500(1.645) + 10{,}000 = I_0$$
$$I_0 = 10{,}822.5$$

OTHER PRINCIPLES OF CHOICE

In a variety of actual contexts the inventory decision has been based upon some sort of an aspiration level principle. This comes about in many situations because of the impossibility of actually measuring the values of C_1 and C_2 which are required for application of the expectation principle. Often the cost of a shortage must in fact reflect the loss of customer good will, the administrative difficulties, and a variety of other consequences not easily measured in dollar terms. In such situations it is common for management to use a principle such as: *Establish the inventory level so that the probability of a shortage is no greater than some specified value* p_a. This has great appeal when management is able to specify the risk it is willing to run of being short but is unable to determine the dollar costs of shortages and overages.

One may formulate other versions of the aspiration level principle for use in connection with the inventory decision. For example, we might wish to fix the inventory level so that the sum of the probability that $C_1(I - D) > A_1$ plus the probability that $C_2(D - I) > A_2$, is minimized. The sum of these probabilities may be expressed as

$$\int_0^{I - \frac{A_1}{C_1}} p(D)\,dD + \int_{I + \frac{A_2}{C_2}}^{\infty} p(D)\,dD$$

This sum will be minimized when

$$p\left(I - \frac{A_1}{C_1}\right) = p\left(I + \frac{A_2}{C_2}\right)$$

For example, in the continuous problem suggested previously suppose we take $A_1 = A_2 = \$20$. We then wish to fix I so that

$$p(I - 2{,}000) = p(I + 105)$$

Using the fact that the normal distribution is symmetric around the mean, we can see by inspection that $I = 10{,}947.5$.

It is also possible to compute the variance of the cost associated with any inventory level and to determine a level which will minimize some function of expected cost and variance of cost. The mathematics of such a principle is not especially simple and neat, however. By far the most widely used principles in this class of decision problems are the expectation principle and the aspiration level principle in the form first suggested. In Chapter 18 we will return to the problem of inventory policy, considering it as a decision under conditions of uncertainty.

ENRICHING THE DECISION

It is perfectly clear that the formulation of the inventory problem which we have just given is the simplest possible version of any interest at all. It is also clear that, in actuality, the general class of decisions about which we are speaking will be complicated by a wide variety of other considerations which we have not included. Many of these complications have been studied extensively and much is known about them. Several obvious enrichments are suggested in the following paragraphs.

1. It may be that the time between deciding on an inventory level and the realization of that level, the reorder time, is not zero as we have assumed, but is better described as a finite but variable period of time. The reorder time itself may be a random variable, thus adding an additional source of risk.

2. The amount ordered to bring the inventory up to the desired level may differ from what is actually delivered. The actual amount received to replenish the inventory may be a random variable whose mean depends on the amount ordered, for example.

3. The amount ordered to replenish the inventory may be actually delivered in amounts which are to some extent random, at times which are also random.

4. The decision may be only the choice of the mean rate of input to the inventory in situations which prevent precise control of what is put into stock.

5. The amount ordered to replenish the inventory may itself influence costs. That is, we may have an economic order quantity problem in connection with an inventory level problem. Again, there may be price discounts for quantity buying which may influence the amount ordered.

6. The cost functions may be more complicated than we have suggested.

7. There may be a variety of ways of, say, responding to a shortage. The firm might hire additional workers, it might work the present force overtime, or it might simply back order. The real decision problem is thus more complex than simply that of fixing the inventory level.

All these and many other complications may be brought to bear upon the determination of inventory policy. Our point is not so much to achieve the rich detail of realistic analysis as to point out a decision-making principle which emerges here. There are a variety of decision problems which might be classed as decisions requiring the matching of a random output by means of a fixed input. The inventory problem is one example, and the facilities planning problem discussed in Chapter 12 is another. The principle simply suggests that once we have decided that the output or demand is random, the best thing to do is pick a given input level and stick with it. "Best" here is used in the sense of minimizing expected costs. It is thus logically consistent to respond to a random demand prediction with a fixed inventory level. It does, of course, take courage to maintain a given inventory level when demand is fluctuating dramatically from period to period.

SUGGESTION FOR FURTHER STUDY

HANSSMANN, FRED. *Operations Research in Production and Inventory Control.* New York: John Wiley & Sons, Inc., 1962.

PROBLEMS

14–1. A manufacturer stocks a certain spare part for one of his production machines. As soon as a breakdown occurs and one of the spares is used, another is immediately ordered. The lead time for the delivery of a spare part is fixed and known. The number of breakdowns per lead time is a random variable having a Poisson distribution. How many spares should be stocked to assure that the probability of not having enough spares is less than some value p?

14–2. The monthly demand for an item is given by a Poisson distribution with a mean of 20 items per month. The item may be restocked only at the beginning of a month. The cost of stocking an item if it is not sold during a month is taken to be $1.50. The cost of being unable to supply a unit when one is required is assumed to be $8.50. What should be the stock level in order to minimize total expected costs?

14–3. Discuss the application of other principles of choice to the problem given in 14–2.

14–4. In problem 14–2, suppose the density function of demand were unknown, but you were willing to assume that demand would be at least

4 units per month and never more than 36. What inventory level would you suggest?

14–5. An electric utility firm has studied its past records and tabulated the frequency with which various peak demands occur. Peak demand is measured in megawatts and is tabulated for each day. The frequency of occurrence is expressed in terms of the expected number of days per month on which a given peak load will occur.

Peak Demand (Megawatts)	Expected No. of Days/Month
1,000	.10
1,050	1.12
1,100	2.25
1,150	3.80
1,200	4.50
1,250	6.46
1,300	4.50
1,350	3.80
1,400	2.25
1,450	1.12
1,500	.10

Generating equipment is available to the firm in 50 megawatt units. Management wishes to establish sufficient capacity so the expected number of days per month on which peak demand exceeds capacity is less than k. Plot a graph showing the required capacity as a function of k.

14–6. The demand for a commodity over a fixed planning period is described by a normal distribution with a mean of 100 and a standard deviation of 10.

a) If $C_1 = \$5$ and $C_2 = \$40$, plot the optimal inventory level as a function of the standard deviation of the demand distribution.

b) Plot the optimal inventory level as a function of the ratio of C_1 to C_2.

14–7. The number of units of a given item sold in a month by a retail store is a random variable with the following probability distribution:

$$p(D) = \frac{N!}{D!(N-D)!}(p)^D(1-p)^{N-D}$$

where $N = 10$ and $p = .10$. Plot the optimal inventory level as a function of C_2 if $C_1 = \$.20$. Assume the item can be stocked only at the beginning of a month.

14–8. A gas station finds that its weekly sales of regular gas may be described by a random variable with a uniform distribution over the range 1,800 to 2,200 gallons. It is able to replenish its stock only once each week. It reckons the shortage cost at $\$.04$ per gallon and the storage cost for gas unsold at the end of the week at $\$.005$ per gallon. Find the optimal stock level.

14–9. With the aid of the theorem given in Chapter 12, derive the expression for the optimum inventory level in the continuous case.

14–10. If the daily demand for an item is given by the probability distribution

$$p(d) = e^{-m} \frac{(m)^{d-d_0}}{(d-d_0)!} \quad for \ d \geq d_0$$

then it follows that the probability distribution of demand for a period of t days is

$$e^{-mt} \frac{(mt)^{d-d_0}}{(d-d_0)!}$$

For fixed values of C_1 and C_2 show how the optimal inventory level varies as a function of the number of days between replenishments.

14–11. The demand for a commodity is given by a uniform distribution with a range of 100 to 150 units per day. Replenishment is possible once each day. The storage cost for items not sold during a day is \$.10. The shortage cost is \$.20 per unit for shortages up to 10 units and \$.25 per unit for shortages in excess of 10 units. Find the optimal inventory level.

14–12. Find the inventory level which will maximize expected profit under the following conditions. The purchase price of each unit is C_0. Units not sold at the end of the inventory period are worthless. The revenue from the sale of each unit is R. There is a storage charge of C_1 per unit based on the number of units left over at the end of an inventory period. Demand is predicted in the form of a probability distribution. Assume inventory level and demand are continuous variables.

14–13. Write an expression for the cumulative probability distribution of cost for the model developed in the chapter. Discuss the relevance of this distribution for management.

14–14. Convert the model developed in the chapter to a profit model by adding the condition that there is a revenue of R per unit for each unit sold. For the continuous case find the inventory level which maximizes the expected profit.

14–15. Write an expression for the probability that profit will be less than or equal to zero for the model developed in problem 14–14.

14–16. An inventory level may be chosen at the start of a period, but cannot be altered during the period. Demand is predicted in the form of a random variable. Two costs are considered:

C_1 = cost per unit for the starting inventory
C_2 = cost per unit for shortages

Assume the commodity is infinitely divisible.

a) Find the policy which will minimize expected costs.

b) Formulate and apply an aspiration level principle.

c) Suggest an industrial or commercial situation in which each (a and b) would be appropriate.

14–17. Find the inventory level which will minimize expected costs in the following situation:

$$C_1 = \$100,000 \qquad C_2 = \$300,000$$

D	1	2	3	4	5	6
$f(D)$	.10	.20	.30	.20	.10	.10

What inventory level would maximize the probability that costs are less than or equal to $400,000?

14–18. The demand for a commodity is modeled by a normal probability distribution with mean $A + Bt$, and standard deviation $C + Dt$. An inventory must be established at the beginning of each month, t, to meet the demand throughout the month. If the cost of having inventory left over at the end of the month is C_1 and the cost of running short is C_2 (per unit), what is the best inventory level, as a function of t?

14–19. Using the data of problem 14–8 find

  a) An expression for the stock level which will meet the demand with probability p.

  b) An expression for the probability that cost will exceed a level A, as a function of the stock level.

14–20. Demand for a commodity in a given period is predicted in the form of a normally distributed random variable with a mean of 1,000 units and a standard deviation of 200 units. Plot the inventory level which will make the probability of a shortage equal to p for $.01 \leq p \leq .10$.

14–21. Demand for an item takes the values 0,1,2,3, and 4 with equal probabilities. There is a storage cost of $100 per unit, based on the number remaining at the end of an inventory period, and a cost of $200 per unit for shortages. At the start of an inventory period management is advised of the number of units left on hand from the previous period. They may choose to continue with the number on hand or to make a production run in order to add more units to the inventory. If they decide to make a production run, there is a fixed setup cost of $50 which is independent of the number of units produced. Find a policy for deciding when to make a production run and how many to produce which will minimize expected costs.

14–22. Suppose the demand for an item is predicted in the form of a uniformly distributed random variable over the range $1 \leq d \leq 6$. The cost of having units left over at the end of an inventory period is $1,000 per unit. The cost of being unable to meet a demand is $2,000 per unit.

  a) How many units should be stocked?

  b) If careful study could produce a prediction that demand is equally likely to be d, $d + 1$, or $d + 2$ for values of $d = 1,2,3,4$, how much would such information be worth?

  c) How much would it be worth to know in advance the exact demand?

Chapter 15

BIDDING POLICY

THE BIDDING PROBLEM

MANY BUSINESS undertakings involve the submission of bids in the hope of being awarded a contract to carry out some activity. This is almost universally true of projects undertaken for governmental agencies. For many large projects, such as highway construction or missile manufacture, an elaborate structure of bids is necessary, involving a prime contractor and many subcontractors. An understanding of bidding policy as a guide to bidding decisions is thus of interest, not only because of its general application, but also because it may be studied as another example of decision making under risk. While there are several schemes for obtaining bids and awarding contracts, we will be concerned with only the sealed bid competition where the award is made to the lowest bidder. The decision is simply what to bid for a given contract. Clearly, the considerations in making this decision would involve an estimate of the cost of performing the contract, the profit desired, the anticipated behavior of competing bidders, and perhaps how badly the firm wanted the contract. There are at least two sources of risk in such a decision—the risk associated with estimating the cost of performance, and the risk associated with predicting the action of competitors. We will consider a situation in which the firm has been for some time submitting bids in a specific field of activity. Such a situation implies that the firm is in a position to keep records of past competitions as a basis for prediction, and that an expectation principle of choice might be a reasonable basis for policy.

ESTIMATING ABILITY

We begin by supposing that the firm is in a position to study its own ability to estimate the costs of performing the type of contract in question. Specifically, we assume that it has data on bids and actual performance costs for the contracts which it has had in the past. For each such contract we form the ratio

$$e = \frac{\text{our estimate}}{\text{actual cost}}$$

and we assume that e is a random variable with probability distribution $f(e)$. Now e may differ significantly for large and small contracts, among various types of projects, or as the firms estimating ability improves. We will assume that these effects have been studied and that $f(e)$ is appropriate for the size and type of project under consideration. Thus, it reflects the firm's current estimating ability. We compute first the mean and variance of e:

$$\bar{e} = \int e\, f(e)\, de$$

$$\sigma^2 = \int (e - \bar{e})^2\, f(e)\, de$$

The mean of e is a measure of the accuracy of the estimate, and indicates whether or not they are good in the long run. If $\bar{e}$ is not equal to 1, there is a constant bias in the estimates for which one may correct. This correction can be made by dividing any future cost estimate, c, by $\bar{e}$, and thus removing the constant bias. For example, if $\bar{e}$ turns out to be 1.05, it means that on the average our estimates run 5 per cent above actual cost. It would be useful then to correct any estimate by dividing it by 1.05. We define a corrected cost estimate then as

$$c' = \frac{c}{\bar{e}}$$

The variance of e is a measure of the precision of our estimates and we would like to have it as small as possible. The only way to reduce this variance, however, is to strive continually to identify and reduce the sources of error in the estimating process. This is likely to be a long-term undertaking. The change in variance over time is a good measure of how the estimating process is being improved.

EXPECTED PROFIT

The alternatives in the decision are the various amounts, B, which might be bid for the contract. For a given bid B, if it turns out to be the winning bid, our best estimate of the profit from the contract would be $B - c'$. Supposing that we knew the probability that a bid of B would win, say $p(B)$, then the expected profit from such a bid would be

$$E(B) = (B - c')\, p(B)$$

We assume that if our bid does not win, then neither profit nor loss results. Clearly, if we could write out $p(B)$, it would be possible to find the bid which would maximize expected profit.

ESTIMATING THE PROBABILITY OF WINNING

Again we suppose that the firm has records of its own bids on past contracts, and has also kept records of bids submitted by competitors on these contracts. This information is often made public when the bids are opened. Let us first assume that the competition is among a number of firms who bid with some regularity for the contracts in question. Then, for a specific competitor, firm X, we could obtain data on the ratio of X's bid, b, to our cost estimate over past contracts. Let

$$x = \frac{b}{c}$$

$g(x) =$ the probability distribution of x

In a competition in which we were opposed only by X, the probability of our winning with a bid of B would then be

$$W(X) = \int_{x=\frac{B}{c}}^{\infty} g(x)dx$$

If we know that we are to be opposed by several competitors, X, Y, and Z, we would compute the probability of winning against Y and Z individually, as we have done for X. Let the resulting probabilities be $W(Y)$ and $W(Z)$. The probability of winning in a competition against all three will then be the product

$$W(X)\ W(Y)\ W(Z) = p(B)$$

Given $p(B)$, we could then find the bid which would maximize expected profit.

Another approach to estimating the probability of winning might be more appropriate if we were not so certain which or how many firms would be opposing us.

In such a situation one might simply choose to view the competitors as being essentially the same with respect to bidding behavior and use the concept of an average or stereotypic competitor. The bidding data on all competitors might then be pooled to obtain a description of an average competitor. This would be an alternative to attempting to identify specific competitors and quantify the individual bidding patterns.

Consider an average or stereotypic competitor, T, whose bidding behavior may be represented by the quantity t.

$$t = \frac{b}{c} = \text{the ratio of an average competitor's bid to our cost estimate}$$

$$g(t) = \text{density function of } t$$

The probability of a bid B winning against a single average competitor is given by

$$W(T) = \int_{t=\frac{B}{c}}^{\infty} g(t)dt$$

Given that we are opposed by k average bidders, the probability of winning the contract with a bid of B is $\{W(T)\}^k$. To complete the analysis we would need data on the number of bidders against whom we had competed in the past. This would permit the estimate of a density function for k, say $h(k)$. This would give the probability of being opposed by exactly k competitors. The expected profit from a bid of B is then

$$E(B) = \sum_{k=0}^{\infty} h(k)\{W(T)\}^k (B - c')$$

By taking the first derivative of expected profit with respect to B, we could find the bid which would maximize this quantity. The general nature of the problem is now somewhat clearer. As the amount of the bid is increased, the profit also increases, given that the bid wins. However, as the amount of the bid increases, the probability of winning decreases. Usually the expected return rises to a maximum and then declines as the bid is increased. The typical behavior is shown in Figure 15–1.

EXAMPLE

Consider a bidding problem in which the number of opposing bidders has the following probability distribution.

k	2	3	4
$h(k)$	⅙	⅔	⅙

These competitors are to be viewed as average competitors and their bidding behavior is described by the density function

$$f(t) = \text{uniform over the range}$$
$$.95 \leq t \leq 1.35$$

Figure 15–1

Expected Profit versus Amount Bid

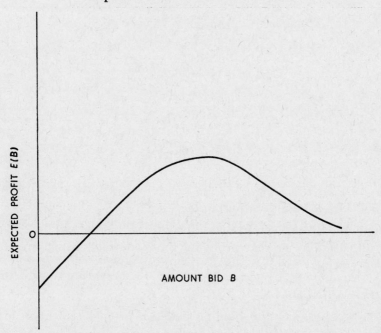

Given a bid of B, the probability of winning against one average competitor is

$$W(T) = \frac{1.35 - \dfrac{B}{c}}{.40}$$

and the expected profit in this case is

$$E(B) = (B - c')\left\{ \frac{1}{6}\left(\frac{1.35 - \dfrac{B}{c}}{.40} \right)^2 \right.$$
$$+ \frac{2}{3}\left(\frac{1.35 - \dfrac{B}{c}}{.40} \right)^3$$
$$\left. + \frac{1}{6}\left(\frac{1.35 - \dfrac{B}{c}}{.40} \right)^4 \right\}$$

We will assume for simplicity that $c = c'$. The determination of the bid which will maximize expected profit is illustrated by Table 15–1. This table suggests that the way to maximize expected profits is to bid about 10 per cent more than the corrected cost estimate. If this

TABLE 15–1

B	$B - c'$	$W(t)$	$p(B)$	$E(B)$
$1.05c'$	$.05c'$	$\dfrac{1.35 - 1.05}{.40}$	.428	$.0214c'$
$1.07c'$	$.07c'$	$\dfrac{1.35 - 1.07}{.40}$	.350	$.0245c'$
$1.10c'$	$.10c'$	$\dfrac{1.35 - 1.10}{.40}$	.252	$.0252c'$
$1.12c'$	$.12c'$	$\dfrac{1.35 - 1.12}{.40}$	.200	$.0240c'$
$1.15c'$	$.15c'$	$\dfrac{1.35 - 1.15}{.40}$	.140	$.0210c'$
$1.20c'$	$.20c'$	$\dfrac{1.35 - 1.20}{.40}$	.062	$.0124c'$
$1.25c'$	$.25c'$	$\dfrac{1.35 - 1.25}{.40}$	.020	$.0050c'$

is done, the average profit over all contracts bid on will be 2.52 per cent of cost. The average profit for those contracts which are actually performed will, of course, be 10 per cent.

OTHER PRINCIPLES OF CHOICE

The establishment of bidding policy is often based upon other principles of choice than expectation maximizing. The firm may simply aspire to a profit of x per cent on any contract which it obtains. It may simply bid its estimated cost plus x per cent on all bids. Alternatively, the firm may be short of work and willing to undertake contracts for any price which exceeds the variable cost of performance. This excess will then help to reduce the fixed cost loss which the company would suffer without the contract.

In formulating the bidding problem in this manner it has been assumed that the firm's bidding behavior does not directly influence that of its competitors. In other words, the bids of the competition are taken to be independent of the firm's bid. An alternative approach is suggested by the "Theory of Games," in Chapter 19, which would not require this assumption.

SUGGESTION FOR FURTHER STUDY

FRIEDMAN, LAWRENCE. "A Competitive Bidding Strategy," *Operations Research*, Vol. 4, No. 1 (February, 1956).

PROBLEMS

15–1. On the basis of a study of the performance of its estimating department, a firm concludes that the ratio of estimated cost to actual cost for past contracts is a random variable. It may reasonably be de-

scribed by a normal distribution with mean 1.00 and standard deviation
.03. It views its competitors as stereotypic bidders. The ratio of a competitor's bid to the firm's cost estimate is also a random variable. It may
be described by a normal distribution with mean of 1.00 and standard
deviation .10. The number of competitors which have bid for past contracts is suggested by the following frequency distribution:

Number of Competitors	Relative Frequency
2	.10
3	.60
4	.30

Find the bidding policy (in terms of the firm's cost estimate) which will
maximize expected profit.

15–2. Find the bid which will maximize expected profit in the following situation: The density function of the ratio of estimated to actual
cost, based on the firm's experience, is taken to be normal with mean 1.05
and standard deviation .053. The competitors are viewed as stereotypic
bidders. The ratio of a competitor's bid to the firm's cost estimate is
normally distributed with mean 1.00 and standard deviation .04. The
probability that the firm will be opposed by k other bidders is as follows:

k	0	2	3	4
Probability	.05	.20	.65	.10

Interpret your answer.

15–3. Given:

$$f(e) = \text{normal } (\mu = 1.00, \sigma = .10)$$
$$g(t) = \text{uniform } (.95 \leq t \leq 1.35)$$

k	2	3	4
$h(k)$	$\frac{1}{5}$	$\frac{3}{5}$	$\frac{1}{5}$

Find the bid which will maximize expected profit.

15–4. Discuss the application of principles of choice other than the expectation principle to the bidding policy decision. How may the current
financial and workload status of the firm influence the principle of choice
used?

15–5. What are the sources of risk in the bidding policy decision?
How might the decision be treated if it were not possible to express this
risk in the form of probability distributions?

15–6. A firm's estimating success is described by the density function:

$$f(e) = \text{normal } (\mu = 1.05, \sigma = .03)$$

In a certain contract competition it expects to be opposed by three familiar competitors, X, Y, and Z. From public bid openings in the past, evi-

dence on the ratio of each of these competitors' bids to the firm's cost estimates has been obtained.

$$g(x) = \text{uniform } (.92 \le x \le 1.12)$$
$$g(y) = \text{uniform } (.99 \le x \le 1.21)$$
$$g(z) = \text{normal } (\mu = 1.02, \sigma = .04)$$

Find the bidding policy which will maximize expected profit on a job for which the firm's uncorrected cost estimate is $10,000.

15–7.   How might one obtain the information necessary for an analysis such as that of problem 15–6? For an analysis such as that of problem 15–1?

15–8.   Given

$$c = \$1850$$
$$f(e) = \text{uniform } (.95 \le e \le 1.05)$$
$$\text{Two competitors: } X; \ g(x) = \text{uniform } (1.03 \le x \le 1.23)$$
$$Y; \ g(y) = \text{uniform } (\ .88 \le y \le \ .98)$$

Find the bid which maximizes expected profit.

15–9.   In what situations would you consider expected profit maximization a suitable basis for bidding policy? What arguments would you offer in its support? In what situations would some other principle be preferred? Explain.

15–10.   Write the cumulative probability distribution of profit for the model developed in the chapter. How might this be useful in making recommendations to management?

15–11.   A company keeps records for some time of the *lowest competing* bid, X, in bidding competitions. It finds that the ratio of X to its own (uncorrected) cost estimate can be described by a random variable having a uniform density function over the range .95 to 1.35. It finds also that the ratio of its own cost estimates to actual costs is a normally distributed random variable with mean of 1.00 and standard deviation of .10. What should be the firm's bid if it wishes to maximize expected profit?

Chapter 16

PURCHASING POLICY

INTRODUCTION

The problem of purchasing a commodity on the open market involves risk because of the movement of the market price which cannot be known with certainty in advance. The purchasing officer who purchases for his firm such commodities as leather, scrap iron, or grain must contend with this risk in the formulation of buying strategy. The basic decision involves the determination of when and in what quantities to buy so as to satisfy the requirements of the firm in some "best" way. This is made difficult both by the fluctuations of the prices quoted by the market and by the transitory nature of any given price quotation. Once a price is known, a quick decision is required to take advantage of it. In this chapter some simple approaches to purchasing decisions under conditions of risk will be discussed. The reader is invited to consider these not only because of the importance of the purchasing decisions themselves to many firms, but also because the analysis brings to light two important points. First, most decisions in the ongoing development of the firm appear as members of a sequence of decisions. In such a sequence, past decisions may have an important bearing on present decisions, and, in turn, future decisions may not be entirely independent of present decisions. Here we have an illustration of the sequential nature of decisions. Second, these purchasing decisions will provide an instance of choice where an aspiration level principle seems most appropriate, and the aspiration levels themselves can be chosen on the basis of a reasonable principle of choice.

It is interesting to note the similarity between the problems faced by the person who invests or speculates in securities and the purchasing agent who buys commodities for his firm. Successful trading for both depends upon the ability to predict future price movements and to formulate a strategy for taking advantage of the predicted movements. Here we will explore the logic of various market strategies under the assumption that the decision maker views future prices as random variables with predicted density functions. In the field of industrial purchasing such strategies as forward buying, "hand-to-mouth" buying, and speculation have been discussed. In the realm of the stock market, somewhat more complicated strategies have been used, going under the names of dollar cost averaging, formula planning, leverage, and so forth. For simplicity, what is being purchased will simply be referred to as "the commodity." Strategies which involve more than one market, such as hedging, and strategies which involve more than one commodity, such as leverage, will not be discussed. Rather, the problem of purchasing a single commodity in a single market will be examined.

SINGLE PROCUREMENT STRATEGY

Consider first the problem of purchasing a given amount of a commodity before a known future deadline. It will be assumed that the market can supply the required quantity, but at a price which is quoted periodically (daily). Each day a market price becomes known which is good for that day, but that day only. Market prices for future days are predicted, and these predictions are taken to be random variables. The purchaser has a variety of strategies open to him in making this procurement. He might decide in advance how much he will buy on each of the days which remain before the deadline. Alternatively, he may wait until the day's price has been quoted and then buy some quantity which might depend on the quoted price and the amount yet to be purchased. To begin the analysis we suppose that the purchaser has determined to obtain his requirements in a single procurement and seeks a good strategy for making this single procurement. The problem may be simplified by omitting several features of importance in actual purchasing problems. Thus it is assumed:

1. That the quantity required is determined.
2. That no costs or restrictions are associated with storing the commodity.
3. That there are no costs or brokerage fees for executing the procurement.

Because of the transitory nature of each day's market price, the purchaser can never make sure that he procures at the lowest possible price. Instead, he must consider each quotation as it is made and decide whether to buy or to wait in the hope of a better price at some future time. The core of the problem is to determine the critical price level, below which he buys, and above which he waits. Given probabilistic forecasts of future prices, these critical levels may be determined so as to minimize the expected price paid for the commodity. To show this, we define:

$$x = \text{a price quotation}$$
$$f_k(x) = \text{density function of price for day } k$$
$$N = \text{number of days available before the deadline}$$
$$X_k = \text{critical price level for day } k$$

The purchasing strategy may be expressed as:

if on day k, $x \leq X_k$, then buy
$$x > X_k, \text{ then wait}$$

These critical price levels are, of course, aspiration levels and each day's choice is based upon an aspiration's level principle.

Using such a policy, the probability that the price on day k will be below (or equal to) X_k is

$$P_k = \int_0^{X_k} f_k(x)dx$$

and assuming no purchase has been made on days 1 through $k - 1$, the expected price paid on day k is

$$e_k = \int_0^{X_k} x f_k(x)dx$$

Price is taken to be a continuous variable for the moment, although later it will be convenient to consider it as a discrete variable. The expected price paid on day k is (unconditionally):

$$E_k = \{e_k\} \prod_{i=1}^{k-1} (1 - P_i)$$

and the expected price paid over the period of N days available for procurement is

$$V = \sum_{k=1}^{N} E_k$$

The reader should examine these statements carefully to make sure he really agrees with them. It is helpful to keep in mind that the statements refer to prices paid as opposed to prices quoted. Since one does not always buy, the price paid may be zero when the price quoted on the market is above the critical price level. It may help also to examine the following simple example. Suppose we let

$$N = 3 \qquad f_k(x) = \frac{1}{b-a} \quad \text{for } a \leq x \leq b \text{ and}$$

$$\text{for all } k$$

$$X_k = \frac{a+b}{2} \quad \text{for } k = 1, 2$$

No critical price level is given for $k = 3$ since, if the purchase has not been made by that time, it must be made at whatever price is quoted.

Clearly, since the critical price levels for day 1 and day 2 lie at the mean of a uniform distribution, the probability that the quoted price will be below this level on either of these days is one half. This may be confirmed using the expression for P_k

$$P_k = \int_a^{\frac{a+b}{2}} \frac{1}{b-a} \, dx = \frac{\frac{b-a}{2}}{b-a} = \frac{1}{2}$$

For day 1 there is a probability of one half that we will not buy and thus pay a price of zero. There is also a probability of one half that we will buy. If we do, the expected price we pay will lie half way between a and $a + b \div 2$. Thus, the expected price paid is

$$\tfrac{1}{2}(0) + \tfrac{1}{2} \left\{ \frac{a + \dfrac{a+b}{2}}{2} \right\} = \frac{3a+b}{8}$$

This may be confirmed by use of the expression for e_k.

$$e_1 = \int_a^{\frac{a+b}{2}} \frac{x}{b-a} \, dx = \frac{x^2}{2(b-a)} \bigg|_a^{\frac{a+b}{2}} = \frac{3a+b}{8}$$

We now have

$$e_1 = \frac{3a+b}{8}$$

$$e_2 = \frac{3a+b}{8}$$

$$e_3 = \frac{a+b}{2}$$

It must be recalled that these are conditional expectations. They give the expected price paid on a particular day, given that the procurement has not been made previously. We may remove this condition simply by multiplying the expectations by the probability of the event upon which they are conditioned. The expected price paid on day 1 is unconditionally e_1 since we cannot buy prior to day 1.

$$E_1 = e_1$$

Note especially the way in which the limits on the product are interpreted in this case. The expectation for day 2 is conditional for not having purchased on day 1. The probability of not buying on day 1 is one half. This gives

$$E_2 = \frac{1}{2} \cdot e_2$$

Similarly

$$E_3 = \frac{1}{2} \cdot \frac{1}{2} \cdot e_3$$

We now need only note that what we pay on the average, over the three-day period, is the sum of the average amount paid on the individual days. Thus, from V we obtain the expected price paid for the three-day period as a whole. This expectation may be interpreted as the average price paid if the purchasing policy assumed is used for a very large number of three-day periods.

FINDING THE CRITICAL PRICE LEVELS

It is clear that the expected price paid, V, is a function of the critical price levels, X_k. Thus, one could go ahead to choose the X_k in such a way as to minimize the expected price paid. This gives us the interesting possibility of using the expectation principle to obtain aspiration levels which will actually be used in the execution of the policy. This is an example of one of the instances in which the aspiration levels can themselves be chosen in a best way.

For each k, the partial derivative of V with respect to X_k may be obtained and set equal to zero. It may easily be confirmed that the solutions of the resulting equations for the X_k will yield the set of critical price levels which will minimize V, the expected price paid. Thus, for $k \neq N$,

$$\frac{\partial V}{\partial X_k} = X_k f_k(X_k) \left\{ \prod_{i=1}^{k-1} (1 - P_i) \right\} + \sum_{j=k+1}^{N} e_j \left\{ \prod_{\substack{i=1 \\ i \neq k}}^{j-1} (1 - P_i) \right\} f_k(X_k)(-1) = 0$$

which yields

$$X_k = \sum_{j=k+1}^{N} e_j \left\{ \prod_{i=k+1}^{j-1} (1 - P_i) \right\}$$

It will be noted that the right hand side of this equation is simply the expected price paid over the days remaining before the deadline. Thus, the result has an interpretation which agrees with one's notions of strategy for the problem. Each day the purchaser compares the day's price quotation with the expected price he will pay if he waits and on each future day uses an optimal X_k. If the day's quotation is lower than his expected price using the optimal policy in the future, then he buys; if his expected price is lower, then he waits.

To illustrate the nature of the critical price levels obtained by this method, consider the following simple problem in which it is assumed that

$$1.\ f_k(x) = f(x),\ \text{for all } k$$
$$2.\ f(x) = \frac{1}{200},\ \text{for } 1,000 \le x \le 1,200$$

For $k = N$, the purchaser has no choice, if he has not previously made the procurement. Because of the deadline he must buy at whatever price is quoted on day N. Thus,

$$e_N = 1,100$$

For $k = N - 1$

$$X_{N-1} = 1,100$$
$$P_{N-1} = .50$$
$$e_{N-1} = \int_{1,000}^{1,100} \frac{x}{200}\,dx = 525$$

For $k = N - 2$

$$X_{N-2} = 525 + (.50)(1,100) = 1,075$$
$$P_{N-2} = .375$$
$$e_{N-2} = \int_{1,000}^{1,075} \frac{x}{200}\,dx = 389$$

Similarly we obtain

$$X_{N-3} = 1,061$$
$$X_{N-4} = 1,052$$
$$X_{N-5} = 1,045$$
. . . .
. . . .

Figure 16–1 shows the critical buying levels for ten periods.

It is perhaps true that this result agrees with one's notions about the problem. If there is plenty of time before the procurement must

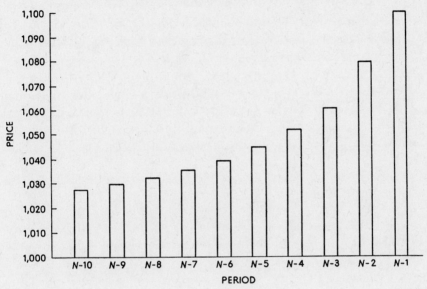

FIGURE 16–1

Critical Buying Levels for Periods $N-10$ through $N-1$

be made, then one may hold out for a relatively low price. As the deadline for the procurement approaches, one is willing to accept a higher and higher price.

GENERAL PROCUREMENT STRATEGY

It is sometimes argued, in connection with policy problems similar to that just discussed, that the purchaser would do better to distribute his purchases in some way over the time available before the deadline. Many such policies indicate that the amount purchased should depend on the quoted price, or more generally, on the price and the number of days remaining. While such policies may have appeal for purchasers who are unable to obtain predictions of future price movements, their value in the problem considered here is questionable. A little reflection on the foregoing analysis may serve to convince one that if the purchaser wishes to minimize expected cost of the procurement, then the single purchase strategy will do this. Nothing is to be gained by any strategy which involves multiple procurements. This important result may be more clearly established as follows. Suppose, as before, that Q units of the commodity must be purchased within N days, and that the basis for procurement is a function $q(x,k)$ which gives the quantity to be purchased. That is, on day k, if the quoted price is x, then the purchaser buys an amount $q(x,k)$. It is assumed that procurement ceases when Q units have been obtained.

It is convenient here to treat price as a discrete variable. Let the expected price quoted on day k be given by

$$A_k(x) = \sum_x x f_k(x)$$

and let

$$V_N = \text{total expected cost of the procurement over } N \text{ days}$$

For $N = 1$, the purchaser can only buy all his requirements at the quoted price. Thus,

$$V_1 = Q A_1(x)$$

For $N = 2$,

$$V_2 = \sum_x x\, q(x, 1)\, f_1(x) + \sum_x \{Q - q(x, 1)\}\, A_2(x)\, f_1(x)$$

The problem is thus to find the function $q(x, 1)$ which will minimize the expected cost V_2, subject to the restriction that

$$0 \leq q(x, 1) \leq Q, \text{ for all } x$$

This is a simple linear programming problem, the solution of which may be obtained by inspection. The expression for V_2 may be reduced to

$$V_2 = \sum_x \{x - A_2(x)\}\, q(x, 1)\, f_1(x) + Q A_2(x)$$

It may be seen that this function will be minimized under the given restrictions by taking

$$q(x, 1) = 0, \text{ if } x - A_2(x) > 0$$
$$q(x, 1) = Q, \text{ if } x - A_2(x) < 0$$

This is precisely the same as saying, "If the quotation on day 1 is below the expected price on day 2, buy the entire amount required; otherwise buy nothing until day 2." This is simply the single procurement strategy already given. However, it is now seen that (for $N = 2$, at least) no policy involving more than a single purchase is desirable.

For $N = 3$

$$V_3 = \sum_x x\, q(x, 1)\, f_1(x) + \sum_x \left\{ Q - q(x, 1) \right\} \frac{V_2}{Q} f_1(x)$$

$$= \sum_x \left\{ x - \frac{V_2}{Q} \right\} q(x, 1)\, f_1(x) + V_2$$

In general, if N days are available before the deadline, we have an N-stage process in the form of a dynamic programming problem. The expected cost is given by

$$V_N = \sum_x \left\{ x - \frac{V_{N-1}}{Q} \right\} q(x, 1)\, f_1(x) + V_{N-1}$$

or in the more usual form

$$V_N = \sum_x x\, q(x, 1)\, f_1(x) + V_{N-1} \left\{ 1 - \frac{1}{Q} \sum_x q(x, 1)\, f_1(x) \right\}$$

The solution is of the form obtained previously. Thus take

$$q(x, 1) = 0, \text{ if } x - \frac{V_{N-1}}{Q} > 0$$

$$q(x, 1) = Q, \text{ if } x - \frac{V_{N-1}}{Q} < 0$$

The optimal policy at any stage consists of computing the expected unit cost using optimal buying prices for all future stages and buying all requirements immediately if the current quotation is below this amount, otherwise buying nothing at present. This provides a demonstration of the optimal character of the single procurement strategy.

At this point certain complications may be easily introduced. If there are brokerage charges or other expenses which depend only on the number of procurements made, the single procurement strategy clearly minimizes these costs. Thus, no change in the policy will result. If known holding costs or storage charges are to be introduced, the price in any period may simply be increased by an amount equal to the unit cost of holding from that period until the deadline. For example, if a procurement were made in period $N - k$, and if holding costs were simply c dollars per unit per period, then the price in period $N - k$ may be taken as $x + ck$. While this will change the critical price levels, it does not detract from the optimality of the single procurement strategy.

DOLLAR AVERAGING

Although the optimality of the single procurement strategy has already been demonstrated under a particular set of assumptions, it is worthwhile to investigate certain other strategies which are in wide use. One form of purchasing policy in which the amount purchased is a function of price is called "dollar averaging" or "dollar cost averaging." This policy suggests that, at each purchasing opportunity, a fixed dollar amount should be expended, regardless of the price. Thus, for example, one is encouraged to invest $50 each month in a security without being concerned as to the price. The purpose of this policy is to free the purchaser from having to make a forecast of future price movements and to average down the mean price of the stock held, as more and more purchases are made. It accomplishes this latter result by leading to the purchase of relatively few units when the price is high, and relatively many units when the price is low. For the investor, this policy is supposed to increase the proportion of the time that his portfolio is "in the black," in the sense that the average price of units held is lower than the current quotation. Some of the properties of this policy may be illustrated in the following simple fashion.

Consider a series of purchasing opportunities which may occur daily, weekly, monthly, or according to the needs of the purchaser. We assume that a policy of spending exactly d dollars at each opportunity is to be used, and that the density function of price for the jth opportunity, $f_j(x)$, is given. Then the expected number of units purchased on the jth opportunity is

$$\int_x \frac{d}{x} f_j(x) \, dx$$

In N opportunities the expected total number of units purchased is

$$\sum_{j=1}^{N} \int_x \frac{d}{x} f_j(x) \, dx$$

The amount expended in N opportunities is Nd. Thus the expected unit cost after N opportunities is

$$E(c) = \frac{Nd}{\displaystyle\sum_{j=1}^{N} \int_x \frac{d}{x} f_j(x) \, dx} = \frac{N}{\displaystyle\sum_{j=1}^{N} \int_x \frac{1}{x} f_j(x) \, dx}$$

It is clear that the expected unit cost is independent of the fixed purchase expenditure d, but dependent upon the number of opportunities N.

For simplicity assume that $f_j(x) = f(x)$, for all j. In this case

$$E(c) = \frac{N}{N\int_x \frac{1}{x} f(x) \, dx} = \frac{1}{E\left(\frac{1}{x}\right)}$$

and the expected unit cost becomes independent of the number of opportunities as well. To show that the policy does, in fact, tend to reduce the expected unit cost of units purchased, assume further that

$$f(x) = \frac{1}{b - a}$$

To show that $E(c) < E(x)$, we simply compute, in Table 16–1, a few values of these expectations as functions of b and a.

TABLE 16–1

b/a	$E(x)$	$E(c)$
1......................	a	a
2......................	$1.5a$	$1.44a$
3......................	$2.0a$	$1.82a$
4......................	$2.5a$	$2.16a$

In general, of course, dollar averaging cannot offer any special protection against portfolio losses in a declining market. Returning to the more general expression for $E(c)$

$$E(c) = \frac{N}{\sum_{j=1}^{N} E_j\left(\frac{1}{x}\right)}$$

it is of interest to note that $E(c)$ does not increase with N if

$$\frac{N-1}{\sum_{j=1}^{N-1} E_j\left(\frac{1}{x}\right)} - \frac{N}{\sum_{j=1}^{N} E_j\left(\frac{1}{x}\right)} \geq 0$$

which yields

$$E_N\left(\frac{1}{x}\right) - \frac{1}{N} \sum_{j=1}^{N} E_j\left(\frac{1}{x}\right) \geq 0$$

Thus, in a rising market, the value of $E(c)$ must rise also. If the rise is followed by a decline, then the portfolio may pass through an extended period "in the red." Table 16–2 illustrates a simple instance of this. Here it is assumed that the price quotation for opportunity j is given by

$$f_j(x) = \frac{1}{b_j - a_j}$$

where

$$b_j/a_j = 2, \text{ for all } j$$

TABLE 16–2

j	a	$E_j(x)$	$E(c)$
1	10	15.0	14.4
2	12	18.0	15.8
3	14	21.0	16.9
4	12	18.0	17.1
5	10	15.0	16.4
6	8	12.0	15.3
7	6	9.0	13.8
8	8	12.0	13.4
9	10	15.0	13.6

From the viewpoint of purchasing policy, dollar averaging cannot improve the purchaser's expectation beyond the single procurement strategy. However, it does have some appeal in situations where capital becomes available in regular amounts and at regular intervals. Perhaps its most appealing application is to the situation in which the purchaser does not wish, or is not able, to obtain a forecast of future price movements.

The fundamental idea of dollar averaging, increasing the number of units purchased as the price declines, suggests immediately that the results might be improved by making the amount purchased even more sensitive to price. Thus, one might buy d/x^2 units on each opportunity, instead of simply d/x. Such a policy might be called "accelerated dollar averaging." It does in fact serve to reduce the expected unit cost of the units purchased. Returning to Table 16–1, it is easy to show that, under the conditions for which this table is valid, if one uses a d/x^2 policy, then for $b/a = 2$, $E(c) = 1.39a$. This represents an improvement over the results for the ordinary dollar averaging policy which yields $E(c) = 1.44a$. Extension of the idea of accelerated dollar averaging leads directly to the single purchase strategy discussed previously.

SPECULATION

While speculation is not a policy viewed with favor by many industrial enterprises, the simplest aspects of speculative buying and selling will be illustrated by way of contrast. The analysis is suggested by that of Marschak. (131) Assume that a speculator wishes to maximize expected profit, and that he is confronted with a current price quotation, y, and a density function for the price on the next opportunity, $f(x)$. To maximize expectation, the speculator computes the expected price for the next opportunity $E(x)$ and applies the following rule:

If $y - E(x) > 0$; sell as much as possible
$y - E(x) < 0$; buy as much as possible

It follows directly that the expected unit profit is given by

$$| y - E(x) |$$

for each opportunity. If one assumes that the costs of making a transaction are small enough to be neglected, and that there is no problem of the speculator being ruined, then at every opportunity as much as possible should be bought or sold, according to the rule. If one takes $f(y) = f(x)$, then the expected unit of profit over a series of opportunities is

$$E\{|x - E(x)|\}$$

which is the average deviation of x. Thus, the greater the variability in the price of the commodity, the greater the expected profits from speculation.

In practice, many speculators modify this policy by not trading at every opportunity, and by restricting the amount bought or sold so as to limit the maximum possible losses. Of special interest is the problem of finding the probability that the speculator's wealth will fall below some given level within a certain number of opportunities.

The attempt has been made to give some insight into the nature of several purchasing policies by means of simple analysis. Perhaps the most typical procurement situation is that of obtaining a fixed amount of a commodity before a given deadline. If the market is characterized by probabilistic future price quotations, then it has been shown that the expectation minimizing policy is to make a single procurement. This procurement is made according to a set of buying price levels which determine whether or not a purchase is made, given a price quotation.

PROBLEMS

16–1. A man has two days within which to sell his house. If it is not sold on the first day it must be sold on the second.
Let:

$$x = \text{the highest offer received on the first day}$$
$$f(x) = \text{the probability distribution of } x$$
$$y = \text{the highest offer received on the second day}$$
$$f(y) = \text{the probability distribution of } y$$

Offers are good only on the day received. The man desires to set an acceptance price for the first day, say A, such that

$$\text{if } x > A \text{ he sells at price } x \text{ on the first day}$$
$$\text{if } x < A \text{ he sells at price } y \text{ on the second day}$$

Find the acceptance price A which will maximize the expected price he obtains. Does this policy make sense from his point of view? Explain.

16–2. A firm wishes to buy 10,000 units of a commodity over the next five days. Its prediction of the price movements over this period takes the form of a probability distribution for the daily price, x.

$$f_k(x) = \text{uniform } (1,100 < x \leq 1,200)$$

Find the purchasing policy which will minimize the expected total cost of the procurement.

16–3. Given:

$$f_k(x) = \text{normal } (\mu = 1,000 + 50[k - 1], \sigma = 100)$$
$$N = 6$$

Find the procurement policy for the purchase of 100 units which will minimize expected costs. Compute the minimum expected cost of the procurement. Interpret this quantity.

16–4. What other principles of choice would you consider good possibilities for the purchasing policy problem which is defined in this chapter?

16–5. What relation between the expectation principle and the aspiration level principle is demonstrated by this decision? What can be said in support of computing aspiration levels in this way?

16–6. In what ways does the analysis of this chapter fail to agree with the formulation of industrial purchasing policy as you understand it? Is the analysis of this chapter typical of the way people buy stocks in the stock market?

16–7. How would you handle the problem of purchasing policy if the market price were not independent of the firm's purchase, and depended on the quantity bought?

16–8.   Explain the meaning of the expression

$$E_k = \{e_k\} \prod_{i=1}^{k-1} (1 - P_i)$$

16–9.   What happens to the purchasing problem if the time deadline is removed?

16–10.   You are invited to play the following game. You may draw a sample of one number from a population of numbers having a uniform distribution over the range −5 to 5. The numbers are restricted to integers. After each such draw you have two alternatives. You may accept a number of dollars from your opponent equal to the number drawn if it is positive, or pay your opponent an amount in dollars equal to the number if it is negative. Alternatively, you may discard the number and go on to another draw. At most you are allowed five draws, and when you decide to stop the payoff is the last number drawn. How should this game be played in order to maximize expectation?

16–11.   Discuss the uses and advantages of dollar cost averaging. Design a plan for accelerated dollar cost averaging.

16–12.   In what respects does the model of speculation suggested in the chapter fail to describe actual speculative behavior as you understand it? Is an expectation principle suitable for the ordinary speculator?

16–13.   What are the values of analysis such as has been done here if exact quantification is not possible?

16–14.   A policy of accelerated dollar cost averaging might be based on the following rule: When the price is x, buy d/x^2 units where d is a positive constant. Write expressions for

  a) The average number of units bought on the jth opportunity
  b) The average total number of units bought in N opportunities
  c) The average amount spent on the jth opportunity
  d) The average amount spent over N opportunities
  e) The average unit cost for N opportunities
  f) The average unit cost for N opportunities if

$$f_j(x) = f(x) = \frac{1}{b - a}, \qquad \text{for all } j$$

  g) Compute the average unit cost from part *f*) for values of b/a of 2, 3, and 4.

Chapter 17

DECISIONS UNDER UNCERTAINTY

INTRODUCTION

CONSIDER A MANUFACTURER using steel as a major input to his production process. The expiration of union contracts in the steel industry is approaching, and there is considerable public and private speculation concerning the possibility of a steel strike. Some
steel users are buying extra quantities of steel as a protective inventory in the event of a strike. Our manufacturer raises the questions of whether or not he should provide such an additional inventory and what size it should be. Suppose as analysts we begin
to make the decision explicit by considering the alternatives to be
various amounts of extra steel inventory, the possible futures to be
various durations of a steel strike, and the values of the outcomes
to be the marginal (incremental) costs resulting from the various
inventory size–strike duration combinations. The remaining difficult question is what probabilities to associate with the possible
futures.

Our first attempt might be the usual one of looking for available
data on which to base these probabilities or trying to design some
sort of experiment which will produce the data. Perhaps we find
this difficult, even impossible, in this case. The obvious move of
examining the history of past steel negotiations with a view toward
finding some data which will lead to the required probabilities may
be rejected because in our opinion the economic, political, profit,
inventory, and union-strength situation is not sufficiently similar
to past instances. Thus, lacking the ability to get data on which to
base probabilities, we are faced as analysts with a decision under
uncertainty.

Our next step might be to confront our management with our
inability to proceed further by our usual methods of data collection
and analysis, asking them for their own judgments as to the likeli-

hood of steel strikes of various durations. Perhaps we could even transform these judgments into numbers which would behave as probability theory suggests that probabilities behave. (They add to one over a collectively exhaustive and mutually exclusive set of events, for example.) If so, we might express these judgments as subjective probabilities. This term suggests the fact that the data on which they are based, the methods by which this data is processed into probabilities, and all the assumptions involved are not made explicit. In producing so-called objective or relative frequency probabilities of the usual sort dealt with in science and engineering, the analyst inserts his own (subjective) judgments at many points (such as choosing significance levels), but the attempt is made to keep the process as explicit as possible. Judgment leading to subjective probabilities is largely an internalized, implicit process. We will examine in Chapter 20 the sorts of questions one might ask a manager in order to elicit answers which could be expressed in the form of subjective probabilities. Given, however, these subjective probabilities we would then be able to treat the decision as one under conditions of risk by the methods we have previously suggested. We might take care to point out to management that any recommendation we made should be considered a recommendation of a course of action consistent with management's own subjective probabilities, rather than one consistent with probabilities based on data we have collected and explicitly analyzed.

Another similar possibility might be that of consulting some person or group believed to be experts in the field of labor relations in general or the steel situation in particular. We might decide to recommend to management a course of action consistent with the opinion obtained from such an expert. Again we might succeed in expressing the experts' judgment in terms of subjective probabilities, thus transforming what we had originally conceptualized as a decision under uncertainty into one under conditions of risk.

Instead of any of these responses we might finally be led to deal with the problem as one in the face of uncertainty—that is, to take our conception of the decision lacking probabilities and apply some principle of choice for decisions under uncertainty. In this chapter we will examine some principles of choice of this sort.

To illustrate but one such principle, suppose we confer with management asking them only to place an upper bound on the length of a steel strike which they consider possible. Presumably this is easier for them to judge than the likelihoods of strikes of various lengths. Suppose they agree that it is unlikely, indeed in their opinion virtually impossible, that a strike last more than four weeks. Of course this opinion may turn out to be wrong, but we will assume that they agree that policy for the firm is to be determined as though it were correct. That is, affairs will be managed in a fashion consistent with the opinion that it is impossible (has probability zero) for a strike to last more than four weeks. With this in mind suppose we express the incremental costs involved in the matrix shown below.

One principle of choice which has been proposed for processing data of this sort is the "minimax" principle. It suggests that one choose the alternative which would minimize the maximum cost. The maximum costs for the alternatives are listed to the right of the matrix. The minimum of these maxima is associated with the alternative, "Stock three weeks' supply of steel."

		\multicolumn{5}{c}{Length of Strike (weeks)}	Maximum Cost
		0	1	2	3	4	
	0	0	$20,000	$40,000	$60,000	$80,000	$80,000
	1	$10,000	1,000	20,000	40,000	60,000	60,000
Extra inventory (*weeks' supply*)	2	20,000	10,000	2,000	20,000	40,000	40,000
	3	30,000	20,000	10,000	3,000	20,000	30,000
	4	40,000	30,000	20,000	10,000	4,000	40,000

CONDITIONS LEADING TO UNCERTAINTY

The analyst aims at making predictions of possible future events by means of an explicit prediction model and historical or experimental data. When this cannot be done, then he may choose to conceptualize the decision as one under conditions of uncertainty. Several futures are possible, but evidence is not available upon which to base statements of their probabilities. Uncertainty does not mean that complete ignorance prevails nor that there is no relevant experience. The analyst, as a scientifically trained person, may not himself have experience with the business situations in question, and if he had, he might well be reluctant to inject his opinions into the analysis. Management, however, may have considerable relevant experience, or experts may be available whose experience may be called upon. Uncertainty indicates what is really an unspecified degree of ignorance, and the task of the analyst is to bound uncertainty and to make it more specific. His first step, we will suppose, is to make explicit what futures are possible, in the judgment of management or experts, and what futures are impossible. Thus if uncertainty characterizes his view of the sales of a new product during its first year, he may begin by setting upper and lower bounds on possible sales. This leaves him with several possible futures but still without grounds for stating their probabilities. He may proceed no further, or he may go on to seek more refined managerial or expert judgments, as we will shortly suggest.

There are several reasons why the probabilities might not be available for a decision problem. It may be that relative frequency knowledge is not at hand at the time the decision is being made. Thus, in introducing a new product, one may have no evidence upon which to base an estimate of the probability distribution of demand. It may not be possible to do the kind of experiment that would be necessary to obtain the probabilities. For example, in considering the safety features of a proposed piece of equipment, one would like to know the probabilities that the operator will sustain certain kinds of injuries. Perhaps there is no way to get this evidence, without actually obtaining the machine, assigning the operator, and waiting for him to get hurt. Again, it may not even be possible to conceive of the kind of experiment necessary to obtain relative frequency probabilities. This is the case, for example, if we wish to know the probability of a team winning a certain football game. Even if we could get the teams to engage each other repeatedly, the probability of winning would change through injuries, familiarity with strategy, and so on. Many methods for predicting possible futures upon which the decision maker must rely are not sufficiently well developed to yield evidence on probabilities. For example, many attempts to predict stock market movements will yield statements about the direction of the market, but nothing about the probabilities associated with these statements. Many, many problems are simply too complicated and too little understood to result in probabilistic predictions.

Contingencies, or future events which cannot readily be forecast by means of historical data, are a major source of uncertainty for the analyst. Events such as research discoveries, technological innovations, the emergence of new competitors, and so on may not yield readily to predictions based on past data.

RESPONSES TO UNCERTAINTY

Speaking generally, if, as an analyst, one conceives of a management decision as one under uncertainty, then among the possible responses are (see Figure 17–1)

FIGURE 17–1

Responses to Uncertainty

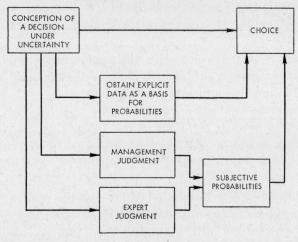

1. Get the data or do the experiment on which some probabilities may be explicitly based, thus transforming the decision into one under risk by the addition of the ordinary sort of relative frequency probabilities. There are many cases in which this is simply impossible; and where it is possible, it involves the difficult questions of how much ought to be spent and how much data collected.

2. Obtain expert judgments or the judgments of managers themselves, expressing these in the form of subjective probabilities. This again transforms the decision into one under risk. The possibilities and difficulties associated with this response will be examined more closely in Chapter 20.

3. Treat the decision as one under uncertainty, using some principle of choice which does not require probabilities as part of its input data.

We are thus confronted with a series of difficult questions. Which of these responses will provide the best basis for understanding management decisions? Which will provide the best method of producing recommendations for management action? Once again, the answers to such questions cannot be given in general, and the analyst must develop experience and judgment of his own in the matter. In this chapter and several which follow, we will examine the problems and possibilities associated with these responses. We begin by examining a number of principles of choice which do not depend on the presence of probabilities in the analyst's conception of the decision and thus may be used directly for decisions under uncertainty.

PRINCIPLES OF CHOICE

As an example of a decision under uncertainty, consider the following decision matrix. The numbers in the matrix are to be taken as profits or gains.

	S_1	S_2	S_3	S_4
a_1	4	4	0	2
a_2	2	2	2	2
a_3	0	8	0	0
a_4	2	6	0	0
a_5	0	1	1	0

As before, we will suggest several principles of choice which might be applied, and then discuss the considerations surrounding each of them.

Dominance. If of two alternatives one would always be preferred no matter what future occurs, this preferred alternative is said to dominate. The other alternative may then be discarded, since there is no further reason to consider it. In the example it is clear that, for any future, the profit from a_2 will be greater than the profit from a_5, and thus a_5 may be eliminated. The first step in approaching any decision under uncertainty is to eliminate any alternatives which are thus dominated. Formally stated the principle of dominance suggests: *If there is a pair of alternatives* a_i *and* a_k *such that* $V(\theta_{ij}) \geqslant V(\theta_{kj})$ *for all* j, a_i *is said to dominate* a_k. *The alternative* a_k *may then be discarded from the decision problem.* This principle may not yield a unique alternative which would be recommended, but it may help to reduce the range of alternatives which must be further considered.

Laplace Principle (Principle of Insufficient Reason). There is a common tendency toward the assumption that all the futures will simply be considered equally likely. Having made this assumption, one may then maximize expectation. It is sometimes suggested that, in the absence of any evidence to the contrary, one might just as well assume that the futures are equally likely. This argument, of highly questionable merit, has led to the name "principle of insufficient reason." To state the principle precisely: *Assume all possible futures are of equal probability, then select the alternative which maximizes expectation.* In the example, this leads to assuming

$$p_1 = p_2 = p_3 = p_4 = \tfrac{1}{4}$$

and the expected profits would be

$$E(a_1) = 2.5$$
$$E(a_2) = 2.0$$
$$E(a_3) = 2.0$$
$$E(a_4) = 2.0$$

The Laplace principle would lead them to the selection of a_1.

Maximin or Minimax Principle. A widely discussed principle suggests that we examine the minimum profit associated with each alternative, and then select the alternative which maximizes the minimum profit. This is clearly a conservative or pessimistic principle which directs attention to the worst outcome and makes the worst outcome as desirable as possible. It says: *Select the alternative,* i, *associated with* $\max_i \min_j V(\theta_{ij})$.

From this it derives the obvious name, maximin. If we were dealing with a decision in which costs instead of profits were given, the principle would be reinterpreted. It would suggest that we examine the maximum cost associated with each alternative, and then select the alternative which minimizes the maximum cost. In this form it is called the "minimax principle."

The obvious antithesis of the maximin principle might be called the "maximax principle." It suggests that we examine the maximum profit associated with each alternative, and then select the alternative which maximizes the maximum profit: *Select the alternative,* i, *associated with* $\max_i \max_j V(\theta_{ij})$.

The maximax principle is thus as optimistic and adventurous as the maximin principle is pessimistic and conservative. In the example, the minimum profits for a_1 through a_4 are 0, 2, 0, and 0, respectively. Thus, a_2 would be selected as the alternative which maximizes the minimum profit.

Hurwicz Principle. Most decision makers find their outlook somewhere between the extreme pessimism of the minimax principle and the equally extreme optimism of the maximax principle. A principle which accounts for all levels of moderation between these two extremes is called the Hurwicz principle. It suggests that the degree of optimism of the decision maker be measured on a scale from 0 to 1. If the decision maker is relatively pessimistic, this scale would supply an index, α, close to 0. If he is relatively optimistic, his α would be close to 1. Having obtained a measure of optimism, α, for the decision maker, we then multiply the maximum profit for each alternative by α, and the minimum profit for each alternative by $1 - \alpha$. The sum of these products for each alternative is called the "Hurwicz criterion," and the alternative which maximizes this criterion is selected. The principle says explicitly: *Select an index of optimism α, such that $0 \leq \alpha \leq 1$. For each a_i compute $\alpha \{max\ V(\theta_{ij})\} + (1 - \alpha) \{min\ V(\theta_{ij})\}$ and select the alternative which maximizes this quantity.*

Note that if the decision maker is optimistic in the extreme, $\alpha = 1$, and the Hurwicz principle becomes the maximax principle. The extreme of pessimism gives $\alpha = 0$, and we have the minimax principle. In the example we have

	$\max_j V(\theta_{ij})$	$\min_j V(\theta_{ij})$
a_1	4	0
a_2	2	2
a_3	8	0
a_4	6	0

In Figure 17–2 the value of the Hurwicz criterion has been plotted for each alternative over the entire range of α. From this diagram it

FIGURE 17–2

Application of the Hurwicz Principle

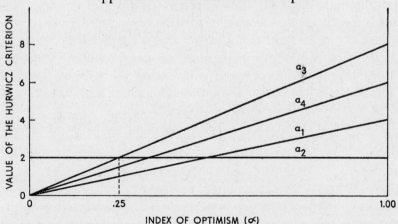

may be seen that if $\alpha < .25$, a_2 is the preferred, but if $\alpha > .25$, then a_3 would be selected.

Savage Principle (Minimax Regret). Still another principle has been proposed for decisions under uncertainty which has certain desirable features. This principle, proposed by L. J. Savage, suggests that a new matrix called a "regret matrix" be computed first. For each alternative-future combination, the difference should be computed between the profit that will result and the maximum profit that could be obtained for the future under consideration. This quantity is called "regret." In the example, the regret for a_1 and S_2 is found by subtracting the profit, 4, from the maximum profit that could be obtained given S_2, 8. The difference of 4 is the regret for the cell a_1, S_2. Having completed the regret matrix, the alternative is selected which minimizes the maximum regret. Regret is given by the relation

$$\text{Regret for } a_k \text{ and } S_j = \max_i V(\theta_{ij}) - V(\theta_{kj})$$

The regret matrix for the example is

	S_1	S_2	S_3	S_4	*Maximum Regret*
a_1	0	4	2	0	4
a_2	2	6	0	0	6
a_3	4	0	2	2	4
a_4	2	2	2	2	2

The alternative which minimizes the maximum regret is thus a_4. The intuitive appeal of the regret principle may be suggested by the following line of thought. If, after a course of action has been selected and carried out, we discover that some particular future, say S_2, actually turns out, then we might wish we had chosen a_3. The choice of a_3, from this hindsight position, would clearly have been the best. If we have in fact chosen some other alternative, say a_2, then we are disappointed or regretful about our choice. A measure of this disappointment or regret is the difference between the value of the best possible choice and our actual choice, given that a particular future has happened.

Note that in this example each of the four principles leads to a different choice.

Laplace........................a_1
Maximin........................a_2
Hurwicz ($\alpha > .25$)..............a_3
Savage.........................a_4

Thus, there is in general a difference between the four principles although in some problems they may yield the same results.

These principles may be understood in several ways. For example, a person faced with a complex decision under uncertainty may have a psychological need for a rule of thumb, a guide to behavior which simplifies the situation for him. These principles may be understood as such devices for simplifying the environment. In choosing among principles for this purpose a person would want to select one which reflected his feelings about the decision problem he faced. The principle would then be an aid to making his attitudes explicit. As analysts we might consider a principle to be a first, very simple hypothesis about management behavior. Testing the hypothesis with past decisions, or by means of direct questions to the manager, the analyst might select a principle as a model for predicting consistent management choices in future decisions. Thus, just as in the case of decisions under risk, a recommendation based on a principle of choice could be considered a prediction of how the manager would choose if he were logically consistent.

Notice that these principles can be thought of as equivalent to expressing the attitudes of the decision maker in the form of subjective probabilities. The Laplace principle is obviously equivalent to a uniform subjective probability distribution over the possible futures. The minimax principle is equivalent to the belief that the probabilities of the possible futures *depend on* which action is chosen and for any action the worst possible future will occur with probability one. Notice, however, that a manager who finds this principle useful may not hold this belief, but may simply be cautious and wish to protect himself against the worst that could happen. Similarly, in the Hurwicz and Savage cases, one may think of these as equivalent to subjective probabilities which are not independent of the action chosen.

THE LAPLACE PRINCIPLE

The very statement of this principle raises strong feelings of doubt. Its highly gratuitous character leaves little to be said for it, except that it is simple and gives definite selections among the alternatives. Its application is complicated by difficulties in obtaining statements of possible futures which form collectively exhaustive and mutually exclusive sets of futures. For example, in the decision to invest in a certain machine, it is generally no simple matter to decide on a way of listing the possible futures. Many listings might be given and the choice may well depend simply on which list is used. For example, suppose we are deciding between a general-purpose machine and a special-purpose machine. Assume that we are negotiating for three contracts, any one of which would load the machine, and no more than one of which we would accept if negotiations are successful. There are two ways of listing the futures, among the several which might be used, which appear sensible:

I. S_1 = we get no contract   II. S_1 = we get no contract
     S_2 = we get a contract S_2 = we get contract A
                                      S_3 = we get contract B
                                      S_4 = we get contract C

Assuming that under S_1 we might still have use for the general-purpose machine, the profit matrix might be.

Using List I:

	S_1	S_2	$E(a_i)$
a_1 = special-purpose machine	−1	6	2.50
a_2 = general-purpose machine	1	5	3.00

Using List II:

	S_1	S_2	S_3	S_4	$E(a_i)$
a_1 = special-purpose machine	−1	6	6	6	4.25
a_2 = general-purpose machine	1	5	5	5	4.00

Thus the choice might depend simply on the way in which we decided to list the possible futures.

Now one may argue against this that the possible futures should be listed in such a way as to make them equally likely, but this presumes that we have some knowledge of the probabilities. If we do, then it would perhaps be better to formulate the problem as a decision under risk rather than as a decision under uncertainty. This places the decision maker in that vague and difficult area where he is not willing to admit he is completely ignorant of the probabilities, but he finds it extremely difficult to make the precise statements about their values that are required to treat the problem as one involving risk.

Another symptom of this same difficulty arises in the application of the Laplace principle to problems such as the following: Suppose an investment decision depends importantly on the salvage value of equipment at some future time. To say that we are "completely ignorant" of this salvage value is to say that it could be any number from negative infinity to positive infinity. This is clearly foolishness, and the decision maker must admit that he is not completely ignorant. In fact, what he may wish to do, is to say that a certain range of salvage values is possible, and that values outside this range are impossible. He may then assume that all values within the range are equally likely. As later examples will illustrate, the outcome of this process depends heavily on the range of possible

values selected, and the Laplace criterion gives no guidance as to
how this should be done.

THE MAXIMIN OR MINIMAX PRINCIPLE

The decision maker who chooses so as to maximize his minimum
profit or minimize his maximum loss may certainly be described as
conservative, pessimistic, security conscious, timid, and unadventur-
ous. These principles have their most useful application in situations
where conservatism and security are desired and seem appropriate
to the decision maker. Life insurance is a typical example. Decisions
made in many stable, "old line," conservative companies are characterized by these principles. There are other situations in which
these ideas lead to such extreme conservatism as to be nonsensical
and thus they are cast aside in favor of others. An extreme example
of the kind of decision in which many feel ill at ease with the
maximin principle is the following:

	S_1	S_2
a_1	$0	$1,000
a_2	1	1

Maximin clearly leads to a_2, while many feel that there is something
intuitively more desirable about a_1. This is reinforced by the observation that the payoffs for a_2 could be reduced to one cent and
the payoff for a_1, S_2 raised to a billion dollars without altering the
choice indicated by the maximin principle. Another objection which
might be raised against this principle is that it does not possess a
property called "column linearity." This may be illustrated by the
following example.

In the following matrix of profits, the maximin principle would
clearly lead to the choice of a_1:

	S_1	S_2
a_1	$ 5	$8
a_2	10	2

Now suppose that it is stated that if S_2 is the possible future which
is actually realized, the decision maker will receive an additional
income of $4.00, no matter which alternative he has chosen. This
simply has the effect of adding a constant to the column headed
S_2. Many have argued that, since this constant depends only on
which possible future is realized, and is in no way connected with
which alternative is chosen, it should not change the decision
maker's selection. However, this is not the case with the maximin

principle, as an examination of the following modified matrix will reveal:

	S_1	S_2
a_1	\$ 5	\$12
a_2	10	6

Now a_2 is chosen. To put it another way, it is argued that, since the additional \$4.00 has exactly the same effect on both alternatives, it should not influence one's choice. The fact that the maximin principle does not have this property is taken by some to detract from its suitability as a useful principle of choice. It will be noted that the Laplace principle does have the property of column linearity.

THE HURWICZ PRINCIPLE

The Hurwicz principle was originated to avoid the extreme conservatism of minimax or the radicalism of a principle such as maximax. Thus, it allows various degrees of moderation according to the optimism or pessimism of the decision maker. The most obvious operational criticism of this principle centers around the method for determining the proper value of the index α. If this is simply left "to the judgment" of the decision maker, then the principle loses to some degree its objectivity. There is perhaps no other way of getting at the value of α; however, it has been suggested that such a judgment might be sharpened and made explicit. One way to do this might be to confront the decision maker with a choice problem of the following form:

	S_1	S_2
a_1	0	1
a_2	x	x

Assuming the values in the matrix are profits, the decision maker is then asked to indicate for what value of x he would be indifferent as to which alternative he chose. For what value of x would the alternatives be equally desirable? If he can state a value of x, then the Hurwicz principle may be applied to quantify the equivalence of the alternatives.

$$\alpha(1) + (1 - \alpha)(0) = \alpha x + (1 - \alpha)x$$

The solution of this equation yields

$$\alpha = x$$

There are several difficulties with this process, which arise in many other places in the study of decision making. It may be difficult to find a sample choice problem which has enough meaning to elicit a reasonable response from the decision maker as to his value of x, or in turn, α. One must also assume that the α so determined is a general measure of his degree of optimism which can be applied to other decision problems. Clearly, also, a particular decision maker may be very sensitive to outside influences (such as the morning paper) and thus may change his attitude considerably over time. To clarify this process, consider the following simple example. A firm is about to undertake an engineering project, the success of which depends heavily on whether or not a large corporation decides to build a plant on the outskirts of town. Suppose analysis reduces the decision to the following profit matrix (in millions of dollars):

	Plant Built	Plant Not Built
Project	−1	5
No Project	0	0

Being unable to obtain any information about the probability that the corporation will build its plant in the area, the analyst decides to apply a maximin principle, which leads to the decision that the project should not be undertaken. Being dissatisfied with this, he decides to try the Hurwicz principle. To find α he confronts the decision maker with two wagers:

a_1: If the plant is built, the analyst will pay the decision maker $10. If the plant is not built, the analyst will pay the decision maker nothing.

a_2: Whether or not the plant is built, the analyst will pay the decision maker x dollars.

The decision maker is then invited to state the value of x for which he would be willing to pay the same amount for either wager. This example has the same structure as was given previously, but possibly has the advantage of being somewhat interesting and realistic to the decision maker. One might be willing to assume that the α elicited in this way would be relevant to the actual decision under consideration.

Several other difficulties have been pointed out in connection with the Hurwicz principle. For many the principle leads to counterintuitive results in decisions of the following sort:

| a_1 | 1 | 0 | 0 | 0 | 0 | 0 | 0 | 0 | 0 | 0 |
| a_2 | 0 | 1 | 1 | 1 | 1 | 1 | 1 | 1 | 1 | 1 |

The Hurwicz principle suggests that these alternatives are equivalent to the decision maker. Many people find a strong preference for a_2 and thus find fault with the principle. Such a preference seems inevitably to involve some preconceived notion about the probabilities of the possible futures. One must assert that, if estimates of the probabilities can be made, they should be used and the decision treated as one under conditions of risk. If the problem is treated as one under uncertainty, then by definition the probabilities are unknown, and no argument based upon them is relevant. Thus, we encounter here a criticism which can only be based upon taste, rather than logic. It should be noted that this argument applies also to the maximin principle and to the regret principle as well.

Column linearity is also not a characteristic of the Hurwicz principle. To demonstrate this once more suppose we are given the following decision where the numbers in the matrix may be taken as profits:

1	4
3	3

For any $\alpha < \frac{2}{3}$, a_2 will be preferred, but if we add the constant 5 to the first column of the matrix, it will be seen that the choice is switched to a_1 for any $\alpha < \frac{1}{3}$.

"Convexity" is the name given to another property which is not possessed by the Hurwicz principle. Suppose for $\alpha = \frac{3}{4}$ we have the following decision:

a_1	0	1	0
a_2	1	0	0

The value of the Hurwicz criterion is $\frac{3}{4}$ for each alternative and the decision maker would be indifferent as to which he chose. It is then argued that if he is really indifferent there would be no harm in using a_1 some of the time and a_2 some of the time if the decision is to be made repeatedly. Thus, we could think of a third alternative which would be a combination of a_1 sometimes and a_2 at other times. Clearly this third alternative should be just as good as the previous two. To be specific, suppose the decision maker decides to use a third alternative which involves flipping a fair coin and using a_1 if heads comes up and a_2 otherwise. Call this a_3. The decision then looks as follows:

a_1	0	1	0
a_2	1	0	0
a_3	½	½	0

The Hurwicz criterion for a_3 turns out to have a value of ⅜, indicating that a_3 is not as good as a_1 and a_2. This is called "lack of convexity." The property of convexity suggests that any combination (in the sense of the foregoing example) of equivalent alternatives, should also be equivalent.

THE SAVAGE OR MINIMAX REGRET PRINCIPLE

The Savage principle is intended to counter some of the ultra-conservative results given by the minimax principle. For example, the problem used to illustrate the counterintuitive results sometimes given by the minimax principle was (maximin in this case)

	S_1	S_2
a_1	0	$1,000
a_2	$1	1

The regret matrix for this problem is

	S_1	S_2
a_1	$1	0
a_2	0	$999

and the principle thus leads to the selection of a_1 which is intuitively more satisfactory to many decision makers.

In many problems the regret matrix is simply equal to the loss matrix and both minimax and minimax regret have the very same results. This will be true in all problems for which the minimum in each and every column of the loss matrix is zero. More explicitly regret is simply the negaive of loss if and only if max $V (\theta_{ij}) = 0$. This may be illustrated by the following decision:

LOSS MATRIX

	S_1	S_2	S_3
a_1	5	0	2
a_2	9	8	0
a_3	0	6	3

The minimax principle selects a_1. The regret matrix for the decision is

	S_1	S_2	S_3
a_1	5	0	2
a_2	9	8	0
a_3	0	6	3

yielding the same problem as before.

One of the logical difficulties associated with the regret principle is that it is not independent of the addition of irrelevant alternatives. Consider a decision maker who is confronted by the following problem:

PROFIT MATRIX

	S_1	S_2	S_3
a_1	1	6	4
a_2	5	3	6

The regret matrix is

$$\begin{matrix} 4 & 0 & 2 \\ 0 & 3 & 0 \end{matrix}$$

leading to the selection of a_2. Now suppose a third alternative becomes available

a_3	4	8	1

The regret matrix of the new problem is

$$\begin{matrix} 4 & 2 & 2 \\ 0 & 5 & 0 \\ 1 & 0 & 5 \end{matrix}$$

The distressing result is that a_3 is clearly not preferred by the decision maker, but its presence shifts his choice from a_2 to a_1. Thus, the appearance of a third alternative, which itself is of no interest to the decision maker, has the effect of changing his preferences among the original two alternatives.

This is distracting to many decision makers, but others try to point out that there are situations in which this sort of thing is not so unreasonable. Consider a manager who is deciding which of two machines to purchase. Both of the machines appear on the surface to be of the same capabilities, but prices differ markedly. Machine A is offered for $12,000 and Machine B for $10,000. The manager would like to buy B but it is manufactured by a company which is little known and without reputation, thus he decides on A, which is made by a prominent manufacturer with an excellent reputation for quality and dependability. Just as the manager is about to authorize the purchase, the salesman from company B calls to point out that a precision thread grinding machine has been introduced by his company. The manager then says, "Thank you but I have no use for a thread grinder; however, we will place an order for your Machine *B*." The manager has reasoned, and perhaps rightly so, that if company *B* can put out a thread grinder, they are probably capable of making a good quality product, and thus their Machine *B* is a good buy.

CHOOSING A PRINCIPLE

The kind of arguments advanced against the various principles of choice for decisions under uncertainty clearly do not take the form of deductive proofs. They are based either on intuitions about the application of a principle in a specific decision problem, or upon the failure of a principle to exhibit some property which is taken to be desirable. We can do little about the variety of intuitions we have, except to agree where we can and disagree where we cannot. People have produced various lists of desirable properties which a principle should have, such as column linearity, convexity, and so on. One of the best known is that of Milnor (131), who was able to show that none of the principles of choice we have discussed had all the properties on the list. One might go back one step further and argue about what properties should appear on such a list. It seems, however, more reasonable to simply conclude that the choice of a principle must remain a matter of reflecting a decision maker's attitude toward uncertainty in a given decision-making context.

SUGGESTION FOR FURTHER STUDY

LUCE, R. DUNCAN, and RAIFFA, HOWARD. *Games and Decisions.* New York: John Wiley & Sons, Inc., 1957.

PROBLEMS

17–1. Suggest an example of a decision from your own experience which you feel is best treated as a decision under uncertainty. What principle of choice would seem appropriate?

17–2. For each principle of choice suggest an example of a decision which illustrates its applicability.

17–3. Formulate a principle of choice of your own for decisions under uncertainty. Show by an example how it would be used. What can be said for and against your principle?

17–4. Discuss the following ideas:

a) We do not deal with "real" decisions but with our views or perceptions of decisions.

b) How we view a decision may depend on accumulated experience, the evidence at hand, as well as a considerable amount of judgment.

Compare your thoughts with those set down in answer to problem 12–1.

17–5.   What rough principles could be formulated to help one decide when to treat a decision as one under uncertainty?

17–6.   In formulating a view of a decision, how can we handle the feelings we have about probabilities which are not supported by objective relative frequency evidence? What is meant by "complete ignorance of the probabilities of the possible futures"?

17–7.   Apply the various principles of choice to the following matrix. The numbers in the matrix are costs.

18	18	10	14
14	14	14	14
5	26	10	10
14	22	10	10
10	12	12	10

Form a new matrix from the one above by taking each number, adding 2, and multiplying the result by 3. Again apply the principles of choice. What does this suggest with respect to value measurement?

17–8.   What general description could you give of the appropriate circumstances for the use of each principle?

17–9.   What difficulties would you expect to encounter in applying the Hurwicz principle in actual practice?

17–10.   In your own terms, explain the reasoning behind the Savage or regret principle.

17–11.   What is column linearity? Why is it to be desired in a principle of choice? Answer the same questions with respect to convexity.

17–12.   Comment on the following argument: "Any principle of choice ought to select alternatives which would maximize expectation for *some* set of probabilities. If there is an alternative for which *there exists no* set of probabilities which would make it the expectation maximizing alternative, then no principle of choice should lead to its selection."

17–13.   Suppose a gambler were to confront the decision as to how to bet at roulette. Consider the alternatives RED, BLACK, and 0 AND 00. Suppose he knows the wheel to be biased but has no evidence as to how it is biased. How should he bet?

17–14.   Consider an insurance policy which insures against a loss of amount L on payment of a premium P. Suppose no evidence is available to aid in estimating the probability of the loss. What principle of choice would you suggest for the decision to insure or not to insure?

17–15.   Consider a gamble in which the probability of winning is unknown. An amount W may be won as the result of placing a bet B. What principle of choice would you suggest in deciding whether or not to bet?

17–16.   An urn contains N balls. You are given N dollars and asked to decide how many black balls are in the urn. If your decision differs from the actual number, then a number of dollars equal to the amount of the difference will be taken away from you.

a) What would be your decision if you were given no opportunity to obtain further information?

b) What would be your decision if you were permitted to take a sample of three balls (with replacement) from the urn? Assume that N is very much greater than 3.

17–17. A six-horse race is about to be run and you are determined to bet on one of the horses to win. How would you place your bet if:

a) You had no other information?

b) You could see the tote board?

17–18. Regret has been called a measure of the loss which may be suffered as a result of imperfect information. Explain the sense of this interpretation.

17–19. Suppose you know that the instructor in a certain course gives only the grades A, B, or C. He makes you the following offer: If you can guess the grade which he has already assigned you, he will raise it by one letter (except in the case of A); if you guess wrong, he will lower it by one letter; and if you choose not to guess at all, you will of course receive the assigned grade. Explain your choice.

17–20. Two bettors at a race track both believe in using the Laplace principle. They are considering a bet on a horse which carries the number 1 and wondering whether to bet $2 on this horse or not to bet on the race at all. If number 1 wins he is expected to pay $6, yielding a profit of $6 − $2 = $4. One bettor argues that there are two possible futures, the horse either wins or loses. The other bettor feels that there are six possible futures since one of the six horses in the race will win. What conclusions will they reach?

17–21. A retailer is wondering how many units of a perishable item to stock. The demand for the item during a stocking period could, in his opinion, be 0, 1, 2, 3, or 4 units, but he does not feel able to estimate the probabilities. He will suffer a loss of $1 for each unit stocked but not sold, and make a profit of $10 on each unit sold. Would you advise a policy of minimizing the maximum loss?

Chapter 18

DECISIONS UNDER UNCERTAINTY— EXAMPLES

INTRODUCTION

IN THIS CHAPTER a number of examples will be discussed to illustrate the flavor of the analysis of decisions under uncertainty. In many cases the application of several principles of choice will be discussed, without any particular attempt to resolve the question of which might best be used. It will be beneficial for the reader to check the results given by the various principles against his common sense, and to try to be explicit about the various decision-making contexts which might support the use of one principle as opposed to another. Still other examples of decision making under conditions of uncertainty follow in Chapters 19 and 20, as well as in the problems at the end of this chapter.

OPERATOR SAFETY

To begin with a simple example, assume that a firm has purchased a new press and is offered an expensive safety device designed to protect the press operator from injury. Suppose that because of the design of the press the choice is between this safety device or none, and that if the operator is injured by the press the nature of the injury can be rather closely predicted. We will divide the actions of the operator into safe and unsafe classifications. Unsafe actions are those acts which will result in injury to the operator if the safety device is not in use. All other actions are classified, for purposes of this decision, as safe actions. It would be extremely useful in this decision to have some information on the probability that an operator would commit an unsafe action during some specified time interval, since this would suggest the possibility of analysis as a decision under risk. We will suppose, however, that no such information is available. This is perhaps the most common situation. Assume that the cost of the safety device is $1,200 and that the alternatives are:

a_1 = install the safety device
a_2 = do not install the safety device unless an injury occurs, in which case the device will be immediately installed after the injury

Let:

S_1 = no unsafe action is committed by the operator during the useful life of the press
S_2 = at least one unsafe action is committed by the operator during the useful life of the machine

Then:

a_1	$1,200	$1,200
a_2	0	V(injury and $1,200 expense)

We begin by applying the Laplace principle, which simply suggests that the probabilities of S_1 and S_2 each be taken equal to $\frac{1}{2}$. The expected costs would then be:

$$E(a_1) = \frac{1}{2}(\$1,200) + \frac{1}{2}(\$1,200) = \$1,200$$
$$E(a_2) = \frac{1}{2}(0) + \frac{1}{2}\{V(\text{injury and \$1,200 expense})\}$$

Alternative a_1 will be preferred if $E(a_2) > E(a_1)$ which implies

$$\frac{1}{2}\{V(\text{injury and \$1,200 expense})\} > \$1,200$$

If we are willing to make the simplifying assumption about the decision maker's value system that:

$$V(\text{injury and \$1,200 expense}) = V(\text{injury}) + \$1,200$$

then it may be said that a_1 will be preferred if

$$V(\text{injury}) > \$1,200$$

Thus, if the firm attaches a cost to such an injury of more than $1,200, the safety device should be installed. Aside from its lack of logical appeal, the Laplace principle may be questioned here by the decision maker who feels that the probability of at least one unsafe act during the life of the machine is nowhere near one half. If this response is made, then the decision maker is not completely ignorant of the probabilities involved. It would perhaps be better to treat the decision as one under conditions of risk, using the decision maker's judgments of the probabilities.

The minimax principle is easily seen to lead to the choice of a_1 as long as the injury has any value associated with it whatsoever. The maximum losses are:

$$\text{for } a_1: \$1,200$$
$$\text{for } a_2: V(\text{injury and } \$1,200)$$

Here it is seen that if the firm will install the safety device after an injury occurs it would clearly be wiser to install it immediately. This reflects the familiar principle which suggests the futility of closing the barn door after the horses have departed.

The Hurwicz criterion for a_1 is simply

$$\alpha(\$1,200) + (1 - \alpha)(\$1,200) = \$1,200$$

and for a_2

$$\alpha(0) + (1 - \alpha)\{V(\text{injury and } \$1,200)\} \quad \text{or}$$
$$(1 - \alpha)V(\text{injury}) + (1 - \alpha)(\$1,200)$$

Now a_1 will be preferred if

$$(1 - \alpha)V(\text{injury}) + (1 - \alpha)(\$1,200) > \$1,200$$
$$V(\text{injury}) > \frac{\alpha}{1 - \alpha}(\$1,200)$$

If $\alpha = 1$, meaning the decision maker is ultimately optimistic, the safety device will only be installed if an infinite cost is associated with the injury. If $\alpha = 0$, meaning complete pessimism, this reduces to the minimax principle.

It will be noted that, in this decision problem, the selection of an α is logically equivalent to the selection of a probability distribution on the possible futures. This, however, is not the case in any problem where there are more than two possible futures. In spite of the equivalence in the foregoing case, it is worthwhile to maintain a distinction between measuring the level of optimism of a decision maker, and obtaining estimates of the probabilities, if only for purposes of discussion.

The Savage principle requires the computation of a regret matrix which will appear thus:

	S_1	S_2
a_1	$1,200	0
a_2	0	$V(\text{injury})$

Minimizing the maximum regret leads to the selection of a_1 as long as V (injury) $>$ \$1,200.

EQUIPMENT INVESTMENT

Consider the decision as to which of two production machines should be purchased for a given application. The requirement for a machine is expected to continue for either three or four years, but the probabilities of these events cannot be estimated. When the requirement no longer exists the machine will be disposed of. Neither of those under consideration are expected to have any net salvage value at any time. The following information is assumed to be known with certainty:

	Machine A	Machine B
Investment...........................	\$10,000	\$12,000
Annual operating cost.................	4,000	3,200

Each of the machines contains a major component which will require a complete overhaul in either the third or fourth year of use. No data are available for either machine which permit the estimation of the probabilities that this overhaul will occur in the third year or the fourth year. Thus, for each machine we have two possible predicted patterns of maintenance expense:

	Machine A		Machine B	
	M_1	M_2	M_3	M_4
Year 1.........	\$ 500	\$ 500	\$ 200	\$ 200
2.........	500	500	300	300
3.........	1,500	500	2,800	300
4.........	500	1,500	200	2,800

A possible future in this problem may be specified by stating a maintenance prediction for each machine and a duration for the machine requirement. Evaluating the outcomes in terms of average annual cost and using the symbol L to stand for the duration of the machine requirement, the decision appears as:

	M_1 M_3 $L = 3$	M_1 M_4 $L = 3$	M_1 M_3 $L = 4$	M_1 M_4 $L = 4$	M_2 M_3 $L = 3$	M_2 M_4 $L = 3$	M_2 M_3 $L = 4$	M_2 M_4 $L = 4$
A	\$8,167	\$8,167	\$7,250	\$7,250	\$7,833	\$7,833	\$7,250	\$7,250
B	8,300	7,467	7,075	7,100	8,300	7,467	7,075	7,100

These machines are clearly rather closely matched. The numbers were chosen this way to show something of how the principles of choice behave under such conditions. The Laplace principle indicates that the probability of each of the possible futures should be taken to be $\frac{1}{8}$. The expected costs under this assumption are

$$E(a_1) = \$7{,}625 \qquad E(a_2) = \$7{,}485$$

Thus, machine B would be preferred by a very small margin.

The minimax principle leads to the selection of machine A with a maximum average annual cost of \$8,167, as compared with \$8,300 for machine B. The regret matrix is easily computed with the following result:

0	700	175	150	0	366	175	150
133	0	0	0	467	0	0	0

The maximum regret in each case is 700 for a_1 and 467 for a_2, indicating the selection of machine B.

The Hurwicz principle yields:

for a_1: $(\alpha)(\$7{,}250) + (1 - \alpha)(\$8{,}167)$
for a_2: $(\alpha)(\$7{,}075) + (1 - \alpha)(\$8{,}300)$

It may be confirmed that for any $\alpha < .432$, a_1 will be preferred, but again by a small margin.

It seems clear that these two machines are, from any viewpoint, very similar with respect to cost performances. Review of the results obtained from various principles of choice will show that slight variations in the cost performance could tip the balance in favor of one machine or another, depending upon which principle is used. As long as this is the case it seems fair to say that, in this application, none of the principles lead to a highly counterintuitive choice.

INVENTORY POLICY

In Chapter 14 we examined in some detail the problem of fixing an inventory level in the face of demand which was predicted in the form of a probability distribution. There we defined

$C_1 = $ the unit cost of being overstocked
$C_2 = $ the unit cost of being understocked
$D = $ the number of units demanded during the period for which the inventory level is being established
$p(D) = $ the probability distribution of D
$I = $ an inventory level

Using these variables and treating the decision as one under conditions of risk, the expected cost associated with any inventory level I was expressed as

$$E(I) = C_1 \int_{D=0}^{I} (I - D)p(D)dD + C_2 \int_{D=I}^{\infty} (D - I)p(D)dD$$

The stock level choice, I_0, which minimizes expected cost was shown to be that stock level which satisfies the following equation:

$$\int_0^{I_0} p(D)dD = P(I_0) = \frac{C_2}{C_1 + C_2}$$

This assumes that I is a continuous variable.

The application of this model may present various data collection difficulties, but the one of interest here concerns the density function of demand, $p(D)$. Clearly, in many situations it will be possible through the study of past demand, trends, and possible future contingencies, to form an estimate of the demand probability distribution. However, in some situations this may not be possible. For example, the commodity stocked may be a new one for which no demand data are available. It may be that (as so often happens) no records are available on past demand for a commodity, and thus no basis for prediction exists. Again, it may be that some of the factors which determine demand are believed to have altered to such an extent that predictions are not possible. The best move in such situations is, of course, to set in motion the process of collecting data upon which predictions may be based in the future. This, however, does not solve the problem of fixing a stock level for the present.

An immediate possibility is, of course, to treat the decision as one under conditions of uncertainty. This presents a number of interesting insights, as the following analysis using various principles of choice will show. Before examining these principles, it is necessary to be somewhat more explicit about the analyst's "degree of ignorance" of the demand probability distribution. If he is literally "completely ignorant" of the demand distribution, this must mean that demand could be anywhere between minus infinity and plus infinity. Not much can be done in this case, but it is hardly a realistic situation. On the other hand, the analyst may be only "slightly ignorant" of the demand distribution, in the sense that he may have a rough idea of the mean and variance of the distribution, and possibly even some notion of its form. If this is the situation, then perhaps the best thing to do is to use these rough notions in the original model, or appeal to some limit theorem such as Tchebycheff's Inequality. The degree of ignorance presumed here lies between these two. It will be assumed that the analyst is able to predict a finite minimum and a finite maximum for demand, and nothing more. We assume, without loss of generality, that the minimum demand is taken to be zero and the maximum demand is taken to be D units.

The Laplace principle is easily applied in this decision for it simply suggests that the density function of demand be taken as a uniform density function. In this problem it would be taken to be uniform over the range O to $\bar{D}$. Thus

$$p(D) = \frac{1}{\bar{D}} \qquad P(D) = \frac{D}{\bar{D}}$$

Using the result obtained before

$$\int_0^{I_0} p(D)dD = P(I_0) = \frac{I_0}{\bar{D}} = \frac{C_2}{C_1 + C_2}$$

This yields

$$I_0 = \frac{C_2\bar{D}}{C_1 + C_2}$$

Now in spite of the fact that little can be said about the merits of the Laplace principle, it does yield a definite answer to the problem of fixing an inventory level under uncertain demand. A little reflection will perhaps convince one that the answer is not highly unreasonable. It is important to note, however, that the answer is highly sensitive to the assumption one makes about the maximum possible demand.

The application of the minimax principle is best understood by referring to Figure 18–1. This figure shows a plot for any inventory level of the maximum cost due to overstock, $C_1(I - 0)$, and the maximum cost due to understock, $C_2(\bar{D} - I)$. For a given level, I, the maximum cost due to overstock will occur when demand turns out to be zero. Similarly, the maximum cost due to understock will be suffered when demand turns out to be $\bar{D}$. For any inventory level the maximum cost will simply be the maximum of these two quantities, as is shown by the heavy line in Figure 18–1. It is easy to see that the inventory level, I_0, is the level which corresponds to the minimum point on the heavy line, or the intersection of the two maximum cost lines. This means that I_0 must satisfy the equation

$$C_1(I_0 - 0) = C_2(\bar{D} - I_0)$$

Solving this for I_0 we have;

$$I_0 = \frac{C_2 \bar{D}}{C_1 + C_2}$$

Interestingly enough, this is precisely the same result obtained with the Laplace principle.

The Hurwicz principle suggests that for each stock level one compute the maximum possible total cost, $TC(I)_{max}$, and the min-

FIGURE 18–1

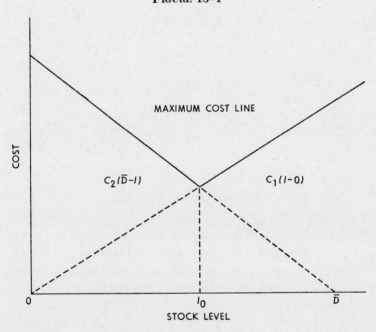

imum possible total cost, $TC(I)_{min}$. Then the stock level should be selected which will maximize the function

$$\alpha\, TC(I)_{min} + (1 - \alpha)TC(I)_{max}$$

Returning to Figure 18–1, it will be seen that for

$$I \leq \frac{C_2 \bar{D}}{C_1 + C_2}; \ TC(I)_{max} = C_2(\bar{D} - I)$$
$$TC(I)_{min} = 0$$

The Hurwicz criterion takes the form

$$\alpha(0) + (1 - \alpha)C_2(\bar{D} - I)$$

This function will be minimized, for any α, if I is made as close to D as possible. Here this means

$$I_0 = \frac{C_2 \bar{D}}{C_1 + C_2}$$

Now for

$$I \geq \frac{C_2 \bar{D}}{C_1 + C_2}; \; TC(I)_{\text{max}} = C_1 I$$
$$TC(I)_{\text{min}} = 0$$

and the criterion function becomes

$$\alpha(0) + (1 - \alpha)C_1 I$$

Minimization is now achieved by making I as small as possible, thus

$$I_0 = \frac{C_2 \bar{D}}{C_1 + C_2}$$

Finally over the entire range of I and for any α whatsoever, the Hurwicz principle suggests that the stock level should be

$$I_0 = \frac{C_2 \bar{D}}{C_1 + C_2}$$

which is again the very same result obtained before.

Finally, the Savage or regret principle may be applied to the decision. It defines, for any stock level and any demand, the difference in cost between the minimum cost achievable had demand been known in advance and the cost resulting from the stock level in question, as the decision maker's regret. Thus, for any demand, if a stock level had been chosen equal to demand, cost would be 0, and the regret associated with any other I would be $C_1(I - D)$ or $C_2(D - I)$, depending on whether I was greater or less than D. Having computed the regret for each I and D combination, the principle suggests that one select the stock level which will minimize the maximum regret. Since, for any D, the minimum possible cost is 0, the maximum regret turns out to be equal to the maximum cost for any I. Thus, Figure 18–1 may be interpreted as a plot of maximum regret, and the minimizing value of I is the one previously found.

It is interesting to note, then, that whatever principle one selects the suggested stock level is the same. It must be emphasized that this is not true of all decision problems. It is easy to construct or discover examples for which each principle yields a different result. No great significance can be attached to this fact in connection with the inventory problem, for it is the mathematical result of the problem formulation, rather than any subtle generality which has emerged. The result has, however, a certain practical value for situations in which inventory policy must be formulated without demand information. It gives a definite answer to the question of stock level, and the answer is the same when the question is approached from four points of view. Best of all, perhaps, the answer has certain demonstrable properties, such as minimizing the maximum cost, which are directly appealing to the decision maker.

EXAMPLES

In Chapter 14, an example was suggested involving the establishment of an inventory for a liquid fuel. The relevant costs were

$$C_1 = \$.01 \text{ per gallon}$$
$$C_2 = \$.19 \text{ per gallon}$$

Instead of assuming that demand is predicted as a random variable, let us now assume that it is estimated the demand will fall in the range of 8,000 to 12,000 gallons per week. Nothing, however, can be estimated about its probabilities within this range.

$$8{,}000 \leq D \leq 12{,}000$$

Clearly we will stock at least 8,000 gallons since, under our assumptions at least, we will always require this much or more. To simplify computations, define a new variable, d, to be the demand in excess of 8,000 gallons.

$$D = 8{,}000 + d \qquad 0 \leq d \leq 4{,}000$$

The Laplace principle leads to the assumption that the probability distribution of demand is uniform.

$$p(d) = \frac{1}{4{,}000 - 0} = \frac{1}{4{,}000}$$
$$\text{for } 0 \leq d \leq 4{,}000$$

The expression for the optimal stock level is now

$$I_0 = 8{,}000 + \frac{C_2 \bar{D}}{C_1 + C_2}$$

which gives

$$I_0 = 8,000 + \frac{(.19)(4,000)}{.20} = 11,800 \text{ gallons}$$

Here $\bar{D}$ is the upper limit of d.

In Chapter 14 it was shown that the condition for optimality was

$$P(I_0) = \frac{C_2}{C_1 + C_2}$$

To indicate that this gives the same result for this problem, we take

$$P(d) = P(I_0 - 8,000) = \frac{d}{4,000} = \frac{.19}{.01 + .19} = .95$$
$$d = (.95)(4,000) = 3,800$$
$$I_0 = 8,000 + d = 11,800 \text{ gallons}$$

For the other principles it is helpful to have a graph of the maximum and minimum costs associated with any inventory level. The minimum cost for any level is zero, and occurs when demand just equals the level. The maximum cost occurs when demand takes one or the other of its extreme values. For any inventory level I, the maximum cost is either an overstock cost for $d = 0$,

$$C_1 I = .01 I$$

or an understock cost for $\bar{D} = 4,000$

$$C_2(\bar{D} - I) = .19(4,000 - I)$$

Here we define I as the inventory in excess of 8,000 units.

The minimax principle leads to minimizing the maximum cost, which occurs at the intersection of the two lines on the graph. The value of I which is common to both lines may be found by equating their functions.

$$.01 I = .19(4,000 - I)$$

This is easily solved to obtain

$$I = 3,800$$

As this has been defined as the inventory in excess of 8,000 units, the actual choice is

$$8,000 + 3,800 = 11,800$$

The reader may quickly satisfy himself that the regret principle and the Hurwicz principle, for any z whatsoever, will yield the same result.

It is interesting to look also at a discrete problem, such as the boat builder's decision introduced in Chapter 14. A discrete commodity was involved, the demand for which was predicted in the form of a probability distribution over the range $1 \leqq D \leqq 6$. The costs were

$$C_1 = \$100$$
$$C_2 = \$300$$

Assume that it is now felt that demand will fall in the range from one to six units, but that nothing can be said of the probabilities over this range. There are thus six possible futures in the decision, and our choice of an inventory level will more than likely be restricted to the same six alternatives.

		Demand					
		1	2	3	4	5	6
	1	0	300	600	900	1200	1500
	2	100	0	300	600	900	1200
	3	200	100	0	300	600	900
Inventory Level	4	300	200	100	0	300	600
	5	400	300	200	100	0	300
	6	500	400	300	200	100	0

Assuming that the probability of each possible future is $\frac{1}{6}$ and computing expectations we obtain

$$\begin{array}{ll} E(1) = \$750 & E(4) = \$250 \\ E(2) = \$517 & E(5) = \$217 \\ E(3) = \$350 & E(6) = \$250 \end{array}$$

The Laplace principle thus leads to a choice of five units as the best inventory level. This corresponds to the result obtained if we use the relation

$$P(I_0 - 1) \leq \frac{C_2}{C_1 + C_2} \leq P(I_0)$$

$$P(I_0 - 1) = P(4) = .67 \leq \frac{300}{400} = .75 \leq P(I_0) = P(5) = .83$$

I	1	2	3	4	5	6
Maximum cost	\$1,500	\$1,200	\$900	\$600	\$400	\$500

The minimax principle thus reinforces the choice of five units as the best inventory level.

The Hurwicz principle requires the computation of the Hurwicz criterion for each alternative.

I	α(minimum cost) + (1 − α)(maximum cost)
1	$\alpha(0) + (1 - \alpha)(1{,}500)$
2	$\alpha(0) + (1 - \alpha)(1{,}200)$
3	$\alpha(0) + (1 - \alpha)(\ \ 900)$
4	$\alpha(0) + (1 - \alpha)(\ \ 600)$
5	$\alpha(0) + (1 - \alpha)(\ \ 400)$
6	$\alpha(0) + (1 - \alpha)(\ \ 500)$

It may be seen that, whatever the value of α, the Hurwicz criterion will be maximized for an inventory of five units.

Since each column of the cost matrix contains as a minimum cost the value zero, the regret matrix will be identical to the cost matrix. Minimizing the maximum regret is thus equivalent to minimizing the maximum cost.

PRODUCTION PROCESSES

Suppose it is possible to produce a certain part on either an engine lathe or a turret lathe. The engine lathe is characterized by a small setup cost but a relatively high unit direct labor cost. The turret lathe has a higher setup cost but a lower unit direct labor cost. One of the machines is to be chosen for production, but it is not known in advance just what the size of the production run will be. Let

$$a_1 = \text{engine lathe}$$
$$a_2 = \text{turret lathe}$$
$$D = \text{size of the production run}$$
$$A_i = \text{setup cost for alternative } i$$
$$B_i = \text{unit direct labor cost for alternative } i$$
$$C(a_i, D) = \text{total cost for alternative } i \text{ if the production}$$
$$\text{run is } D \text{ units}$$

Then

$$C(a_i, D) = A_i + B_i D$$

Assume that the total cost functions are as shown in Figure 18–2 and that it is possible to say that D will fall within the range

$$\underline{D} \le D \le \bar{D}$$

but nothing can be said about the probability of D in this range. It is easily shown that the various principles for decisions under uncertainty will yield the following results:

Laplace: Select the alternative which minimizes

$$E(a_i) = A_i + B_i \frac{D + \bar{D}}{2}$$

Minimax: Select a_2.
Hurwicz: Select the alternative which minimizes

$$A_i + B_i\{\alpha \underline{D} + (1 - \alpha)\bar{D}\}$$

Savage: Select a_1 if

$$A_1 + B_1\bar{D} - A_2 - B_2\bar{D} < A_2 + B_2\underline{D} - A_1 - B_1\underline{D}$$

otherwise select a_2.

A little reflection will suffice to show that this approach to the decision problem is to some extent incompatible with a common sense notion about this type of decision problem. For example, in the application of the minimax principle it is clear that the maximum

FIGURE 18–2

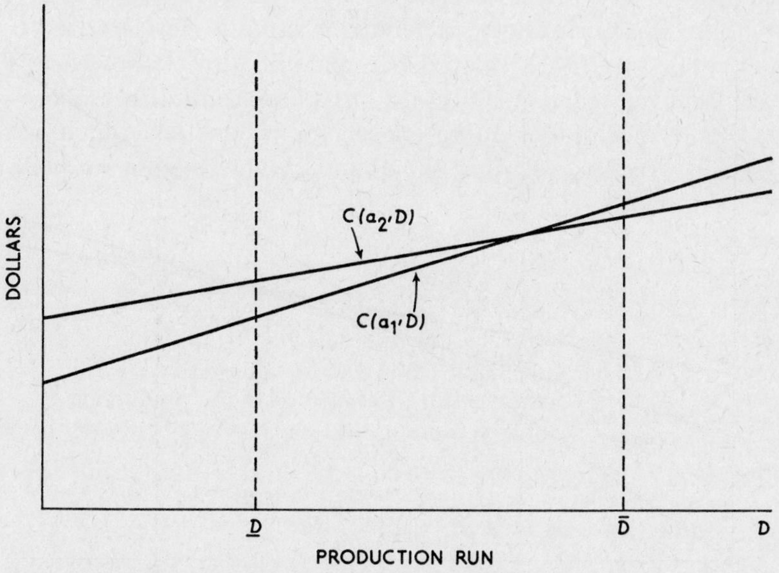

cost for either alternative will occur when $D = \bar{D}$, and that the selection of a_2 will minimize this maximum cost. However, it may well be that the most desirable event would be to have D take on its maximum value since this would mean that profit would be maximized. If we were really pessimistic our attention might be directed to what would happen if D takes its smallest value. Similarly, the

Hurwicz principle is most naturally used to associate feelings of optimism with large production runs and pessimism with small production runs. Thus it might make more sense to assume a total revenue function in connection with such a problem and compute profits rather than cost. Suppose we take the total revenue function to be simply

$$TR(D) = PD$$

as is shown in Figure 18–3. Our principles of choice then yield somewhat more sensible results. The Laplace principle requires the maximization of

$$E(a_i) = (P - B_i)\left(\frac{D + \bar{D}}{2}\right) - A_i$$

which results in the same choice as before. The minimax principle is now interpreted as maximizing the minimum profit or minimizing the maximum loss. In this case the maximum loss for each alterna-

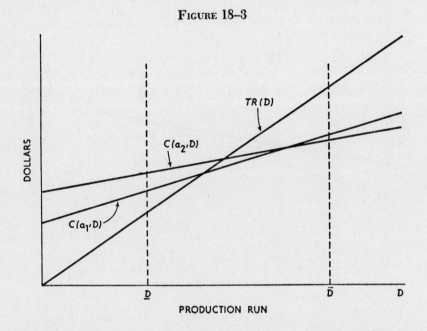

FIGURE 18–3

tive will occur when D is smallest. By inspection it may be seen that alternative a_1 will minimize the maximum loss. The Hurwicz principle leads to the selection of the alternative which maximizes

$$\alpha\{(P - B_i)\bar{D} - A_i\} + (1 - \alpha)\{(P - B_i)\underline{D} - A_i\}$$

The maximum profit will occur when the production run is as large as possible, and the minimum profit will occur when it is as small as possible. The Savage principle leads to the same choice as before.

EXAMPLE

Assume that for an engine lathe the cost to set up for a run of a particular part is

$$A_1 = \$26.00$$

and the unit production cost is

$$B_1 = .40$$

For a turret lathe which might be used for the same job the corresponding costs are

$$A_2 = \$200.00$$
$$B_2 = .10$$

The reader may verify that if the problem is stated simply in this form the results are as shown in Figure 18–4. Suppose it is possible to

FIGURE 18–4

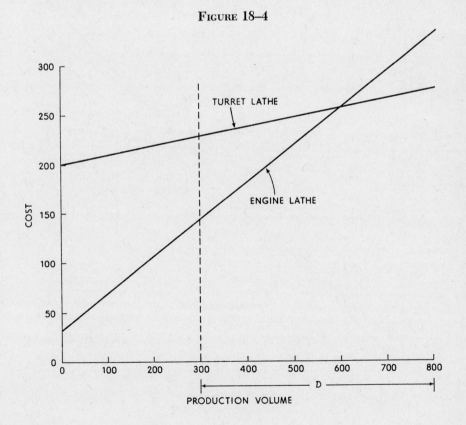

say that the size of the run which will be required lies in the range

$$300 \leq D \leq 800$$

Then

Laplace: $E(D) = 550$, select the engine lathe
Minimax: select the turret lathe
Hurwicz: for $\alpha \leq 11/25$ select the engine lathe
Regret: select the engine lathe

Now suppose that the decision can be looked at from the viewpoint of profit and that a total revenue function can be estimated.

$$TR = (.50)D$$

These functions are shown in Figure 18–5. Using the Laplace assumption the expected volume of production is 550 units. It is

FIGURE 18–5

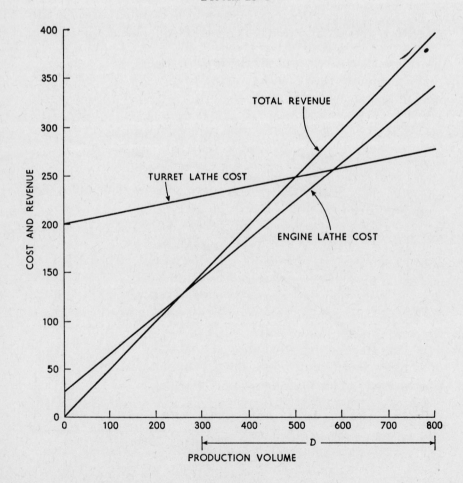

easily shown that, for volume less than 580 units, the engine lathe will have lower costs, while above this it will be more economical to use the turret lathe. Thus the Laplace principle suggests the engine lathe.

The minimax principle is now applied so as to maximize the minimum profit. Examination of Figure 18–5 shows immediately that this will lead to the selection of the engine lathe.

For the Hurwicz criterion we have

$$\alpha(\text{maximum profit}) + (1 - \alpha)(\text{minimum profit})$$

for each alternative. For the engine lathe this is

$$\alpha(400 - 346) + (1 - \alpha)(150 - 146)$$

and for the turret lathe

$$\alpha(400 - 280) + (1 - \alpha)(150 - 230)$$

It can be shown that the two machines yield the same value of the Hurwicz criterion for $\alpha = {}^{14}\!/_{25}$. For any value of α above this the turret lathe is chosen, otherwise the engine lathe.

The maximum regret will be experienced at one extreme or the other of the range of production volume.

	Regret	
	$D = 300$	$D = 800$
Engine lathe...............	0	\$66
Turret lathe...............	\$84	0

Thus, the engine lathe will be chosen if one wishes to minimize the maximum regret.

RECTIFYING INSPECTION

In Chapter 13 the problem of choosing an acceptance sampling inspection plan was treated as a decision under risk. The assumption was made that the probability distribution of the fraction defective on the incoming lots of product was known. In many interesting quality control situations one has no way of knowing either the fraction defective of an incoming lot of product, or its probability distribution. Thus, the decision may be more properly treated as one under conditions of uncertainty.

Let us compare the same three sampling plans as before, and once again make the assumption that when a lot is rejected it is then inspected 100 per cent, the defective items are repaired or replaced, and the rectified lot is then accepted.

Plan	Sample Size (N)	Acceptance Number (c)
a_1 100		1
a_2 200		1
a_3 100		3

The product is shipped in lots of 1,000 units. Suppose it is possible to assert that the incoming lots will have a fraction defective in the range from 1 to 4 per cent, but nothing can be said about the probability distribution within that range.

$$.01 \leq p' \leq .04$$

The unit cost of inspection is

$$C_1 = \$.30$$

and the cost of accepting a defective item is

$$C_2 = \$10.00$$

As before, we compute the average amount of inspection per lot

$$ATI = N + (1 - P_a)(S - N)$$

and the average number of defective items accepted per lot

$$ADA = P_a p'(S - N)$$

The total cost for any alternative, as a function of P_a and p' is

$$TC = C_1(ATI) + C_2(ADA)$$
$$= C_1\{N + (1 - P_a)(S - N)\} + C_2 P_a p'(S - N)$$

The probability of accepting a lot is

$$P_a = \sum_{x=0}^{c} \frac{N!}{x!\,(N - x)!}\,(p')^x(1 - p')^{N-x}$$

Carrying through computations in the usual way, we obtain the total cost for selected values of p' shown in the following table:

	.010	.015	.020	p' .025	.030	.034	.040
a_1	$167	$224	$263	$286	$300	$305	$307
a_2	232	275	294	298	300	300	300
a_3	123	175	223	266	296	319	340

These values have been plotted in Figure 18–6.

With no knowledge of the probability distribution of p', the lot fraction defective, we are forced to resort to the principle of choices

FIGURE 18–6

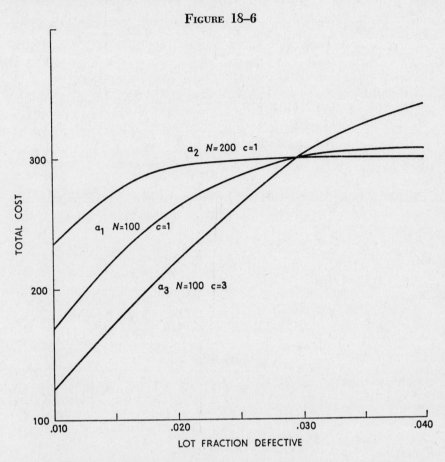

for uncertain decisions. The Laplace principle suggests that one assume a uniform distribution for p'. To find the expectation for each alternative it would be necessary to integrate.

$$E(a_i) = \int_{p'=.01}^{.04} TC\,(a_i, p')\,f(p')\,dp'$$

Inspection for Figure 18–6 may, however, be sufficient to satisfy us that a_3 does in fact have the lowest expected cost under this assumption.

The minimax principle focuses attention on the maximum total costs associated with each alternative.

Maximum Total Cost

a_1..............................	$307
a_2..............................	300
a_3..............................	340

Minimizing the maximum total cost suggests that we choose a_2. The Hurwicz criterion for each alternative may be written as shown:

Hurwicz Criterion

a_1 . . . . $\alpha(167) + (1 - \alpha)(307) = 307 - 140\alpha$
a_2 . . . . $\alpha(232) + (1 - \alpha)(300) = 300 - 68\alpha$
a_3 . . . . $\alpha(123) + (1 - \alpha)(340) = 340 - 217\alpha$

The reader may verify that for

$$0 \leq \alpha \leq .102 \qquad a_2 \text{ is preferred}$$
$$.102 \leq \alpha \leq .43 \qquad a_1 \text{ is preferred}$$
$$.43 \leq \alpha \leq 1 \qquad a_3 \text{ is preferred}$$

The regret principle is easily applied for it is clear that the maximum regret for any alternative will occur at one of the extremes in the range of p'.

Regret

	$p' = .01$	$p' = .04$
a_1	44	7
a_2	109	0
a_3	0	40

The choice under the regret principle falls upon a_3.

PROBLEMS

18–1. A firm is considering the purchase of either an engine lathe or a turret lathe for the manufacture of a certain item. The production quantity x is unknown. Total production costs for the engine lathe are given by the function $A + Bx$ and for the turret lathe by the function $C + Dx$. Assume that $A < C$ and $B > D$. Which machine would you purchase?

18–2. Your company, which requires a site for a new plant, is given a 48-hour option on a piece of land which is satisfactory for its purposes. The price is reasonable but not cheap, and the land is good but not outstanding. You must decide within the 48 hours whether to take up the option or let it go and look for another site. How would you treat this as a decision under uncertainty?

18–3. Kelvin's Law suggests that the cost of an electrical transmission cable may be expressed as follows:

Total Cost = Investment Cost + Cost of Energy Loss

or symbolically

$$TC(A) = C_1 K_1 A + \frac{C_2 K_2}{A}$$

where C_1 is the unit investment cost, C_2 is the unit cost of energy, and K_1 and K_2 are constants of proportionality. The decision variable is A, the area of the cable. Show how A might be chosen if *a*) C_1, C_2, K_1 and K_2 are assumed to be certainly known.

b) C_1, C_2, and K_1 are assumed to be certainly known, but K_2 can be predicted only in the form of a probability distribution, say $f(K_2)$.

c) C_1, C_2, and K_1 are assumed to be certainly known and K_2 is assumed to fall in the range $K_{2L} \leqq K_2 \leqq K_{2U}$ with unknown probabilities.

18–4. Treat problem 13–1 as a decision under uncertainty assuming that the probability of a defective casting, p, will fall within some range whose limits are known, but that nothing further can be said about its probability distribution.

18–5. Show how problem 13–2 might be considered as a decision under uncertainty if the probability distribution of the present worth of future profits for the population of investment opportunities were not known.

18–6. Discuss problem 11–24 as a decision under uncertainty.

18–7. Refer to problem 13–10. How would you analyze the decision to insure or not to insure, if the probability of a fire were unknown?

18–8. Refer to problem 13–14. What alternative would you suggest if the probability that a spare would be needed during the life of the machine could not be reasonably estimated?

18–9. After having formulated a decision as one under uncertainty, one always has the choice of whether to select an alternative or to try to collect enough information so as to treat the decision as one under risk. How would you make this choice? What principles could you formulate as guides?

18–10. Refer to problem 13–15. Which alternative would you recommend if it were not possible to obtain data on the probability distribution of the number of breakdowns per year? Suppose it could reasonably be assumed that this number would lie in the range from 0 to 8.

18–11. How would you treat problem 13–16 as a decision under conditions of uncertainty?

18–12. Refer to problem 13–27. Suppose no evidence were available to permit estimates of the probabilities of failure. Which alternative would be selected by each principle of choice? What would be your choice?

18–13. Formulate the problem of maintenance policy discussed in Chapter 13 as a problem of decision making under uncertainty. What would be the effect of each principle of choice? Which would you advocate?

18–14. Analyze problem 13–33 as a decision under uncertainty using the assumption that the incoming fraction defective will fall in the range from 0 to .04, but its probability distribution is not known.

18–15. Given two single-sample, fraction defective sampling plans with known average outgoing quality curves. Assuming that average outgoing quality is taken to be a measure of effectiveness for a plan, what principle of choice would be most appropriate for choosing between the two?

18–16. Consider two quality control charts for process fraction defective, each having three standard deviation limits. Chart A uses a sample size of 9 and Chart B uses a sample size of 16. The process is to be brought into control with a process mean of .20. Assuming a sample is to be taken once each hour, which chart would you select on the basis of an hour's performance? The production rate is k units per hour, the inspection cost is C_1 per unit, and the cost for defective production is C_2 per unit.

18–17. Consider two single-sample, fraction defective sampling plans to be used for lots of size 5,000;

Plan A: sample size $= 100$; acceptance number $= 2$
Plan B: sample size $= 500$; acceptance number $= 10$

Using the assumption of 100 per cent screening of rejected lots with replacement of defectives, which plan would you select? The cost of inspection is C_1 per unit, and the cost of passing bad product is C_2 per unit. The incoming fraction defective is unknown.

18–18. Refer to problem 13–4. If the range of bar lengths is known to be from k units below the mean to k units above it, but the distribution of lengths is unknown, what would you suggest?

18–19. Consider the problem of determining an economic purchase quantity discussed in Chapter 3. Suppose the total procurement cost associated with the purchase of a total of D units in lots of size L over a period of time T is given by

$$C(L) = C_1 \frac{D}{L} + C_2 \frac{LTP}{2}$$

Here C_1 is the fixed cost of making a procurement and C_2 is the cost of carrying inventory, based upon the average value of the inventory. The price paid is P, and the average number of units in stock is $L/2$. The number of unit-periods of inventory is $LT/2$, and the value per unit is taken to be P. Then C_2 is simply a fraction representing carrying costs as a proportion of inventory value.

Now suppose that it is known that the price paid will vary in the future. Clearly, the economic purchase quantity may be influenced by this variation. Assuming that it is not possible to obtain a probabilistic prediction of P, suppose it is only possible to estimate the upper and lower limits of P, say P_2 and P_1 respectively. If it is necessary to fix the economic purchase quantity before the price is known any more precisely, one may consider the problem as a decision under uncertainty.

   a) Find the economic purchasing quantity if P is assumed to be known with certainty.

   b) Apply the Laplace, Hurwicz, and minimax principles.

   c) Apply the regret principle under the assumption that the alternatives are limited to those which are optimal for some possible future. That is, the alternatives considered fall in the interval $L_1 \geqslant L \geqslant L_2$ where

$$L_1 = \sqrt{\frac{2C_1D}{C_2TP_1}} \quad \text{and} \quad L_2 = \sqrt{\frac{2C_1D}{C_2TP_2}}$$

18–20.   Apply the analysis of problem 18–19 to the purchasing decision in which the following data are given:

$$C_1 = \$500$$
$$C_2 = .02$$
$$T = 12 \text{ months}$$
$$D = 60,000 \text{ units}$$
$$P_1 = \$4.50 \le P \le P_2 = \$5.50$$

18–21.   Management wishes to establish an appropriate inventory level in a situation where the cost of storing excess inventory is $5 per unit per month and the cost of a shortage is $10 per unit. The inventory level may be adjusted at the beginning of a month only. Demand for a month is essentially unknown; however, management is willing to state that in no case will it fall below 501 units nor above 1500 units. Show the inventory level which would result from the application of each of the four principles of choice.

18–22.   Formulate the problem of the number of machines for a department treated in Chapter 12, as a decision under uncertainty. Show the use of each principle of choice.

18–23.   Refer to problem 14–6. Suppose the probability distribution of demand were unknown but it seemed reasonable to assume that demand would fall in the range from 80 to 130 units. What inventory level would you suggest?

18–24.   Analyze problem 14–7 under the assumption that p is unknown. Show how your choice of inventory level would vary as a function of N.

18–25.   Suppose in problem 14–8 the density function of demand were not known, but the range was taken to be from 1,800 to 2,200 gallons. What inventory level would you suggest?

18–26.   On Sunday a man is informed that, before the market closes on the following Wednesday, he must buy 100 shares of a certain stock in order to cover a previous commitment. This man does not feel that he can predict the price movements of the stock in terms of probabilities, but he is willing to estimate the limits of the range within which he expects the price to move. Further, he is willing to plan his purchasing on the basis of the limits. His estimates are as follows:

| | | Day | |
Price per Share:	Monday	Tuesday	Wednesday
Upper Limit	$24	$28	$30
Lower Limit	20	16	12

Treating the purchasing policy decision as one under uncertainty, apply each of the four principles of choice. For simplicity assume that a single integer price quotation is made each day. Thus on Monday the price is $20, $21, . . . , or $24.

18–27. Consider the purchasing policy decision presented in Chapter 16. Suppose that the density function of future prices is not known but that the range within which they will fall can reasonably be specified. Develop a formulation of the purchasing problem as a decision under conditions of uncertainty. How would you compare this formulation of the problem with that given in Chapter 16?

18–28. Refer to problem 16–1. Assume $f(x)$ and $f(y)$ are unknown but that the ranges of x and y may be stated. What policy would you suggest?

18–29. Refer to problem 3–15. Suppose the situation is modified by the addition of the following assumptions:

a) The sum of the annual operating and maintenance costs for the Detroit Model 303 is estimated to fall in the range from $10,000 to $13,-000. The probability distribution of these costs cannot be estimated from the data at hand.

b) The sum of the annual operating and maintenance costs for the Giant Special is estimated to fall in the range from $10,500 to $12,000, but the probability distribution within this range cannot be estimated. Treating the decision as one under conditions of uncertainty, what would be your recommendation?

18–30. Solve problem 3–3 if the annual mileage is known to be in the range from 3,000 to 10,000 miles, but no further information can be obtained.

18–31. Solve problem 3–18 if the firm's requirement for the services of a jig boring machine are expected to last from 3 to 7 years. Assume no probabilities can be estimated for the duration of this requirement.

18–32. Suppose in problem 3–23 that the annual operating costs can neither be estimated precisely, nor expressed in the form of probability distributions. Only the ranges in which they might possibly fall can be specified. Show how the choice might vary as a function of the ranges specified. Do this for various principles of choice.

18–33. Formulate the bidding policy decision discussed in Chapter 15 as a decision under uncertainty. Do you feel that this is a satisfactory formulation of the problem? Explain.

18–34. A firm engaged in bidding finds that very limited historical data on the behavior of competitors is available. Management is willing to assume that the ratio of the lowest competing bid to their own cost estimate will be not less than .95 nor greater than 1.35. The evidence seems insufficient to say anything about the probabilities, however. They are willing to suppress the risk associated with estimating errors in performance costs. Show how various principles of choice for decisions under uncertainty might be applied.

18–35. Consider problem 11–38 as a decision under uncertainty. What response would you make as a manager?

Chapter 19

GAME THEORY
COMPETITIVE DECISIONS

ONE VERY IMPORTANT class of decisions under uncertainty is the class of decisions which involve conflict or competition between two or more decision makers. These situations include such games as chess, competitive decisions made by businessmen, and decisions of military commanders in combat. They have been extensively studied and a philosophy for understanding them has been produced, called the "theory of games." The word "game" here is used in a special technical sense and in no way denotes a restriction of the theory to the trivial analysis of parlor games. It should be emphasized that the following introduction to this elaborate theory is presented with the idea that, while the direct application of its consequences to engineering decision making may be rather limited, it is rich in fundamental ideas which are of significance in the general understanding of decision problems.

As an example, consider the following conflict situation which is a game in the ordinary sense of the word. Two decision makers are involved in the game of matching coins. One decision maker, called Red, has two alternatives. He may show heads or tails. Likewise, the other decision maker, called Blue, may show either heads or tails. Suppose the rules say that if Red's coin shows the same side as Blue's, Red wins Blue's coin; otherwise Red loses his coin to Blue. This may be represented in the usual matrix form:

		Blue	
		H	*T*
Red	*H*	1	-1
	T	-1	1

where the numbers in the matrix represent the profit or return to Red. From Red's point of view this is clearly a decision under uncertainty, but with a very special feature. That is, the possible

423

futures are now controlled by Blue who is presumed to be both intelligent and in competition with Red. Thus, Blue may be expected to do his best to get Red's money. It is this feature which distinguishes competitive decisions from those studied so far. Previously we had assumed that the possible futures were not under the control of an intelligent competitor who was trying to do us in, but rather that they were events which were simply beyond the control of the decision maker.

GAME THEORY

The theory of games has certain very special suggestions to make in a decision of this sort. These suggestions may be accepted or rejected as one sees fit. It is our purpose here to merely explain them, and not necessarily to advocate their use. The theory approaches the decision as follows. Clearly, if the game is to be played only once it makes no difference what Red does; either alternative is as good as the other. The same is true of Blue. However, suppose the game is to be played repeatedly. Red might show heads consistently, but if he does Blue will soon discover this and respond by showing tails consistently, thus causing Red to lose. Similarly, Red might show tails consistently, but Blue will discover this and win from Red by responding with heads. The theory of games suggests what is almost obvious. The thing for Red to do is to show heads and tails at random, each with probability one half. This has two advantages. First, the randomness will make it impossible for Blue to predict from Red's behavior what he is going to do next. Secondly, it guarantees Red that, whatever Blue does, his expectation will be at least zero. That is, on the average he will at least break even. Taking Blue's point of view, the very same arguments hold, and it becomes clear that Blue should also randomize his choice between heads and tails with probability one half. It may then be added that if Blue does anything else, Red will eventually detect it, and take advantage of Blue, raising his expectation above the break-even point. Thus, the randomized choice has a third advantage for Red. It may further be seen that if both players use these recommendations, the expected outcome for each is zero. To demonstrate these points mathematically, assume the Blue shows heads with probability p, and tails with probability $1 - p$. If Red shows heads with probability one half and tails with probability one half, his expected profit will be

$$\tfrac{1}{2}(p)(1) + \tfrac{1}{2}(1 - p)(-1) + \tfrac{1}{2}(p)(-1) + \tfrac{1}{2}(1 - p)(1) = 0$$

No matter what value Blue assigns to p, Red's expectation will be equal to zero. A similar equation can be written from Blue's point of view.

Now suppose Blue is ignorant of these arguments and decides to play heads with a probability .60, regardless of what Red does. Red may then take advantage of this mistake and play heads with probability 1.00. His expected profit will then be

$$(.60)(1) + (.40)(-1) = .20$$

In the long run such an error will ruin Blue. Note, however, that if Blue suddenly discovers what is happening, Red must immediately return to his original random mixture of heads and tails, each with probability one half.

TERMINOLOGY

The theory of games has technical names for many of the aspects of this situation. It is referred to as a "two-person, zero-sum, game," since there are two "players" and since the losses of one player exactly equal the gains of the other. This makes the sum of losses and gains always equal to zero. The alternatives are referred to as "pure strategies" and a randomized choice among the alternatives is called a "mixed strategy." The mixed strategy or pure strategy which has the properties described in the foregoing example is called an "optimal" strategy. The expected outcome when both players use their optimal strategies is called the "value" of the game. Games, such as the coin-matching game, which have values of zero are called "fair" games. A single episode is called a "play" of the game. Finding the optimal strategies and the value of a game is called "solving" the game. We shall always refer to the maximizing player as Red, and show his pure strategies along the left-hand side of the matrix, and to the minimizing player as Blue and exhibit his pure strategies along the top of the matrix. The theory of games is not limited to the study of zero-sum, two-person games, but this discussion will be so limited, since it purports only to be an introduction.

SOLUTION

In order to further explore the approach of the theory of games consider the following abstract game:

Blue

		1	2	3
	1	4	1	0
	2	3	2	3
Red	3	0	1	4
	4	2	1	0

The first step in attempting the solution of any game is to examine the pure strategies of each player for instances of dominance, and to cross out any strategies which are dominated. In this example Red 2 clearly dominates Red 4, and thus Red 4 may be dropped from consideration. Always assuming that neither player is able to cheat and discover in advance what his opponent will do, the theory of games suggests the following analysis. As Red looks at the game he must fear that, whatever he does, Blue will respond in such a way as to make his gain as small as possible. Red thus initially adopts a conservative viewpoint and looks for the strategy that will maximize his minimum profit. In this case Red 2 is the result, making his minimum profit 2. Blue uses exactly the same approach to find the pure strategy which will make Red's maximum profit as small as possible, fixing upon Blue 2. Now if both players adopt these pure strategies the gain to Red (and the loss to Blue) will be exactly 2 on every play of the game. This line of thinking might be called "first-order analysis."

The players, however, attempt to be more insightful than this, according to the theory. Red thinks, "I must assume that Blue is clever and follows the same reasoning that I have used. Blue will then discover that Blue 2 will minimize my maximum profit. Thus, if I expect Blue to play Blue 2, what would my best strategy be?" The answer is still Red 2. Thus Red's choice is the same on the basis of both first and second-order analysis. Blue, reasoning in the same way, concludes that second-order analysis leads him to Blue 2 as before. Thus we have a solution which has the property of being stable under the assumption that one's opponent is also acting according to the philosophy of the theory of games. This stability is characteristic of the optimal strategies which the theory suggests.

In this example the optimal strategies are pure strategies for each player, whereas in the previous example the optimal strategies were mixed. The easiest games to solve are those which lead to optimal strategies which are pure, and these games are characterized by what is called a "saddle point." If the minimum of the column maxima is equal to the maximum of the row minima, then the game has a saddle point. The optimal strategy for each player is then the pure strategy associated with the row or column of the saddle point, and the value of the game is the value of the payoff at the saddle point. Such a game is said to be strictly determined. In summary:

$$\text{value} = \text{min of col max} = \text{max of row min}$$

Thus, the first step in solving a game is to test for dominance, and the second step is to look for a saddle point.

If the game does not have a saddle point then the optimal strategy of at least one player will be mixed. The discovery of optimal mixed strategies may be complicated, but certain cases can be handled easily. The simplest case is that in which each player has exactly two pure strategies, called a "two-by-two" game. Consider the example:

Blue

		1	2
Red	1	5	2
	2	3	4

Examination will show neither dominance nor a saddle point. The following simple rule may then be used:

- *a)* For Red 1, find the absolute value of the difference in payoff between Blue 1 and Blue 2 (here we obtain $|5 - 2| = 3$), call this result A.
- *b)* For Red 2, do the same ($|4 - 3| = 1$), call this result B.
- *c)* The optimal mixed strategy for Red is then to play Red 1 with probability

$$\frac{B}{A + B}$$

and to play Red 2 with probability

$$\frac{A}{A + B}$$

In this example Red should play Red 1 with probability $\frac{1}{4}$ and Red 2 with probability $\frac{3}{4}$. It is common to express a mixed strategy as $(\frac{1}{4}, \frac{3}{4})$. Applying the same method to Blue will show that Blue's optimal strategy is $(\frac{1}{2}, \frac{1}{2})$. It is then easy to show that if Red uses $(\frac{1}{4}, \frac{3}{4})$ his expectation will be 3.5, no matter what Blue uses. Likewise, if Blue uses ($\frac{1}{2}$, $\frac{1}{2}$) his expectation will be -3.5, no matter what Red uses. Further, it will be seen that if Blue through ignorance or error fixes upon any other strategy, Red may take advantage of this to improve his expectation. For example, if Blue plays ($\frac{1}{3}$, $\frac{2}{3}$) then Red may play (0, 1) and improve his expectation to 3.67.

Mathematically, if Blue uses any strategy (p, $1 - p$) and Red uses his optimal strategy, Red will expect to gain:

$$\tfrac{1}{4}\{(p)(5) + (1 - p)(2)\} + \tfrac{3}{4}\{(p)(3) + (1 - p)(4)\} = 3.5$$

If Red uses any strategy (q, $1 - q$) and Blue uses his optimal strategy, Blue will expect to lose:

$$\tfrac{1}{2}\{(q)(5) + (1 - q)(3)\} + \tfrac{1}{2}\{(q)(2) + (1 - q)(4)\} = 3.5$$

LARGER GAMES

For problems in which at least one of the players has more than two pure strategies, the foregoing rule does not apply. There are a variety of methods for solving such larger games, two of which will be presented. Consider first a game in which one of the players has exactly two pure strategies, but the other player has three or more. This is called a "2-by-n game." Such a game yields easily to a graphic method of solution. To illustrate we will use the example:

		Blue		
		1	2	3
Red	1	1	2	6
	2	4	3	1

We begin by constructing a graph with an abscissa which represents the probability, x, with which Red plays his pure strategy Red 1. On the ordinate we represent the payoff to Red. Figure 19–1 illustrates such a graph. For each of Blue's pure strategies we now plot the payoff to Red for all values of x, the probability of Red 1. Thus, for pure strategy Blue 1, if Red plays Red 1 with probability x, his payoff is given by:

$$(x)(1) + (1 - x)(4) = 4 - 3x$$

This function is then plotted on the graph. For Blue 2 and Blue 3 we obtain:

Blue 2 $\quad (x)(2) + (1 - x)(3) = 3 - x$
Blue 3 $\quad (x)(6) + (1 - x)(1) = 1 + 5x$

These functions are also shown in Figure 19–1. An examination of the graph reveals that if Blue were to play Blue 1, Red could respond with Red 2 ($x = 0$) and his payoff would be 4, and so on. Blue can minimize Red's maximum payoff by using the mixture of Blue 2 and

FIGURE 19–1

Graphical Solution

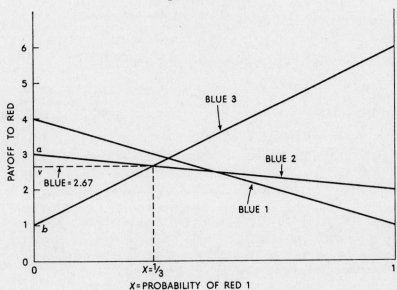

Blue 3 which fixes Red's payoff at the ordinate value represented by the intersection of the payoff functions for these two pure strategies. That is, if Blue can find the right combination of Blue 2 and Blue 3, he can limit Red's payoff to no more than

$$3 - x = 1 + 5x$$

Red notices that this is true and decides to maximize his payoff by adopting the value of x which will satisfy this equation. Thus, either graphically or analytically, we discover that Red should play Red 1 with probability $\frac{1}{3}$, since $x = \frac{1}{3}$ satisfies this equation. This means obviously that Red 2 should be played with probability $\frac{2}{3}$.

Blue notices that Blue 1 is of no use to him, and that he must find the proper mixture of Blue 2 and Blue 3. Having thus eliminated Blue 1, there are three ways we might proceed.

1. With Blue 1 disposed of we have a 2-by-2 game which could be solved by the previous method.

$$2 \qquad 6$$
$$3 \qquad 1$$

The optimal strategy for Red is $(\frac{1}{3}, \frac{2}{3})$ as we have already shown, and for Blue $(\frac{5}{6}, \frac{1}{6})$. Returning to the original game, Blue's optimal strategy would be written $(0, \frac{5}{6}, \frac{1}{6})$.

2. From the graph we can see that if Red uses $(\frac{1}{3}, \frac{2}{3})$ then the value of the game will be

$$3 - \frac{1}{3} = 1 + 5(\frac{1}{3}) = \frac{8}{3}$$

Supposing that Blue's optimal strategy is $(0, y, 1 - y)$, then it must be that

$$(y)(2) + (1 - y)(6) = \frac{8}{3}$$

Solving this for y, yields $y = \frac{5}{6}$, and thus $1 - y = \frac{1}{6}$.

3. Still a third way of obtaining Blue's optimal strategy is from the graph itself. If we let av stand for the distance between point a and point v then

$$\text{Probability of Blue 2:} \frac{bv}{ab} = \frac{5}{6}$$

$$\text{Probability of Blue 3:} \frac{av}{ab} = \frac{1}{6}$$

This method is satisfactory for any 2-by-n game, and if one wishes to draw three dimensional graphs, it may be used for a 3-by-n game. Notice that it makes no difference which of the players has the 2 strategies and which has the n.

A special case of a 2-by-n game is represented by the following example:

			Blue	
		1	2	3
	1	1	2	6
Red	2	4	2	1

The graph of this game shown in Figure 19–2 indicates that the optimal strategy for Blue is $(0, 1, 0)$, a pure strategy. For Red, any value of x in the range $x = \frac{1}{5}$ to $x = \frac{2}{3}$ will be optimal. Thus Blue has an optimal pure strategy and Red has an infinity of optimal mixed strategies.

N-BY-N GAMES

Rather than embark upon some rather complicated mathematics, we will simply illustrate an approximate method of estimating the solution of larger games, where each player may have $n > 2$ pure strategies. The method is called the "method of fictitious play," and is of some interest in its own right.

This method involves playing the game using a special set of rules

FIGURE 19–2

Graphical Solution

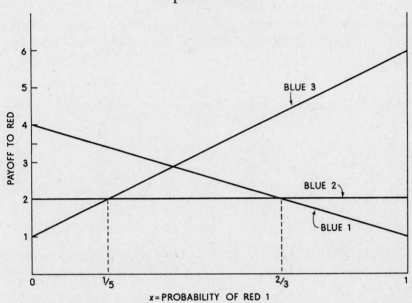

for the behavior of each player. A record is kept of the play and from this record the optimal strategies and value may be estimated. The rules are:

1. On the first play, Red plays Red 1 and Blue plays Blue 1.

2. On any succeeding play, each player uses the pure strategy which is best from hindsight. Each player looks back on the plays of his opponent and selects the pure strategy which would have been best. He then uses this pure strategy on the next play.

3. In case two pure strategies appear equally good, the one with the lowest number attached to it will be used. (Any such rule is satisfactory for breaking ties, as long as it is consistently applied.) To illustrate this simulated or fictitious play, we will use the following example:

		Blue		
		1	2	3
	1	1	2	3
Red	2	4	0	1
	3	2	3	0

On the first play of the game each player uses his number 1 strategy. Red then notices that Blue has played Blue 1 and thus his payoff would have been 1 if he had played Red 1, 4 if Red 2, and 2 if Red 3. From hindsight Red 2 is best and he plays this on the next play. Blue applies similar reasoning and decides to play Blue 1 on the next play.

When the second play is over Red sees that his total payoff over both plays, given Blue's choices, would have been 2 if he had used Red 1, 8 if he had used Red 2, and 4 if Red 3. On this basis Red 2 looks best and is selected for the third play. Blue's similar reasoning leads him to Blue 2 for the third play. Several plays are shown below.

			Red's Hindsight			Blue's Hindsight		
Play	Red Plays	Blue Plays	Red 1	Red 2	Red 3	Blue 1	Blue 2	Blue 3
1......1	1	1	4	2	1	2	3
2......2	1	2	8	4	5	2	4
3......2	2	4	8	7	9	2	5
4......2	2	6	8	10	13	2	6
5......3	2	8	8	13	15	5	6
6......3	2	10	8	16	17	8	6
7......3	3	13	9	16	19	11	6
8......3	3	16	10	16	21	14	6
9......1	3	19	11	16	22	16	9
10......1	3	22	12	16	23	18	12

This represents only a small sample of plays and thus will give only crude results. Precision requires that much larger samples be obtained. The optimal strategies of each player may be estimated by simply computing the relative frequencies with which the pure strategies have been used in the fictitious play. On the basis of these first ten plays the estimates would be

Red (3/10, 3/10, 4/10)   Blue (2/10, 4/10, 4/10)

To estimate the value of the game define

v_i = minimum of Blue's hindsight values on play i
v_i' = maximum of Red's hindsight values on play i

It is then true that the value of the game lies in the range

$$\frac{v_i}{i} \leq \text{value} \leq \frac{v_i'}{i}$$

These quantities for the first ten plays are

Play	v_i/i	v_i'/i
1	1	4
2	1	4
3	2/3	2 2/3
4	1/2	2 1/2
5	1	2 3/5
6	1	2 2/3
7	6/7	2 2/7
8	6/8	2
9	1	2 1/9
10	1 2/10	2 2/10

It then follows that the value must lie between the maximum of the $\frac{v_i}{i}$ and the minimum of the $\frac{v_i'}{i}$. We could then estimate that the value must be in the range

$$1.20 \leq \text{value} \leq 2.00$$

If this simulated play is carried on for additional trials the results are:

	Red's Optimal Strategy	Blue's Optimal Strategy	Value
After 20 plays	(13/20, 3/20, 4/20)	(6/20, 4/20, 10/20)	$1.81 \leq \text{value} \leq 2.00$
After 30 plays	(17/30, 9/30, 4/30)	(13/30, 7/30, 10/30)	$1.81 \leq \text{value} \leq 2.00$

It can be shown that this method will converge upon the solution of the game.

APPLICATIONS

The part of game theory which has been discussed, the theory of zero-sum, two-person games, is somewhat too simple to find direct application in a wide range of competitive decisions faced by a firm. It is useful, however, to suggest a few hypothetical examples of its use in order to suggest some of its possibilities. Most of the direct conflict or competition engaged in by a firm is represented by decisions concerning advertising, sales effort, pricing policy, new product development, and so on. Thus, most applications which have been studied are from these areas.

1. Suppose two firms are competing for a given market. For simplicity assume that each firm has a fixed advertising budget and must devote its entire budget to one promotional medium, or not advertise at all. If the market research department of Red could figure out the net gain in revenue for all possible contingencies, a matrix such as the following might be developed:

		Blue			
		Radio	TV	Magazines	No Advertising
	Radio	0	−4	−1	4
Red	TV	4	0	6	5
	Magazines	1	−6	0	3
	No advertising	−4	−5	−3	0

In this game TV is clearly the dominant strategy for both firms, and the game has a saddle point with value 0. Thus each firm will use a TV campaign but end up with the same result as would have been obtained if they had not advertised at all. Neither firm, however, dares not to advertise.

2. Now suppose that the firms, having decided on television promotion, find two networks which offer them programs, ABS and DBC. Again we suppose that skillful market research can predict the results. ABS is the more effective network, as long as only one of the firms uses it. If both firms use the same network, then their efforts tend to cancel each other.

		Blue	
		ABS	*DBC*
	ABS	0	$-k$
Red			
	DBC	k	0

Both firms will use DBC and the result will be a sort of a draw.

3. Suppose in the previous examples that Red's advertising agency produces promotion messages which are not as effective as those used by Blue. It is predicted that if Red can get on one network by itself it will have some success, but if Blue uses the same network Red will fall behind.

		Blue	
		ABS	*DBC*
	ABS	$-k$	K
Red			
	DBC	K	$-k$

The game suggests a mixed strategy of $(\frac{1}{2}, \frac{1}{2})$ for each player. One is tempted to interpret this as saying that Red should spend half of its money on each network. A better interpretation is probably that, for any given period, Red should use only one network but should randomize between the networks from period to period.

4. Two firms are competing for a market which is divided into two sales districts. Each firm has a promotional budget which it must allocate betwen the two territories. Let

s_1 = sales potential of territory 1
s_2 = sales potential of territory 2 $(s_1 + s_2 = S)$
R = Red's promotional budget
B = Blue's promotional budget
r_1, r_2 = amounts spent by Red in territories 1 and 2, respectively
b_1, b_2 = amounts spent by Blue in territories 1 and 2, respectively

Now suppose it can be predicted that the difference between Red's sales and Blue's sales in territory 1 is given by the function

$$\frac{r_1 - b_1}{r_1 + b_1} s_1$$

An identical function is applicable to territory 2. In this game a pure strategy for Red is represented by a choice of r_1 and r_2, subject to the restriction that $r_1 + r_2 = R$. Red thus has an infinity of pure strategies and the game is called a continuous game. The same is true for Blue. Friedman (52) has shown that the solution of this game requires that each firm allocate its funds in proportion to the sales potential of the territory.

$$r_1 = \frac{Rs_1}{S} \qquad r_2 = \frac{Rs_2}{S}$$

$$b_1 = \frac{Bs_1}{S} \qquad b_2 = \frac{Bs_2}{S}$$

If this is done, the value of the game is

$$\frac{R - B}{R + B} S$$

This example is interesting because it tends to confirm the decision rules actually used in many promotional programs.

USES OF GAME THEORY

It requires some stretch of the imagination to see much realism in the foregoing examples, and this seems to be generally true of attempts to apply the theory of zero-sum, two-person games to business situations. It is perhaps true that the more complex aspects of game theory, which deal with nonzero-sum games with several players will be more fruitful. Nevertheless, the difficulties of prediction and computation appear to be formidable. Knowledge of the theory is not by any means useless, however. It suggests a philosophy for approaching decisions involving competition or conflict. It provides a framework for attempts to make such decisions explicit. It also introduces the very important notion of a mixed strategy as a means of countering competitive pressures. Its most important function is to give insight to decision makers who face conflict situations, rather than to yield exact computations of optimal strategies.

SUGGESTIONS FOR FURTHER STUDY

WILLIAMS, J. D. *The Compleat Strategyst*. New York: McGraw-Hill Book Co., 1954.

McKINSEY, J. C. C. *Introduction to the Theory of Games*. New York: McGraw-Hill Book Co., 1952.

SHUBIK, MARTIN. "The Uses of Game Theory in Management Science," *Management Science*, Vol. 2, No. 1 (October, 1955).

PROBLEMS

Solve the following games:

19–1. *a*) 4 7   *b*) 4 7   *c*) 4 7
             5 3   3 5   3 9

19–2. *a*) 22 12 32   *b*) 13 14 13
             36   1 15   11 38 10

19–3. *a*) 5   6 5   *b*) −10   6   2   40
             4 10 6   10 10   8   12
                                  −8 −4   0 −10

19–4. *a*)   1 −7   *b*) 8 6 7
             −1   2   5 9 4

19–5. *a*) 5 0 1   *b*) 3 1 1   *c*) 1 8 2
             1 6 4   1 1 5   6 2 8
             4 4 8   1 4 1   5 1 6

19–6. *a*) 3 4 12   *b*) 1 3 10
             8 6   3   6 3   1

19–7. *a*) 1 0 0   *b*) 3 2 3 1 6
             0 1 0   4 4 0 4 3
             0 0 1   1 5 3 6 4
                                 3 2 4 3 2

19–8. Two auto manufacturers, Red and Blue, are competing for a fixed market. If both manufacturers make major model changes in a given year, their respective shares of the market remain constant. Likewise, if both do not make major model changes, their shares of the market also remain constant. If Red makes a major model change and Blue does not, Red is able to take an amount x of the market away from Blue. If Blue makes a major model change and Red does not, Blue is able to take an amount y of the market away from Red.

19–9. Refer to the fourth example given in the chapter (p. 434). Let

$$s_1 = \$1,000,000 \qquad s_2 = \$200,000$$
$$R = \$6,000 \qquad B = \$4,000$$

By testing several strategies for each player, show that the game has a saddle point. Find the value of the game.

19–10. Consider a 2-by-2 game in which the optimal strategy for each player is mixed. Suppose we plot the payoff to Red as a function of the probability with which Red plays Red 1 as in Figure 19–3.

a) Show that the payoff to Red resulting from a mixed strategy used by Blue can be represented by a straight line such as the line AB.

b) Why does the line CD represent the optimal mixed strategy for Blue?

FIGURE 19-3

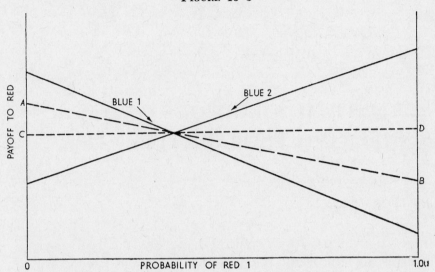

19-11. Find the optimal strategies and the value of the following game. Red and Blue both show coins simultaneously. If both are heads, Red wins $1; if both are tails, Red wins nothing; and if one head and one tail are shown, Red loses $.50.

19-12. Two partners own a business which has a net worth of C. Each owns half of the business and in addition has a personal bank account in amount N. After a long and bitter argument, they decide that one will buy the other's share of the business, according to the following plan: Each partner submits a *sealed* bid B. $(0 \leqq B \leqq N)$ The partner making the highest bid pays the amount bid to his associate in return for full ownership of the business. If the bids are equal, the business is assigned to one by flipping a coin and without any payment. Find the optimal strategies and the value of the game.

19-13. It is sometimes suggested that the reasoning of game theory does not reasonably apply to competitive situations which are not encountered repeatedly. How would you answer this argument in view of the discussion of Chapter 11?

19-14. What difficulties would you expect to encounter in attempting to apply the theory of zero-sum, two-person games to union-management conflict over wages, hours, and working conditions?

19-15. Make up a game matrix which illustrates the following remark: "If two or more numbers exist which satisfy the saddle-point rule, each is a saddle point and each is a solution to the game."

19-16. One of the difficulties in applying zero-sum, two-person game theory to conflicts between nations is that the value of an outcome to one nation is not simply the negative of the value of that outcome to the other nation. Give an example of this.

Chapter 20

STATISTICAL DECISIONS AND
SUBJECTIVE PROBABILITY

INTRODUCTION

THE TRADITIONAL USES of statistics have been the drawing of inferences from samples in the form of point estimates, interval estimates, the testing of hypotheses, and the relationship among variables. For some scientific purposes such inferences are a sufficient end in themselves. In management decisions, however, inferences are of interest because they form the basis for action. Modern developments in statistics have led to a much closer integration of the process of inference and the processes of decision and action, thus leading to the notion of statistical decision. A statistical decision differs from the decisions studied so far only in that the process of collecting the data, drawing inferences from it, and determining the decision are included in a single body of theory. Thus, this is not really a new type of decision. It simply includes such features as the cost of collecting information about the possible futures and the costs of the outcomes which result from errors of inference.

This does, however, represent an important difference in viewpoint from ordinary approaches to statistical inference. For example, it is usual in selecting estimators to look for such properties as unbiasedness, or for maximum likelihood estimators. The new notion recognizes that the estimate is to be used in the decision process and, if the estimate is wrong, the result will be a cost to the decision maker. Thus, if we knew the costs of being wrong by various amounts, we might be able to form an estimate which would minimize the maximum cost to the decision maker. This estimate, of course, would be selected in reference to a particular decision problem, considering the alternatives, outcomes, and the value system involved. Again, in hypothesis testing it has become general practice to consider two types of errors of inference: the rejection of a hypothesis when in fact it is true (type 1 error), and the acceptance of a hypothesis when in fact it is false (type 2 error). The selection of hypothesis testing methods has been roughly based on the following criterion: *For a given probability of a type 1 error, select the test which minimizes the probability of a type 2 error.* The statistical decision approach suggests the consideration of the costs of these two errors in terms of a particular decision situation. It also includes directly the cost of sampling, thus permitting a balancing of sampling costs against the reduction in error cost which will result from taking larger samples.

STATISTICAL DECISIONS UNDER RISK

Suppose we are confronted with a decision under risk having several possible futures, the probabilities of which are given. Suppose further that we have an opportunity to make some sort of observations which will yield information about these probabilities and thus increase our knowledge of them. The original probabilities are referred to as "a priori" probabilities, and those obtained as a result of the observations are called "a posteriori" probabilities. We will neglect, for the present, the cost of making these observations and simply show how they become an integral part of the decision process.

To take a specific example, let us suppose a foundry has poured ten lots of castings from ten heats of iron during a day. Under normal process operating conditions, the product averages about 2 per cent defective. After the day's production has been completed, it is discovered that an important additive was omitted from the metal on one of the heats. When this happens, past experience has shown that the castings will average about 12 per cent defective. To make the problem interesting, let us assume that because of administrative errors it is no longer possible to tell just which lot of castings was made with this bad metal. Thus there are ten lots, one of which is from a process which averages 12 per cent defective, and the others from a process which averages 2 per cent defective. Suppose it is necessary to ship one lot of castings immediately and that, if the bad lot is shipped, a penalty cost of $1,000 is incurred by the company. If the good lot is shipped, no penalty cost arises.

Under these conditions it is reasonable to say that, if any one of the ten lots is selected at random, the probability that it will be the bad lot is .10, and the expected penalty cost if it is shipped is

$$(.10)(\$1,000) = \$100$$

If there is no possibility of further investigation, then it makes little difference which lot is chosen for shipment.

Suppose, however, it is possible to take a sample of two castings from any one lot and inspect them. The inspection of a casting will result in its classification as either good or bad. The decision to be made after the sample has been obtained is whether to ship the lot sampled from or to ship any other lot. Let

a_1 = ship the lot sampled
a_2 = ship any other lot
S_1 = the lot sampled comes from a process with a fraction defective of 2 per cent
S_2 = the lot sampled comes from a process with a fraction defective of 12 per cent
p_1 = the a priori probability of S_1 = .90
p_2 = the a priori probability of S_2 = .10

In a sample of two castings there are three possible sets of observations which will be symbolized as follows:

x_1 = both castings good
x_2 = one casting good and one bad
x_3 = both castings bad

Having obtained one of these observations, we wish to compute the a posteriori probabilities of the possible futures. In general, for decisions under risk, these may be computed from Bayes' theorem which states that the a posteriori probability of S_j given an observation x is

$$P(S_j|x) = \frac{p_j P(x|S_j)}{\sum_j p_j P(x|S_j)}$$

It is first necessary to compute the conditional probabilities $P(x|S_j)$. Assuming that S_1 is the case, the probability of observing x_1 in the sample is

$$P(x_1|S_1) = \frac{2!}{2!}(.98)^2 = .9604$$

This is the familiar binomial distribution. Similarly, the conditional probability of observing x_1 given S_2 is

$$P(x_1|S_2) = \frac{2!}{2!}(.88)^2 = .7744$$

The additional probabilities required are

$$P(x_2|S_1) = .0392 \qquad\qquad P(x_2|S_2) = .2112$$
$$P(x_3|S_1) = .0004 \qquad\qquad P(x_3|S_2) = .0144$$

These results are now used together with Bayes' theorem to compute the a posteriori probabilities of the possible futures. If x_1 is observed then

$$P(S_1|x_1) = \frac{(.90)(.9604)}{(.90)(.9604) + (.10)(.7744)} = .9182$$

and similarly

$$P(S_2|x_1) = \frac{(.10)(.7744)}{(.90)(.9604) + (.10)(.7744)} = .0818$$

If x_2 is observed the a posteriori probabilities are

$$P(S_1|x_2) = .6255 \qquad\qquad P(S_2|x_2) = .3745$$

and if x_3 is observed

$$P(S_1|x_3) = .2000 \qquad\qquad P(S_2|x_3) = .8000$$

The problem of choice is again one under conditions of risk, with the probabilities being the a posteriori probabilities, thus:

	$P(S_1\|x)$ S_1	$P(S_2\|x)$ S_2
a_1	0	\$1,000
a_2	⅑(\$1,000)	0

dependent upon what has been observed in the sample. If x_1 has been observed, the expectations are

$$E(a_1) = (.0818)\,(1,000) = \$\,81.80$$
$$E(a_2) = (.9182)\left\{\frac{1,000}{9}\right\} = \$102.02$$

Thus a_1 would be preferred. If x_2 has been observed we have

$$E(a_1) = \$374.50$$
$$E(a_2) = \$\ 69.50$$

leading to the choice of a_2. Finally, if x_3 is observed

$$E(a_1) = \$800.00$$
$$E(a_2) = \$\ 22.22$$

which suggests a preference for a_2.

Clearly, expected cost can be reduced by the sampling process if the optimal choice is made in the above manner. If the cost of taking the samples is small compared to the possible losses involved, then it would be clearly beneficial. If, however, the cost of inspection is large, then some doubt may exist as to whether the samples should be taken at all. To explore this question, we begin by asking, "Before the samples are taken, what is the expected cost of the optimal decision given the results of sampling?"

If the samples are taken and the result is x_1, then the choice will be a_1. The probability that x_1 will be observed, based upon the a priori probabilities is

$$P(x_1) = P(x_1|S_1)p_1 + P(x_1|S_2)p_2$$
$$= (.9604)(.90) + (.7744)(.10)$$
$$= .9418$$

In the same manner we obtain

$$P(x_2) = .0564 \qquad\qquad P(x_3) = .0018$$

We may now formulate a new decision as to whether or not the samples should be taken. Let

A_1 = do not sample—ship a lot selected at random
A_2 = take the samples—select the alternative which minimizes
expected cost based on the a posteriori probabilities

This decision may be arrayed in the following form:

	$P(x_1) = .9418$ x_1 is observed	$P(x_2) = .0564$ x_2 is observed	$P(x_3) = .0018$ x_3 is observed
A_1	$100	$100	$100
A_2	$E(a_1) = \$81.80$ $+C$	$E(a_2) = \$69.50$ $+C$	$E(a_2) = \$22.22$ $+C$

where C is the cost of taking the samples.

In this decision the expectations are

$$E(A_1) = \$100.00$$
$$E(A_2) = \$\ 81.01 + C$$

Thus, if C, the cost of sampling, is less than or equal to $18.99, it would pay to go ahead and take the samples. Otherwise it would be better to choose a lot for shipment at random, without the benefit of the information to be obtained from the sample.

At this point it is natural to ask about the efficacy of a sample of two castings. Might it not be better to take a sample of one, or three, or n castings? We could answer this question before taking any samples, by analysis similar to the foregoing. However, it may turn out that if we decide to inspect ten castings, and the first eight examined turn out to be bad, then there is little to be gained by inspecting the remaining two. Thus, the decision about sample size might better be revised continually as sampling progresses. This suggests the idea of a sequential sampling plan. Such a plan involves a series of decisions which begins with the choice of either selecting an alternative immediately on the basis of the a priori probabilities. or of taking a sample of at least one casting. If it is decided to do the latter, then a sample of one is taken and the a posteriori probabilities are computed. It is then necessary to decide between the immediate selection of an alternative, and taking a sample of at least one more casting. This series goes on until the decision is finally made to stop sampling and select a course of action. At each stage the choice is based upon an examination of the expected return from the best alternative, computed on the basis of the a posteriori probabilities at that stage, and the expected return if the sampling process is continued and optimum decisions are made at each future stage. The computation of these expectations may be extremely difficult, but the principle on which sequential sampling is based is of universal importance. It suggests that in any information collection process one should continually balance the expected cost of making the decision, using the information available, against the cost of collecting at least one more increment of information and then making the best decision. This is a direct interpretation of the principles of search discussed in Chapter 4.

STATISTICAL DECISIONS UNDER UNCERTAINTY

The reader with any familiarity in the application of techniques of statistical inference will recognize that the a priori probabilities required to produce a statistical decision under risk are seldom available in interesting problems. If these probabilities are not present then the decision becomes one under conditions of uncertainty. To illustrate, let us modify the previous example slightly. Let the alternatives be

$$a_1 = \text{ship the lot sampled}$$
$$a_2 = \text{scrap the lot sampled}$$

If a_2 is chosen, we will not be particularly concerned with which lot is shipped, but presumably the sampling process would have to be carried out on the other lots until one is selected for shipment. Using the possible futures as previously defined the decision now appears as follows:

	S_1	S_2
a_1	0	$1,000
a_2	$500	0

We have included a new assumption, namely that the scrapping of a good lot results in a cost of $500. The decision might arise in this form if it were discovered that several heats were made without the essential additive, but the number and identification of the bad lots are both unknown.

Statistical decision theory now suggests that we formulate all possible decision rules, where a decision rule simply specifies what alternative will be selected for each possible observation.

In our problem there are three possible observations and two possible alternatives. This results in $2^3 = 8$ possible ways of associating alternatives with observations, each of which is a particular decision rule. The following table indicates all eight rules. The symbol R_k is used to designate the kth decision rule.

Rule		Observation	
	x_1	x_2	x_3
R_1	a_1	a_1	a_1
R_2	a_1	a_1	a_2
R_3	a_1	a_2	a_1
R_4	a_1	a_2	a_2
R_5	a_2	a_1	a_1
R_6	a_2	a_1	a_2
R_7	a_2	a_2	a_1
R_8	a_2	a_2	a_2

The decision is then viewed as a choice among these eight rules. In order to make this choice it is necessary to compute the expected cost associated with each rule, for each possible future. This is done in several steps. We have already obtained the conditional probability of an observation, x, given a future S_j, symbolized by $P(x|S_j)$. This, together with the above table, will permit the computation of the probability that any alternative will be selected, given a rule R_k and a future S_j. Let this be $P(a_i|S_j,R_k)$. Since the cost for any selection a_i and any future S_j is known, we may then obtain the expected cost for a rule R_k given a future S_j.

For rule 1, the probabilities of selection for the alternatives are simple.

$$P(a_1|S_1,R_1) = P(x_1|S_1) + P(x_2|S_1) + P(x_3|S_1) = 1$$
$$P(a_2|S_1,R_1) = 0$$
$$P(a_1|S_2,R_1) = 1$$
$$P(a_2|S_2,R_1) = 0$$

For rule 2 we have

$$P(a_1|S_1,R_2) = P(x_1|S_1) + P(x_2|S_1) = .9996$$
$$P(a_2|S_1,R_2) = P(x_3|S_1) = .0004$$

and so on. The complete set of such probabilities are tabulated in Matrix 1.

Matrix 1

		S_1	S_2
R_1	a_1	1.00	1.00
	a_2	0	0
R_2	a_1	.9996	.9856
	a_2	.0004	.0144
R_3	a_1	.9608	.7888
	a_2	.0392	.2112
R_4	a_1	.9604	.7744
	a_2	.0396	.2256

		S_1	S_2
R_5	a_1	.0396	.2256
	a_2	.9604	.7744
R_6	a_1	.0392	.2112
	a_2	.9608	.7888
R_7	a_1	.0004	.0144
	a_2	.9996	.9856
R_8	a_1	0	0
	a_2	1.00	1.00

It is now possible to compute the expected cost for each rule under each possible future. The expected cost for R_1 and S_1 is

$$V(R_1,S_1) = P(a_1|S_1,R_1)V(\theta_{11}) + P(a_2|S_1,R_1)V(\theta_{21})$$
$$= (1.00)(0) + (0)(\$500) = 0$$

For R_1 and S_2

$$V(R_1,S_2) = P(a_1|S_2,R_1)V(\theta_{12}) + P(a_2|S_2,R_1)V(\theta_{22})$$
$$= (1.00)(\$1,000) + (0)(0) = \$1,000$$

and so on. The final decision matrix for the choice between rules under conditions of uncertainty is given in Matrix 2.

Matrix 2

	S_1	S_2
R_1	0	1000.00
R_2	.20	985.60
R_3	19.60	788.80
R_4	19.80	774.40
R_5	480.20	225.60
R_6	480.40	211.20
R_7	499.80	14.40
R_8	500.00	0

Now any of the principles of choice which have been suggested
for decisions under uncertainty might be applied. This would lead
to the selection of a rule which would associate a course of action
in the original decision with every possible outcome of the program
of observation. Within the context of statistical decision theory
it has been customary to suggest that the decision should be viewed
as a game. That is, one might imagine the possible futures as being
the pure strategies of nature. The decision maker then assumes that
it is important to protect himself as best he can against the worst
possible "play" by nature, where nature is thought of as having the
intelligence and aims of an opponent in the game theory sense. Thus,
the decision maker may sometimes be led to the use of a mixed
strategy, that is, a randomized mixture of the decision rules. For the
foregoing example, the game theoretic solution is carried out graphically in Figure 20–1. The optimal strategy for the decision maker
is mixed. It suggests that R_4 should be used with probability .601,
and that R_8 should be used with probability .399. Nature's optimal
strategy is (.617, .383). The value of the game is $308.50.

As will be recalled, the optimal strategy for the decision maker
has the property that, if used, the decision maker's expectation will
be just the value of the game, no matter what nature does. Thus,
viewing the decision as a game has the advantage that the expected
cost after sampling can be computed and compared with the expected cost before sampling to see if the sampling process will be
economic. If no sampling is done, we have a game of the form

$$
\begin{array}{cc}
0 & 1{,}000 \\
500 & 0
\end{array}
$$

The optimal strategy for the decision maker is to select a_1 with
probability $\frac{1}{3}$, and a_2 with probability $\frac{2}{3}$. The value of this game is
then $333.33. If the cost of sampling is greater than $333.33 −
308.50 = $24.83, then it will not be economic to perform the in-
spection.

There has been considerable discussion as to whether it is useful
to view nature as an intelligent competitor and as to whether mixed
strategies have a place in decisions of this sort. Few will argue that
nature is in any real sense an opponent who plays against the decision maker in the style recommended by game theory; however,
some feel that this is a useful and conservative assumption to make.
Having made this assumption, then the use of mixed strategies follows logically, even though it may be difficult to think of nature

Figure 20–1

Graphical Solution as a Game

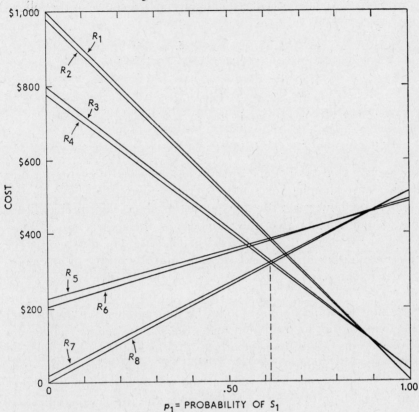

p_1 = PROBABILITY OF S_1

as responding to the decision maker's choices in such a way as to require the secrecy obtained by mixing these choices.

SUBJECTIVE PROBABILITY

In Chapter 17 it was suggested that a possible response to uncertainty was to seek probabilities through the judgments of experienced managers or knowledgeable experts. These expressions of opinion may be called personalistic or subjective probability to distinguish them from probabilities produced by the analyst on the basis of explicit relative frequency evidence. The present discussion of statistical decisions suggests that if the a priori probabilities are subjective, then Bayes' theorem provides a possible model for combining experience with explicit data to produce a posteriori probabilities upon which a decision is based. The statistical decision model indicates how the judgment of the manager might be influenced by the evidence collected by the analyst in certain instances.

Suppose we confront a decision maker with a choice of the following form:

	S_1	S_2	S_3	S_4
a_1	K	0	0	0
a_2	0	K	0	0
a_3	0	0	K	0
a_4	0	0	0	K

We assume that the possible futures are meaningful events for him in the sense that he has some experience with them. We do not supply him, however, with any statements about their probabilities. We assume further that the numbers in the matrix are utilities assigned by means of the method of Chapter 11; thus consistent behavior implies utility maximization, and the utility of any prospect is its expected utility. Now we ask the decision maker which alternative he prefers. Suppose, after careful consideration, he reports that he is indifferent among the four actions. We understand this to mean that he would not make the slightest effort to take one of the actions rather than the others, that he would let his choice be determined by a chance device, or that he would delegate the decision with no concern as to what action was taken. Suppose further that we wish to explain his choice using the utility maximization model. We could say that his report is equivalent to the statement

$$U(a_1) = U(a_2) = U(a_3) = U(a_4)$$

This will be true if

$$p_j = .25 \qquad \text{for all } j$$

since then

$$U(a_i) = (.25)(K) \qquad \text{for all } i$$

We could then say that the decision maker acts as though he attached equal weights of .25 to each of the possible futures. These weights are then called subjective probabilities. Notice that these numbers are indicative of his attitudes toward risk in this decision and make no direct reference to relative frequencies.

The example is of the same form as a lottery with four tickets and a prize of utility K. We could imagine a lottery with 100 tickets;

and, if the decision maker was indifferent as to which ticket he held, we could then say that the drawing of any ticket was an event with which he associated the subjective probability .01. This lottery may be used as a measuring device in the following manner. To find the subjective probability he associates with the event "he will win a certain contract" we ask him, "How many tickets in the lottery would you find equivalent to the prospect of winning a prize of utility K in the event that you win the contract?" If he is able to answer this question, after due consideration, by saying that he would be indifferent between twenty tickets in the lottery and the prospect of winning the prize if he is awarded the contract, then we would call .20 his subjective probability of the event "he wins the contract." If we wished we could start with a lottery of 1000 tickets and perhaps learn that his subjective probability is .203.

It would be convenient to be able to use the theorems of probability theory to make calculations of the subjective probabilities of complex events based on the subjective probabilities of simple events. The theorems are used in this way in the case of relative frequencies. To make this reasonable, we assign subjective probability zero to any event which the decision maker believes is impossible and subjective probability one to any event which he feels is certain to occur. Further, we insist that the sum of the subjective probabilities of a mutually exclusive and collectively exhaustive set of events must be one. For any two mutually exclusive events, we insist that the subjective probability of either one or the other be equal to the sum of their individual subjective probabilities. If the results obtained from a decision maker are not in agreement with these axioms, then we must ask him to reconsider and correct his "inconsistency." If his subjective probabilities do agree with them, then we have some justification for using them to predict consistent choices according to the theorems of probability theory. Just as in the case of utilities, recommendations based on subjective probabilities would be predictions of consistent choices for the decision maker.

Several important points should be noted about the notion of subjective probability.

1. The decision maker must be able to think about his attitudes toward risk and answer the sort of questions which have been suggested. Without doubt this is a difficult sort of thing to bring off in actuality. Inconsistencies may arise, the results may be unreliable, and the whole thing may appear quite "fuzzy" to the manager.

2. If experience transforms subjective probabilities in the manner suggested by Bayes' theorem, then subjective probabilities will, through experience, approach relative frequencies. In many cases it can be shown that this will happen rather quickly. Thus "reasonable" men could be expected to have similar subjective probabilities for events with which they have had similar experience.

3. In many routine situations, a manager's subjective probabilities will be determined by routine data collection and analysis methods. In these cases, the determination of probabilities can be delegated to the analyst and the manager may be freed for the more difficult decisions.

4. Relative frequencies (sometimes called objective probabilities) are themselves the product of considerable subjective judgment by the analyst. They differ mainly in that the data on which they are based and the rules for processing the data are made more explicit.

5. If a manager's experience is not considered most extensive and most relevant on a particular question, then an expert may be brought in. The expert is someone believed to have considerable knowledge and experience on the matter in question. He is then integrated into the decision process by obtaining from him his subjective probabilities. One could suggest certain qualifications that might be used as tests to determine a person's admissibility as an expert. For example, we might require that he

    a. have personalistic probabilities which are reasonably stable over time, providing he receives no new evidence,

    b. have probabilities which are affected in the right direction by new evidence,

    c. be selected for his past predictive performance, his demonstrated record of success and accuracy.

Thus a good deal of what is most subjective about subjective probabilities would be removed in the case of the expert. He is in fact treated as a kind of powerful computer in the decision process. He digests rich and complex past experience, producing the probabilities as his output.

CONCLUSION

The statistical decision model suggests a way in which data collection and processing can be integrated with the decision process itself. While its exact quantitative application may be limited to those situations in which one is willing to assume a good deal about the relevant probability distributions, it provides a useful conceptualization of one aspect of decision-making dynamics. Subjective probability offers the analyst a possible response to uncertainty which utilizes the reservoir of experience possessed by management. Subjective probabilities coupled with the statistical decision model suggest a way in which this management experience may be combined with the data provided by the analyst, thus further enlarging our conception of the dynamics of the decision process.

SUGGESTIONS FOR FURTHER STUDY

CHERNOFF, HERMAN, and MOSES, LINCOLN E. *Elementary Decision Theory.* New York: John Wiley & Sons, Inc., 1959.

HELMER, OLAF, and RESCHER, NICHOLAS. "On the Epistemology of the Inexact Sciences," *Management Science,* Vol. 6, No. 1 (October, 1956).

SCHLAIFER, ROBERT. *Introduction to Statistics for Business Decisions.* New York: McGraw-Hill Book Co., Inc., 1961.

WAGNER, HARVEY M. "Statistical Decision Theory as a Method for Information Processing," *Journal of Industrial Engineering,* Vol. 10, No. 1 (January–February, 1959).

PROBLEMS

20–1. Large lots of solid-fuel rocket engines are received from a manufacturer. They may be tested only by actually firing a sample of a few engines. Suppose that it is known in advance that the engines will come from a process which is either producing 8 per cent defective product or one which is producing 3 per cent defective product. Suppose we are permitted to take a sample of two engines from each lot for test firing. For purposes of analysis, the cost of testing an engine is taken to be $1,000, the cost of accepting a defective engine is $15,000, and the cost of rejecting a good engine is $1,000. Assume a lot size of 50.

a) If the a priori probabilities are

$$p' = .03 \qquad \text{probability} = .50$$
$$p' = .08 \qquad \text{probability} = .50$$

analyze the decision as a statistical decision under risk.

b) Assume the a priori probabilities are unknown and treat the problem as a statistical decision under uncertainty.

c) Discuss the application of various principles of choice in part (b).

20–2. Explain the process whereby a priori probabilities are transformed by sampling into a posteriori probabilities.

20–3. From a study of statistical decisions, what general guides for decisions of all sorts can be derived?

20–4. Outline the general steps in a sequential statistical decision-making process. How would such a process be related to the analysis of Chapter 16?

20–5. Suggest how the model developed in this chapter might be interpreted as

a) A model of learning.

b) An adaptive control system.

c) An illustration of decision making as a sequential process.

d) A model of how people's beliefs are changed by experience.

e) A model of how staff results are integrated into a manager's conceptualization of a decision.

20–6. Show that if observations are independent, the a posteriori probability resulting from a given a priori probability and a sample of size two is the same as that resulting from obtaining the same observations in two samples each of size one.

20–7. A business man must make travel plans in advance and the success of these plans depends heavily on the weather. Let S_1 represent the condition "good weather on the day of travel" and S_2 stand for "bad weather on the day of travel." In the business man's opinion, the chances of good weather on the day in question are .70. His utilities are shown in the matrix below.

	S_1	S_2
Air	1.0	0
Rail	.25	.75
Auto	.50	.25

A long-range weather prediction is available which is right 60 per cent of the time. (The prediction is either "good" or "bad.") Assume that the results of the long-range weather forecast can, for simplicity, be considered independent of the business man's opinion. What would be a consistent choice

a) Without the prediction?
b) Given the prediction?
c) What is the value of the prediction to him?

20–8. Four men examine a potential oil property. Their respective subjective probabilities for the event "oil will be found if a well is drilled on this property" are .01, .20, .80, and .99. They agree that there are three methods of testing for the presence of oil, one of which is right half of the time, one of which is right 90 per cent of the time, and one of which has never been wrong. If the results from the use of each of these testing methods were to be processed according to Bayes' theorem, how would the belief of each man change?

20–9. Consider a manager whose firm places new consumer products on the market from time to time. Suppose for simplicity that he considers a product which at least breaks even, a success, and a product which does not break even, a failure. When a new product possibility is brought to his attention he makes his own estimate of its chance of success. He may then submit the item to a consumer test panel. Again for simplicity, the results of the panel test are either "success" or "failure." The product may be either discarded, marketed, or submitted to a test marketing at this point. The results of the test marketing are also either "success" or "failure." It is known that the result of the test marketing is *not* independent of the consumer panel result. Show symbolically how the statistical decision model might be adapted to this situation. What data would be required for its application? What difficulties would you expect to encounter in obtaining this data?

20–10. A manufacturer is considering the possibility of introducing a new product and the advisability of a test marketing prior to making the final decision. His alternatives are

$$a_1 = \text{market the product}$$
$$a_2 = \text{do not market the product}$$

For simplicity, only three possible futures are considered which are shown below together with his a priori probabilities associated with them.

	Profit	A Priori Probability
S_1: the product captures 10 per cent of the market	$10,000,000	.70
S_2: the product captures 3 per cent of the market	$ 1,000,000	.10
S_3: the product captures less than 1 per cent of the market	$-$ 5,000,000	.20

If the test marketing is made, three possible results are considered:

$Z_1 =$ test sales of more than 10 per cent of the market
$Z_2 =$ test sales of 5 to 10 per cent of the market
$Z_3 =$ test sales of less than 5 per cent of the market

The conditional probabilities of the test results are given in the table below.

	Z_1	Z_2	Z_3
$P(Z\|S_1)$	.60	.30	.10
$P(Z\|S_2)$	.30	.60	.10
$P(Z\|S_3)$	.10	.10	.80

Assume that utility is linear in money.

a) What is his best alternative before the test?

b) How much would it be worth to have perfect knowledge of the outcome?

c) What action is best for each possible result of the test marketing?

d) What is the value of the test marketing?

Adapted from Bass, *Journal of Business*, Vol. 36, No. 1 (1963).

Chapter 21

DIVERSIFICATION

INTRODUCTION

IN THIS CHAPTER we shall attempt to illustrate the sometimes subtle, sometimes obvious point that much analysis of decisions has as
its chief result general understanding, rather than exact quantification. Many analytic abstractions or models of decisions encounter
two sorts of difficulties. First, the actual or "real" decision problem
is so complex that no analytic representation of it, which the analyst
can readily construct, can capture the full richness of reality. Much
is necessarily left out. Second, many of the variables which do enter
into the analysis turn out to be very difficult to measure. In fact,
these difficulties have so troubled some that they have come to feel
that all attempts to rationalize decisions are largely futile. This
view we take to be somewhat pessimistic, at the same time attempting to be fully aware of the limitations of our attempts to make
sense out of the choices which confront the firm. In the face of these
shortcomings, analysis does have a contribution to make. Its function is to assist the decision maker in including more variables in
his choice processes than might otherwise be possible and to contribute to his understanding of the relationships between the relevant variables which might not be obvious. It performs the further
service of providing a framework into which the rough approximations or qualitative statement about the hard-to-measure variables
may be fitted. If values, probabilities, and other quantities can be
only roughly stated, the analysis at least shows how these rough
guesses combine and relate.

While all this may appear needlessly subtle, two points seem to
emerge quite clearly from the recent progress which has been made
in the analysis of management decisions.

1. No analytic model, whether or not it is limited to easily measurable variables, is likely to capture very completely the variety and complexity of the actual decision under study.

2. In spite of this, analysis can contribute importantly in the ways we have suggested to the improvement of decision-making activities. One must be careful to keep in mind that, just as nothing really comes out of a computing machine which the programmer did not put into it, the analytic solution of a decision problem relates only to that much of the actual problem which the analyst abstracted and included in his work. Inevitably the process is incomplete.

Another way of sketching these ideas is this. One of the primary functions of the analyst is to provide decision makers with an explicit understanding of the consequences of policy. The most-sought-after description of these consequences is a quantified prediction of the outcome resulting from the application of a particular policy to a particular decision situation. Ordinarily, the amount of information necessary for such quantified statements is beyond the resources or abilities of the analyst. However, this may not preclude the manager from making use of a logical analysis of the consequences of policy. Such an analysis, while lacking quantification, leads the decision maker toward greater explicitness in the decision process and toward greater consistency. It is in this spirit that the policy of diversification is discussed in this chapter.

These points must be set forth in terms of an example, since this is presently the only way we know to explore them. The analysis of diversification as a policy for the firm has been chosen, not only in the hope of providing a simple yet novel example, but to cast some light on a policy problem which is of continuing central interest to many firms.

THE USES OF DIVERSIFICATION

Diversification is widely used by investors in the selection of security portfolios. Its use is often based on such notions as, "Don't put all your eggs in one basket." The rough purpose being that, no matter what the future course of the economy and the securities market, *some portion* of the investor's holdings will yield a profit (or at least not a total loss).

It is a far more general policy in its application, however, for some firms attempt to offer a diversified line of products, sell to a diversified group of customers, avoid dependence on a single source of supply, and even employ interdisciplinary research teams. Diversification of product line is perhaps the most common instance of the policy. It is used to absorb excess capacity, as in smoothing out seasonal variations in demand and production. The traditional examples are the firm which combined the sale of ice in the summer with the sale of coal in the winter, or the summer vacation area which installed a ski tow. The firm may diversify its product line to protect itself against longer-range shifts in demand which may arise through changes in consumer tastes, the emergence of new substitute products, new marketing methods and so on. For example, many aircraft manufacturers have made important attempts to avoid complete dependence on government business. In fact, nearly all of the great industrial concerns of our time indicate the efficacy of diversification. One especially prominent form of product line diversification is vertical integration as exhibited by certain large automobile and steel companies.

The policy of diversification, roughly considered, indicates that, in the allocation of resources to alternative activities or opportunities, one should not allocate all resources to a single opportunity but should somehow spread them out among the various alternatives. Just how this allocation should be made and exactly what is to be gained from this policy is often only vaguely understood. The following discussion is an attempt to understand the policy and in particular to give some general answers to these questions. No attempt is made at mathematical sophistication, but rather a few very simple situations will be examined to understand when diversification is a rational policy and how it might be carried out. The necessity for explicit formulation of values, expectations, and objectives will, as with all such models, limit the possibilities for exact quantitative solutions.

THE ANALYTIC MODEL

A very simple decision situation will be used to illustrate the consequences of this policy. A single resource which is perfectly divisible, such as capital, is considered. The decision maker is faced with two opportunities for the employment of this resource. These opportunities involve risk in the sense that, for each opportunity, two outcomes are possible and the decision maker is able to state the probabilities of these outcomes. The outcomes are simple functions of the amount of resource allocated to the opportunity; in particular, a given outcome will be taken as simply multiplying the amount of resource by a constant. The decision maker is further able to evaluate these outcomes. That is, he has a set of objectives and a value system which somehow relates outcomes to the attainment of objectives. To make this structure explicit the following symbolism is used. Let

x = the total amount of resource available

x_i = the amount of resource allocated to alternative i

a_i = alternative i $(i = 1, 2)$

$K_i x_i$ = a possible outcome resulting from the allocation of x_i units of resource to alternative i

$k_i x_i$ = the other possible outcome resulting from the allocation of x_i units of resource to alternative i (these outcomes are measured in the same units as the resource itself)

$V(y)$ = the value of an outcome of y resource units (V is called in economics the utility function of the decision maker.)

D = a program of allocation of resources among both alternatives

The outcomes will be thought of in such a way that $k_i < K_i$, and it will always be required that all of the resource available be used, that is $x_1 + x_2 = x$. The probability distributions of the outcomes are assumed to be independent.

$$p_i = \text{probability of } k_i x_i$$
$$1 - p_i = \text{probability of } K_i x_i$$

THE EXPECTATION PRINCIPLE

Consider a decision maker who forms the expectation of the value of outcomes and seeks to choose so as to maximize this expectation. A simple value system that might be used is expressed by the function

$$V(y) = y$$

The expectation if all of the resource is devoted to alternative a_i is given by

$$E(a_i) = k_i x p_i + K_i x (1 - p_i)$$

Let the numbering of the alternatives be such that

$$E(a_1) > E(a_2)$$

Ruling out the possibility for the moment that

$$E(a_1) = E(a_2)$$

Thus

$$E(a_1) = k_1 x p_1 + K_1 x (1 - p_1) > E(a_2) = k_2 x p_2 + K_2 x (1 - p_2)$$

Now if it is possible to allocate some amount of resource to each of these opportunities, the decision maker is interested in whether or not this will improve his expectations. For a diversified program:

$$E(D) = \{k_1x_1 + k_2x_2\}p_1p_2 + \{k_1x_1 + K_2x_2\}p_1(1 - p_2)$$
$$+ \{K_1x_1 + k_2x_2\}(1 - p_1)p_2 + \{K_1x_1 + K_2x_2\}(1 - p_1)(1 - p_2)$$

Recalling that $x_2 = x - x_1$, the derivative of $E(D)$ with respect to x_1 may be obtained.

$$\frac{dE(D)}{dx_1} = \text{constant}$$

Thus

$E(D)$ is maximum for $x_1 = 0$ or $x_1 = x$
For $x_1 = 0$, $E(D) = k_2xp_2 + K_2x(1 - p_2) = E(a_2)$
For $x_1 = x$, $E(D) = k_1xp_1 + K_2x(1 - p_1) = E(a_1)$

Under these conditions no diversified program can improve the expectations.

This situation represents the decision maker who invests dollars and seeks to maximize the expected dollar return. Diversification is thus not a reasonable policy in this rather common case. If $E(a_1) = E(a_2)$, then for any diversified program

$$E(D) = E(a_1) = E(a_2)$$

and the decision maker is indifferent with respect to the policy. Suppose the value system of the decision maker is a linear function of the outcome. The value of y resource units would be given by

$$V(y) = a + by$$

The expectation from a diversified program is

$$E(D) = \{a + b(k_1x_1 + k_2x_2)\}p_1p_2 + \{a + b(k_1x_1 + K_2x_2)\}$$
$$p_1(1 - p_2) + \{a + b(K_1x_1 + k_2x_2)\}(1 - p_1)p_2$$
$$+ \{a + b(K_1x_1 + K_2x_2)\}(1 - p_1)(1 - p_2)$$

For this type of utility function it is easily seen that

$$\frac{dE(D)}{dx_1} = \text{constant}$$

and, as before, no diversified program is rational. This result can be readily extended to the case of more than two opportunities, and more than two outcomes for any opportunity.

Thus, the result is that a policy of diversification is not rational for a decision maker whose utility function is linear in the outcome (measured in resource units) and who wishes to maximize expectations.

VALUE SYSTEMS LEADING TO DIVERSIFICATION

In the simple two-opportunity, two-outcome-per-opportunity problem, the requirements for using a diversified program are that

$$\frac{dE(D)}{dx_1} = 0$$

for some value of x_1 in the interval $0 < x_1 < x$, and that

$$\frac{d^2E(D)}{dx_1^2}$$

be negative at this point.

The question of what class of value systems or utility functions is necessary for these conditions to exist will now be examined. Representing a utility function simply by $V(y)$ we have:

$$E(D) = V[k_1x_1 + k_2(x - x_1)]\, p_1p_2 + V[k_1x_1 + K_2(x - x_1)]$$
$$p_1(1 - p_2) + V[K_1x_1 + k_2(x - x_1)](1 - p_1)p_2$$
$$+ V[K_1x_1 + K_2(x - x_1)](1 - p_1)(1 - p_2)$$

Let consideration be limited to the class of utility functions $V(y)$ which are increasing functions of y. This is simply to say that the decision maker prefers more of the resource to less of it.

Consider the four terms in the foregoing expression for $E(D)$. The individual behavior of these terms as x_1 changes depends clearly on the relationship among the rates of return. It has already been assumed that $K_i > k_i$, for all i. Again let the alternative opportunities be numbered so that $E(a_1) > E(a_2)$. One may then distinguish four possible orderings for the rates of return:

$$\text{I. } K_1 > k_1 > K_2 > k_2$$
$$\text{II. } K_1 > K_2 > k_1 > k_2$$
$$\text{III. } K_1 > K_2 > k_2 > k_1$$
$$\text{IV. } K_2 > K_1 > k_1 > k_2$$

The first of these orderings represents the case in which opportunity a_1 dominates, and thus no policy of diversification will be attractive. For all the other orderings at least one of the terms in the expression for $E(D)$ will increase as x_1 increases, and at least one term will decrease as x_1 increases. For ordering II, the second term decreases and the other terms increase with increasing x_1. For ordering III, the first and second terms decrease, and for ordering IV, the second and fourth terms decrease, while the remaining terms increase as x_1 increases.

Let $g(x_1)$ stand for the sum of those terms which increase with x_1, and let $h(x_1)$ stand for the sum of those terms which decrease. Thus

$$\frac{dg(x_1)}{dx_1} = \text{positive}$$

$$\frac{dh(x_1)}{dx_1} = \text{negative}$$

and

$$\frac{dE(D)}{dx_1} = 0$$

when

$$\frac{dg(x_1)}{dx_1} = \frac{dh(x_1)}{dx_1}$$

The crucial result arises when it is noticed that each of the four terms in the expression of $E(D)$ will have a second derivative with respect to x_1 which has the same sign as

$$\frac{d^2 V(y)}{dy^2}$$

Thus, if the second derivative of the utility function is negative, then the second derivative of each of the terms in the expression for $E(D)$ is negative, thus

$$\frac{d^2 E(D)}{dy^2}$$

is itself negative.

We have restricted attention to utility functions which are increasing functions of the amount of resource. It may now be seen under the conditions of the foregoing form of rationality, a concave utility function is a necessary condition for diversification. The results so far may be summarized as follows:

In the two-opportunity, two-outcome decision problem, a decision maker who wishes to maximize expectation will find diversification rational if

$$\frac{dE(D)}{dx_1} = 0$$

for some value of x_1 in the interval $0 < x_1 < x$, and if his utility function is concave and increasing. This second condition is sometimes called "positive and decreasing marginal utility."

REDUCTION OF VARIANCE: THE EXPECTATION-VARIANCE PRINCIPLE

Another property of the policy of diversification may now be illustrated. Under conditions of decreasing and positive marginal utility, the decision maker seeks to maximize the expected quantity of the resource if the variance of the quantity of resource is held constant, or to minimize the variance if the expected quantity is held constant. This was shown in Chapter 11. To recall, the value of an amount of resource y may be expanded in a Taylor series.

$$V(y) = V(a) + (y - a)\frac{dV(a)}{dy} + \tfrac{1}{2}(y - a)^2\frac{d^2V(a)}{dy^2} + \ldots\ldots$$

Letting

$$a = E(y)$$

and taking expected values

$$E\{V(y)\} = V\{E(y)\} + \tfrac{1}{2}\sigma_y^2\frac{d^2V\{E(y)\}}{dy^2} + \ldots\ldots\ldots\ldots$$

Since the second derivative of $V(y)$ is negative, the decision maker will prefer opportunities with small variances, for fixed expected returns. It will now be shown that diversification does in fact serve this end. If y represents the number of resource units obtained from a program, it will be recalled that for an opportunity a_i

$$E(y) = k_i x_i p_i + K_i x_i(1 - p_i)$$

The variance of y is easily computed with the following result:

$$\sigma_y^2 = x_i^2(k_i - K_i)^2 p_i(1 - p_i)$$

We now define

$$\sigma_i^2 = (k_i - K_i)^2 p_i(1 - p_i)$$

Thus, if x_i units are allocated to a_i the resulting return has variance

$$x_i^2\sigma_i^2$$

If all x units are allocated to a single opportunity a_i the variance of the result is given by

$$\sigma_y = x^2\sigma_i^2$$

However, if a diversified program is used, the variance of the result is

$$\sum_i x_i^2\sigma_i^2$$

Let this latter quantity be signified by $S_D{}^2$. If there exists a diversified program such that

$$S_D{}^2 < x^2\sigma_i{}^2 \text{ for all } i$$

then clearly this diversified program has a smaller variance than any nondiversified program. To show this we define

$$\sigma_D{}^2 = S_D{}^2/x^2$$

and demonstrate that there always exists a diversified program which will make

$$\sigma_D{}^2 < \sigma_i{}^2 \text{ for all } i$$

To show this, we assume the opportunities to be numbered such that

$$\frac{\sigma_1{}^2}{\sigma_2{}^2} \geqq 1$$

Then

$$\sigma_D{}^2 = \frac{x_1{}^2}{x^2}\sigma_1{}^2 + \frac{(x - x_1)^2}{x^2}\sigma_2{}^2$$

$$\frac{d(\sigma_D{}^2)}{dx_1} = \frac{x_1{}^2}{x^2}\sigma_1{}^2 + \frac{(-2x + 2x_1)}{x^2}\sigma_2{}^2$$

Setting

$$\frac{d(\sigma_D{}^2)}{dx_1} = 0$$

then

$$x_1 = \frac{x\sigma_2{}^2}{\sigma_1{}^2 + \sigma_2{}^2} = x\left(\frac{r}{1 + r}\right)$$

which is the value of x_1 which will minimize $\sigma_D{}^2$. Substituting this value of the expression for $\sigma_D{}^2$

$$\sigma_D{}^2 = \frac{r\sigma_1{}^2}{(1 + r)}$$

Since $\sigma_1{}^2 < \sigma_2{}^2$, then $\sigma_D{}^2 < \sigma_1{}^2 < \sigma_2{}^2$, which was to be shown.

The essential nature of the policy of diversification is evident. It is a policy which tends to reduce the variance of the amount of resource returned and is sometimes rational for maximizing expected utility, when conditions of positive and decreasing marginal utility prevail.

DEPENDENT OPPORTUNITIES

So far the independence of the opportunities has been assumed. In order to understand what happens if the opportunities are dependent, rewrite the expression for $E(D)$ as follows:

$$E(D) = V(k_1x_1 + k_2x_2)P_1 + V(k_1x_1 + K_2x_2)P_2 + V(K_1x_1 + k_2x_2)P_3 \\ + V(K_1x_1 + K_2x_2)P_4$$

Positive correlation among the opportunities implies that P_2 and P_3 tend to zero and $P_1 + P_4$ tends to one as the degree of correlation increases. Negative correlation implies that P_1 and P_4 tend to zero and $P_2 + P_3$ tends to one as the degree of negative correlation increases. Consider the four ordering relations among the rates of return discussed previously. In the following table are shown the direction of change of the terms in the foregoing expression for $E(D)$ as x_1 increases under each of these four orderings.

Quantity	Ordering I	Ordering II	Ordering III	Ordering IV
$V(k_1x_1 + k_2x_2)$	+	+	−	+
$V(k_1x_1 + K_2x_2)$	+	−	−	−
$V(K_1x_1 + k_2x_2)$	+	+	+	+
$V(K_1x_1 + K_2x_2)$	+	+	+	−

The following statements may be made regarding diversification with correlated opportunities.

1. As before, ordering I is immediately ruled out since the first opportunity is dominant.
2. For perfect positive correlation, ordering II yields a preference for opportunity a_1, while orderings III and IV admit the possibility of preference for a diversified program.
3. For perfect negative correlation, orderings II, III, and IV admit the possibility of diversification.
4. For anything less than perfect correlation, diversification may be desirable for orderings II, III, and IV.

In each case where the possibility of diversification is present, actual preference for diversification in particular situations must be determined by the foregoing tests.

THE ASPIRATION LEVEL PRINCIPLE

If k is the amount of resource available, then the aspiration level may be expressed in resource units, as $A = x + Y$. As before we will consider two opportunities whose expected returns in resource units are given by

$$E(a_i) = p_i k_i x + (1 - p_i) K_i x$$

In order for an opportunity to be considered at all it must be that $E(a_i) > A$. Assume this relation holds for a_1. If $E(a_2) < A$, then a_1 will clearly be chosen. If $E(a_2) > A$ then one of the following policies might be used.

Rule I: Select a_1 if $E(a_1) \geqq E(a_2)$, otherwise select a_2.
Rule II: Select a_1 if $(1 - p_1) \geqq (1 - p_2)$, otherwise select a_2.

These rules might be modified by using one of the following orderings.

Rule III: Select the opportunity which will maximize the probability of achieving the aspiration level. If the probabilities are equal, select the alternative which maximizes the expected return.
Rule IV: Select the alternative which maximizes the expected return. If the expected returns are equal, select the alternative which maximizes the probability of achieving the aspiration level.

Now if the possibility of a diversified program is entertained, one may ask if conditions exist under which any of these rules will lead to the selection of such a program. Rule I is equivalent to the situation discussed formerly where $V(y) = y$, for which it has been shown that diversification will never be used.

For Rule II it is clear that if one or both of the opportunities will achieve the aspiration level with probability one, no diversified program need be chosen. A more interesting case arises when one assumes that

$$k_1 x < A \qquad\qquad K_1 x \geq A$$
$$k_2 x < A \qquad\qquad K_2 x \geq A$$

Defining the expected return for a diversified program as

$$E(D) = (k_1 x_1 + k_2 x_2)p_1 p_2 + (k_1 x_1 + K_2 x_2)p_1(1 - p_2)$$
$$+ (K_1 x_1 + k_2 x_2)(1 - p_1)p_2 + (K_1 x_1 + K_2 x_2)(1 - p_1)(1 - p_2)$$

there are four possible sets of relations between the resource terms in this equation and the aspiration level.

Quantity	Case 1	Case 2	Case 3	Case 4
$k_1 x_1 + k_2 x_2$	$< A$	$< A$	$< A$	$< A$
$k_1 x_1 + K_2 x_2$	$< A$	$< A$	$\geq A$	$\geq A$
$K_1 x_1 + k_2 x_2$	$< A$	$\geq A$	$\geq A$	$< A$
$K_1 x_1 + K_2 x_2$	$\geq A$	$\geq A$	$\geq A$	$\geq A$

For Case 1 the probability of achieving the aspiration level is

$$(1 - p_1)(1 - p_2)$$

Since

$$(1 - p_1) > (1 - p_1)(1 - p_2)$$

and

$$(1 - p_2) > (1 - p_1)(1 - p_2)$$

no diversified program will be chosen.

For Case 2 the probability of achievement is

$$(1 - p_1)p_2 + (1 - p_1)(1 - p_2) = (1 - p_1)$$

Thus the decision maker will be indifferent between the diversified program and a_1. A similar argument shows that in Case 4 indifference will exist between D and a_2.

For Case 3 the probability of achievement is

$$p_1(1 - p_2) + (1 - p_1)p_2 + (1 - p_1)(1 - p_2) = (1 - p_1) + p_1(1 - p_2)$$
$$= (1 - p_2) + (1 - p_1)p_2$$

A diversified program will thus be preferred to both opportunities. The range of x_1 which will be suitable is given by

$$\frac{A - xk_2}{K_1 - k_2} \le x_1 \le \frac{xK_2 - A}{K_2 - k_1}$$

if

$$\frac{A - xk_2}{K_1 - k_2} \le \frac{xK_2 - A}{K_2 - k_1}$$

or

$$0 < x_1 \frac{xK_2 - A}{K_2 - k_1}$$

and

$$\frac{A - xk_2}{K_1 - k_2} \le x_1 < x$$

if

$$\frac{A - xk_2}{K_1 - k_2} > \frac{xK_2 - A}{K_2 - k_1}$$

For Rule III a direct synthesis of the results for Rules I and II shows that, although diversified programs exist which have the same probability of achievement as the opportunities themselves, no diversified program can improve the expected return.

For Rule IV it is easily shown that if a diversified program exists such that either

$$E(D) = E(a_1)$$

or

$$E(D) = E(a_2)$$

then it must be that

$$E(D) = E(a_1) = E(a_2)$$

The analysis of Rule II then indicates the conditions under which a diversified program will increase the probability of achieving the aspiration level.

These results may be summarized by stating that diversification may sometimes be a rational policy under the following conditions:

1. If the decision maker wishes to maximize the expected value of the outcomes and if conditions of positive and decreasing marginal utility prevail.
2. If the decision maker wishes to maximize the probability of achieving some aspired level of return.

Under these conditions optimum diversified programs may be obtained by simple methods in the two-opportunity, two-outcome problem discussed here.

SOME GUIDES TO CONSISTENCY

At this point one might proceed in several ways. For example, the analysis of a particular diversification decision for a given firm might be undertaken. This might involve, in addition to several difficult measurement problems, some basic modifications of the analysis. If we think in terms of investments, then clearly we must modify the analysis to include several alternatives and several outcomes. Investment opportunities also tend to be "lumpy" or discontinuous for industrial firms, as in the case of equipment investment. A relatively restricted variety of equipment is available which may be acquired only in discrete units, thus the amount invested in any given opportunity is not a continuous variable. The problems of measurement and prediction are obviously difficult. Perhaps the most troublesome is that of the value system or utility function of the firm.

Our point is, however, that perhaps one can contribute something to the decision maker's understanding of diversification, which might not have otherwise been obvious to him. In most firms management is likely to be something less than enthusiastic about the prospect of plumbing through the analysis which we have developed. However, it may be that out of such analysis one can extract some rough and ready principles which may provide some useful guides to consistent decision making.

It is often reasonable to conclude that a firm actually manifests the phenomenon of diminishing marginal utility of money. This can be supported either by introspection on the part of management or by a study of the firm's policies and past decisions. Most conservative policies which tend to aim at the preservation of the firm's existence or maintaining a reasonable level of profit, may be thought of as being consistent with diminishing marginal utility of money. Given such a conclusion, then our analysis has suggested that diversification will be a *consistent* policy for the firm. To put it negatively: *Given a firm or decision maker wishing to maximize expected dollar profits, then diversification among investments promising differing dollar returns is inconsistent with this objective.*

This kind of principle, which is perhaps not obvious at the outset, may provide a rough but basic insight for the decision maker. More precise measurement and quantification are not required, at least with respect to the choice of whether or not to diversify. Other closely related principles may be formulated:

A decision maker wishing to reduce the variance of his return may do so through proper diversification.

Diversification may be a consistent policy if the decision maker wishes to maximize the probability of achieving some aspired level of return.

The reader will find others which can be similarly advanced. The point is that such guides to consistent decision making do in fact emerge from this sort of analysis, and may be useful without precise quantification.

SUGGESTIONS FOR FURTHER STUDY

ANSOFF, H. I. "A Model for Diversification," *Management Science,* Vol. 4, No. 4 (July, 1958).

MARKOWITZ, HARRY M. *Portfolio Selection, Efficient Diversification of Investments.* New York: John Wiley & Sons, Inc., 1959.

PROBLEMS

21–1. A research director about to undertake a project has a choice between assigning one full-time man to the task or four men at one-quarter time each. Assume that the project is one for which success and failure are clearly defined and that evidence of the past performance of the men in question on similar projects is available. What arguments can be advanced for and against the alternatives? To what extent can the choice be quantified?

21–2. A gray iron foundry now sells almost exclusively to machinery manufacturers in a two-state area. The firm is owned largely by its employees. Would you suggest that it diversify its market and product line? If so, how?

21–3. What explanation can be given for the diversification programs which have been undertaken by many of the major aircraft manufacturers? What would be the characteristics of an ideal expansion program for such a firm?

21–4. What are the basic similarities and differences between a policy of diversification among alternatives and a mixed strategy in the sense of game theory? (See Chapter 19.)

21–5. If you had $10,000 to invest in securities, would you diversify? Explain the reasons behind your answer. If you decide to diversify, how would you do it? Would the number of persons dependent on you for their support make any difference in this decision?

21–6. Given two investments of one-year duration:

a_1 promises a return of $k_1 x_1$ where k_1 is a random variable having a normal distribution with mean 1.15 and standard deviation .08.

a_2 promises a return of $k_2 x_2$ where k_2 is a random variable having a normal distribution with a mean of 1.10 and standard deviation of .04.

An investor seeks a diversified program for a sum x which will maximize the function

$$a(\text{expected return}) - b(\text{variance of return})$$

Given that $a = 1$, plot the value of x_1 which will maximize this quantity as a function of b.

21–7. Repeat problem 21–6 for an investor who wishes to maximize the quantity

$$E\{b \, ln(y)\}$$

where y is the return in dollars.

21–8. A firm may invest to any extent it wishes in two lines of activity.

a_1 promises a return of $k_1 x_1$ with probability .20 and $K_1 x_1$ with probability .80. Here k_1 is .90 and K_1 is 1.20.

a_2 promises a return of $(1.10)x_2$ with probability .20 and $(1.15)x_2$ with probability .80.

The firm has $10,000 available for such investments.

a) Find a program which will maximize expectation if the firm's value system suggests that

$$V(y) = y$$

where y is the dollar return.

b) Find the program which will maximize expectation if

$$V(y) = ln(y)$$

c) Find the program having minimum variance of return.

d) Plot the program which maximizes the probability of achieving a level of return A as a function of A.

21–9. Suggest some of the symptoms which would reveal diminishing marginal utility for money in a firm. In an individual.

21–10. Formulate some rough principles to guide management in approaching diversification policy.

Chapter 22

DECISIONS UNDER PRESSURE

INTRODUCTION

DEADLINES ARE AN EVER-PRESENT and troublesome feature of the ongoing operations of any firm. There are target dates to be met, production schedules to be satisfied, delivery dates on which customer satisfaction may depend, and so on. The firm is continually under the pressure of time in many of its activities. It must bring together all the inputs to the production process according to some coordinated time schedule, get the production out, and bring its product into the market with timeliness. This inevitably means that many of the decisions, such as which machine to purchase, what inventory level to hold, or when to buy its raw materials, cannot be made in an atmosphere of leisurely investigation and reflection. The pressure which these deadlines place on the decision process constitutes perhaps the most striking difference encountered in going from an academic discussion of management decisions into the world of action. Admittedly at present there seems to be nothing very subtle to be said about how decisions should be made under this pressure, but its existence must be clearly recognized. There is a certain feeling of disillusionment which comes to the analyst who is equipped to make an effective analysis, say of replacement policy, but discovers there just is not time. The decision is quickly made instead on the basis of hunches, experience, or intuition.

The chief effect of time pressures is to force one into making decisions with something less than the amount of information which would otherwise be desired. Time pressure is in fact one of the principal reasons why the analysis of decisions in the face of incomplete information is of interest. However, other pressures also act within the context of the firm to force decisions under meager knowledge of the consequences. One of these is the pressure of cost, in particular the cost of collecting the information and carrying out the analysis of the decision. Every manager knows that, before introducing a new product, it would be very useful to have the results of a thorough market study, including test marketings, consumer panels, and so on. This, however, is simply too expensive for many firms. It is also well known that, before buying a machine, a great many alternatives might be carefully investigated if funds were available to carry out such an investigation. Indeed, some information just cannot be obtained at any cost, such as information about the future or perhaps information about a competitor's financial position.

Time and cost then act, sometimes together and sometimes individually, to exert pressures on the decision process, the chief consequence of which is to force decisions to be made with incomplete information. One might characterize the scientist who works undisturbed in his laboratory supported by a grant for pure research, as a man who has little concern for deadlines in his information-gathering and decision-making activities. In fact, scientists seldom if ever feel that they have enough information on which to base a scientific decision. The executive in his decision-making activities is at the other extreme. He is conscious of the deadline imposed upon him by the progress of the firm, thoroughly accustomed to making decisions on the basis of very little information, and has confidence in his hunches and judgments. Somewhere in between is the analyst, who is engaged in the application of scientific results to decisions under the pressure of executive action. The analyst inevitably must feel the conflict between his desire to do definitive analysis and the need to get an answer in a hurry. In this situation the analyst has little choice but to present the best possible analysis of the decision within the time available. If he does not, the decision will probably be made without the benefit of his work. On the other hand, deadlines are sometimes not as absolute as they are made to seem, and it may be the case that a decision can be held up while better analysis is made available.

In the next section we will try to point out some of the effects of time pressure on the decision process, and offer some highly simplified examples of how one might react to this pressure.

EFFECTS OF PRESSURE

In the absence of any very general evidence on the nature of the effects of pressure on decision making in the firm, we will suggest some hypotheses. These hypotheses can best be viewed as suggestions of things to be watched for in particular situations, rather than general statements of facts.

As we have pointed out, the general effect of time pressure is to reduce the available information and the extent of analysis accomplished in preparation for an actual choice. This means that fewer alternatives will be identified under conditions of time pressure. It means also that less evidence will be obtained on the outcomes, their probabilities, and their values. In the absence of this evidence, it is increasingly difficult to do analysis. This leads to the formulation of a simple, but possibly revealing, principle of a tentative nature: *Pressure favors intuition as against analysis.*

We might also say that as pressure increases we are more likely to find the firm making its decisions on the basis of judgment, unorganized experience, and implicit processes of choice. All these are, of course, arrayed in contrast to our attempts to move toward rationality through data collection and analysis. This may mean that, in some firms, the only decisions on which anything like effective staff assistance can be given, are those which provide sufficient time for the staff to perform its routine functions. One of the major differences between staff organizations is their ability to do nonroutine analysis in the face of executive decision deadlines. It is perhaps true that the most difficult aspect of staff work is to put knowledge into the hands of those who make decisions, under the conditions of pressure which characterize these decisions.

Time pressure may also have an important effect on the process of searching for alternative courses of action. The Simon-March hypothesis examined in Chapter 4 emphasized the tendency toward searching out and selecting satisfactory alternatives, as opposed to optimal alternatives. Now time pressure may increase the rate of search, but it also probably reduces the total number of alternatives examined. This may happen in the following way. The Simon-March hypothesis suggests that one searches for alternatives and as each is obtained it is immediately evaluated. If the alternative is acceptable, or meets the decision maker's aspiration level, it is immediately chosen, thus concluding the decision process. This method is sequential—obtaining and evaluating the alternatives in sequence, selecting the first acceptable one. It stands in contrast to the method of first obtaining a number of alternatives, then evaluating them, and finally choosing one of them. Now it is possible to suppose that, if in fact search and selection are sequential, the aspiration level or definition of acceptability may be influenced by time pressures. We would hypothesize that, as the deadline for a choice approaches, the aspiration level will be reduced. This is exactly what happened in the example of purchasing policy given in Chapter 16. As the deadline for the procurement approached, the price at which the decision maker was willing to buy increased. The same phenomenon may be hypothesized for the man who has 30 days in which to sell his home. As the 30th day nears, he is willing to accept less and less for the house. We may summarize by saying that it is hypothesized that, under conditions of time pressure, alternatives will be searched out and evaluated in sequence. The first one which meets the decision maker's aspiration level will be accepted, thus completing the decision process. The aspiration level will decline as the deadline approaches.

Control decisions, such as those relating to quality control, production control, or inventory control are inherently time-pressure decisions. If management hopes to control a production process, it must be able to make quick decisions as to what action to take when something goes wrong with the process. It is hypothesized that relatively simple policies are established to cover the common repetitive situations in which a control choice must be made. These policies are then followed almost automatically through to the selection of an alternative. This indicates the obvious way of reacting to repetitive decisions made in the face of time pressures. This way is, of course, the formulation of policy which effectively predetermines the choice.

Finally, we suggest two well-known problems which will indicate some of the relevant considerations.

THE PISTOL PROBLEM

Consider two persons determined to fight a duel with single-shot pistols. When one of them fires, the shot is either fatal or a miss. Having fired and missed, one duelist can only stand there until his assailant walks up and delivers the fatal shot. For each duelist a function is given which tells the probability of a hit as a function of the distance between the persons. One form of this problem is to ask, "When is the optimal time to fire?" There is an advantage in delaying the decision to fire, since this improves the probability of a hit. However, the longer the delay, the more likely the opponent will fire, perhaps with devastating effect. The pressures of time are obvious.

THE FIANCÉ PROBLEM

A young lady has determined that N gentlemen are potential husbands, but she knows none of them. She proposes to become engaged to them one at a time. She begins by selecting one man at random and becoming engaged. The question is, then, should she marry him, or discard him in the hope of finding a more suitable mate. If she becomes engaged a second time, she will perhaps discard the man if he is not more desirable than the first man, but otherwise she faces the same problem again. Here pressures are again in evidence. She is quite ignorant of those men to whom she has not yet been engaged. The supply of men is limited because, after breaking an engagement, it is difficult to take up again with a man. Time presses also, since this process leaves her a little older at each stage. The question is, "To how many men should she become engaged before marrying one?"

DEALING WITH PRESSURES

There is a real need for some method of dealing with the pressure which will be effective in the context of management decisions. Modern statistics has, of course, recognized the financial pressures involved by introducing considerations of the cost of taking data and the costs associated with say type 1 and type 2 errors. Little has been offered so far as to how one should take into account the pressures of time, and it is the purpose of the discussion which follows to explore an approach to this problem.

Before proceeding, a word of caution is necessary. These very pressures themselves may make it impossible for the analyst to behave optimally under pressure, if the rules for optimal behavior are complicated, costly, and time consuming. Thus, the analyst faces a sort of double dilemma. He would like to know the rules for rational behavior under pressure, but if the answer you give him is too complicated, pressure will prevent him from using it. Ideally what is sought is some rough guide to behavior in making decisions under pressure which can be economically applied. If a missile is in flight in our general direction, we are unlikely to be interested in a complicated scheme for calculating the best direction in which to run. These kinds of results are not generally available at present.

We suggest below a hypothetical problem which is intended to illustrate three basic notions.

1. The principal reason for postponing a decision is to gather additional information. If no additional information can be obtained, the choice may as well be made, and the time available before the deadline used for advance preparation or early action.

2. The basic problem of dealing with deadlines is knowing when to stop gathering additional information and make the choice. In this respect the problem is much like a statistical sequential sampling plan.

3. In order to deal rationally with decisions in the face of deadlines, a great deal must be known about the characteristics of the information which has not yet been obtained. Here, as in the problem of searching for alternatives, reasonable behavior seems to require more information than is likely to be available in most situations.

AN EXAMPLE

This is the problem of the political opportunist who tries to pick the candidate who will win the election, attach himself to this candidate, and thus obtain a comfortable appointment as a reward for his loyalty. If he picks the wrong candidate, the loser, of course all is wasted, for the loser has no jobs to distribute to his followers. The earlier in the campaign that the opportunist becomes associated with a candidate, the greater his reward if his man wins the election. The election is, of course, a rather definite deadline, because no elected official has much sympathy for followers who only declare themselves after the returns are in. The time between the present and election day is divided by the opportunist into three periods. He has the possibility during any of these periods of making a survey of voter opinion which will presumably reveal to him something of the way in which the election will go. Let us suppose that his payoff is given as a function of the time he declares his support, as shown in the following matrix.

	Present	Period 1	Period 2	Period 3	After Election
He supports the winner	10	9	8	7	0
He supports the loser	0	0	0	0	0

The surveys of voter opinion which he may wish to make not only take time, but cost money. In the same units as the payoff data, the cost of a survey will be taken as .25, no matter in which period it is made. To make things simple, let us further assume that the result of a survey is simply a statement, "Candidate A will be elected" or "Candidate B will be elected." A survey gives no other information. From past experience with surveys, our political opportunist knows that, as the surveys are made closer to the time of the elec-

tion, they are more and more likely to be correct. In fact, he estimates the probability that a survey will be correct as follows:

Period	1	2	3
Probability of a correct prediction	.60	.70	.90

For simplicity we will assume that the outcomes of the surveys are
probabilistically independent.

At the present time the information which the opportunist has in
hand leads him to estimate that the probability of A being elected
is .55, thus the probability of B being elected is .45, since this is a
two-party contest. These are called "a priori probabilities."

The political opportunist is thus faced with the choice of whether
to go ahead with one or more surveys before declaring his choice, or
to associate himself with a candidate immediately. Whoever decides to declare for a candidate must, of course, decide which one.

Assume for the moment that he decided to dispense with any future surveys and declare a choice immediately. His decision is then
represented by the following matrix:

	$p_1 = .55$ A is elected	$p_2 = .45$ B is elected
Support A	10	0
Support B	0	10

It may readily be shown that the application of the expectation
principle will lead him to support A, with an expected payoff of
5.5. We will continue to use the expectation principle throughout
the analysis of this decision.

Now what might happen if he were to take one or more surveys
of voter opinion during the three future periods available to him before the election? After any survey, he will want to consider the information thus obtained and decide once more whether to stop or
continue. Let us assume that he contemplates the possible outcomes
of a series of three such surveys. These outcomes are listed below.
The letter A indicates the survey results in the statement, "A will
be elected."

Period 1	Period 2	Period 3
A	A	A
A	A	B
A	B	A
A	B	B
B	A	A
B	A	B
B	B	A
B	B	B

This listing of possible outcomes might be called the sample space by the statistician. The effect of these surveys will clearly be to change his probabilities of the possible futures. Our first step will be to show for each possible result how the probabilities would be changed. Given these probabilities, the expectations for various alternatives of stopping or continuing may be computed, which will finally suggest a method of dealing with the time pressure so as to maximize expectations.

To simplify our symbolism let

S_1 = A is elected
S_2 = B is elected
p_1 = probability of S_1 at present (a priori)
p_2 = probability of S_2 at present (a priori)
$f_k(S_j)$ = probability of S_j given the results of k surveys (the a posteriori probability) $k = 1,2,3$
$p(K|S_j)$ = the conditional probability of the survey results represented by K, given S_j (for example, K may stand for A or AB, or ABA)

Using Bayes' theorem (see Chapter 10) we may write

$$f_k(S_j) = \frac{p(K|S_j)p_j}{\sum_j p(K|S_j)p_j}$$

which gives us the a posteriori probability of S_j, given its a priori probability p_j, and k surveys with the result K. This will tell us then how the political opportunist's probabilities change as the result of his surveys.

Suppose, as before, that the first survey gives the result $K = A$. The a priori probability of S_1 is $p_1 = .55$. Now if we assume that S_1 is true, namely that A will be elected, the probability of the first survey yielding the result A is the probability of the first survey being correct in its prediction. Thus

$$p(A|S_1) = .60$$

Substituting in Bayes' theorem we obtain

$$f_1(S_1) = \frac{(.60)(.55)}{(.60)(.55) + (.40)(.45)} = .65$$

Thus, if the first survey is made and the result is A, the probability of S_1 is increased to .65 and the probability of S_2 is decreased to .35.

Now suppose the first survey has been taken with the result A as before, and the second survey is made also yielding the result A. Given that S_1 is true, the conditional probability that both surveys will yield A is simply the probability that both will be correct. This is the product of their individual probabilities of being correct.

$$p(K = A,A|S_1) = (.60)(.70) = .42$$

Again using Bayes' theorem we have

$$f_2(S_1) = \frac{(.42)(.55)}{(.42)(.55) + (.12)(.45)} = .81$$

Finally, if three surveys are made and all yield the result A, similar calculations yield

$$p(K = A,A,A|S_1) = (.60)(.70)(.90) = .38$$
$$f_3(S_1) = \frac{(.38)(.55)}{(.38)(.55) + (.012)(.45)} = .97$$

Similarly, the probabilities of S_1 may be calculated for all possible results of one, two, and three surveys. These are shown in Table 22–1.

TABLE 22–1

Survey Results	$f_1(S_1)$	$f_2(S_1)$	$f_3(S_1)$
A A A	.65	.81	.97
A A B	.65	.81	.32
A B A	.65	.44	.88
A B B	.65	.44	.08
B A A	.45	.66	.94
B A B	.45	.66	.17
B B A	.45	.26	.76
B B B	.45	.26	.04

The probabilities of S_2 are simply one minus those given in Table 22–1.

After any survey, if the opportunist decides to declare his choice, then it is not hard to see that he maximizes expected payoff by declaring for the candidate whose probability of success is largest at that point. Let $R_k(K)$ stand for the expected return after k surveys the result of which are given by K, if the candidate whose probability of success is greatest is chosen. For example, after one survey, which is taken at a cost of .25, if the result turns out to be A, the best choice at that point would be A. The expected payoff from such a choice is

$$R_1(A) = (.65)(9) - .25 = 5.60$$

Similarly

$$R_1(B) = (.55)(9) - .25 = 4.70$$

The expectations associated with stopping and making the best choice for other numbers of surveys with various results are as follows:

$$
\begin{aligned}
R_2(AA) &= (.81)(8) - .50 = 5.98 \\
R_2(AB) &= (.56)(8) - .50 = 3.98 \\
R_2(BA) &= (.66)(8) - .50 = 4.78 \\
R_2(BB) &= (.74)(8) - .50 = 5.42 \\
R_3(AAA) &= (.97)(7) - .75 = 6.04 \\
R_3(AAB) &= (.68)(7) - .75 = 4.01 \\
R_3(ABA) &= (.88)(7) - .75 = 5.41 \\
R_3(ABB) &= (.92)(7) - .75 = 5.69 \\
R_3(BAA) &= (.94)(7) - .75 = 5.83 \\
R_3(BAB) &= (.83)(7) - .75 = 5.06 \\
R_3(BBA) &= (.76)(7) - .75 = 4.57 \\
R_3(BBB) &= (.96)(7) - .75 = 5.97
\end{aligned}
$$

It will be recalled that the expected payoff if no survey activity is undertaken is 5.50. Thus we now know the expected payoff for a decision made at any point in the information collection process. The problem may now be posed differently. If the political opportunist wishes to maximize expectation, then wherever he is in the data collection possibilities, he must make the following choice:

a_1 = continue with more data collection, making the expectation maximizing choice at each future stage

a_2 = stop and choose the candidate associated with the larger expectation in view of presently available information.

Let us suppose that two surveys have been taken with the results A,A. If the decision maker stops at this point, his best choice is A, and the expected payoff is 5.98. The symbol $E_{AA}(a_2)$ will represent the expectation of a_2 after two surveys which resulted in A,A.

$$E_{AA}(a_2) = R_2(AA) = 5.98$$

If he decides to go on, taking the third survey, it may result in either A or B. The probability that the third survey will yield A is

(Prob. of S_1)(Prob. of correct survey)

$\qquad\qquad$ + (Prob. of S_2)(Prob. of wrong survey)

After two surveys yielding A,A, the probability of S_1 may be obtained from Table 22–1.

$$f_2(S_1) = .81$$

Then the probability that the third survey will result in A is

$$(.81)(.90) + (.19)(.10)$$

By similar reasoning, the probability that the third survey will give B as a result is

$$(.81)(.10) + (.19)(.90)$$

If the third survey is taken, the deadline forces a choice immediately afterward. If the third survey results in A, the best choice will be A with expected payoff

$$R_3(AAA) = 6.04$$

If the third survey results in B, then the best choice will be B, with expectations

$$R_3(AAB) = 4.01$$

Putting these together, the expected return if he decides to continue with the third survey is

$$E_{AA}(a_1) = \{(.81)(.90) + (.19)(.10)\}6.04 + \{(.81)(.10) + (.19)(.90)\}4.01$$
$$= 5.53$$

Thus, having two surveys with the results A,A, the best choice would be to stop immediately and declare support for candidate A. This has an expected return of 5.98, which is clearly better than an expected return of 5.53 if he decides to go on.

The same choice may be evaluated for another possible stage of information collection. These computations are shown in the following paragraphs.

It must be emphasized that these expectations are computed on the premise that the decision maker elects the expectation maximizing choice at each future stage. Thus, given one survey which resulted in A, we reason as follows in exploring the expected return from a second survey and optimal future choices. If the second survey results in A, then the decision maker would be in the position of comparing

$$E_{AA}(a_1) = 5.53$$

and

$$E_{AA}(a_2) = 5.98$$

Making the expectation maximizing choice, he would at that point elect to stop. Again starting from the position of one survey with the result A, if the second survey yields B, the comparison will be made between

$$E_{AB}(a_1) = 5.56$$

and

$$E_{AB}(a_2) = 3.98$$

Thus, after the results A,B, the choice will be to continue, with an expectation of 5.56. In summary, after A,A, stop; after A,B, continue.

Given then the single result A, the expectation from continuing is

$$E_A(a_1) = \{(.65)(.70) + (.35)(.30)\}5.98 + \{(.65)(.30) + (.35)(.70)\}5.56$$
$$= 5.79$$

Given that the result of the first survey is A, the choice would be to continue since

$$E_A(a_1) = 5.79 > E_A(a_2) = 5.60$$

The complete set of such computations is as follows:

$$E_{AA}(a_1) = \{(.81)(.90) + (.19)(.10)\}6.04 + \{(.81)(.10) + (.19)(.90)\}4.01$$
$$= 5.53$$

$E_{AA}(a_2) = 5.98$

$$E_{AB}(a_1) = \{(.44)(.90) + (.56)(.10)\}5.41 + \{(.44)(.10) + (.56)(.90)\}5.69$$
$$= 5.56$$

$E_{AB}(a_2) = 3.98$

$$E_{BA}(a_1) = \{(.66)(.90) + (.34)(.10)\}5.83 + \{(.66)(.10) + (.34)(.90)\}5.06$$
$$= 5.54$$

$E_{BA}(a_2) = 4.78$

$$E_{BB}(a_1) = \{(.26)(.90) + (.74)(.10)\}4.57 + \{(.26)(.10) + (.74)(.90)\}5.97$$
$$= 5.54$$

$E_{BB}(a_2) = 5.42$

$$E_A(a_1) = \{(.65)(.70) + (.35)(.30)\}5.98 + \{(.65)(.30) + (.35)(.70)\}5.56$$
$$= 5.79$$

$E_A(a_2) = 5.60$

$$E_B(a_1) = \{(.45)(.70) + (.55)(.30)\}5.54 + \{(.45)(.30) + (.55)(.70)\}5.54$$
$$= 5.54$$

$E_B(a_2) = 4.70$

$$E(a_1) = \{(.55)(.60) + (.45)(.40)\}5.79 + \{(.55)(.40) + (.45)(.60)\}5.54$$
$$= 5.67$$

$E(a_2) = 5.50$

All of these calculations are brought together in Figure 22–1, which shows the possible evolutions of the information collection process, and indicates at each stage whether the political opportunist

Figure 22–1

The Political Opportunist

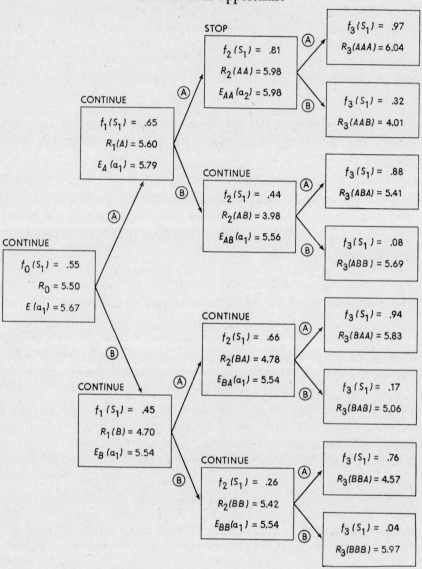

should stop or continue. Several points may be drawn from the example of the political opportunist.

1. The example, though highly simplified, does in fact suggest a rational method of reacting to time pressure so as to maximize the expected return. Thus, the question of how to face time pressures is not unanswerable.

2. The example includes the interesting features of more real-

istic time pressure problems. A deadline is in evidence at a known point in time. In some cases, the deadline itself may be unknown. When two opposing military forces are moving to occupy a strategic position, the deadline for force A's arrival is the time of force B's arrival, which is not definitely known. The example also includes a benefit for early choice which may arise through advance preparation for the deadline. This is the familiar concept "Time is money." It leads also to a more general notion of deadlines. Instead of a definitive point in time at which the payoffs change dramatically, one may think of simply the payoff being a nonincreasing function of time. The example also includes directly the cost of information collection, which is reckoned into the expected payoffs.

3. Out of this example it may be possible to formulate a rough principle for dealing with deadlines. *After each increment of information is obtained the decision is reviewed in the light of the new evidence. The cost of stopping immediately and making the best possible choice is compared with the cost of continuing. The expected cost of continuing is computed under the assumption that at each future stage of information collection, the optimal choice between stopping and continuing is made. On the basis of expected payoff, stop or continue the process.*

To apply this principle quantitatively it is necessary to be able to enumerate the possible outcomes of future data collection efforts, and further, to compute the probabilities of these outcomes. In addition, it must be possible to indicate just how the information will quantitatively change the decision maker's view of his choice. In the example this was done by means of Bayes' theorem. It is essential also to begin with some a priori probabilities.

4. It is probably true that, in most actual situations of decision making under pressure within the firm, the foregoing method requires more information and computation ability than will be available. The principle then may best serve as a rough guide for sharpening judgments about how to deal with deadlines. In this rough form it might suggest the following:

   a) Study information as fast as it becomes available.
   b) If no more information can be obtained, there is little point in waiting and the choice should be made.
   c) At every stage of information development, the best present choice should be compared (by judgment or however) with the expectation from continuing and making the same choice at each future stage.

As in several previous decision problems we have examined, one reaches the conclusion that an exact quantitative response to deadline is seldom possible. The study of exact analysis of the problem does, however, give the decision maker some possibility of sharpening his intuitions and perhaps improve his responses in nonquantitative situations.

PROBLEMS

22–1. Discuss explicitly the pressure aspects of the purchasing policy decision presented in Chapter 16.

22–2. What is the relation between a decision under pressure as formulated in this chapter and a sequential sampling plan?

22–3. What effects of pressure on a decision are not captured by the analysis presented in this chapter?

22–4. Formulate a set of hypotheses which will help you understand decision making under pressure.

22–5. Describe some examples from your own experience which tend to confirm the hypothesis that, as a deadline approaches, aspirations tend to be reduced.

22–6. Solve the problem of the political opportunist under the following conditions: Two periods are available in which to collect data on voter intentions. The payoffs are:

	Now	End of Period 1	End of Period 2	After the Election
Correct choice	100	80	70	0
Wrong choice	0	0	0	0

The cost of each survey is 2 units. The a priori probabilities held by the opportunist are .60 for candidate R and .40 for candidate D. The probabilities of correct inferences from the surveys are

Period	1	2
Probability	.80	.90

22–7. Formulate some rough guides for decision-making behavior in the following situations:

a) A limited time option to purchase a potential plant site.

b) Getting a cigarette on the market which contains no tobacco.

c) Deciding to repair or replace a machine which has failed and is vital to the operation of the plant.

22–8. Formulate some guides to decision-making behavior in the following situations:

a) Which supplier to choose in the face of a fast-approaching deadline for the delivery of a new part for a firm's product.

b) Deciding whether to hold or to sell a stock in a presently declining market.

22–9. Suppose in the example of the political opportunist, the results of the surveys were not taken to be independent. Show symbolically what data would be necessary and how they would enter into the calculations of the a posteriori probabilities.

Chapter 23

SIMULATED DECISION MAKING

INTRODUCTION

THE TRADITIONAL PEACETIME OCCUPATION of professional military men has been the fighting of simulated battles. These exercises in military decision making often take the form of map exercises, or when the budget permits, actual field exercises involving troops, equipment, and field conditions. These simulated decision-making exercises have evolved for the military into the Link trainer and its descendants, air defense simulation systems of great complexity, and a general reliance on simulation to train officers in decision making for all sorts of weapons and combat conditions. A natural offshoot of this was, of course, the simulation of management decision-making situations. The development of simulated decision-making problems related to the business enterprise has been carried on with considerable enthusiasm in recent years, until at present there are a rather large number and variety of such problems in existence.

Anyone who has played the well-known game called "Monopoly" will recognize it as a simulated decision-making device with some relevance to business notions. The basic ideas are simple. An artificial situation is created for the decision maker or player, within which he makes some choices more or less similar to those which might be required in a business situation. These choices then in a variety of more or less realistic ways determine the progress of his business through time. Soon he must make more choices which are influenced by his past decisions, and so on. After it is all over, presumably something is to be learned from this pseudoexperience in being a business manager.

AN EXAMPLE

To clarify all this, let us examine immediately a simple inventory decision "game" or simulation. While this game is so simple that it would hardly simulate any interesting real situation, it does illus-

485

trate the basic ideas. It has, nevertheless, proved of considerable interest to a rather large number of persons who have "played" it.

In speaking of these games we shall refer to the decision makers as "players," and to the operator of the game as the "referee" or "administrator." In this inventory decision game the administrator gives the players a brief description of the situation in which they are asked to place themselves. He goes over the situation to make sure that each player understands it.

THE SITUATION

"As a manager, part of your job is to make a decision about the quantity of an important item to be stocked. The choice of a stock level is made at the beginning of each period, and cannot be changed during the period. As the basis for making this decision you have:

1. A *Usage Report* which shows the number of units of this item used in each of the last twelve periods.
2. A *Cost Analysis* which shows that if you stock more than the demand for a given period, a cost of $1.00 is suffered for each unit overstocked. If you stock less than the demand for a given period, a cost of $2.00 is suffered for each unit understocked."

EXAMPLE

"Suppose you decide on a stock level of 10 units for the first period. If demand turns out to be 7 units, you find yourself overstocked by 3 units. This costs $3.00. If, however, demand turns out to be 14 units, you will be understocked by 4 units. This costs $8.00 (4 units understocked at $2.00 each)."

When the administrator is satisfied that the game is understood, he instructs the players to examine the Usage Report (Figure 23–1) and make a decision as to their inventory for the first period. They are allowed two minutes in which to do this.

No additional information is supplied by the administrator, who must be noncommital on any questions requesting additional data. The point is to simulate some of the lack of information which would be present in a real situation of this sort. The time limitation is provided so as to simulate in a very crude way some of the pressure under which one might actually have to make such a choice.

When the two-minute period is up, the players are instructed to record their decision for the first period on the score sheet (Figure 23–2). The administrator then reports to the players the actual demand for the first period, after which they are given a few seconds

Figure 23–1

Usage Report—Last Twelve Periods

Period	1	2	3	4	5	6	7	8	9	10	11	12
No. of units used	52	64	57	52	50	69	51	63	67	54	56	53

This information is presented graphically below:

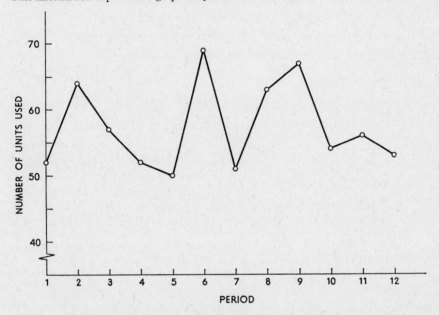

to compute the amount by which they were overstocked or under-stocked, and the cost of their decision. Then a 60-second period is begun, at the end of which they must record their decisions for the second period. The administrator then announces the actual demand for the second period, allows the players time to score themselves, and times them for a decision with respect to the third period. The game goes on in this manner for as long as one wishes. For a game of this simplicity, about ten periods have been found to be an interesting length, allowing the players to try the development of simple policies, but not leading to boredom.

The administrator of such a game has an endless variety of actual demand patterns with which to confront the players. In one series of plays the following actual demand data were used.

Period	1	2	3	4	5	6	7	8	9	10
Actual demand	76	60	65	53	70	58	54	63	67	72

These data, with the exception of the first period, and that shown in the Usage Report, are simply random samples from a uniform dis-

FIGURE 23–2

Score Sheet

RECORD YOUR DECISIONS ON THIS SHEET

Period	Record Your Decision Here	Actual Demand	Amount Over	Amount Under	Cost
1					
2					
3					
4					
5					
6					
7					
8					
9					
10					
11					
12					
13					
14					
15					
16					
17					
18					
19					
20					

Total Cost ———→

tribution over the range from 51 to 70. The first period, having a demand of 76, was put in to try to detect certain changes in the player's policy. Ignoring this, if the player also reached the conclusion
that demand was simply random and independent, the analysis of

Chapter 14 would apply immediately. The expectation maximizing policy would then be to select the proper inventory level and stick to it.

The administrator could present the players with demand patterns reflecting trends, seasonal effects, cycles, and so on. Often, in actuality, demand is not independent, but in fact a given month's demand may be correlated with the demand of the previous month or months. This could, of course, be reflected in the demand presented by the administrator.

From the player's viewpoint there is really no right answer to the problem. To be rational the player must form some hypothesis which is supported by the data and formulate a policy accordingly. In the example given, several kinds of behaviors have been tentatively identified among players, most of whom had not been instructed in the analysis of inventory policy.

1. Some evidently came to the conclusion that the best thing to do was to select a given inventory level and remain with it.

2. Some adopted a "following" policy. If demand went up, their inventory level moved up. If demand went down, so did their choice. This is perfectly reasonable if one forms the hypothesis of nonindependence or correlation between the data for successive months.

3. Others moved with the demand in a more gradual manner, apparently on the basis of trends which they perceived in the data.

4. Still others adopted an "antifollowing" policy. If demand went up, their chosen inventory level went down. If demand went down, they moved their inventory level up.

5. Finally, many made decisions which did not fit into any of these simple patterns, and which could not be classified in any obvious way.

This is perhaps the simplest conceivable example of a management decision-making game; nevertheless, it serves to introduce the idea.

A SURVEY OF SIMULATION POSSIBILITIES

The first major classification of simulated decision-making problems or games separates those in which the player competes against an impersonal environment from those in which the player competes against other players. In the simple inventory game outlined previously, the player is pitted against the market, or a more or less impersonal environment which generated demand for the product in question. These are really not competitive games at all in the sense of game theory discussed in Chapter 19. The possible futures are not within the control of an intelligent adversary who seeks to win out over the decision maker. The production management game which will be presented subsequently is also a noncompetitive game.

More complex and in many ways more interesting games organize the players into teams. Each team becomes the management of a firm, and the firms compete directly with each other. Usually the competition takes place in the market, as opposed to competition for resources or through mergers and monopolies. Direct competitive decisions are involved, such as advertising expenditure, sales territories to be served, price, quality, volume, product development and differentiation, and so on. In these competitive games a decision, for example, by firm *A* to lower its selling price, may have consequences which are highly unpredictable from the viewpoint of firm *A*'s management. As in reality, the effect of such a price reduction may depend on what firms *B, C,* and *D* do with their prices and marketing programs. Thus, something of the uncertainty of competition in the game theory sense is captured by competitive decision simulations.

An example of such a competitive game is one developed by IBM. There are many others, but this will be described because it is typical in many ways. (59)

THE IBM MANAGEMENT DECISION GAME*

PURPOSE

The purpose of this game is to simulate business conditions so that participants can make decisions regarding allocation of funds within a company as well as decisions of strategy involving competitive companies.

MECHANICS

Participants are divided into three groups each of which will constitute the management team of a company. At the outset, each company has good possibilities, but currently is not in a good financial position. The goal of each team is to put the company in a good position and, at the same time, develop a long-range plan of operation.

The necessary company decisions are made and entered into the

---

* Quoted with permission from instructional material prepared by the International Business Machines Corporation.

IBM Electronic Computer by people conducting the game. The computer which holds a mathematical model of the game then correlates the decisions for all three companies and computes all inter- and intracompany reactions. These results are then returned to each company (team) so that the decisions for the next operating period can be made. The operating period is three months.

AREAS OF DECISION

(Each company produces and sells the same product)

SALES AREAS

Each company has a "home" territory in which that company can sell its product without incurring transportation costs. A company can sell in another company's territory but does so at high transportation costs. Each company, therefore, has an advantage at home. In addition, there is a fourth common sales area in which all companies can operate at equal costs. A company can sell different volumes in each sales area.

PRICE

Each company sets its own selling price according to competition, profit goals, and so on. Prices can vary in each of the four sales areas.

MARKETING EXPENDITURES

According to its sales goals, each company can determine how much money it wants to spend in each sales area to attain its goal. (This expenditure is comparable to all sales expenses in normal business, such as, commissions and advertising.)

PRODUCTION COSTS

To meet anticipated sales, each company must produce the proper volume. Overproduction means increased inventory, hence loss of working capital, while underproduction means loss of sales. Each company knows its production cost per unit initially, and hence can project production costs according to sales forecasts. Thereafter, this cost per unit varies according to the number of units produced. Higher production means lower unit cost.

PLANT INVESTMENT

There is a production capacity for each company according to its current plant facilities. To increase production beyond capacity, a company must increase facilities by allocating money to plant investment. As sales volume increases, this investment is usually necessary. Of course, as facilities increase, if production should decrease, then the cost for each unit produced would increase.

RESEARCH AND DEVELOPMENT

This allocation can benefit two areas. Primarily, production costs are lowered because this money improves production methods. Secondarily, a greater number of sales can be realized because this money could conceivably cause the product to be more appealing to the market (for example, eye-catching packaging or design of the product).

GENERAL

In general, the model as built into the computer takes the foregoing information from each company and computes all competitive effects, determines the number of sales for each company in each area, and then develops for each company an abbreviated operating statement showing the financial results for this period.

Results can be affected by how much each company expends in marketing as compared to the total expended by all companies, as in most businesses prices—relative to competitive prices—are important. All in all the model is simple, but does present most of the finances, decisions, and strategy encountered in a business today.

*   *   *   *   *

The second major classification for decision-making games divides those games which require a computing machine from those which can be operated with hand computation alone. The IBM and most games of similar complexity cannot be satisfactorily played without a computer into which the decisions may be fed. The computer has the response functions stored within it and very quickly produces the detailed results of a complex set of interacting decisions. The need for a computer limits the use of such games since computer time is expensive.

On the other hand, the inventory control game and the production control game to follow, do not require automatic computation equipment. They can, in fact, be played by groups of any size whatsoever, since each player does his own computation and scoring. Noncomputer games are obviously restricted to fewer decisions and less complicated response functions, but there is every possibility that they will prove both interesting and useful.

POSSIBLE USES

At the present state of the art of management decision gaming, there seems to be little evidence available which can strongly confirm the usefulness of such devices. Those who have used them, however, are generally enthusiastic about their possibilities. Some of these possibilities are indicated in following paragraphs, with the strong proviso that their validity appears yet to be demonstrated.

1. *Teaching.* Such games should have definite uses as teaching devices. They seem suitable for several purposes. For example, one excellent way to motivate and reinforce the analysis of particular decisions is to design a game which the student might play both before and after studying analytical approaches to the decision. They also are used to give the student some appreciation for the uncertainty, pressure, and lack of definition which is characteristic of actual decisions.

2. *Training.* Perhaps the most widely explored use of games has been to gain some experience in decision making. The notion is that the experience of playing the game will provide transferable learning which will in some way improve on-the-job decision-making ability. The validity of this concept has yet to be established. It has dangers as well. No simulation is likely to approach anything like the extreme complexity of a real situation. One must, therefore, be very careful that the player is not given to understand that the policies which worked well in the game will naturally prove as successful in the actual operations of the firm. A more conservative kind of training is probably the legitimate outcome. That is, the need of the executive to get the information relevant to a decision and the need to organize toward some specialization of function in decision making have been reinforced by game experiences. Games appear also to have been used successfully to communicate the point of view of the executive to the specialist, or the viewpoint of one specialist to another. Thus, research people have, through games, obtained some insight into the president's problems and perhaps some appreciation of why research is not given an unlimited budget. Marketing men have been shown something of the production man's view of the firm, and so on, with sales, finance, purchasing, and accounting.

3. *Testing a Policy.* Another possibility is the use of simulation to test the effectiveness of some particular policy. For example, we might think up several policies for inventory control, and then conduct a controlled experiment using the inventory management game

to get some idea of which of these policies is best. It is particularly true in more complex decision problems, where the analytical approach to the derivation of an optimal policy becomes difficult or impossible, that the simulated test of several trial policies may point the way to good ones. In the production management games the reader may find it instructive to analyze the problem in an attempt to derive an optimal policy. Failing this, it is interesting to think up several possibilities for production management decision rules and perhaps test them by means of simulation.

4. *Psychological Experimentation.* Finally, for the psychologist who is interested in ways in which people make decisions, the simulation technique provides a possible laboratory experiment. It has even been suggested that someday a simulation problem will be developed and validated for use in the selection of executives for promotion to greater decision-making responsibilities. So far as is known, nothing of the kind has been developed at the present time.

Perhaps the greatest advantage of simulated decision making for any of these purposes is the motivating force which they seem to have. Even the two simple, noncompetitive games included in this chapter have been found to be capable of getting and holding the interest of both students and business executives alike. Some players get deeply involved in the games and play with intense concentration. The more complicated competitive games, such as the IBM game, are even more effective in motivating the participants. Indeed, it may well be that the acceptance of these games has been so satisfactory that more may be claimed for them than can really be expected.

Games also give the player a kind of pseudoexperience with decision-making problems which is richer and stronger than the experience of making sample problems or talking about the decision. They provide a degree of involvement which cannot be easily achieved in other ways. They may develop eventually to the point of providing the clinical training for students of engineering and management, which corresponds to the hospital experiences of the medical student.

Finally, games allow us to work with far more complicated decisions than could be encompassed within the bounds of our present mathematical abilities. Most games which have been developed, even seemingly simple ones, defy mathematical solution. That is, they are too complex to permit the analysis and derivation of probably optimum policies. Thus, we are able to go further down the road toward the complexity of realism in simulation.

A PRODUCTION MANAGEMENT GAME

This game represents a level of complexity slightly above that of the inventory game, but is still simple enough for rapid individual scoring. The player is required to make a decision about the volume of production for the coming day in his plant. An outline of the instructions presented to the players is as follows:

PRODUCTION MANAGEMENT GAME

The following information is available:

1. Sales records—see attached report.
2. Quality report—"About one unit in every ten is scrapped at final inspection."
3. Production times—Department A ....1 day.
   Department B ....1 day.
   Final inspection ......1 day.
4. Production capacity, Department A = 6 units per day.
5. No inventory may be accumulated between departments.
6. Estimated costs—Holding costs at finished
   goods inventory ($/unit/day) ....$10.
   Shortage costs ($/unit/day) ....$30.
   For each unit change in the
   production level of Dept. A ....$20.
7. The initial status of the plant will be given.

Information is available on past sales as shown in the "Sales Report" (Figure 23–3). The player must contend not only with fluctuations in sales, but with the possibility that some of the production may be scrapped. The costs incurred include a holding cost for finished goods inventory, a cost for changing the production level in the plant, and a shortage cost if finished goods inventory is not sufficient to cover sales.

The product moves from Department A to Department B, and thence to final inspection (Figure 23–4). It must spend one day in each of these departments, after which it is placed in finished goods inventory. No storage is permitted in the plant itself. The player takes over the production management task at the end of Day 11, and the status of the plant at that time is given to him. His first decision is the production order for Day 12. The record sheet shown in Figure 23–5 makes a convenient device for playing the game.

FIGURE 23-3
Sales Report

Day	1	2	3	4	5	6	7	8	9	10
Units sold	3	6	3	3	5	4	4	2	4	4

This information is presented graphically below:

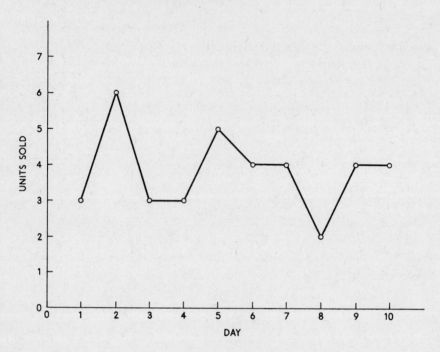

FIGURE 23-4

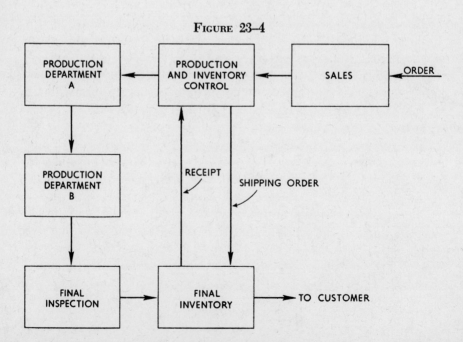

FIGURE 23–5

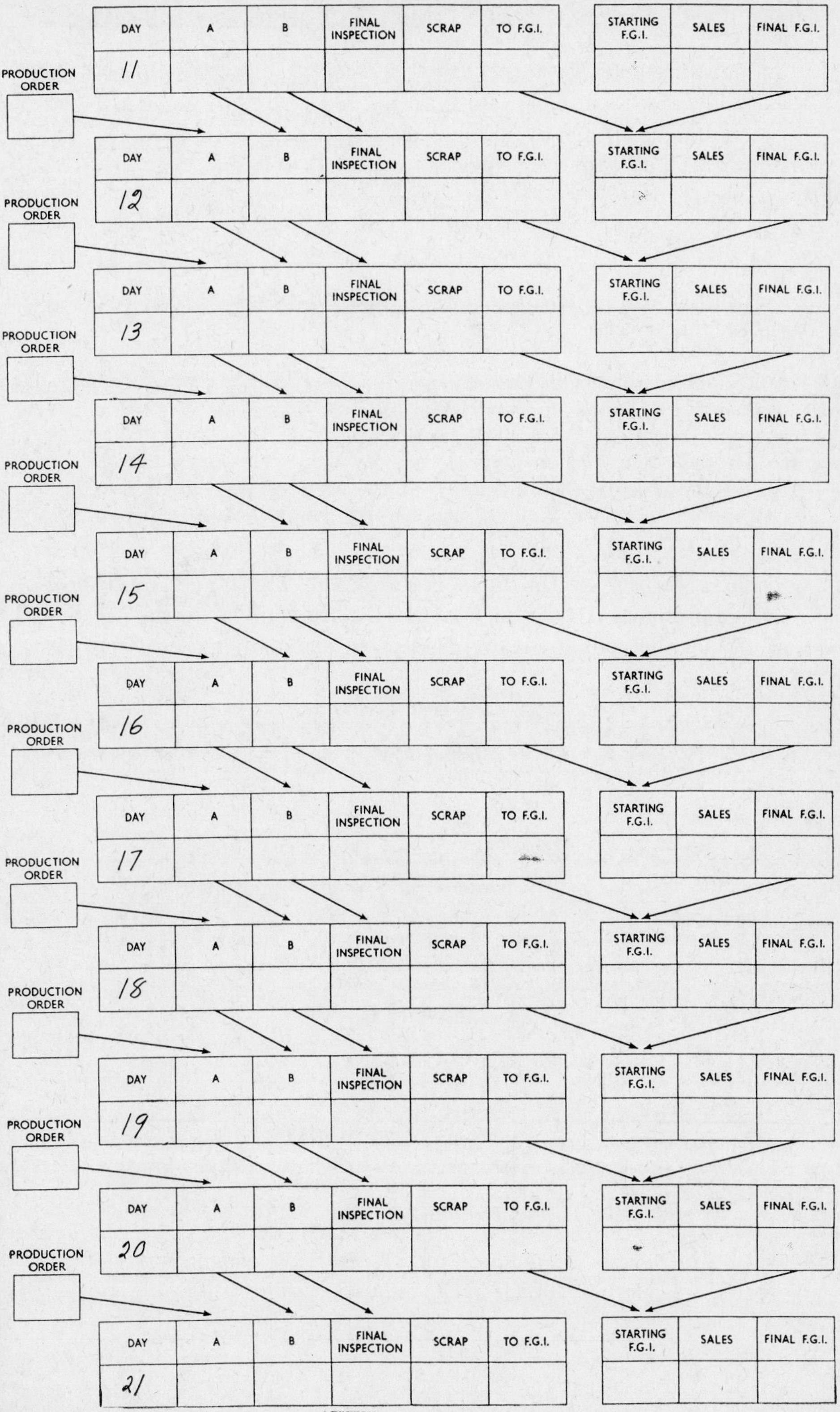

The administrator must have two series of numbers, the sales for each day and the number of units scrapped at final inspection. These can be made up in any number of ways, using a table of random numbers. The following suggests one such series:

Day	12	13	14	15	16	17	18	19	20	21
Sales	2	7	5	3	3	4	3	4	1	6
Scrap	0	1	0	0	0	2	0	0	0	0

To illustrate play, suppose that the initial status of the plant at the end of Day 11 is as follows:

2 units completed in Department A
3 units completed in Department B
1 unit completed at final inspection
No units scrapped on Day 11
Initial finished goods inventory at the start of Day 11 of 6 units
Sales on Day 11 of 3 units, thus leaving a final finished goods inventory of $6 - 3 = 3$ units

These figures are shown in Figure 23–6. The player must now write a production order for Day 12. His order will be for the number of units which will go into production in Department A on Day 12.

FIGURE 23–6

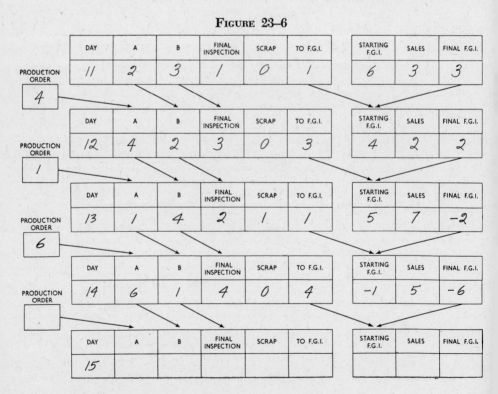

It must not exceed 6 units. Before making this decision he may make the following extensions to Day 12:

1. The 2 units in Department A on Day 11 will go into Department B on Day 12.
2. The 3 units in Department B on Day 11 will go into final inspection on Day 12.
3. The 1 unit in final inspection on Day 11, less units scrapped on Day 11 (in this case none), goes into starting finished goods inventory for Day 12.
4. The starting finished goods inventory for Day 12 is made up of the 1 unit obtained in step 3 plus the 3 units of final finished goods inventory remaining at the end of Day 11.

The player then writes his production order for Day 12, which in this example we have supposed to be 4 units. The administrator asks him to imagine himself at the end of Day 12 and reports sales of 2 units and no scrap for that day. Several such days are shown in Figure 23–6. Negative finished goods inventories are carried as such to denote shortages which must be satisfied out of future production.

The scoring instructions are shown in Figure 23–7.

FIGURE 23–7

Production Management Game Scoring Instructions

Enter here the total of all positive final finished goods inventories.	
Multiply the result by 10 and record.	
Enter here the sum of all negative final finished goods inventories.	
Multiply the result by 30 and record; neglect the minus sign.	
Enter here the sum of all the changes in production level for Department A. Changes up and down should both be taken as positive numbers.	
Multiply the result by 20 and record.	
Enter here the total of the numbers in the right-hand boxes. This is your score.	

SUGGESTIONS FOR FURTHER STUDY

CLARK, CHARLES E., *et al.* "On the Construction of a Multi-Stage, Multi-Person Business Game," *Operations Research*, Vol. 5, No. 4 (August, 1957).

COHEN, KALMAN J., and RHENMAN, ERIC. "The Role of Management Games in Education and Research," *Management Science*, Vol. 7, No. 2 (January, 1961).

GREENE, JAY R., and SISSON, ROGER L. *Dynamic Management Decision Games.* New York: John Wiley & Sons, Inc., 1959.

GREENLAW, PAUL S.; HERRON, LOWELL W.; and RAWDON, RICHARD H. *Business Simulation in Industrial and University Education.* Englewood Cliffs, N.J.: Prentice-Hall, Inc., 1962.

RICCIARDI, F. M., *et al.* *Top Management Decision Simulation.* New York: American Management Association, 1957.

Chapter 24

HOW DECISIONS ARE MADE

INTRODUCTION

THIS IS A CHAPTER of hypotheses. In terms of objective, verifiable evidence, very little is really known about how decisions are actually made either in firms or in other contexts. There are, however, a great many hypotheses about decision-making behavior, with various amounts of evidence to support them. The aim of this chapter is to present a sampling of such hypotheses about decision making. The purpose is not to support any claim of the general validity of these ideas, but rather to offer them as things to watch for in decision-making situations. They can best be used as cues or guides to intelligent observation of the decision-making process within the firm. Such observation will hopefully lead to a measure of understanding of the process, which may be an important basis to effective action, both for the staff analyst and for the line decision maker himself.

The evidence which reveals how decisions are made appears in a variety of forms. The literature in the field of management contains a continuing stream of articles which report how a particular decision was made within a particular firm. These reports usually emphasize the use of an approach or a technique, and have relatively little to say about the personalities and peculiarities of the firm or about the actual process of reaching a decision. Few people are interested in exhibiting publicly the blind alleys, the mistakes, and the seemingly irrational steps in a decision process in which they were involved. Still other kinds of evidence come from psychologists who are interested in decision making as a fundamental category of human behavior; from sociologists who are interested in group decision making as carried on by families, work groups, and so on; from political scientists who are interested in the decision-making methods of society as a whole; and from economists whose special interest is the decisions made by consumers and businessmen in economic contexts. This list could be extended indefinitely, but our particular interest will be in a sample of those hypotheses which seem to have something to say about the firm and the decision makers in it.

Out of these hypotheses one could build theories of decision making. It is important to distinguish two kinds of such theories. This book is filled with statements of the form, "If the firm has certain objectives, then in this or that decisions it ought to choose such and such an alternative." We have been talking about what the firm *ought* to do in order to achieve its objectives. Theories about how people or firms ought to make decisions are called "normative theories." Later in this chapter some hypotheses will be presented about how businessmen actually do behave in making decisions. It is obvious in everyone's experience that businessmen do not always make decisions the way they ought to in order to achieve their objectives. Theories about how people or firms actually do make decisions are called "descriptive theories." Normative theories recommend and offer guides to decision making; descriptive theories attempt to predict how a decision maker will actually choose. This chapter suggests some hypotheses which may become a part of a descriptive theory of decision making.

In the previous chapters we have already introduced a number of hypotheses about how firms make decisions which we will risk repeating here in a somewhat more organized context. We will not bother to identify all of the following statements as hypotheses, although the reader must interpret them as such.

RATIONALITY

In looking at decisions one sooner or later comes to ask, "Is it rational?" by which is usually meant, "Does the decision process measure up to some set of requirements which define rationality?" At the outset we have established some requirements for rationality which included explicitness of the decision process, logical consistency, and agreement with the "facts." It will, of course, hardly be a surprise to suggest that most decision-making activity does not in fact measure up to these requirements. Another set of requirements for rationality are those of the model of "economic man" who has complete information as to the alternatives available, has complete information on the outcomes (certainty), and always chooses so as to maximize something. Very little decision making actually measures up to these standards either. We wish to indicate a few of the hypotheses which have to do with the limits of rationality which are achieved by typical decision makers.

The alternatives in a decision are not given exhaustively. The decision maker must search for them and either deliberately or by mistake will miss some. It has been the main line of thought in the previous chapters that a principal difficulty in achieving rationality is the lack of complete information available to the decision maker. We take this to be a most general hypothesis about the firm's activity in choosing. We have spoken also about the problem of making explicit the goals and values of the firm, which constitutes a second major hypothesis about the bounds of rationality.

Actual decisions are probably most often made within the context of a limited and highly approximate abstraction of the actual situation. One person's perception of the situation will differ from another's; thus, we have a basic difficulty in passing judgment on the rationality of other people's decisions. The elements in a particular decision maker's abstraction of a situation probably are chosen and arise in a complicated way which is a function of his entire psychological makeup and the sociological environment which is the firm in which he operates. These notions lead directly to the Simon-March hypothesis introduced in Chapter 4.

Most human decision making is concerned with the discovery and selection of satisfactory alternatives; only in exceptional cases is it concerned with the discovery and selection of optimal alternatives. If the decision maker can define the requirements for acceptability, or as we have previously spoken of it, if he can fix an aspiration level, then any alternative which meets his aspirations is called acceptable. In order to find an optimal alternative one must find a method of value measurement by which all alternatives can be compared, and then discover an alternative which can be shown to be preferred to *any other*. This hypothesis, simple as it is, may perhaps be a major key to the understanding of a great variety of business decisions.

Several interesting sets of hypotheses supplement this basic notion of acceptable as opposed to optimal choices. The limitations of the human being may provide a partial explanation. The human mind is limited in the number of alternatives or the amount of information upon which it can focus at any one time. The abilities of the human to handle information, to store it in the memory, to recall it when required all play a part. The computational and reasoning ability of the human also tend to limit the achievement of elaborate forms of rationality. These limitations are probably intensified by the time pressure under which many of the firm's decisions must be made. For example, the greater the pressure of time, the fewer the number of alternatives which will be explicitly considered by the decision maker. The greater the time pressure, the smaller the amount of information which will be obtained in the effort to reduce uncertainty and risk.

ORGANIZATION FOR DECISION MAKING

One way to overcome the limitations of the individual is to organize the firm for decision making in such a way that many individuals participate in the decision process. Part of this organization is designed to bring to bear the specialized talents or reservoirs of information and experience which are represented by the individuals who form the management of the firm. While this does in part help overcome the limitations of the individual, it brings with it problems of its own. Because of the limitations of those with whom the decision may ultimately rest, the mass of information which is relevant must be coded or summarized. Thus, a probability distribution may be summarized by one or two of its parameters. This process, called uncertainty absorption, clearly economizes the use of information handling capacity, but on the other hand tends to filter out considerable information. The basic principle of management by exception is another instance of the same effect.

A great deal might be said about organizational decision making, or the division of labor in the decision process. We will mention only one basic hypothesis. Clearly the values held by the members of an organization will in general differ. These values must somehow be reconciled if the firm is to make decisions. This process of reconciliation manifests itself in various leadership forms ranging from authoritarian or dictatorial, to completely permissive or democratic. The reconciliation also generates conflict within the organization, power struggles, and perhaps even breakdowns of the decision process. This extremely complex field of organizational decision making has been summarized by March and Simon. (91)

SEARCH

At the heart of the limitations on rationality is the process of search itself. For example one might offer the following set of hypotheses (91):

a) As the satisfaction of the decision maker with presently available alternatives decreases, the search for new alternatives will increase.

b) As the search for new alternatives increases, the expected payoff will also increase.

c) As the expected payoff increases, the decision maker's satisfaction with the alternatives under consideration will increase also.

d) As the expected payoff of the alternatives in hand increases, the aspiration level of the decision maker also increases.

e) As the aspiration level increases, the satisfaction of the decision maker with the alternatives available decreases.

Such a set of hypotheses agree with an interesting hypothesis about persistence in decision making. It is suggested that decision makers will give special preference to alternatives which represent a continuation of activities already under way in the firm. There is a tendency to favor the equipment, operating policies, and programs which are in use by the firm, as opposed to choosing alternatives which represent change. This may come about partially through the psychological phenomenon of resistance to change, and partially through a crudely rational calculation of the costs of change. However, it may well be explained by suggesting that the firm simply does not engage in active search for alternatives when those available are satisfactory. The amount of search decreases with satisfaction, and clearly, if little search is going on, there is a strong tendency to persist in the utilization of existing alternatives.

These hypotheses give a clue also to the interaction of search, success, and aspiration levels. They indicate something of how the aspiration levels of a firm might change with experience. If it is easy to discover good alternatives, aspirations will rise; if it is difficult, they will be reduced.

Search is also related to the difficulty which the decision maker encounters in making the choice among the alternatives which are perceived as being available. The following set of hypotheses suggests some possibilities:

If, among the alternatives perceived by the decision maker, one is clearly preferred, and if this preferred alternative is acceptable, then there will be little difficulty in making the decision.

If their decision maker finds that all of his perceived alternatives either: (*a*) cannot be compared so as to identify a preferred alternative, or (*b*) lack predictions of the associated outcomes (uncertainty), or (*c*) are not acceptable, then difficulty will be experienced in making the choice.

The decision maker will move to overcome this difficulty. In the case of uncertainty, it is hypothesized that the first move will be an attempt to obtain more information about the outcomes. If this is not successful, then a search will be undertaken for new alternatives. The rate at which this search effort is carried on will increase as the time pressure felt by the decision maker increases. If this search fails to turn up an acceptable alternative, then eventually the level of aspiration will be reduced.

If the perceived alternatives contain several which are acceptable but cannot be compared, then the choice will depend on the focus of the decision maker's attention and be sensitive to the order in which the alternatives are examined.

POLICY

Policy is simply the premeditation of decision. Most large firms make decisions by means of an extensive policy structure. Policy flourishes best in connection with those decisions which it can anticipate. Those which can be anticipated include, as an important part, decisions which must be made repeatedly by the firm. Policy may tend to be more rational and carefully considered than will nonrepetitive decisions. Time pressure is not conducive to the formulation of policy. Such pressure may also arise out of the day-to-day activities of decision making, which may occupy the attention of the firm to the exclusion of policy formulation.

Policy formulation serves to routinize decision making and thus relieve individuals for nonroutine problems. If policy can be formulated with sufficient objectivity and explicitness, then the decisions may be carried on by a computing machine, relieving the humans entirely.

Policy also provides top management with a measure of control over the organization. Given a policy, they may be fairly certain how subordinate decision makers will choose, and this may be used as a basis for further policy formulation. The subordinate decision makers find it easy to justify any decision which agrees with policy, but extremely difficult to justify one which does not. This means that, at the lower levels, decision making consists largely of associating problems with the most relevant policy, and making the choice accordingly.

We might continue to suggest a great number of hypotheses about individual and organizational decision making, but perhaps this sample will be sufficiently suggestive. The possibilities for explaining decision-making behavior vary from the model of economic man who is highly rational, to a model called "heroic man." Heroic man chooses action alternatives without any calculation whatever of the consequences of his actions. Admittedly, there are instances within everyone's experience of decisions which seem to be well described by one of these extreme models. However, the majority of behavior falls perhaps in the middle ground of limited rationality. In order to illustrate this in connection with some decisions of interest, and in the general vein of those discussed previously, the major results of two studies will be summarized. The first of these, by Cyert, Dill, and March, examines in detail four decisions which were made in the context of industrial firms. The second, that of Meyer and Kuh, studies statistically the investment decisions made by a very large number of firms. Both studies indicate the limits of rationality involved, as well as a number of interesting additional hypotheses.

FOUR DECISIONS OBSERVED

Cyert, Dill, and March (29) observed in detail four decisions made by industrial firms. These concerned:

1. The replacement of control devices on overhead cranes with new controllers which were thought to be safer and easier to operate and maintain.
2. The selection of new quarters for a department which had a questionable future with the firm.
3. The selection of a consulting firm to study the possibilities of using electronic data-processing in a company.
4. The selection of automatic data-processing equipment.

It is not possible to reproduce the rich and fascinating details of the decision processes which were observed in each case. The major conclusions which might be offered in the form of hypotheses are suggested in the following paragraphs.

1. In each case the investment or expenditure involved was made or not made with only a very crude comparison of alternatives. Expenditures and investments were always considered within the constraints of the firm's budget. In some cases comparison among alternatives involved only such considerations as prior commitment rather than relative desirability.

2. Sometimes comparison was not made between alternatives at all. Instead, rules of thumb, such as acceptable costs, acceptable net return, or payoff period were applied to the alternatives.

3. The evidence indicated that any alternative which satisfied such rules of thumb and received the support of those persons who were influential in management was likely to be accepted. This support may come as a result of a complicated mixture of individual, departmental, and firm values.

4. The search for alternatives seemed to involve the immediate attempt to discover a few alternatives which would be examined in some detail. A rather strong commitment to action was often made before the information necessary for this examination was available to any great extent. As the time for implementation approached, search activity intensified.

5. The search for information consisted largely of discovering the considerations which various departments or subunits of the firm felt were relevant for the decision. If the organization has considerable funds available, each subunit is somewhat unconcerned about their use. Thus, this kind of search will be relatively routine. If, however, a shortage of funds exists, the subunits will be much concerned about their disposition and this type of search will be more active.

6. In making the decisions only a few simple criteria were used to evaluate the alternatives. Basically, attention seemed to focus on the feasibility of alternatives where "feasibility" meant two things:

a) Is the money available for the alternative?
b) Is it clearly better than the existing action?

The extreme difficulty of value measurement in terms of a single criterion seemed to promote this kind of simplicity as the only possible approach.

7. To the extent that the expected benefits associated with the alternatives were formulated and considered, these expectations were influenced by the hopes, desires, and internal bargaining attempts of the subunits of the firm.

It is perhaps possible to say that the conclusions obtained from the study of these four decisions agree in a rough way with a great part of the folklore of business decision making. The brand of rationality exhibited is clearly limited in many of the ways suggested by the hypotheses previously listed.

EQUIPMENT INVESTMENT DECISIONS

We have maintained a central interest in decisions involving investments in new or replacement equipment. In this section some hypotheses will be advanced with respect to how these decisions are actually made by firms.

Of primary interest is the stimulus which brings to the firm the realization that an equipment investment decision must be faced. In the simplest case, the irreparable failure of presently used equipment may be such a stimulus. It is probably true that many replacement decisions arise simply as the result of such failures. Again the firm may find itself with inadequate capacity to meet the demand for its product, thus confronting a decision about investment in new equipment. The alternatives in this decision may of course include such things as overtime work, subcontracting, allowing a backlog of orders to accumulate, and so on. It is perhaps true that firms are confronted with equipment investment decisions because of a tendency to imitate competitors or leaders in the industry. If a competitor replaces his equipment with the most modern available, this may act as a powerful stimulus to the firm to take a look at its own equipment. Finally, the decision may arise within the context of a policy of periodic review of equipment. Thus there may be an annual survey to identify those pieces of equipment which are candidates for replacement.

Given that an equipment replacement decision has been recognized, how is the choice made? It is tenable to hypothesize the use of rules of thumb such as payoff period, rate of return, and so on. These appeared in the study noted previously and are perhaps in rather general use. At a somewhat more rational level of decision making, it is well known that many firms use replacement decision techniques similar to those suggested in the previous chapters. The Machinery and Allied Products Institute has developed and widely advocated a special form of these methods. This technique has a considerable following among progressive firms. (127)

It appears that many firms make these decisions on the basis of considerations other than those we have suggested and achieve a somewhat more limited level of rationality than is represented by the approaches given earlier. An extensive recent study of this class of decision-making behavior has been done by Meyer and Kuh. (94) This study involved the collection of a variety of financial data from which could be inferred something of the decision-making methods of a sample of business firms. The sample consisted of 750 manufacturing firms in twelve manufacturing industries. The firms selected all had securities registered with the Securities and

Exchange Commission. A five-year period from 1946 through 1950 was covered in the study.

THE MEYER-KUH STUDY

The Meyer-Kuh study begins with a survey of contemporary theories which propose to explain the investment decisions made by the firm. These explanations can be grouped in three classes: those based upon marginal analysis, those based upon the accelerator principle, and those based upon actual empirical studies.

Theories about investment decision based upon marginal analysis are simply those discussed in the previous chapters of this book. The suggestions we have made for the analysis of investment decisions are simply normative interpretations of possible descriptive theories of such decision-making behavior. Marginal analysis is simply another term for profit maximization or utility maximization. Under conditions of risk the maximization of expected profit or expected utility would be hypothesized. In investment decisions under uncertainty, the minimax principle might be suggested. In other words, one theory which might be used to explain and predict the investment decisions of the firm would simply be, "It is predicted that the firm will make investment decisions as prescribed in this book." That is simply to take our normative theory and turn it into descriptive theory.

As we have seen, this "marginalist" or profit maximization analysis in connection with investment, is usually taken to include a reckoning of the interest charges on the investment. In the simplest interpretation, the firm which does in fact borrow money to make investments, does so at the going interest rate or market rate. It might be hypothesized, then, that as the market interest rate went down, firms would find more and more profitable investments and thus the volume of investment for an industry or for the economy would increase. This is not to insist that the interest rate is the central variable in investment decisions, but the marginal theory insists that it is of some importance. The interesting fact is that a considerable number of empirical studies summarized by Meyer and Kuh show that market interest rate is not important in this connection. The railroad and electric utility industries are possible exceptions to this conclusion. Thus, some evidence has accumulated to show that the marginalist position may not be a completely satisfactory explanation of investment decisions.

The acceleration principle holds that the rate at which a firm invests in new, as opposed to replacement equipment, is a linear function of the rate of change of output. Suppose a firm has a capacity of 100,000 units of output each year, and is operating at that capacity. Assuming that the only way to increase output is to add more capacity, then, as demand increases, capacity must be increased in direct proportion. An illustrative history is shown below:

Year	Demand	Required Capacity	Investment in New Capacity
1	100,000	100,000	0
2	100,000	100,000	0
3	110,000	110,000	10,000
4	110,000	110,000	0
5	120,000	120,000	10,000
6	140,000	140,000	20,000

The acceleration principle assumes that capacity is well defined and that, when it is reached, such alternatives as overtime, subcontracting, and back-ordering are not available. It purports to explain only new investment or net investment. One must still look for an explanation of the firm's investment for replacement purposes. The principle also assumes that the firm is able to obtain the funds to finance the indicated expansion. Just what happens when a decline in sales sets in is not too important, unless one assumes that the firm sells off some of its equipment. This would be a kind of negative investment or disinvestment.

A number of empirical studies of firm investment seem to indicate a general preference for financing from the inside with the firm's own funds, rather than through debts incurred outside the firm. Associated with this is the obvious result that the volume of investment is directly constrained by the funds available within the firm, or its internal liquidity. Obtaining funds outside the firm is beset with the usual difficulties of interest charges and fixed obligations in the case of bonds, and high financing costs and dilution of control and earnings in the case of common stocks. In addition, management tends to be cautious about debt financing since they themselves find it somewhat less attractive than internal financing. If, for example, an investment made with borrowed funds fails, management may find itself forced into bankruptcy and voted out by the stockholders. If it succeeds, they gain relatively little because they are likely to own only limited amounts of stock themselves. On the other hand, if they finance a project internally through retained earnings, the resultant reduction in dividend payments is of slight consequence to the managers personally.

Another consideration in investment decisions which is supported by empirical studies, is that of the firm's position in its industry. It appears that many firms are concerned with maintaining their competitive position in an industry and will undertake investments in order to maintain this position.

With these theories as a background, Meyer and Kuh proceed to empirical tests of many of the notions which they include. Their results are summarized in the following paragraphs.

1. One especially simple explanation of investment decisions suggests that the older the equipment owned by a firm, the greater will be the volume of investment required for replacement purposes. This would also suggest that, if abnormally heavy investments are made in a given year, then some years later abnormally heavy investments must again be made for replacement. This explanation has a reasonable and obvious basis in our analysis of replacement policy. It has been given the name "echo effect." One way to estimate the age of the equipment used by a firm is to look at the size of its depreciation reserve. A firm which has predominantly old equipment will have built up a large depreciation reserve. This provided the basic measurements for a test of the echo effect.

Studying the correlation between investment and depreciation reserve, it was shown that very little reaction could be demonstrated between the two. Thus, the echo effect is not a useful explanation of the investment decisions made by the firms in the sample. This remarkable result suggests that the investment for replacement made by a firm may not be importantly related to the age of its equipment. Possible exceptions to this were the machine tool and basic textile industries.

This surprising finding is, however, consistent with another view of investment decisions called the "senility effect." This name is given to the notion that firms which have predominantly old equipment as a result of low levels of investment in the past will continue to have old equipment in the future. Firms whose equipment is becoming outmoded through lack of replacement are unlikely to reverse this trend. On the other hand, firms which have maintained modern equipment through relatively high rates of investment are likely to continue to do so. This is not unreasonable if one grants that the firms with older equipment are likely to be less profitable. Lower profits mean less money available within the firm for investment purposes. The firm is thus forced into a decline in the rate of equipment replacement which can only be stopped by drastic methods.

2. A variable which is often supposed to have a significant influence on investment decisions is the rate at which assets are depreciated. It is suggested, for example, that when the government allows firms to depreciate their equipment at an accelerated rate for tax purposes, the effect is to increase investment.

Since depreciation expense accounts for an important part of the cash flowing into the firm, it is argued that accelerated depreciation will improve the liquid assets position of the firm. Under the usual assumption that firms prefer to finance investments internally, this clearly makes additional funds available for investment. Accelerated depreciation also makes investments more attractive since it reduces the time during which funds are tied up in a given asset. Quicker investment recovery reduces the risk of not recovering investment. Clearly, also, accelerated depreciation will reduce the interest charges or the time capital is tied up, thus effectively increasing the profit on any investment.

After attempting to remove the effect of differing useful lives for equipment, the study yields the following major conclusions:

a) Under conditions of stable or deflationary economic climates, increased depreciation rates do in fact significantly increase investments.

b) The mechanism for this increase is primarily through the increased internal liquidity of the firm.

c) During inflationary periods, the firm is likely to have adequate internal funds in any case, thus accelerated depreciation is of slight importance in increasing investment.

This evidence continues to reinforce the hypothesis that firms regard internal liquidity as a dominant factor in investment decisions.

3. The next portion of the study investigated the effects of several variables.

a) The flow of liquidity into the firm as measured by profits and depreciation expense.

b) The liquidity position of the firm.

c) The effect of capacity limitations as suggested by the acceleration principle.

d) The position of the firm in its industry.

These variables were studied during various phases of the business cycle and their interactions were also investigated. The major conclusions appear to be:

a) During stable or deflationary movements of the economy, the flow of liquidity is of significant importance. These variables are directly related to the volume of investment. The data supported the argument that during such times money becomes scarce for the firm due to decreased profits, and is thus a major determinant of its investing ability. The liquidity position of the firm, as opposed to the liquidity flow, is of little significance.

b) The capacity limitations suggested by the acceleration principle provide a reasonably good explanation of investment behavior during inflationary periods. At these times the firm has sufficient internal funds to expand and meet increases in the demand for its output. This represents also the attempt by the firm to maintain its share of the market through investment in additional facilities. More precisely, the data support the following statement of the acceleration principle: "Investment will increase when sales undergo a nontemporary increase, if existing capacity is already fully utilized and if sufficient funds are available to finance the acquisition of new capital goods." (94) The premise that funds be available is a major consideration in the relevance of this principle as an explanation of investment decision making.

c) In the long run, the investment decisions of a firm depend more on the capacity considerations of the acceleration principle than on liquidity considerations.

4. While the inference from all of this is strongly that firms prefer to finance their investments from internally obtained funds, in the sample were many instances of the use of external funds. During the period from 1946 to 1950, those firms in the sample which did resort to investment financed externally showed a strong preference for debt financing as opposed to equity. The reasons for resorting to the use of externally obtained funds are many. Of these, two were investigated. It was shown that there was evidence to support the conclusion that growth of the firm had at least some influence. A firm which is growing rapidly may find it necessary to obtain external funds in order to finance this growth.

Competitive pressures, that is, pressures which must be overcome if the firm is to maintain its market position, seem to have only slight relation to the use of outside funds for investment. It was also shown that, in an expanding industry, a firm which maintained a liberal dividend policy was likely to be more successful in obtaining the outside funds which it might need for expansion. Such a policy appeared to enhance the firm's position in the money market, thus giving it access to funds for rapid expansion.

5. A study of investment decisions in small and large firms produced a number of interesting results. Here, "small" is used to refer to firms which have $4.9 million or less in gross fixed assets.

a) Small firms are able to grow just as rapidly using internal funds as are large firms.

b) Although the evidence is not especially clear, it appeared that small firms had about as much success in obtaining outside funds as did large firms on an over-all basis.

c) However, in rapidly expanding industries where outside funds are most important, small firms appeared to be less successful in obtaining such funds.

d) Plans for investment in small firms are more sensitive to levels of cash flow and less sensitive to capacity requirements than investment plans of large firms.

6. A final study of the effect of three variables which would be of interest in marginal analysis of investment decisions showed

a) The market rate of interest was not significantly related to investment decisions.

b) Labor costs were not related to investment. (One might hypothesize that, as labor costs rose relative to capital costs, the firm would use more equipment and less labor, moving toward automation.)

c) The movements of prices on the stock market did appear to vary closely with investment in equipment. It may be that both are influenced by the same basic factors, or that firms look to the stock market for an indication of future economic conditions.

SUGGESTIONS FOR FURTHER STUDY

CYERT, RICHARD M.; DILL, WILLIAM R.; and MARCH, JAMES G. "The Role of Expectations in Business Decision Making," *Administrative Science Quarterly*, Vol. 3, No. 3 (December, 1958).

CYERT, RICHARD M., and MARCH, JAMES G. *A Behavioral Theory of the Firm.* Englewood Cliffs, N.J.: Prentice-Hall, Inc., 1963.

EISNER, ROBERT. *Determinants of Capital Expenditures.* Urbana: University of Illinois, Bureau of Economic and Business Research, 1956.

MARCH, JAMES G., and SIMON, HERBERT A. *Organizations.* New York: John Wiley & Sons, Inc., 1958.

MEYER, JOHN R., and KUH, EDWIN. *The Investment Decision—An Empirical Study.* Cambridge, Mass.: Harvard University Press, 1957.

Appendix A

INTEREST CALCULATIONS

CONSIDER AN INVESTMENT of an amount of money in a project which will earn a return of interest on the investment. Say $100 is invested in a project which earns 5 per cent each year. If the interest is not withdrawn but is reinvested in the project, then the amount of the investment increases from year to year. If the interest rate remains fixed, the dollar amount of the interest received will also increase, and we have the process of compounding, or compound interest. The history of such an investment is illustrated as follows:

Year	Interest Earned during Year	Amount of Investment at Year End
1...............	$5.00	$105.00
2...............	5.25	110.25
3...............	5.5125	115.7625
4...............	5.7881	121.5506
and so on		

In more general terms let:

P = a sum of money at the present time
S = a sum of money at the end of n periods in the future
i = interest rate expressed as a decimal

The foregoing table may then be expressed by the function

$$S = (1 + i)^n P$$

If, for example, we are interested in the value of the investment at the end of ten years, the factor $(1 + .05)^{10}$ may be obtained from the interest tables.

$$(1 + .05)^{10} = 1.629$$
$$P = \$100$$
$$S = (1.629)(\$100) = \$162.90$$

Thus, an investment of $100 at 5 per cent compound interest will yield the sum of $162.90 at the end of ten years.

We can also compute the amount which would have to be invested at the present time in order to yield a future sum of a given amount.

$$P = \frac{1}{(1 + i)^n} S$$

The present sum which is "equivalent" in this sense to a given S, is called the present worth of S. A future sum which is equivalent to a given present sum P, is called the future worth of P.

Next consider an investment which will result in a series of n end-of-period payments, each of an equal amount, R. What is such an investment worth in dollars paid today or what is its present worth? We could compute the present worth of each of the equal, end-of-period payments, and then add the present worths.

$$P = \frac{1}{1 + i} R + \frac{1}{(1 + i)^2} R + \frac{1}{(1 + i)^3} R + \frac{1}{(1 + i)^4} R + \cdots$$
$$+ \frac{1}{(1 + i)^n} R$$

The right-hand side of this equation represents the first n terms of a geometric series. It will be recalled that if the nth term of such a series is of the form ar^{n-1}, the sum of the first n terms is given by

$$a\left(\frac{r^n - 1}{r - 1}\right)$$

Using this result we obtain

$$P = \frac{(1 + i)^n - 1}{i(1 + i)^n} R$$

This amount invested now at interest rate i would be sufficient to yield a series of n end-of-period payments each of amount R.

Having found the present worth of such a series of payments, this may easily be transformed into a future worth using the relation already developed between P and S. This gives

$$S = \frac{(1 + i)^n - 1}{i} R$$

This is the amount which will be accumulated at the end of n years if we pay an amount R into a fund each year and the fund earns interest at rate i. For example, suppose a firm contributes \$10,000 annually to its employees' retirement fund, and the fund is kept fully invested at 4 per cent. What will be the value of the fund after 20 years? The interest tables give

$$\frac{(1 + .04)^{20} - 1}{.04} = 29.778$$

Thus

$$S = (29.778)(\$10,000) = \$297,780$$

The interest tables found on pages 529–39 give numerical values for the six factors which relate the three variables P, S, and R.

INTEREST FOR PERIODS OTHER THAN ONE YEAR

In some problems it is necessary to deal with interest which is compounded more frequently than once each year. Suppose, for example, interest is compounded k times per year at a rate of I per period. We may be interested in what annual rate of interest i would be equivalent to compounding k times each year at a rate I. If we were to deposit $1.00 in a bank which compounded in this latter way, at the end of one year the dollar would have grown to an amount

$$S = (\$1.00)(1 + I)^k$$

If we then subtract the original dollar, the remainder will be the interest earned in a year on $1.00, or the annual rate of interest expressed as a decimal:

$$(\$1.00)(1 + I)^k - \$1.00 = i$$

If, for example, interest is compounded monthly at a rate of 1 per cent per month, the annual interest rate equivalent to this is

$$i = (1 + .01)^{12} - 1$$
$$= 1.127 - 1 = .127 \text{ or } 12.7 \text{ per cent per year}$$

CONTINUOUS DISCOUNTING

Throughout this book interest calculations will be based on the assumptions that time is divided into discrete periods (usually years), that an interest rate is stated as an annual rate, and that income or expenses occurring during a year are considered to have occurred at the end of the year. Interest is thus compounded annually, in accordance with the practice of many of our financial institutions.

An alternative approach, which may be used chiefly for its mathematical convenience, is to consider interest to be compounded continuously or instantaneously. This has the advantage of making the functions encountered in decision problems continuous functions rather than discrete functions. This makes it possible to differentiate and thus quickly find the solution to many problems.

Suppose a sum of money S, when deposited at continuously compounded interest, grows at the rate

$$\frac{dS}{dt}$$

The rate of growth divided by S gives the unit rate of growth (the rate of increase per dollar deposited)

$$f(t) = \frac{1}{S}\frac{dS}{dt}$$

Let us assume, as will be most often the case, that this rate of growth is constant over time.

$$f(t) = \text{a constant} = f$$

The equation

$$f = \frac{1}{S}\frac{dS}{dt}$$

is a linear differential equation, whose solution is found in any standard work on the subject. This solution is

$$S_t = S_0\, e^{ft} = P\, e^{ft}$$

or

$$P = S_o = S_t\, e^{-ft}$$

Here P stands for the initial sum deposited (a present sum) and S_t stands for the sum accumulated at time t (a future sum).

This second equation corresponds in continuous compounding computations to the equation

$$P = S\frac{1}{(1+i)^n}$$

in discrete annual compounding computations. The relation between f and i is shown by letting $t = n$. Then

$$e^{-ft} = \left(\frac{1}{1+i}\right)^t$$

$$e^{-f} = \frac{1}{1+i}$$

It follows immediately that

$$i = e^f - 1 = f + \frac{f^2}{2!} + \frac{f^3}{3!} + \cdots\cdots$$

and

$$f = ln(1 + i) = i - \frac{i^2}{2} + \frac{i^3}{3} - \cdots\cdots$$

An examination of these series will show that there is likely to be little difference between f and i. Thus, as an approximation in continuous compounding, the relation

$$P = S_t\, e^{-it}$$

is used, where i is the annual rate of interest in the usual sense.

To illustrate the mathematical convenience of this method, consider the problem of finding the present worth of the costs associated with a certain machine. Let

$$P = \text{initial investment}$$
$$S(t) = \text{operating cost at time } t \text{ expressed as an annual rate}$$
$$i = \text{annual interest rate}$$
$$T = \text{service life}$$

Using discrete compounding the present worth is

$$P + \sum_{t=1}^{T} \frac{S_t}{(1 + i)^t}$$

Using continuous compounding we obtain

$$P + \int_{t=o}^{T} S(t)\, e^{-it}\, dt$$

Expressions of the second type may be chosen because they may be differentiated by the well-known methods of the calculus and because they may be evaluated with fewer computational steps.

The relevance of this will appear especially in Chapter 9, where the reader will recognize that all of the functions could be restated in continuous form, thus greatly easing the difficulties of the minimizing or maximizing operations.

PROBLEMS

A–1. A man who is disabled in an industrial accident is awarded damages by the court equal to the present worth of all his future earnings, using an interest rate of 5 per cent. He has fifteen years of working life remaining and his earnings are estimated as follows:

Years	Annual Income
1–5	$7,000
6–10	$8,000
11–15	$8,500

Compute the amount of the award.

A–2. A successful manufacturing firm "plows back" an amount equal to 6 per cent of its net worth out of earnings each year. If the firm now has a net worth of $10 million, what will be its net worth in eight years?

A–3. A firm is considering the purchase of a truck which will be used for six years. At the end of that time it will be essentially worthless. The use of the truck will result in an annual savings of $3,400. If the firm expects to make at least 7 per cent on its investments, what is the most it would be willing to pay for the truck?

A–4. The long-range plans of a company indicate that in six years a major element of its production process will be obsolete and will have to be replaced. It is estimated that the cost of replacement will be $500,000. The company decides to invest a fixed amount in 3 per cent bonds each year, in order to have this sum available when the time comes. How much should the annual investment be if the interest is reinvested?

A–5. A $100,000 mortgage specifies repayment of principal and interest on the unpaid balance in a series of equal annual payments over 20 years. If the interest rate is to be 5 per cent, what will be the amount of the payments?

A–6. A firm wishes to set up a sinking fund for future expansion. At the end of each year for five years it deposits $1 million in the fund, which draws interest at a rate of 7 per cent compounded annually. What will be the amount in the sinking fund at the end of this time?

A–7. An equipment salesman estimates that an investment in his equipment of $30,000 will produce an annual revenue of $5,000 for ten years. If the annual operating costs for the equipment are $1,500, what rate of return will be earned on this investment?

A–8. If funds are invested at 5 per cent, how many years are required to double the investment? How many years at 8 per cent? At 10 per cent?

A–9. Obtain from a local newspaper the terms for a home improvement loan, an automobile or appliance "easy payment plan," or a personal loan from a finance company. Compute the rate of interest.

A–10. A small loan company offers to make loans of $100 to be repaid in monthly payments of $5.77 each over 25 months. What annual rate of interest is being paid by a person making such a loan?

A–11. Consider a lump-sum payment of $10,000 to be received at the end of ten years and the same sum to be received at the end of five years. Plot the present worths of these two sums as a function of interest rate. What is the effect of interest rate on predicted future incomes in present worth calculations?

A–12. A firm wishes to depreciate an asset costing $25,000 over a period of ten years. The asset will have a salvage value of $5,000 at the end of this time. The sinking fund method of depreciation is to be used with an interest rate of 10 per cent. What is the amount of the annual sinking fund deposit? What are the amounts of depreciation charged in each of the first three years of the asset's life?

A–13.   A $1,000 bond paying 4 per cent interest and maturing in ten years is purchased by an investor for $920. What rate of interest does he actually receive?

A–14.   A personal finance firm offers to loan $50 for two weeks at a cost of 70 cents. What interest rate is being paid if the 70 cents is paid at the end of the two weeks? If it is subtracted from the $50 before the money is given to the borrower?

A–15.   A bank offers home improvements loans of $300 to be repaid in twelve monthly payments of $26.50 each. What is the annual rate of interest?

A–16.   Consider a ten-year loan of $10,000 to be repaid in equal annual payments. Plot the amount of the payment as a function of the interest rate. What would you say about raising the interest rate as a method of reducing consumer borrowing?

A–17.   An investment of $1,100 produces incomes of $600 at the end of one year, $400 at the end of two years, and $300 at the end of three years. Find the interest rate for which the present worth of this investment will be zero. This interest rate is called the rate of return on the investment.

A–18.   Using the interest rate obtained in problem A–17, compute the unrecovered investment, the amount of the investment recovered, and the amount of return earned on the unrecovered investment for each of the three years.

A–19.   Using the interest rate obtained in problem A–17 and the quantities computed in problem A–18, compute the present worth of the amounts of investment recovered and the return.

A–20.   Consider a sum of $1,000 to be received n years in the future. Plot the present worth of this sum at 5 per cent interest as a function of n. What relation would you expect between the value of n and the difficulty in estimating the amount of a future income? What is the effect of the discounting process on these difficulties?

A–21.   If production increases as management predicts it will, a new plant now under construction will have to be enlarged by 50 per cent in ten years. It appears considerably cheaper to build the enlargement now, at the time of the original construction, than to do it ten years hence. On the other hand the work is financed out of funds that the firm can invest at 5 per cent. Formulate a general policy relating the construction cost now and the construction cost ten years hence to a recommended course of action.

A–22.   A firm buys a new automatic machine for $37,000. It makes a down payment of $14,000 and then annual payments of $3,000. If the equipment is being financed through a bank which charges 6 per cent interest, how long will it take to pay for the machine?

A–23.   A firm brings out a small computer which it hopes to sell to small businesses. The computer sells for $10,000, but potential customers will need financing assistance in order to buy it. Several financing plans are being considered:

a) A $4,000 down payment followed by 20 annual payments. If interest is charged at 6 per cent, what should be the amount of the annual payments?

b) Payments of $872 each year for 20 years after an initial down payment. What should be the amount of the down payment if 6 per cent interest is to be charged?

c) A down payment of $3,000, ten equal annual payments, and a final payment of $3,000 at the end of ten years. What should be the amount of the annual payments if 6 per cent interest is charged?

A–24. A loan company offers to lend $1,000 to be repaid in 25 monthly payments of $48.69 each. What annual rate of interest is actually being paid on such a loan?

A–25. A loan is negotiated with a bank under the following terms: The bank adds 7 per cent to the amount borrowed; the borrower pays back one twelfth of this total at the end of each month for a year. On a loan of $1,000 for example, the payment is $1,070/12 or $89.17. What is the annual rate of interest?

A–26. An investor plans to make twenty end-of-year deposits in a 4 per cent compound interest savings account. At the end of each of the last five of these twenty years he wishes to withdraw $1,000 from his account.

a) What must be the amount of each of the twenty deposits?

b) Set up two different equations, each of which will lead to an answer for part *a*. Show *analytically* that your two equations are equivalent.

Appendix B

REPLACEMENT POLICY AND OBSOLESCENCE

IN THE DISCUSSION of replacement policy in which obsolescence is to be reckoned with, it was suggested that the problem of finding the value of n which would minimize

$$TC_1(n) = I + \sum_{j=1}^{n} \frac{c + (j-1)a}{(1+i)^j} + \frac{I}{(1+i)^n} + \sum_{j=1}^{n} \frac{c + (j-1)a - nb}{(1+i)^{n+j}}$$

$$+ \frac{I}{(1+i)^{2n}} + \sum_{j=1}^{n} \frac{c + (j-1)a - 2nb}{(1+i)^{2n+j}} + \cdots$$

might be solved by substituting the problem of finding the value of n which would minimize

$$AC_2(n) = \left\{ I + \sum_{j=1}^{n} \frac{c + (j-1)(a+b)}{(1+i)^j} \right\} \frac{i(1+i)^n}{(1+i)^n - 1}$$

To show the validity of this assertion, we first convert the present worth $TC_1(n)$ to an annual cost yielding

$$AC_1(n) = \left\{ I + \sum_{j=1}^{n} \frac{c + (j-1)a}{(1+i)^j} \right\} \frac{i(1+i)^n}{(1+i)^n - 1} - \left\{ \sum_{k=1}^{\infty} \sum_{j=1}^{n} \frac{knb}{(1+i)^{kn+j}} \right\} i$$

Now if it can be shown that $AC_1(n)$ and $AC_2(n)$ differ only by a constant, then they will both take minimum values for the same value of n. If this is the case, the solution to the substitute problem is also the solution to the original problem.

We wish then to show that

$$AC_2(n) - AC_1(n) = K$$

for all n. Write $AC_2(n)$ as

524

$$AC_2(n) = \left\{I + \sum_{j=1}^{n} \frac{c + (j-1)a}{(1+i)^j}\right\} \frac{i(1+i)^n}{(1+i)^n - 1}$$

$$+ \left\{\sum_{j=1}^{n} \frac{(j-1)b}{(1+i)^j}\right\} \frac{i(1+i)^n}{(1+i)^n - 1}$$

Then

$$AC_2(n) - AC_1(n) = \left\{\sum_{j=1}^{n} \frac{(j-1)b}{(1+i)^j}\right\} \frac{i(1+i)^n}{(1+i)^n - 1} + \left\{\sum_{k=1}^{\infty}\sum_{j=1}^{n} \frac{knb}{(1+i)^{kn+j}}\right\} i$$

We begin by simplifying the last term on the right hand side of the foregoing equation.

$$\left\{\sum_{k=1}^{\infty}\sum_{j=1}^{n} \frac{knb}{(1+i)^{kn+j}}\right\}i = \left\{\sum_{k=1}^{\infty} \frac{knb}{(1+i)^{kn}}\left(\frac{(1+i)^n - 1}{i(1+i)^n}\right)\right\}i$$

$$= \left\{nb\sum_{k=1}^{\infty} \frac{k}{(1+i)^{kn}}\left(\frac{(1+i)^n - 1}{i(1+i)^n}\right)\right\}i$$

$$= nbi\left\{\frac{\dfrac{1}{(1+i)^n}}{\left(1 - \dfrac{1}{(1+i)^n}\right)^2}\right\}\left\{\frac{(1+i)^n - 1}{i(1+i)^n}\right\} = \frac{nb}{(1+i)^n - 1}$$

The proof may now be completed:

$$AC_2(n) - AC_1(n) = \left\{\sum_{j=1}^{n} \frac{(j-1)b}{(1+i)^j}\right\} \frac{i(1+i)^n}{(1+i)^n - 1} + \frac{nb}{(1+i)^n - 1} = K$$

This may be written as

$$\sum_{j=1}^{n} \frac{(j-1)}{(1+i)^j}(i)(1+i)^n + n - \frac{K}{b}\{(1+i)^n - 1\} = 0$$

This must also be true for $n + 1$

$$\sum_{j=1}^{n+1} \frac{(j-1)}{(1+i)^j}(i)(1+i)^{n+1} + n + 1 - \frac{K}{b}\{(1+i)^{n+1} - 1\} = 0$$

$$\sum_{j=1}^{n+1} \frac{(j-1)}{(1+i)^j}(i)(1+i)^n + \frac{n+1}{1+i} - \frac{K}{b}\left\{\frac{(1+i)^{n+1} - 1}{(1+i)}\right\} = 0$$

These two expressions are equal to zero and thus their difference is also zero:

$$\frac{n}{(1 + i)^{n+1}} i(1 + i)^n + \frac{1 - ni}{1 + i} - \frac{K}{b}\left\{\frac{i}{1 + i}\right\} = 0$$

$$\frac{ni}{1 + i} + \frac{1 - ni}{1 + i} - \frac{K}{b}\left\{\frac{i}{1 + i}\right\} = 0$$

$$ni + 1 - ni = \frac{K}{b} i$$

$$K = \frac{b}{i}$$

which was to be shown.

Appendix C

PROOF OF THE LAW OF LONG-RUN SUCCESS

We begin with a statement of the Weak Law of Large Numbers:

Consider a sequence of decisions numbered $1, 2, \ldots, k, \ldots$
Suppose that the outcome resulting from a choice of alternative a_i on decision k is $V_k(\theta_{ij})$. These outcomes are assumed to be independent random variables which are not necessarily identically distributed. We rule out also infinitely good or infinitely bad alternatives.

Let the sum of the outcomes on the first n decisions be

$$S_n = \sum_{k=1}^{n} V_k(\theta_{ij})$$

Let the sum of the expectations resulting from the choice of a_i on the first n decision be

$$M_n = \sum_{k=1}^{n} E_k(a_i)$$

In these terms the Weak Law of Large Numbers then says:

for any $e_1 > 0$, as $n \to \infty$

$$\text{prob}\left\{ \frac{|S_n - M_n|}{n} > e_1 \right\} \to 0$$

Now suppose that on each decision the choice falls on the alternative which maximizes $E(a_i)$. Let the sum of the first n outcomes resulting from the use of this principle be $S_n{}'$, and let the expected value of this sum be $M_n{}'$. For *any other* principle of choice let the sum be S_n and the expected value of the sum be M_n. We wish to show that as $n \to \infty$

$$\text{prob}\ \{S_n{}' > S_n\} \to 1$$

527

Proof: As $n \to \infty$

$$\text{prob}\left\{\frac{|S_n - M_n|}{n} > e_1\right\} \to 0 \qquad e_1 > 0$$

$$\text{prob}\left\{\frac{|S_n' - M_n'|}{n} > e_2\right\} \to 0 \qquad e_2 > 0$$

It follows directly that

$$\text{prob}\{|S_n - M_n| > ne_1\} \to 0$$

The weaker statements may also be made:

$$\text{prob}\{S_n - M_n > ne_1\} \to 0$$
$$\text{prob}\{S_n' - M_n' > ne_2\} \to 0$$

Subtracting and rearranging these we obtain:

$$\text{prob}\{S_n > S_n' - (M_n' - M_n) + n(e_1 - e_2)\} \to 0$$

Since

$$M_n' - M_n > 0$$

it follows that

$$\text{prob}\{S_n > S_n' + n(e_1 - e_2)\} \to 0$$
$$\text{prob}\{S_n > S_n'\} \to 0$$
$$\text{prob}\{S_n' > S_n\} \to 1$$

Q.E.D.

Appendix D

INTEREST TABLES *

½ Per Cent Interest

n	Given P To find S $(1 + i)^n$	Given S To find P $\dfrac{1}{(1 + i)^n}$	Given R To find S $\dfrac{(1 + i)^n - 1}{i}$	Given S To find R $\dfrac{i}{(1 + i)^n - 1}$	Given R To find P $\dfrac{(1 + i)^n - 1}{i(1 + i)^n}$	Given P To find R $\dfrac{i(1 + i)^n}{(1 + i)^n - 1}$	n
1	1.005	0.9950	1.000	1.00000	0.995	1.00500	1
2	1.010	0.9901	2.005	0.49875	1.985	0.50375	2
3	1.015	0.9851	3.015	0.33167	2.970	0.33667	3
4	1.020	0.9802	4.030	0.24813	3.950	0.25313	4
5	1.025	0.9754	5.050	0.19801	4.926	0.20301	5
6	1.030	0.9705	6.076	0.16460	5.896	0.16960	6
7	1.036	0.9657	7.106	0.14073	6.862	0.14573	7
8	1.041	0.9609	8.141	0.12283	7.823	0.12783	8
9	1.046	0.9561	9.182	0.10891	8.779	0.11391	9
10	1.051	0.9513	10.228	0.09777	9.730	0.10277	10
11	1.056	0.9466	11.279	0.08866	10.677	0.09366	11
12	1.062	0.9419	12.336	0.08107	11.619	0.08607	12
13	1.067	0.9372	13.397	0.07464	12.556	0.07964	13
14	1.072	0.9326	14.464	0.06914	13.489	0.07414	14
15	1.078	0.9279	15.537	0.06436	14.417	0.06936	15
16	1.083	0.9233	16.614	0.06019	15.340	0.06519	16
17	1.088	0.9187	17.697	0.05651	16.259	0.06151	17
18	1.094	0.9141	18.786	0.05323	17.173	0.05823	18
19	1.099	0.9096	19.880	0.05030	18.082	0.05530	19
20	1.105	0.9051	20.979	0.04767	18.987	0.05267	20
21	1.110	0.9006	22.084	0.04528	19.888	0.05028	21
22	1.116	0.8961	23.194	0.04311	20.784	0.04811	22
23	1.122	0.8916	24.310	0.04113	21.676	0.04613	23
24	1.127	0.8872	25.432	0.03932	22.563	0.04432	24
25	1.133	0.8828	26.559	0.03765	23.446	0.04265	25
26	1.138	0.8784	27.692	0.03611	24.324	0.04111	26
27	1.144	0.8740	28.830	0.03469	25.198	0.03969	27
28	1.150	0.8697	29.975	0.03336	26.068	0.03836	28
29	1.156	0.8653	31.124	0.03213	26.933	0.03713	29
30	1.161	0.8610	32.280	0.03098	27.794	0.03598	30
31	1.167	0.8567	33.441	0.02990	28.651	0.03490	31
32	1.173	0.8525	34.609	0.02889	29.503	0.03389	32
33	1.179	0.8482	35.782	0.02795	30.352	0.03295	33
34	1.185	0.8440	36.961	0.02706	31.196	0.03206	34
35	1.191	0.8398	38.145	0.02622	32.035	0.03122	35
40	1.221	0.8191	44.159	0.02265	36.172	0.02765	40
45	1.252	0.7990	50.324	0.01987	40.207	0.02487	45
50	1.283	0.7793	56.645	0.01765	44.143	0.02265	50

* Adapted with permission from H. G. Thuesen, *Engineering Economy* (2d ed.; Englewood Cliffs, N.J.: Prentice-Hall, Inc., 1957).

1 Per Cent Interest

n	Given P To find S $(1 + i)^n$	Given S To find P $\dfrac{1}{(1 + i)^n}$	Given R To find S $\dfrac{(1 + i)^n - 1}{i}$	Given S To find R $\dfrac{i}{(1 + i)^n - 1}$	Given R To find P $\dfrac{(1 + i)^n - 1}{i(1 + i)^n}$	Given P To find R $\dfrac{i(1 + i)^n}{(1 + i)^n - 1}$	n
1	1.010	0.9901	1.000	1.00000	0.990	1.01000	1
2	1.020	0.9803	2.010	0.49751	1.970	0.50751	2
3	1.030	0.9706	3.030	0.33002	2.341	0.34002	3
4	1.041	0.9610	4.060	0.24628	3.902	0.25628	4
5	1.051	0.9515	5.101	0.19604	4.853	0.20604	5
6	1.062	0.9420	6.152	0.16255	5.795	0.17255	6
7	1.072	0.9327	7.214	0.13863	6.728	0.14863	7
8	1.083	0.9235	8.286	0.12069	7.652	0.13069	8
9	1.094	0.9143	9.369	0.10674	8.566	0.11674	9
10	1.105	0.9053	10.462	0.09558	9.471	0.10558	10
11	1.116	0.8963	11.567	0.08645	10.368	0.09645	11
12	1.127	0.8874	12.683	0.07885	11.255	0.08885	12
13	1.138	0.8787	13.809	0.07241	12.134	0.08241	13
14	1.149	0.8700	14.947	0.06690	13.004	0.07690	14
15	1.161	0.8613	16.097	0.06212	13.865	0.07212	15
16	1.173	0.8528	17.258	0.05794	14.718	0.06794	16
17	1.184	0.8444	18.430	0.05426	15.562	0.06426	17
18	1.196	0.8360	19.615	0.05098	16.398	0.06098	18
19	1.208	0.8277	20.811	0.04805	17.226	0.05805	19
20	1.220	0.8195	22.019	0.04542	18.046	0.05542	20
21	1.232	0.8114	23.239	0.04303	18.857	0.05303	21
22	1.245	0.8034	24.472	0.04086	19.660	0.05086	22
23	1.257	0.7954	25.716	0.03889	20.456	0.04889	23
24	1.270	0.7876	26.973	0.03707	21.243	0.04707	24
25	1.282	0.7798	28.243	0.03541	22.023	0.04541	25
26	1.295	0.7720	29.526	0.03387	22.795	0.04387	26
27	1.308	0.7644	30.821	0.03245	23.560	0.04245	27
28	1.321	0.7568	32.129	0.03112	24.316	0.04112	28
29	1.335	0.7493	33.450	0.02990	25.066	0.03990	29
30	1.348	0.7419	34.785	0.02875	25.808	0.03875	30
31	1.361	0.7346	36.133	0.02768	26.542	0.03768	31
32	1.375	0.7273	37.494	0.02667	27.270	0.03667	32
33	1.389	0.7201	38.869	0.02573	27.990	0.03573	33
34	1.403	0.7130	40.258	0.02484	28.703	0.03484	34
35	1.417	0.7059	41.660	0.02400	29.409	0.03400	35
40	1.489	0.6717	48.886	0.02046	32.835	0.03046	40
45	1.565	0.6391	56.481	0.01771	36.095	0.02771	45
50	1.645	0.6080	64.463	0.01551	39.196	0.02551	50

2 Per Cent Interest

n	Given P To find S $(1+i)^n$	Given S To find P $\dfrac{1}{(1+i)^n}$	Given R To find S $\dfrac{(1+i)^n-1}{i}$	Given S To find R $\dfrac{i}{(1+i)^n-1}$	Given R To find P $\dfrac{(1+i)^n-1}{i(1+i)^n}$	Given P To find R $\dfrac{i(1+i)^n}{(1+i)^n-1}$	n
1	1.020	0.9804	1.000	1.00000	0.980	1.02000	1
2	1.040	0.9612	2.020	0.49505	1.942	0.51505	2
3	1.061	0.9423	3.060	0.32675	2.884	0.34675	3
4	1.082	0.9238	4.122	0.24262	3.808	0.26262	4
5	1.104	0.9057	5.204	0.19216	4.713	0.21216	5
6	1.126	0.8880	6.308	0.15853	5.601	0.17853	6
7	1.149	0.8706	7.434	0.13451	6.472	0.15451	7
8	1.172	0.8535	8.583	0.11651	7.325	0.13651	8
9	1.195	0.8368	9.755	0.10252	8.162	0.12252	9
10	1.219	0.8203	10.950	0.09133	8.983	0.11133	10
11	1.243	0.8043	12.169	0.08218	9.787	0.10218	11
12	1.268	0.7885	13.412	0.07456	10.575	0.09456	12
13	1.294	0.7730	14.680	0.06812	11.348	0.08812	13
14	1.319	0.7579	15.974	0.06260	12.106	0.08260	14
15	1.346	0.7430	17.293	0.05783	12.849	0.07783	15
16	1.373	0.7284	18.639	0.05365	13.578	0.07365	16
17	1.400	0.7142	20.012	0.04997	14.292	0.06997	17
18	1.428	0.7002	21.412	0.04670	14.992	0.06670	18
19	1.457	0.6864	22.841	0.04378	15.678	0.06378	19
20	1.486	0.6730	24.297	0.04116	16.351	0.06116	20
21	1.516	0.6598	25.783	0.03878	17.011	0.05878	21
22	1.546	0.6468	27.299	0.03663	17.658	0.05663	22
23	1.577	0.6342	28.845	0.03467	18.292	0.05467	23
24	1.608	0.6217	30.422	0.03287	18.914	0.05287	24
25	1.641	0.6095	32.030	0.03122	19.523	0.05122	25
26	1.673	0.5976	33.671	0.02970	20.121	0.04970	26
27	1.707	0.5859	35.344	0.02829	20.707	0.04829	27
28	1.741	0.5744	37.051	0.02699	21.281	0.04699	28
29	1.776	0.5631	38.792	0.02578	21.844	0.04578	29
30	1.811	0.5521	40.568	0.02465	22.396	0.04465	30
31	1.848	0.5412	42.379	0.02360	22.938	0.04360	31
32	1.885	0.5306	44.227	0.02261	23.468	0.04261	32
33	1.922	0.5202	46.112	0.02169	23.989	0.04169	33
34	1.961	0.5100	48.034	0.02082	24.499	0.04082	34
35	2.000	0.5000	49.994	0.02000	24.999	0.04000	35
40	2.208	0.4529	60.402	0.01656	27.355	0.03656	40
45	2.438	0.4102	71.893	0.01391	29.490	0.03391	45
50	2.692	0.3715	84.579	0.01182	31.424	0.03182	50

3 Per Cent Interest

n	Given P To find S $(1 + i)^n$	Given S To find P $\dfrac{1}{(1 + i)^n}$	Given R To find S $\dfrac{(1 + i)^n - 1}{i}$	Given S To find R $\dfrac{i}{(1 + i)^n - 1}$	Given R To find P $\dfrac{(1 + i)^n - 1}{i(1 + i)^n}$	Given P To find R $\dfrac{i(1 + i)^n}{(1 + i)^n - 1}$	n
1	1.030	0.9709	1.000	1.00000	0.971	1.03000	1
2	1.061	0.9426	2.030	0.49261	1.913	0.52261	2
3	1.093	0.9151	3.091	0.32353	2.829	0.35353	3
4	1.126	0.8885	4.184	0.23903	3.717	0.26903	4
5	1.159	0.8626	5.309	0.18835	4.580	0.21835	5
6	1.194	0.8375	6.468	0.15460	5.417	0.18460	6
7	1.230	0.8131	7.662	0.13051	6.230	0.16051	7
8	1.267	0.7894	8.892	0.11246	7.020	0.14246	8
9	1.305	0.7664	10.159	0.09843	7.786	0.12843	9
10	1.344	0.7441	11.464	0.08723	8.530	0.11723	10
11	1.384	0.7224	12.808	0.07808	9.253	0.10808	11
12	1.426	0.7014	14.192	0.07046	9.954	0.10046	12
13	1.469	0.6810	15.618	0.06403	10.635	0.09403	13
14	1.513	0.6611	17.086	0.05853	11.296	0.08853	14
15	1.558	0.6419	18.599	0.05377	11.938	0.08377	15
16	1.605	0.6232	20.157	0.04961	12.561	0.07961	16
17	1.653	0.6050	21.762	0.04595	13.166	0.07595	17
18	1.702	0.5874	23.414	0.04271	13.754	0.07271	18
19	1.754	0.5703	25.117	0.03981	14.324	0.06981	19
20	1.806	0.5537	26.870	0.03722	14.877	0.06722	20
21	1.860	0.5375	28.676	0.03487	15.415	0.06487	21
22	1.916	0.5219	30.537	0.03275	15.937	0.06275	22
23	1.974	0.5067	32.453	0.03081	16.444	0.06081	23
24	2.033	0.4919	34.426	0.02905	16.936	0.05905	24
25	2.094	0.4776	36.459	0.02743	17.413	0.05743	25
26	2.157	0.4637	38.553	0.02594	17.877	0.05594	26
27	2.221	0.4502	40.710	0.02456	18.327	0.05456	27
28	2.288	0.4371	42.931	0.02329	18.764	0.05329	28
29	2.357	0.4243	45.219	0.02211	19.188	0.05211	29
30	2.427	0.4120	47.575	0.02102	19.600	0.05102	30
31	2.500	0.4000	50.003	0.02000	20.000	0.05000	31
32	2.575	0.3883	52.503	0.01905	20.389	0.04905	32
33	2.652	0.3770	55.078	0.01816	20.766	0.04816	33
34	2.732	0.3660	57.730	0.01732	21.132	0.04732	34
35	2.814	0.3554	60.462	0.01654	21.487	0.04654	35
40	3.262	0.3066	75.401	0.01326	23.115	0.04326	40
45	3.782	0.2644	92.720	0.01079	24.519	0.04079	45
50	4.384	0.2281	112.797	0.00887	25.730	0.03887	50

4 Per Cent Interest

n	Given P To find S $(1+i)^n$	Given S To find P $\dfrac{1}{(1+i)^n}$	Given R To find S $\dfrac{(1+i)^n-1}{i}$	Given S To find R $\dfrac{i}{(1+i)^n-1}$	Given R To find P $\dfrac{(1+i)^n-1}{i(1+i)^n}$	Given P To find R $\dfrac{i(1+i)^n}{(1+i)^n-1}$	n
1	1.040	0.9615	1.000	1.00000	0.962	1.04000	1
2	1.082	0.9246	2.040	0.49020	1.886	0.53020	2
3	1.125	0.8890	3.122	0.32035	2.775	0.36035	3
4	1.170	0.8548	4.246	0.23549	3.630	0.27549	4
5	1.217	0.8219	5.416	0.18463	4.452	0.22463	5
6	1.265	0.7903	6.633	0.15076	5.242	0.19076	6
7	1.316	0.7599	7.898	0.12661	6.002	0.16661	7
8	1.369	0.7307	9.214	0.10853	6.733	0.14853	8
9	1.423	0.7026	10.583	0.09449	7.435	0.13449	9
10	1.480	0.6756	12.006	0.08329	8.111	0.12329	10
11	1.539	0.6496	13.486	0.07415	8.760	0.11415	11
12	1.601	0.6246	15.026	0.06655	9.385	0.10655	12
13	1.665	0.6006	16.627	0.06014	9.986	0.10014	13
14	1.732	0.5775	18.292	0.05467	10.563	0.09467	14
15	1.801	0.5553	20.024	0.04994	11.118	0.08994	15
16	1.873	0.5339	21.825	0.04582	11.652	0.08582	16
17	1.948	0.5134	23.698	0.04220	12.166	0.08220	17
18	2.026	0.4936	25.645	0.03899	12.659	0.07899	18
19	2.107	0.4746	27.671	0.03614	13.134	0.07614	19
20	2.191	0.4564	29.778	0.03358	13.590	0.07358	20
21	2.279	0.4388	31.969	0.03128	14.029	0.07128	21
22	2.370	0.4220	34.248	0.02920	14.451	0.06920	22
23	2.465	0.4057	36.618	0.02731	14.857	0.06731	23
24	2.563	0.3901	39.083	0.02559	15.247	0.06559	24
25	2.666	0.3751	41.646	0.02401	15.622	0.06401	25
26	2.772	0.3607	44.312	0.02257	15.983	0.06257	26
27	2.883	0.3468	47.084	0.02124	16.330	0.06124	27
28	2.999	0.3335	49.968	0.02001	16.663	0.06001	28
29	3.119	0.3207	52.966	0.01888	16.984	0.05888	29
30	3.243	0.3083	56.085	0.01783	17.292	0.05783	30
31	3.373	0.2965	59.328	0.01686	17.588	0.05686	31
32	3.508	0.2851	62.701	0.01595	17.874	0.05595	32
33	3.648	0.2741	66.210	0.01510	18.148	0.05510	33
34	3.794	0.2636	69.858	0.01431	18.411	0.05431	34
35	3.946	0.2534	73.652	0.01358	18.665	0.05358	35
40	4.801	0.2083	95.026	0.01052	19.793	0.05052	40
45	5.841	0.1712	121.029	0.00826	20.720	0.04826	45
50	7.107	0.1407	152.667	0.00655	21.482	0.04655	50

5 Per Cent Interest

n	Given P To find S $(1+i)^n$	Given S To find P $\dfrac{1}{(1+i)^n}$	Given R To find S $\dfrac{(1+i)^n-1}{i}$	Given S To find R $\dfrac{i}{(1+i)^n-1}$	Given R To find P $\dfrac{(1+i)^n-1}{i(1+i)^n}$	Given P To find R $\dfrac{i(1+i)^n}{(1+i)^n-1}$	n
1	1.050	0.9524	1.000	1.00000	0.952	1.05000	1
2	1.103	0.9070	2.050	0.48780	1.859	0.53780	2
3	1.158	0.8638	3.153	0.31721	2.723	0.36721	3
4	1.216	0.8227	4.310	0.23201	3.546	0.28201	4
5	1.276	0.7835	5.526	0.18097	4.329	0.23097	5
6	1.340	0.7462	6.802	0.14702	5.076	0.19702	6
7	1.407	0.7107	8.142	0.12282	5.786	0.17282	7
8	1.477	0.6768	9.549	0.10472	6.463	0.15472	8
9	1.551	0.6446	11.027	0.09069	7.108	0.14069	9
10	1.629	0.6139	12.57	0.07950	7.722	0.12950	10
11	1.710	0.5847	14.207	0.07039	8.306	0.12039	11
12	1.796	0.5568	15.917	0.06283	8.863	0.11283	12
13	1.886	0.5303	17.713	0.05646	9.394	0.10646	13
14	1.980	0.5051	19.599	0.05102	9.899	0.10102	14
15	2.079	0.4810	21.579	0.04634	10.380	0.09634	15
16	2.183	0.4581	23.657	0.04227	10.838	0.09227	16
17	2.292	0.4363	25.840	0.03870	11.274	0.08870	17
18	2.407	0.4155	28.132	0.03555	11.690	0.08555	18
19	2.527	0.3957	30.539	0.03275	12.085	0.08275	19
20	2.653	0.3769	33.066	0.03024	12.462	0.08024	20
21	2.786	0.3589	35.719	0.02800	12.821	0.07800	21
22	2.925	0.3418	38.505	0.02597	13.163	0.07597	22
23	3.072	0.3256	41.430	0.02414	13.489	0.07414	23
24	3.225	0.3101	44.502	0.02247	13.799	0.07247	24
25	3.386	0.2953	47.727	0.02095	14.094	0.07095	25
26	3.556	0.2812	51.113	0.01956	14.375	0.06956	26
27	3.733	0.2678	54.669	0.01829	14.643	0.06829	27
28	3.920	0.2551	58.403	0.01712	14.898	0.06712	28
29	4.116	0.2429	62.323	0.01605	15.141	0.06605	29
30	4.322	0.2314	66.439	0.01505	15.372	0.06505	30
31	4.538	0.2204	70.761	0.01413	15.593	0.06413	31
32	4.765	0.2099	75.299	0.01328	15.803	0.06328	32
33	5.003	0.1999	80.064	0.01249	16.003	0.06249	33
34	5.253	0.1904	85.067	0.01176	16.193	0.06176	34
35	5.516	0.1813	90.320	0.01107	16.374	0.06107	35
40	7.040	0.1420	120.800	0.00828	17.159	0.05828	40
45	8.985	0.1113	159.700	0.00626	17.774	0.05626	45
50	11.467	0.0872	209.348	0.00478	18.256	0.05478	50

6 Per Cent Interest

n	Given P To find S $(1 + i)^n$	Given S To find P $\dfrac{1}{(1 + i)^n}$	Given R To find S $\dfrac{(1 + i)^n - 1}{i}$	Given S To find R $\dfrac{i}{(1 + i)^n - 1}$	Given R To find P $\dfrac{(1 + i)^n - 1}{i(1 + i)^n}$	Given P To find R $\dfrac{i(1 + i)^n}{(1 + i)^n - 1}$	n
1	1.060	0.9434	1.000	1.00000	0.943	1.06000	1
2	1.124	0.8900	2.060	0.48544	1.833	0.54544	2
3	1.191	0.8396	3.184	0.31411	2.673	0.37411	3
4	1.262	0.7921	4.375	0.22859	3.465	0.28859	4
5	1.338	0.7473	5.637	0.17740	4.212	0.23740	5
6	1.419	0.7050	6.975	0.14336	4.917	0.20336	6
7	1.504	0.6651	8.394	0.11914	5.582	0.17914	7
8	1.594	0.6274	9.897	0.10104	6.210	0.16104	8
9	1.689	0.5919	11.491	0.08702	6.802	0.14702	9
10	1.791	0.5584	13.181	0.07587	7.360	0.13587	10
11	1.898	0.5268	14.972	0.06679	7.887	0.12679	11
12	2.012	0.4970	16.870	0.05928	8.384	0.11928	12
13	2.133	0.4688	18.882	0.05296	8.853	0.11296	13
14	2.261	0.4423	21.015	0.04758	9.295	0.10758	14
15	2.397	0.4173	23.276	0.04296	9.712	0.10296	15
16	2.540	0.3936	25.673	0.03895	10.106	0.09895	16
17	2.693	0.3714	28.213	0.03544	10.477	0.09544	17
18	2.854	0.3503	30.906	0.03236	10.828	0.09236	18
19	3.026	0.3305	33.760	0.02962	11.158	0.08962	19
20	3.207	0.3118	36.786	0.02718	11.470	0.08718	20
21	3.400	0.2942	39.993	0.02500	11.764	0.08500	21
22	3.604	0.2775	43.392	0.02305	12.042	0.08305	22
23	3.820	0.2618	46.996	0.02128	12.303	0.08128	23
24	4.049	0.2470	50.816	0.01968	12.550	0.07968	24
25	4.292	0.2330	54.865	0.01823	12.783	0.07823	25
26	4.549	0.2198	59.156	0.01690	13.003	0.07690	26
27	4.822	0.2074	63.706	0.01570	13.211	0.07570	27
28	5.112	0.1956	68.528	0.01459	13.406	0.07459	28
29	5.418	0.1846	73.640	0.01358	13.591	0.07358	29
30	5.743	0.1741	79.058	0.01265	13.765	0.07265	30
31	6.088	0.1643	84.802	0.01179	13.929	0.07179	31
32	6.453	0.1550	90.890	0.01100	14.084	0.07100	32
33	6.841	0.1462	97.343	0.01027	14.230	0.07027	33
34	7.251	0.1379	104.184	0.00960	14.368	0.06960	34
35	7.686	0.1301	111.435	0.00897	14.498	0.06897	35
40	10.286	0.0972	154.762	0.00646	15.046	0.06646	40
45	13.765	0.0727	212.744	0.00470	15.456	0.06470	45
50	18.420	0.0543	290.336	0.00344	15.762	0.06344	50

7 Per Cent Interest

n	Given P To find S $(1 + i)^n$	Given S To find P $\dfrac{1}{(1 + i)^n}$	Given R To find S $\dfrac{(1 + i)^n - 1}{i}$	Given S To find R $\dfrac{i}{(1 + i)^n - 1}$	Given R To find P $\dfrac{(1 + i)^n - 1}{i(1 + i)^n}$	Given P To find R $\dfrac{i(1 + i)^n}{(1 + i)^n - 1}$	n
1	1.070	0.9346	1.000	1.00000	0.935	1.07000	1
2	1.145	0.8734	2.070	0.48309	1.808	0.55309	2
3	1.225	0.8163	3.215	0.31105	2.624	0.38105	3
4	1.311	0.7629	4.440	0.22523	3.387	0.29523	4
5	1.403	0.7130	5.751	0.17389	4.100	0.24389	5
6	1.501	0.6663	7.153	0.13980	4.767	0.20980	6
7	1.606	0.6227	8.654	0.11555	5.389	0.18555	7
8	1.718	0.5820	10.260	0.09747	5.971	0.16747	8
9	1.838	0.5439	11.978	0.08349	6.515	0.15349	9
10	1.967	0.5083	13.816	0.07238	7.024	0.14238	10
11	2.105	0.4751	15.784	0.06336	7.499	0.13336	11
12	2.252	0.4440	17.888	0.05590	7.943	0.12590	12
13	2.410	0.4150	20.141	0.04965	8.358	0.11965	13
14	2.579	0.3878	22.550	0.04434	8.745	0.11434	14
15	2.759	0.3624	25.129	0.03979	9.108	0.10979	15
16	2.952	0.3387	27.888	0.03586	9.447	0.10586	16
17	3.159	0.3166	30.840	0.03243	9.763	0.10243	17
13	3.380	0.2959	33.999	0.02941	10.059	0.09941	18
19	3.617	0.2765	37.379	0.02675	10.336	0.09675	19
20	3.870	0.2584	40.995	0.02439	10.594	0.09439	20
21	4.141	0.2415	44.865	0.02229	10.836	0.09229	21
22	4.430	0.2257	49.006	0.02041	11.061	0.09041	22
23	4.741	0.2109	53.436	0.01871	11.272	0.08871	23
24	5.072	0.1971	58.177	0.01719	11.469	0.08719	24
25	5.427	0.1842	63.249	0.01581	11.654	0.08581	25
26	5.807	0.1722	68.676	0.01456	11.826	0.08456	26
27	6.214	0.1609	74.484	0.01343	11.987	0.08343	27
28	6.649	0.1504	80.698	0.01239	12.137	0.08239	28
29	7.114	0.1406	87.347	0.01145	12.278	0.08145	29
30	7.612	0.1314	94.461	0.01059	12.409	0.08059	30
31	8.145	0.1228	102.073	0.00980	12.532	0.07980	31
32	8.715	0.1147	110.218	0.00907	12.647	0.07907	32
33	9.325	0.1072	118.933	0.00841	12.754	0.07841	33
34	9.978	0.1002	128.259	0.00780	12.854	0.07780	34
35	10.677	0.0937	138.237	0.00723	12.948	0.07723	35
40	14.974	0.0668	199.635	0.00501	13.332	0.07501	40
45	21.002	0.0476	285.749	0.00350	13.606	0.07350	45
50	29.457	0.0339	406.529	0.00246	13.801	0.07246	50

8 Per Cent Interest

n	Given P To find S $(1 + i)^n$	Given S To find P $\dfrac{1}{(1 + i)^n}$	Given R To find S $\dfrac{(1 + i)^n - 1}{i}$	Given S To find R $\dfrac{i}{(1 + i)^n - 1}$	Given R To find P $\dfrac{(1 + i)^n - 1}{i(1 + i)^n}$	Given P To find R $\dfrac{i(1 + i)^n}{(1 + i)^n - 1}$	n
1	1.080	0.9259	1.000	1.00000	0.926	1.08000	1
2	1.166	0.8573	2.080	0.48077	1.783	0.56077	2
3	1.260	0.7938	3.246	0.30803	2.577	0.38803	3
4	1.360	0.7350	4.506	0.22192	3.312	0.30192	4
5	1.469	0.6806	5.867	0.17046	3.993	0.25046	5
6	1.587	0.6302	7.336	0.13632	4.623	0.21632	6
7	1.714	0.5835	8.923	0.11207	5.206	0.19207	7
8	1.851	0.5403	10.637	0.09401	5.747	0.17401	8
9	1.999	0.5002	12.488	0.08008	6.247	0.16008	9
10	2.159	0.4632	14.487	0.06903	6.710	0.14903	10
11	2.332	0.4289	16.645	0.06008	7.139	0.14008	11
12	2.518	0.3971	18.977	0.05270	7.536	0.13270	12
13	2.720	0.3677	21.495	0.04652	7.904	0.12652	13
14	2.937	0.3405	24.215	0.04130	8.244	0.12130	14
15	3.172	0.3152	27.152	0.03683	8.559	0.11683	15
16	3.426	0.2919	30.324	0.03298	8.851	0.11298	16
17	3.700	0.2703	33.750	0.02963	9.122	0.10963	17
18	3.996	0.2502	37.450	0.02670	9.372	0.10670	18
19	4.316	0.2317	41.446	0.02413	9.604	0.10413	19
20	4.661	0.2145	45.762	0.02185	9.818	0.10185	20
21	5.034	0.1987	50.423	0.01983	10.017	0.09983	21
22	5.437	0.1839	55.457	0.01803	10.201	0.09803	22
23	5.871	0.1703	60.893	0.01642	10.371	0.09642	23
24	6.341	0.1577	66.765	0.01498	10.529	0.09498	24
25	6.848	0.1460	73.106	0.01368	10.675	0.09368	25
26	7.396	0.1352	79.954	0.01251	10.810	0.09251	26
27	7.988	0.1252	87.351	0.01145	10.935	0.09145	27
28	8.627	0.1159	95.339	0.01049	11.051	0.09049	28
29	9.317	0.1073	103.966	0.00962	11.158	0.08962	29
30	10.063	0.0994	113.283	0.00883	11.258	0.08883	30
31	10.868	0.0920	123.346	0.00811	11.350	0.08811	31
32	11.737	0.0852	134.214	0.00745	11.435	0.08745	32
33	12.676	0.0789	145.951	0.00685	11.514	0.08685	33
34	13.690	0.0730	158.627	0.00630	11.587	0.08630	34
35	14.785	0.0676	172.317	0.00580	11.655	0.08580	35
40	21.725	0.0460	259.057	0.00386	11.925	0.08386	40
45	31.920	0.0313	386.506	0.00259	12.108	0.08259	45
50	46.902	0.0213	573.770	0.00174	12.233	0.08174	50

10 Per Cent Interest

n	Given P To find S $(1 + i)^n$	Given S To find P $\dfrac{1}{(1 + i)^n}$	Given R To find S $\dfrac{(1 + i)^n - 1}{i}$	Given S To find R $\dfrac{i}{(1 + i)^n - 1}$	Given R To find P $\dfrac{(1 + i)^n - 1}{i(1 + i)^n}$	Given P To find R $\dfrac{i(1 + i)^n}{(1 + i)^n - 1}$	n
1	1.100	0.9091	1.000	1.00000	0.909	1.10000	1
2	1.210	0.8264	2.100	0.47619	1.736	0.57619	2
3	1.331	0.7513	3.310	0.30211	2.487	0.40211	3
4	1.464	0.6830	4.641	0.21547	3.170	0.31547	4
5	1.611	0.6209	6.105	0.16380	3.791	0.26380	5
6	1.772	0.5645	7.716	0.12961	4.355	0.22961	6
7	1.949	0.5132	9.487	0.10541	4.868	0.20541	7
8	2.144	0.4665	11.436	0.08744	5.335	0.18744	8
9	2.358	0.4241	13.579	0.07364	5.759	0.17364	9
10	2.594	0.3855	15.937	0.06275	6.144	0.16275	10
11	2.853	0.3505	18.531	0.05396	6.495	0.15396	11
12	3.138	0.3186	21.384	0.04676	6.814	0.14676	12
13	3.452	0.2897	24.523	0.04078	7.103	0.14078	13
14	3.797	0.2633	27.975	0.03575	7.367	0.13575	14
15	4.177	0.2394	31.772	0.03147	7.606	0.13147	15
16	4.595	0.2176	35.950	0.02782	7.824	0.12782	16
17	5.054	0.1978	40.545	0.02466	8.022	0.12466	17
18	5.560	0.1799	45.599	0.02193	8.201	0.12193	18
19	6.116	0.1635	51.159	0.01955	8.365	0.11955	19
20	6.727	0.1486	57.275	0.01746	8.514	0.11746	20
21	7.400	0.1351	64.002	0.01562	8.649	0.11562	21
22	8.140	0.1228	71.403	0.01401	8.772	0.11401	22
23	8.954	0.1117	79.543	0.01257	8.883	0.11257	23
24	9.850	0.1015	88.497	0.01130	8.985	0.11130	24
25	10.835	0.0923	98.347	0.01017	9.077	0.11017	25
26	11.918	0.0839	109.182	0.00916	9.161	0.10916	26
27	13.110	0.0763	121.100	0.00826	9.237	0.10826	27
28	14.421	0.0693	134.210	0.00745	9.307	0.10745	28
29	15.863	0.0630	148.631	0.00673	9.370	0.10673	29
30	17.449	0.0573	164.494	0.00608	9.427	0.10608	30
31	19.194	0.0521	181.943	0.00550	9.479	0.10550	31
32	21.114	0.0474	201.138	0.00497	9.526	0.10497	32
33	23.225	0.0431	222.252	0.00450	9.569	0.10450	33
34	25.548	0.0391	245.477	0.00407	9.609	0.10407	34
35	28.102	0.0356	271.024	0.00369	9.644	0.10369	35
40	45.259	0.0221	442.593	0.00226	9.779	0.10226	40
45	72.890	0.0137	718.905	0.00139	9.863	0.10139	45
50	117.391	0.0085	1163.909	0.00086	9.915	0.10086	50

$$\frac{i(1 + i)^n}{(1 + i)^n - 1}$$ For Interest Rates from 6 to 50 Per Cent

Given P, to Find R

n	6%	8%	10%	12%	15%	20%	25%	30%	40%	50%	n
1	1.06000	1.08000	1.10000	1.12000	1.15000	1.20000	1.25000	1.30000	1.40000	1.50000	1
2	0.54544	0.56077	0.57619	0.59170	0.61512	0.65455	0.69444	0.73478	0.81667	0.90000	2
3	0.37411	0.38803	0.40211	0.41635	0.43798	0.47473	0.51230	0.55063	0.62936	0.71053	3
4	0.28859	0.30192	0.31547	0.32923	0.35027	0.38629	0.42344	0.46163	0.54077	0.62308	4
5	0.23740	0.25046	0.26380	0.27741	0.29832	0.33438	0.37184	0.41058	0.49136	0.57582	5
6	0.20336	0.21632	0.22961	0.24323	0.26424	0.30071	0.33882	0.37840	0.46126	0.54812	6
7	0.17914	0.19207	0.20541	0.21912	0.24036	0.27742	0.31634	0.35687	9.44192	0.53108	7
8	0.16104	0.17401	0.18744	0.20130	0.22285	0.26061	0.30040	0.34191	0.42804	0.52030	8
9	0.14702	0.16008	0.17364	0.18768	0.20957	0.24808	0.28876	0.33123	0.42034	0.51335	9
10	0.13587	0.14903	0.16275	0.17698	0.19925	0.23852	0.28007	0.32346	0.41432	0.50823	10
11	0.12679	0.14008	0.15396	0.16842	0.19107	0.23110	0.27349	0.31773	0.41013	0.50585	11
12	0.11928	0.13270	0.14676	0.16144	0.18448	0.22526	0.26845	0.31345	0.40718	0.50388	12
13	0.11296	0.12652	0.14078	0.15568	0.17911	0.22062	0.26454	0.31024	0.40510	0.50258	13
14	0.10758	0.12130	0.13575	0.15087	0.17469	0.21689	0.26150	0.30782	0.40363	0.50172	14
15	0.10296	0.11683	0.13147	0.14682	0.17102	0.21388	0.25912	0.30598	0.40259	0.50114	15
16	0.09895	0.11298	0.12782	0.14339	0.16795	0.21144	0.25724	0.30458	0.40185	0.50076	16
17	0.09544	0.10963	0.12466	0.14046	0.16537	0.20944	0.25576	0.30351	0.40132	0.50051	17
18	0.09236	0.10670	0.12193	0.13794	0.16319	0.20781	0.25459	0.30269	0.40094	0.50034	18
19	0.08962	0.10413	0.11955	0.13576	0.16134	0.20646	0.25366	0.30206	0.40067	0.50023	19
20	0.08718	0.10185	0.11746	0.13388	0.15976	0.20536	0.25292	0.30159	0.40048	0.50016	20
25	0.07823	0.09368	0.11017	0.12750	0.15470	0.20212	0.25095	0.30043	0.40009	0.50002	25
30	0.07265	0.08883	0.10608	0.12414	0.15230	0.20085	0.25031	0.30011	0.40002	0.50000	30
40	0.06646	0.08386	0.10226	0.12130	0.15056	0.20014	0.25003	0.30008	0.40001	0.50000	40
50	0.06344	0.08174	0.10086	0.12042	0.15014	0.20002	0.25000	0.30001	0.40000	0.50000	50
100	0.06018	0.08004	0.10001	0.12000	0.15000	0.20000	0.25000	0.30000	0.40000	0.50000	100

SELECTED REFERENCES

1. ANSOFF, H. I. "A Model for Diversification," *Management Science*, Vol. 4, No. 4 (July, 1958).

2. ARMOUR, GORDON C., and BUFFA, ELWOOD S. "A Heurisitic Algorithm and Simulation Approach to Relative Location of Facilities," *Management Science*, Vol. 9, No. 2 (January, 1963).

3. ARROW, KENNETH J. "Alternative Approaches to the Theory of Choice in Risk-Taking Situations," *Econometrica*, Vol. 19, No. 3 (March, 1951).

4. ——— *Social Choice and Individual Values*. New York: John Wiley & Sons, Inc., 1951.

5. ——— "Statistics and Economic Policy," *Econometrica*, Vol. 25, No. 4 (October, 1957).

6. ——— "Decision Theory and Operations Research," *Operations Research*, Vol. 5, No. 6 (December, 1957).

7. BARISH, NORMAN N. *Economic Analysis for Engineering and Managerial Decision Making*. New York: McGraw-Hill Book Co., Inc., 1962.

8. BECKER, G. M. "Sequential Decision Making, Wald's Model and Estimates of Parameters," *Journal of Experimental Psychology*, Vol. 55, No. 2 (February, 1958).

9. BENNETT, WILLIAM S. "Allocation for Acceptable Risk Instead of Expected Value," *Operations Research*, Vol. 9, No. 2 (March–April, 1961).

10. BERKOW, WILLIAM F. "Intracorporate Communications Preliminary to Engineering Economy Studies," *Engineering Economist*, Vol. 5, No. 2 (Winter, 1963).

11. BERNHARD, RICHARD H. "Discount Methods for Expenditure Evaluation—A Clarification of Their Assumptions," *Journal of Industrial Engineering*, Vol. 13, No. 1 (January–February, 1962).

12. ——— "On the Importance of Reinvestment Rates in Appraising Accelerated Depreciation Plans," *Journal of Industrial Engineering*, Vol. 14, No. 3 (May–June, 1963).

13. BIERMAN, HAROLD, JR., and SMIDT, SEYMOUR. *The Capital Budgeting Decision*. New York: The Macmillan Co., 1960.

14. BLACKWELL, DAVID, and GIRSHICK, M.A. *Theory of Games and Statistical Decisions*. New York: John Wiley & Sons, Inc., 1954.

15. BOULDING, KENNETH E. *The Image*. Ann Arbor: The University of Michigan Press, 1956.

16. BOWMAN, E. H. "Consistency and Optimality in Managerial Decision Making," *Management Science,* Vol. 9, No. 2 (January, 1963).

17. BOX, G. E. P. "Evolutionary Operation: A Method for Increasing Industrial Productivity," *Applied Statistics,* Vol. 6 (1957).

18. BROSS, IRWIN D. J. *Design for Decision.* New York: The Macmillan Co., 1953.

19. BROWN, ROBERT G. *Statistical Forecasting for Inventory Control.* New York: McGraw-Hill Book Co., Inc., 1959.

20. BRUNER, JEROME S.; GOODNOW, J. J.; and AUSTIN, GEORGE M. *A Study of Thinking.* New York: John Wiley & Sons, Inc., 1956.

21. CARTER, C. F., and WILLIAMS, B. R. *Investment in Innovation.* London: Oxford University Press, 1956.

22. CHARNES, A.; COOPER, W. W.; and MILLER, M. H. "Application of Linear Programming to Financial Budgeting and the Costing of Funds," *Journal of Business,* Vol. 32, No. 1 (January, 1959).

23. CHERNOFF, HERMAN. "Rational Selection of Decision Functions," *Econometrica,* Vol. 22, No. 3 (March, 1954).

24. CHERNOFF, HERMAN, and MOSES, LINCOLN E. *Elementary Decision Theory.* New York: John Wiley & Sons, Inc., 1959.

25. CHURCHMAN, C. WEST, and ACKOFF, RUSSELL L. "An Approximate Measure of Value," *Journal of the Operations Research Society of America,* Vol. 2, No. 2 (May, 1954).

26. CHURCHMAN, C. WEST. *Prediction and Optimal Decision.* Englewood Cliffs, N.J.: Prentice-Hall, Inc., 1961.

27. CLARK, CHARLES E.; MALCOLM, DONALD G.; CRAFT, CLIFFORD J.; and RICCIARDI, FRANK M. "On the Construction of a Multi-Stage, Multi-Person Business Game," *Operations Research,* Vol. 5, No. 4 (August, 1957).

28. COHEN, KALMAN J., and RHENMAN, ERIC. "The Role of Management Games in Education and Research," *Management Science,* Vol. 7, No. 2 (January, 1961).

29. CYERT, RICHARD M.; DILL, WILLIAM R.; and MARCH, JAMES G. "The Role of Expectations in Business Decision Making," *Administrative Science Quarterly,* Vol. 3, No. 3 (December, 1958).

30. CYERT, RICHARD M., and MARCH, JAMES G. *A Behavioral Theory of the Firm.* Englewood Cliffs, N.J.: Prentice-Hall, Inc., 1963.

31. DAVIDSON, SIDNEY, and DRAKE, DAVID F. "Capital Budgeting and the 'Best' Tax Decpreciation Method," *Journal of Business,* Vol. 34, No. 4 (October, 1961).

32. DEAN, BURTON V. "Replacement Theory," *Progress in Operations Research* (ed. R. L. ACKOFF), Vol. I. New York: John Wiley and Sons, Inc., 1961.

33. DEAN, JOEL. *Capital Budgeting.* New York: Columbia University Press, 1951.

34. ——— *Managerial Economics.* Englewood Cliffs, N.J.: Prentice-Hall, Inc., 1951.

35. Reference deleted in proof.

36. DUNCAN, ACHESON J. *Quality Control and Industrial Statistics.* Rev. ed. Homewood, Ill.: Richard D. Irwin, Inc., 1959.

37. EDGERTON, R. A. D. *Investment Decisions under Uncertainty.* Liverpool: Liverpool University Press, 1960.

38. EDWARDS, WARD. "The Theory of Decision Making," *Psychological Bulletin,* Vol. 51, No. 4 (July, 1954).

39. ——— "Dynamic Decision Theory and Probabilistic Information Processing," *Human Factors,* Vol. 4, No. 2 (April, 1962).

40. ——— "Utility, Subjective Probability, Their Interaction, and Variance Preferences," *Journal of Conflict Resolution,* Vol. 6, No. 1 (May, 1962).

41. EISEN, M., and LEIBOWITZ, M. "Replacement of Randomly Deteriorating Equipment," *Management Science,* Vol. 9, No. 2 (January, 1963).

42. EISNER, ROBERT. *Determinants of Capital Expenditures.* Urbana: University of Illinois, Bureau of Economic and Business Research, 1956.

43. ENGLISH, J. MORLEY. "New Approaches to Economic Comparison for Engineering Projects," *The Journal of Industrial Engineering,* Vol. 12, No. 6 (November–December, 1961).

44. Estes, W. K. "A Descriptive Approach to the Dynamics of Choice Behavior," *Behavioral Science,* Vol. 6, No. 2 (February, 1961).

45. FAIR, WILLIAM R. "Analogue Computations of Business Decisions," *Journal of the Operations Research Society of America,* Vol. 1, No. 4 (August, 1953).

46. FELLER, WILLIAM. *An Introduction to Probability Theory and Its Applications.* Vol. I, 2d ed. New York: John Wiley & Sons, Inc., 1957.

47. FETTER, ROBERT B., and GOODMAN, THOMAS. "An Equipment Investment Analog," *Operations Research,* Vol. 5, No. 5 (October, 1957).

48. Reference deleted in proof.

49. FOLSOM, MARION B. *Executive Decision Making.* New York: McGraw-Hill Book Co., Inc., 1962.

50. FOREHAND, GARLIE A., and GUETZKOW, HAROLD. "Judgment and Decision-Making Activities of Government Executives as Described by Superiors and Co-Workers," *Management Science,* Vol. 8, No. 3 (April, 1962).

51. FRIEDMAN, LAWRENCE. "A Competitive Bidding Strategy," *Operations Research,* Vol. 4, No. 1 (February, 1959).

52. ——— "Game Theory Models in the Allocation of Advertising Ex-

penditures," *Operations Research,* Vol. 5, No. 6 (September–October, 1958).

53. GITZENDANNER, F. A. "Risk Analysis in Engineering Economy Studies," *Journal of Engineering Education,* Vol. 46, No. 2 (October, 1955).

54. GOOD, I. J. "How Rational Should a Manager Be?" *Management Science,* Vol. 8, No. 4 (July, 1962).

55. GORT, MICHAEL. "The Planning of Investment," *Journal of Business,* Vol. 24, No. 1 (April, 1951).

56. GRANT, EUGENE L., and IRESON, W. GRANT. *Principles of Engineering Economy.* 4th ed. New York: The Ronald Press Co., 1960.

57. GREEN, PAUL. "Risk Attitudes and Chemical Investment Decisions," *Chemical Engineering Progress,* Vol. 59, No. 1 (January, 1963).

58. GREENBERGER, MARTIN (ed.). *Management and the Computer of the Future.* New York: John Wiley & Sons, Inc., 1962.

59. GREENLAW, PAUL S.; HERRON, LOWELL W.; and RAWDON, RICHARD H. *Business Simulation in Industrial and University Education.* Englewood Cliffs, N.J.: Prentice-Hall, Inc., 1962.

60. HADAMARD, JACQUES. *The Psychology of Invention in the Mathematical Field.* Princeton, N.J.: Princeton University Press, 1945.

61. HANSSMANN, FRED. *Operations Research in Production and Inventory Control.* New York: John Wiley & Sons, Inc., 1962.

62. HAYNES, W. WARREN, and SOLOMON, MARTIN B. "A Misplaced Emphasis in Capital Budgeting," *Quarterly Review of Economics and Business,* Vol. 2, No. 1 (February, 1962).

63. HEEBINK, DAVID V. "Isoquants and Investment Decisions: Part I," *Engineering Economist,* Vol. 7, No. 4 (Summer, 1962).

64. ——— "Isoquants and Investment Decisions: Part II," *Engineering Economist,* Vol. 8, No. 1 (Fall, 1962).

65. HELLER, WALTER H. "The Anatomy of Investment Decisions," *Harvard Business Review,* Vol. 29, No. 2 (March, 1951).

66. HELMER, OLAF, and RESCHER, NICHOLAS. "On the Epistemology of the Inexact Sciences," *Management Science,* Vol. 6, No. 1 (October, 1959).

67. HIRSCHLEIFER, JACK. "On the Theory of Optimal Investment Decisions," *Journal of Political Economy,* Vol. 66, No. 5 (August, 1955).

68. ——— "Risk, the Discount Rate, and Investment Decisions," *American Economic Review,* Vol. 51, No. 2 (May, 1961).

69. HITCH, CHARLES. "Suboptimization and Operations Research," *Journal of the Operations Research Society of America,* Vol. 1, No. 3 (May, 1953).

70. ——— "Uncertainties in Operations Research," *Operations Research,* Vol. 8, No. 4 (July–August, 1961).

71. HOLT, CHARLES C.; MODIGLIANI, FRANCO; MUTH, JOHN F.; and SI-MON, HERBERT A. *Planning Production, Inventories, and Work Force.* Englewood Cliffs, N.J.: Prentice-Hall, Inc., 1960.

72. HOROWITZ, IRA. "Effects of Changes in the Corporate Tax Rate on the Allocation of Research and Development Funds," *Journal of Industrial Engineering,* Vol. 13, No. 4 (July–August, 1962).

73. HURNI, MELVIN L. "Observations on the Role of Business Research as an Aid to Managers," *Management Technology,* Vol. 1, No. 2 (December, 1960).

74. INTERNATIONAL BUSINESS MACHINES CORPORATION. *General Information Manual—Capital Investments.* White Plains, N.Y.: I.B.M. Technical Publications Department, 1962.

75. ISTVAN, DONALD F. *Capital-Expenditure Decisions—How They Are Made in Large Corporations.* Indiana Business Report No. 33. Bloomington, Ind.: Bureau of Business Research, Graduate School of Business, Indiana University, 1961.

76. KATONA, GEORGE. *Psychological Analysis of Economic Behavior.* New York: McGraw-Hill Book Co., 1951.

77. KIMBALL, B. F. "A System of Life Tables for Physical Property Based upon the Truncated Normal Distribution," *Econometrica,* Vol. 15, No. 4 (October, 1947).

78. KNIGHT, FRANK H. *Risk, Uncertainty, and Profit.* Series of Reprints of Scarce Tracts, No. 16. London: London School of Economics and Political Science, 1933.

79. KOOPMANS, T. C. *The State of Economic Science.* New York: McGraw-Hill Book Co., 1957.

80. KURNOW, E.; GLASSER, G. J.; and OTTMAN, F. R. *Statistics for Business Decisions.* Homewood, Ill.: Richard D. Irwin, Inc., 1959.

81. LANZETTA, J. T., and KANAREFF, V. T. "Information Cost, Amount of Payoff, and Level of Aspiration as Determinants of Information Seeking in Decision Making," *Behavioral Science,* Vol. 7, No. 4 (October, 1962).

82. LESSER, A., JR. "Aims and Content of Engineering Economy," *Journal of Engineering Education,* Vol. 44, No. 5 (January, 1954).

83. LORIE, JAMES H., and SAVAGE, LEONARD J. "Three Problems in Rationing Capital," *Journal of Business,* Vol. 28, No. 4 (October, 1955).

84. LUCE, R. DUNCAN, and RAIFFA, HOWARD. *Games and Decisions.* New York: John Wiley & Sons, Inc., 1957.

85. LUTZ, F., and LUTZ, V. *The Theory of Investment of the Firm.* Princeton, N.J.: Princeton University Press, 1951.

86. McDOWELL, IAN. "The Economical Planning Period for Engineering Works," *Operations Research,* Vol. 8, No. 4 (July–August, 1960).

87. McKEAN, ROLAND N. *Efficiency in Government through Systems Analysis.* New York: John Wiley & Sons, Inc., 1958.

88. McKINSEY, J. C. C. *Introduction to the Theory of Games.* New York: McGraw-Hill Book Co., 1952.

89. MAFFEI, RICHARD B. "Simulation, Sensitivity, and Management Decision Rules," *Journal of Business,* Vol. 31, No. 2 (July, 1958).

90. MAJUMDAR, TAPAS. *The Measurement of Utility.* New York: St. Martin's Press, Inc., 1958.

91. MARCH, J. G., and SIMON, HERBERT A. *Organizations.* New York: John Wiley & Sons, Inc., 1958.

92. MARKOWITZ, HARRY M. *Portfolio Selection, Efficient Diversification of Investments.* New York: John Wiley & Sons, Inc., 1959.

93. MAYER, RAYMOND R. "Problems in the Application of Replacement Theory," *Management Science,* Vol. 6, No. 3 (April, 1960).

94. MEYER, JOHN R., and KUH, EDWIN. *The Investment Decision— An Empirical Study.* Cambridge, Mass.: Harvard University Press, 1957.

95. MILLER, DAVID W., and STARR, MARTIN K. *Executive Deicions and Operations Research.* Englewood Cliffs, N.J.: Prentice-Hall, Inc., 1960.

96. MOOD, ALEXANDER M. *Introduction to the Theory of Statistics.* New York: McGraw-Hill Book Co., 1950.

97. MORONEY, M. J. *Facts from Figures.* Baltimore: Penguin Books, Inc., 1959.

98. MORRIS, WILLIAM T. *Analysis for Materials Handling Management.* Homewood, Ill.: Richard D. Irwin, Inc., 1962.

99. ———— *Management Science in Action.* Homewood, Ill.: Richard D. Irwin, Inc., 1963.

100. NADDOR, ELIEZER. "Some Models of Inventory and an Application," *Management Science,* Vol. 2, No. 4 (July, 1958).

101. NAGEL, ERNEST. "Principles of the Theory of Probability," *International Encyclopedia of Unified Science.* Chicago: University of Chicago Press, 1955.

102. NORDIN, J. A. "A Method of Replacement Analysis," *Engineering Economist,* Vol. 6, No. 2 (Winter, 1961).

103. NORTON, JOHN H. "Economic Evaluations for Innovistic New Products," *Engineering Economist,* Vol. 6, No. 1 (Fall, 1960).

104. OLMER, FRANCOIS J. "A New Approach to the Determination of Replacement Costs," *Management Science,* Vol. 6, No. 1 (October, 1959).

105. REISMAN, ARNOLD, and BUFFA, ELLWOOD S. "A General Model for Investment Policy," *Management Science,* Vol. 8, No. 3 (April, 1962).

106. RICCIARDI, F. M., *et al. Top Management Decision Simulation.* New York: American Management Association, 1957.

107. Roy, A. D. "Safety First and the Holding of Assets," *Econometrica*, Vol. 20, No. 3 (March, 1952).

108. Samuelson, Paul A. *Economics*. 5th ed. New York: McGraw-Hill Book Co., 1961.

109. Sand, William C. "An Economic Study of Data Processing Systems for Arco Oil Company," *Engineering Economist*, Vol. 4, No. 4 (Spring, 1959).

110. Sasieni, Maurice; Yaspan, Arthur; and Friedman, Lawrence. *Operations Research—Methods and Problems*. New York: John Wiley & Sons, Inc., 1959.

111. Savage, L. J. *The Foundations of Statistics*. New York: John Wiley & Sons, Inc., 1954.

112. Schlaifer, Robert. *Introduction to Statistics for Business Decisions*. New York: McGraw-Hill Book Co., Inc., 1961.

113. Scodel, Alvin; Ratoosh, Philburn; and Minas, J. Sayer. "Some Personality Correlates of Decision Making under Conditions of Risk," *Behavioral Science*, Vol. 4, No. 1 (January, 1959).

114. Shackle, G. L. S. *Uncertainty in Economics*. Cambridge, England: Cambridge University Press, 1955.

115. Shubik, Martin. "The Uses of Game Theory in Management Science," *Management Science*, Vol. 2, No. 1 (October, 1955).

116. Siegel, S. "Level of Aspiration and Decision Making," *Psychological Review*, Vol. 64, No. 4 (April, 1957).

117. Simon, H. A. *Administrative Behavior*. 2d ed. New York: The Macmillan Co., 1957.

118. ———— *Models of Man*. New York: John Wiley & Sons, Inc., 1957.

119. Smalley, Harold E., and Newberry, Thomas L. "Profit Maximization and Industrial Engineering," *Journal of Industrial Engineering*, Vol. 12, No. 3 (May–June, 1961).

120. Smith, Nicholas M., Jr. "A Calculus for Ethics," *Behavioral Science*, Vol. 1, Nos. 2 and 3 (April and July, 1956).

121. Smith, Vernon L. "Economic Equipment Policies: An Evaluation," *Management Science*, Vol. 4, No. 1 (October, 1957).

122. Snyder, Richard C., and Paige, Glenn D. "The United States' Decision to Resist Aggression in Korea: the Application of an Analytical Scheme," *Administrative Science Quarterly*, Vol. 3, No. 3 (December, 1958).

123. Solomon, Ezra. "Measuring a Company's Cost of Capital," *Journal of Business*, Vol. 28, No. 4 (October, 1955).

124. ———— (ed.). *The Management of Corporate Capital*. Glencoe, Ill.: The Free Press, 1959.

125. Sprague, Richard E. *Electronic Business Systems*. New York: The Ronald Press Co., 1962.

126. Starbuck, William H. "A Generalization of Terborgh's Approach

to Equipment Replacement," *International Journal of Production Research,* Vol. 1, No. 3 (1962).

127. STARR, MARTIN K. *Product Design and Decision Theory.* Englewood Cliffs, N.J.: Prentice-Hall, Inc., 1963.

128. SUMMER, CHARLES E., JR. "The Managerial Mind," *Harvard Business Review,* Vol. 37, No. 1 (January–February, 1959).

129. TERBORGH, GEORGE. *Dynamic Equipment Policy.* New York: McGraw-Hill Book Co., 1949.

130. —— *Business Investment Policy.* Washington, D.C.: Machinery and Allied Products Institute. 1958.

131. THRALL. R. W.; COOMBS, C. H.; and DAVIS, R. L. (eds.). *Decision Processes.* New York: John Wiley & Sons, Inc., 1954.

132. THUESEN, H. G. *Engineering Economy.* Englewood Cliffs, N.J.: Prentice-Hall, Inc., 1957.

133. THURSTONE, L. L. "The Measurement of Values," *Psychological Review,* Vol. 61, No. 1 (January, 1954).

134. TINTNER, GERHARD. *Econometrics.* New York: John Wiley & Sons, Inc., 1952.

135. ULLMAN, JOHN E. "Investment, Equipment Prices, and Income Tax," *Engineering Economist,* Vol. 5, No. 3 (Spring, 1960).

136. VANDELL, R. F., and VANCIL, RICHARD F. *Cases in Capital Budgeting.* Homewood, Ill.: Richard D. Irwin, Inc., 1962.

137. VATTER, WILLIAM J. "Contributions of Accounting to Measurement in Management Science," *Management Science,* Vol. 5, No. 1 (October, 1958).

138. VON NEUMANN, JOHN, and MORGENSTERN, OSKAR. *Theory of Games and Economic Behavior.* 3d. ed. Princeton, N.J.: Princeton University Press, 1953.

139. WAGNER, HARVEY M. "Statistical Decision Theory as a Method for Information Processing," *Journal of Industrial Engineering,* Vol. 10, No. 1 (January–February, 1959).

140. WALLIS, W. ALLEN, and ROBERTS, HARRY V. *Statistics—A New Approach.* Glencoe, Ill.: The Free Press, 1956.

141. WASSERMAN, PAUL, and SILANDER, FRED S. *Decision-Making, An Annotated Bibliography.* Ithaca, N.Y.: Graduate School of Business and Public Administration, Cornell University, 1958.

142. WEAVER, JAMES B. "Why Income Taxes Must Be Considered in Profitability Studies," *Engineering Economist,* Vol. 3, No. 1 (Summer, 1957).

143. WELLINGTON, ARTHUR M. *The Economic Theory of Railway Location.* New York: John Wiley & Sons, Inc., 1887.

144. WILLIAMS, J. D. *The Compleat Strategyst.* New York: McGraw-Hill Book Co., 1954.

INDEX

549

This book has been set on the Linotype in 11 point Modern #21, leaded 2 points, and 10 point Modern #21 and Modern 8A, leaded 1 point. Chapter numbers and titles are in 21 point and 16 point Caledonia Bold. The size of the type page is 27 by 46½ picas.